FOR ELISE

Unveiling the Forgotten Woman on the Criddle Homestead
by Oriole A. Vane Veldhuis

Published by Oriole A. Vane Veldhuis
Winnipeg, Manitoba, Canada

The author welcomes feedback
oavveld1903@gmail.com

Cover Design by Dawn Huck
Printed in Canada by Friesens

Library and Archives Canada Cataloguing in Publication

Veldhuis, Oriole A., 1934-
For Elise : unveiling the forgotten woman on the Criddle homestead / Oriole A. Vane
Veldhuis.

ISBN 978-1-896150-72-7

Includes bibliographical references.

1. Vane, Elise Harrer, d. 1903.
2. Frontier and pioneer life--Manitoba.
3. Criddle family.
4. Vane family.
5. Women pioneers--Manitoba--Biography. I. Title.

FC3373.1.V35V44 2012   971.27'02092   C2012-903973-X

MIX
Paper from
responsible sources
FSC® C016245
FSC
www.fsc.org

ENVIRONMENTAL BENEFITS STATEMENT
Oriole Veldhuis saved the following resources by
printing the pages of this book on chlorine free paper
made with 100% post-consumer waste.

TREES	WATER	ENERGY	SOLID WASTE	GREENHOUSE GASES
11 FULLY GROWN	5,004 GALLONS	5 MILLION BTUs	335 POUNDS	922 POUNDS

Environmental impact estimates were made using the Environmental Paper Network
Paper Calculator 3.2. For more information visit www.papercalculator.org.

Writing *For Elise* challenged me to read widely and think deeply about the act of rewriting history from the perspective of my great-grandmother. The following quotes inspired me in my struggle.

The authority of the historical narrative is the authority of reality itself: the historical account endows this reality with form, and thereby makes it desirable by the imposition upon its processes of the formal coherency that only stories possess... In this world, reality wears the mask of meaning, the completeness and fullness of which we can only imagine, never experience. Insofar as historical stories can be completed, can be given narrative closure, can be shown to have had a plot all along, they give to reality the odour of the ideal... Has an historical narrative ever been written that was not informed, not only by moral awareness, but specifically by the moral authority of the narrator?"
    Donald T. Siebert, *The Moral Animus of David Hume*

"The goal of all settlers was independence—a fresh start, a freedom from the humiliations of whatever had gone before. As a rule the newcomers found it enough, of course, to forget. Only the most tormented, imaginative immigrants were driven beyond forgetfulness to the creation of a non-existent past... The west allowed them to wear a new skin until it became their own. Their lives became a kind of art."
    Mark Abley, *Beyond Forget: Rediscovering the Prairies*

"History with its flickering lamp stumbles along the trail of the past, trying to reconstruct its scenes, to revive its echoes, and kindle with pale gleams the passion of former days."
    Winston Churchill, House of Commons, 1940

For Elise is dedicated to the memory of my parents,
Ruth (nee Clark) and Rupert Vane.

Acknowledgements

Wagon loads of appreciation go to my husband Art for the countless times he acted as my sounding board, helpful critic and first line editor. Art also excelled as my companion on the ancestral trail he dubbed 'The Harrer Hunt and the Criddle Quest'.

I thank the families who shared their treasured keepsakes to make this book possible. Special thanks go to my late Aunt Mona Vane, the loving model for my heroine, along with my sister Faye with her beautiful voice and vivid imagination.

The process of writing this book has been both depressing and fulfilling. I have walked unknown paths, had rare adventures, and enjoyed rich companionships. My sisters Verna, Faye, and Pearl have supported me, as have 'cousins' Myrna Paquette, Kathy Noel, and until her passing, Nan Criddle Kenyon. Valued contributors have been: Helen Ens, letter translator of old German script; Maija Tyzek, translator and visionary; Vona Guiler, Bridgitte Schludermann, and Chris Dewar, generous with their expertise; June Nobel, researcher extraordinaire; Jane Powell, health keeper; the Alabaster Society—Laraine Hake, Angela Alabaster, Valerie Knobloch, and Ray Williamson; Barbara Becker, linguistic analyst; Helen Dyck, and Kelly Southworth, editors; Leone Banks and Wendy Wilson, encouragers and layout; Jim Hunter, David and Patricia Wotton, readers; the many Manitoba Genealogical Society members who assisted and inspired me. There were patient archivists in Canada, England, and especially Germany, who honoured my search and assisted me to find answers to my questions with grace and clarity.

Not least of those to be thanked are the legions of family and friends who asked, "How is your book coming?" You kept me going.

It's been a twelve year journey and my heart soars as I cross the finish line.

Oriole A. Vane Veldhuis

June 25, 2012

Thanks to all who have embraced Elise's story. You have made this second printing possible.

February 28, 2013

Table of Contents

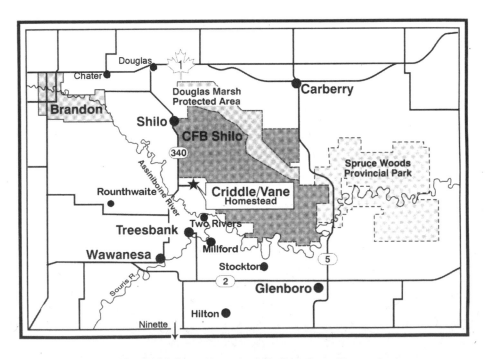

Courtesy of the Criddle/Vane Homestead Heritage Committee, revised.

Family Members

Percy Criddle, London, Nov. 21, 1844

Sabina Elise Harrer/Criddle/Vane, Freiburg, Baden, Nov. 24, 1840
  Engaged to Percy Criddle, Jan. 1863
  Baden passport issued Jan. 17, 1867, no entry stamps.
 All children born in Southwark, part of the city of London:
  Mabel   May 20, 1867
                                            d. March 18, 1868

  Minnie   Oct. 1, 1868
  Isabel (Dido, Dico)   Nov. 29, 1869
  Edwy (The Boy)   July 31, 1871
  Harry   Aug. 25, 1873
  Cecil (Solomon, Shrimp)   Apr. 19, 1875
Alice Nicol Criddle, London, Nov. 24, 1849, married Sept. 8, 1874
  Norman   May 14, 1875
  Evelyn   Nov. 21, 1876
  Stuart   Dec. 4, 1877
  Beatrice (Bobby, Bobo)   Apr. 28, 1880
 Born at homestead:
  Maida   May 2, 1884
  Julia   Aug. 14, 1887
  Talbot   (Tolly)   Aug. 19, 1890
  Alma   Aug. 6, 1893

Elise's Family: The Dukedom of Baden, part of Germany as of 1871
Parents: Karl Harrer, October 2,1805-1849, married 1836,
  Susanna Margaretha Haarbarth 1809-1885
    Carl Friedrich Wilhelm, 1837, married 1865
      Marie Barbara Caroline Bauer (Maria)   May 13, 1839
        Stillborn boy   July 5, 1866
        Anna Maria Catharina   Sept. 13, 1868,
                                                 d. 1870

        Anna Maria Catharina Augusta   May 18, 1872
        Augusta Elise Karoline Susanne (Elsa) Oct. 4, 1874
        Julie Marianne (Julchen)   June 7, 1877

Karl Jacob Wilhelm, 1839, married 1881
    Amalie Franzisca Burgweger   1853-1921
  Sabina Elise   Nov. 24, 1840
  Wilhelm Jacob, unmarried architect   1846-1872

Emily's Family:
Parents: William Henry Steer 1846, married 1870
  Emily Vincent, 1845, England

Emily Louise	April 10, 1871
William Henry (Harry)	Feb. 2, 1874
	d. March 14, 1901
Edwin Patchett (Eddie)	April 26, 1875
	d. May 8, 1898
Reginald Vincent (Reg)	June 7, 1876
Ernest Arthur	May 9, 1878
Gertrude Margaret	Aug. 7, 1879
Agnes Violet (Dolly)	Jan. 30, 1881
Edith Grace (Edie)	July 5, 1882
Herbert Frank	Mar. 10, 1886
	Died in World War 1
May Victoria	April 29, 1887

John Augustus, Tulk England   Nov. 5, 1839
Edward Tulk, younger brother, married 1880
  Anna Pauline Wydler
      Anna Augusta Marie (May)   June 15, 1882
      John Augustus (Johnny)   Aug. 24. 1883

Preface

Welcome. You are invited to share in my family story, a rediscovery of my great-grandmother, Sabina Elise Harrer, and her life as a servant in the 1880s and 90s. As Shirley A. Serviss wrote in *Reading Between the Lines:*

"Women's history disappears like meals placed before hungry men, and kisses on children's cheeks . . ."

Because I knew almost nothing about Elise I spent a great deal of effort for over ten years researching and writing this book. My journey began before the 100th anniversary of Elise's death by having her German letters translated. Beginning in Germany, we found distant cousins, Elise's home, her school, and family records. Gradually I assembled evidence in England and Canada to complete the picture and weave my findings into what I describe as a 'post-modern, creative, non-fiction' story. It is Elise's story, but it is also mine for there has been healing in it for me.

Nan Criddle Kenyon reminded me to make clear that, 'Huckey' as the Criddle children called Elise Vane, was very much loved by all of them. She was their nurse and nurturer. In writing this book I hope to raise Elise's 'life of moral leadership' to a place where her real contribution to the Vane and Criddle families is recognized.

Like other immigrants to Canada, Percy and Alice Criddle brought their attitudes and culture. I could not escape their formality, so despite the passage of 130 years, they remain 'Mr. and Mrs. Criddle'. His diary provided the dates and many events on which I built the story. Could his speech have been even more colourful?

In their Victorian society the gulf between each layer of wealth and class was extremely well defined by language and behaviour. A 'gentleman' lived on money not earned by his own hands. Even a surgeon using his hands, could not be considered a gentleman regardless of how wealthy he was. Men, such as Percy, who made their living by buying and selling, were considered 'tradesmen'. The directories listed Percy Criddle as a merchant from 1873-78. Men in the trades struggled to move upward, and Percy's marriage to a lawyer's daughter was to his advantage. An archivist pointed out Alice's folly in marrying a lowly merchant and asked, "Did she have to get married?" Percy and Alice placed just above the poverty line on the 1881 census by employing two young girls. Families without even one young servant were below that dreaded line.

Rules that seem quaint, even ridiculous to our generation, oppressed all classes of women and children. Not legally persons, women were property, owned body and soul by their men, much as we own pets and livestock. When a husband left his wife, he could take everything, even the children. By the 1880s women won a limited right to own property in England, but few did. In truth, life in 19th century England was a strange mixture—the appearance of gentility hiding cruel realities.

⁓⌖⁓

Many modern historians are uncovering the 'underside of history' and my story joins them in illuminating the past. Born into a loving family, blessed with intelligence, talent and education, Elise trusted a young man who came courting in Heidelberg. Once in London, Percy carefully hid her and their children on the south side of the Thames and attempted to conceal their identity in Canada. It is time to tell Elise's descendants of her heroism and sacrifice.

I treasure the hospitality of the Harrers, my German relatives. They invited me to their homes, listened with compassion to my story, and encouraged me to follow my heart. Now it is my turn to welcome you to Elise's story—FOR ELISE: Unveiling the Forgotten Woman on the Criddle Homestead.

Guide Posts for the Reader

- Footnotes and citations are provided, but not essential for understanding the story.
- Pictures are my own or from family collections. Other sources are noted.
- Although Mr. Criddle's diary is quoted extensively, only some special occasions are footnoted by date. English words often end with a silent letter. In German, every letter is pronounced. This makes Elise-Elisa: Criddle-Criddel.
- Elise's thoughts are written in *italics*.
- Words needing emphases are in **bold.**
- Three dots . . . indicate something has been omitted from a longer quote or letter, and also indicates a pause in thought.
- [Sic] following a word emphasizes the original spelling. Letters and documents retain their original punctuation, expression, and spelling.
- Square brackets [ ] indicate a word or explanation from the writer.
- Round brackets ( ) were used by the original writers.
- Further explanation of the research process can be found at the end of the story.

Prelude

My Promise

Nearing the end of his life, our father, Rupert Vane, had a last piece of business on his mind. He had ordered a small marble marker for his grandmother's grave and asked two of his sons-in-law to help him place it. My sisters, Faye and Pearl, had come home for a last visit with our Dad. On his 77th birthday, September 30, 1977, we were going with him to see it.

He raised his cancer-weakened body from bed, and with Mother's help, dressed in his Sunday best. Mother drove us 'over the river' to the Criddle Place, vacated 17 years earlier. The yard felt eerily empty as Mother parked the car in the windswept grass just down from the abandoned house.

We followed Dad as he slowly picked his way to an overgrown graveyard hidden in the trees. He passed by the Criddle gravestones and stopped to face a weathered cement marker. There, at its base, was Dad's gift, 'Elise Vane 1841-1903' engraved on its polished marble surface.[1] Always a quiet man, my tall, silver-haired father said nothing, but I noticed tears.

I remained beside him wondering why this grass-covered grave held so much meaning. How could my Dad care so deeply? After what seemed like many minutes, I put my hand on his shoulder.

"Tell me about your grandma."

---

1 My father had a 'Copy of Baptism' for Sabina Elise Harrer issued November 17, 1841, Freiburg im Breisgau. Her date of birth was November 24, 1840, according to baptismal record from Staatsarchiv Freiburg.

He hesitated. "She was born in Germany."

He seemed lost in thought; I waited and then asked, "Do you know anything else about her?"

He shook his head.

It wasn't fair, I thought, that he loved his long departed grandma, yet knew so little about her. Once again I broke the silence, "I promise I'll find out more about your grandma."

I wanted to dig deeper but resisted asking, "Why is your grandma buried here? Grandpa and Grandma Vane's graves are in Millford Cemetery with our little sister's."

Long ago conversations at my grandparents' home flashed through my mind. *When our generation is gone no one will know who is buried in the unmarked grave on the Criddle place.* Dad urged them to do more than talk, but Uncle Harry, the last surviving child of Elise Vane, didn't want to upset anyone.

At last Dad had achieved his goal. He turned and carefully retraced his steps. But he didn't stop at our car as we expected. Wading on through tall grass and scrubby trees, he found some rotting logs in the underbrush. "This is all that's left of The Palace . . . I was born here."

I was curious and carried on, "You had an older sister, didn't you?"

Yes, Thyra, and a little brother John. They were born here too, before we moved across the river when I was about six."

"It doesn't look like a very big house for a family of five."

"We had Mr. Criddle's cousin Charlie live with us. And sometimes mother's sisters stayed too. We all got along."

We took pictures and Dad started back to the car. Our special outing was ending and we knew the drive home would be the last with our beloved father. Every landmark heading homeward took on a larger-than-life significance.

From the Criddle yard we drove south to the Treesbank Ferry. Proud of his fine team of horses, Dad had crossed the Assiniboine River with them countless

Gift to our parents on their 50th anniversary. Painted by Terry McLean

times, hauling loads of 'long wood'.[2] We drove onto the ferry and as it 'putt, putt-ed' across the river we looked up towards the Clark home barely visible over the cut-bank. Mom and Dad were married there in 1926. Grandpa Clark's artesian well with its ever flowing clear cold water was a wonder of my childhood, especially for summer's hot dusty feet. Further south was the village of Treesbank, the scene of many a gathering—some heartbreaking, many joyful. At the dances we children dodged moving couples, played under the stage, and finally succumbed to sleep on the pile of coats in the cloakroom. Mom and Dad had recently celebrated their fiftieth anniversary in the little hall with a dinner and concert by their children and families. During the dance following, I had my last old-time waltz with my father. The Treesbank picnic every June had competing ball teams from all the neighbouring towns. We youngsters played 'Hide and Seek' simply for the pleasure of being together. Finally, our day ended with potato salad on a paper plate!

Driving on south we crossed the CPR tracks and descended to the Souris River.

In our childhood, that road had cut diagonally into the side of the valley needing a sharp turn at both bottom and top of the bank. Going down was easy then, as now, but to drive up was a real family affair for us. Four little girls sat

2 Trees not cut into stove-wood lengths.

solemnly in the back seat of our 'not getting any younger' Model A Ford. Three of us crossed our arms and fervently chorused, "Bless me car, get up the hill! Bless me car, get up the hill!" The chant worked its magic and only once, according to little

Destroyed by the flood of 2011.

sister Pearl, did Dad have to back down for a second run.

At the bottom of the hill, a fine cement bridge spanned the Souris River. We called it Dad's Bridge because of the stories he told us of helping— with his team of horses—in

i t s construction in 1921. Continuing up the south side of the river valley we passed Dad's parental home, St. John's. How I remember the warm welcome at the door and Grandpa's trip to the pantry and the taste of that creamy chocolate rose bud. Our bridal bouquets came from Great Uncle Harry Vane's prize-

winning rose garden. Further on, his shelter belts of aging maple trees lined the road protecting the fields from prairie winds.

A left turn took us down to Oak Creek, where on rare summer Sundays, we sisters chased minnows in the creek's shallow water while Dad fished downstream. There were few traces of the thriving pioneer town of Millford, but we knew the area well. Dad had farmed its fields and we'd picked many a pail of saskatoons on the hillside.

On we went, up out of the valley eastward—passing Millford Cemetery. Its trees sheltered the graves of Dad's parents; Mother's parents, and grandparents—Sarah Jane and Alexander Clark.

We did not turn left on the next road leading to the old 'Köhler place', Mom and Dad's first farm. In fancy, I winged north along the dirt road, opened the barbed wire gate at the bottom of the hill, and then, a barefoot child again, ran up to our old farmyard. Happy times flooded back: apple trees in bloom—buzz-

ing with mother's bees; games of 'Anti-I-Over' the long, low henhouse with our cousins; Nancy, our Shetland pony; the warm barn and cows at milking time; baby calves; our dog, Pup; Lummie, my birthday-present lamb; and dear little Ruggit, our beloved pet pig.

Mother had driven straight on leaving only a great cloud of dust. We came to the village of Stockton, passed our tall white church, and just to the east, a cement step on a knoll where our school had stood. Then turning south, we arrived at Many Furrows Farm, our family's home.

Dad grew weaker, yet still very alert. It was time to return a childhood favour. He had read to us on long winter nights while we washed the supper dishes and tidied up the kitchen. That circle of yellow lamplight and our father's voice carried us away to such places as the canyons and mesas of Zane Gray's, *Riders of the Purple Sage*.

I asked, "What would you like me to read?"

He said, "Nellie McLung's, *Black Creek Stopping House*. We knew it by another name."

Later, I went to see Aunt Mona, Dad's youngest sister and asked, "Was there a book Dad liked from your childhood?"

"No, I can't think of any. But he might enjoy his Mother and Dad's letters."

We discovered two lovers, Edwy Vane and Emily Steer, planning a future together. Their brothers and sisters in the letters became more than just names to me. One would not expect Edwy to be thinking much about his own mother as he wrote to his sweetheart; but reading between the lines, who else would be calling, "Breakfast is ready" at five in the morning?

All too soon, on October 17, in his seventy-seventh year, our father died where he wished, at home in his own bed. It was evening; the cows had been milked. We were gathering for supper, and we knew the end had come. Sorrow overwhelmed us.

During my days and months of mourning, I reflected on the scene with my father at his grandmother's grave. A promise made is a promise to be kept! I made it easily, but how could I keep it? Why was Elise Vane's unnamed grave tucked away in the back corner of the Criddle cemetery? Why did my father know so little about her?

The mystery kept churning around in my mind, and a puzzling conversation between my elders resurfaced. Canada introduced Old Age Assistance in 1952 and the Vanes needed proof of age to qualify. Letters had been sent to England requesting their birth registrations. Minnie's, the oldest of the Vanes, returned in due course. But those of her three brothers: Edwy, Harry, and Cecil did not. Minnie suggested, "Try asking for Criddle."

Sure enough, all three were registered as sons of Percy Criddle and Elise Criddle, nee Harrer of 131 St. George's Rd., Southwark. They said not a word to anyone outside the family, for it was their shameful, carefully kept secret, ever since coming to Manitoba.

Years passed, Percy Criddle's granddaughter, Stuart's daughter Nan, became a teacher. As soon as she had enough money in the bank, she booked a flight to England to meet and thank her Nicol great-aunts for all the wonderful presents they had sent her and her little brother, Percy Junior. Her sweet old aunties shocked Nan, "Your grandfather was a dreadful, dreadful man! The Vanes are your father's half sisters and brothers." [3]

Nan's cousin, Alma Criddle, published *Criddle-De-Diddle-Ensis* in 1976 based, she claimed, on her grandfather's diaries. But Nan's discovery made its way into the book. "And what of Elise?' she wrote. "What of the third party of this marital triangle, the second lady of Percy's household for all his married life, until her death in 1903?" [4] Alma opened a can of worms for the Vanes.

The day her book arrived in our home remains as clearly etched in my memory as the day Martin Luther King was shot. Our anguish for our father filled our home. All the Vane elders felt betrayed and deeply wounded! Their shame, tended privately for so long, was now the topic of their neighbours' conversations. My older sister, Faye, understood at last what was meant when a classmate at school squashed her enthusiastic discovery in her British history book.

---

3 Kenyon, Nan Criddle, in conversation with the author.
4 Criddle, Alma, *Criddle-De -Diddle-Ensis.* (Self Published, Friesen and Son, Altona, 1973) p. 208.

"Look, Sir Henry Vane! I wonder if that's where my name comes from!"

Her classmate responded with contempt, "**I** can tell **you** where **your** name comes from!" But she never would.

The Manitoba Museum created an exhibit, *The Criddles of Aweme,* highlighting the pioneering Criddle family and their contributions. Numerous articles have been written about the Criddles over the years, but if they mentioned my great-grandmother, it was briefly as Mr. Criddle's mistress. Nor did they mention her children—Minnie, Isabel, Edwy, Harry, and Cecil.

Meanwhile, my life sped on through 25 demanding years. At retirement, friends wished me a hard-earned rest with coffee and a morning paper. Yet, my father's image at the gravesite remained. Family members shrugged off my questions with, "The past is past, let it be." And equally discouraging, "You won't find anything in Germany. All the records were destroyed in the wars."

Lines from a popular 1850s Victorian melodrama expressed my conflict:

Speaker I: *I'm for plain speaking - Let the truth be shown –*
Speaker II: *Truth's in a well – better leave that well alone-*
                   It's bitter waters why should you uncork? [5]

But, I couldn't leave the well alone, even if the waters proved to be bitter. I began my search for the truth.

In Alma's book, I found Elise, 'the Dutchman', a 'fair of face' beauty from Mannheim, with cameo features much too attractive to Percy Criddle, the young student from England.[6] Her description gave birth to the Mrs. Vane strangers knew more about than her descendants.

Many pioneer women disappeared from history without leaving even a gravestone. I had her stone, but it couldn't talk and the people who knew her had long since been laid in their own graves.

But surely, I thought stubbornly, there must be traces of her life somewhere. I opened the Glenboro community history, *Beneath the Long Grass,* published in 1979. Both Criddle and Vane family accounts were written by the original pioneers. Did either mention coming together in 1882?

The Criddle account read:

> It was with this spirit of adventure and excitement that the Criddles, Percy and Alice, left their home in Addlestone, . . . to establish their home on Section 32-8-16. They had with them the first four members of their family-Norman, Evelyn, Stuart, and two-year-old Beatrice.

---

5 Hammet, Michael ed. *Plays by Charles Reade.* (Cambridge, Cambridge University Press, 1986) p. 78.
6 Elise's family lived in Heidelberg.

The Vane's began:

The Vane family came from England with their mother in 1882 to take out a homestead in South Cyprus, north of the Assiniboine River and the town of Millford. The family was Minnie, Isabel (Dido), Edwy, Harry, and Cecil.

No help there, so I reread published articles about the Criddles. Writers, I soon discovered, had based their articles on those previously published. I asked: did Percy Criddle study music, law, and medicine at the best universities in Europe? Was it possible for Alice Criddle to have graduated with top marks from both Cambridge and Oxford universities prior to her four-year courtship and marriage in 1874? I wondered which seven languages the Criddles spoke so fluently—I had studied both French and Cree, but dared not claim fluency. And when writers described Mrs. Vane as Percy's mistress, were they saying he kept her in a neat little bower similar to British aristocrats? I could only speculate unless I located original documents.

My big break came when I was visiting a cousin. Kathy told me, "We have a package of German letters and papers. But nobody can read them."

My whole being lit up, "If you let me borrow them, I'll find someone who can!"

It was the first step on the long road to keep my promise. The journey could be a book in itself, and one you might have enjoyed. Instead, I have chosen to sift, ever so carefully, through ten years of research in Canada, England, Germany, and Austria in order to recreate Elise's story. My hope is that others may come to understand, as I have, the source of my Dad's tears that golden September afternoon.

Chapter One

Your Name is 'Vane'

It was early Friday morning, July 14, 1882. Elise's old trunk had been filled with precious possessions, the lid forced down, and its latches fastened. Each family member carried a bag of essentials. Everything else had been given to friends. Elise checked her bag once more: baptismal record, her January 1867 Baden passport, her collection of poetry, knitting, envelopes, paper, and two pencils. One, a farewell present, had an eraser on the end. She had a few coins in her pocket and the money from her brothers sewn into the hem of her petticoat.

Elise cast a few last hurried glances at the familiar rooms. Then, with hugs and farewells, especially to Mr. and Mrs. Foulgar, her lodgers, she and her children set forth into the great unknown.

The children had grown up in crowded Southwark. Minnie, almost 14, gave up her education with its prospects for a good future. Isabel, approaching 13, was already missing her friends. Edwy, almost 11; Harry, 10; and Cecil, 7, fancied the adventure. Threats of being locked up in the Clink would no longer scare them. Many things ran through Elise's mind. *No more wretched souls passing the door on their way to the Bedlam Asylum. No more pungent, polluted air from the breweries and leather factories. No more long treks across London Bridge, around the Tower of London to Little Alie Street and the beautiful St. George's German Lutheran Church.*

They walked behind a hired cart down St. George's Road, past their schools to Westminster Bridge Road and finally to Waterloo Street with its bustling station.

Waterloo Station! They'd never seen such a place! Paper boys cried. Pedlars barked! Tramps begged. People rushed. Locomotives erupted! Steam blasted. Black clouds billowed. Conductors shouted, "B-o-a-r-d!" Men stepped down from coaches; others clambered aboard. Beggars, mutts, and pigeons poked about, scrounging for breakfast. In the midst of the throngs some were simply perched, unmoving on their bags.

In all the confusion Elise found the ticket booth and they unloaded the trunk. "We are in time," she told her children. "Papa will find us here." She cleared her throat, and added, "He told me to tell you at the station, 'I want them to call me Mr. Criddle. It's very important – don't call me Papa!'"

They looked puzzled, but their mother looked so serious they dared not question her.

"There's Papa," Little Cecil pointed to a gentleman in a top hat hurrying toward them.

"Hush!" Minnie clamped her hand over his mouth.

Their papa came rushing up, "You've told them I'm Mr. Criddle from now on?"

Elise nodded.

"I will get your tickets – check your trunk. Be sharp. . . . We're late."

That accomplished, he led them to his wife waiting impatiently with her young children near the steam-spouting Liverpool train. They hustled up the steps and into the coach. The frazzled lady settled with a sigh beside her husband and, with a bob of her head toward Elise, said, "So this is the foreign woman who is to take the place of my dear little servants, Ellen and Louisa."[1]

He nodded. When Mrs. Criddle, baby on her knee, caught her breath she leaned across the aisle, "Norman has just turned seven; Evelyn is five and a half; Stuart is four; and this is our little Beatrice. You'll be seeing to their needs."

Elise thought about the situation. *Percy had his family's tickets for America when he came begging. Told me his wife needed help. Clearly she is a lady accustomed to being served. My girls like children; my boys are quick. We'll manage until we get our own home.*

The train jolted forward. Through London they steamed; eager eyes snatched glimpses of tiny backyards—washtubs and clotheslines. Beyond London they saw a magical checkerboard of England's green countryside. They peeked into farmyards with chickens and piglets. Above and beyond were sheep-dotted hillsides.

With everyone settled, Elise could think. Her heart was overflowing with emotion: *another one-way journey.*

The train clattered on and the passing fields blurred into the green hills of her youth. *I loved our family walks in the forest with its clear running streams. I can almost feel the soft spring air. And Percy and I sang Schumann's beautiful songs about*

---

1 English families were considered below the poverty line if they did not have a servant. The Criddles had two teenage domestic servants, one, the children's nanny, listed on the 1882 census.

rippling brooks . . . spring blossoms. Sometimes we stood in the great square looking up at Heidelberg Castle . . . its ruins shining silvery in the moonlight. The church at our backs reached towards the stars. Generations of my mother's family lived in its shadow. . . .

Oh Mama, my dear Mama. When I said good-bye to you, that dreary January day in 1867, I was so happy; you, so sad. You did your best with your small pension . . . sacrificed so I could attend Herr Ekhert's school. I loved my studies: French and English literature, music, painting. . . . Thank you, dear Mama. She felt in her bag again for her precious Poesie book. *I'm going even further now, Mama . . . you'll be as out of reach as Papa.* She was a girl again, hearing the words, "Your Papa is dead." She stared out the window, blinking away tears. *Mama always said, "Our family has weathered storms in the past and will again." Little Wilhelm helped us through our loss. . . . Wilhelm and his buildings . . . took too many risks. My big brothers—dear Friedrich . . . Carl—I'm so homesick. What am I doing?*

Mrs. Criddle broke in, "The servants prepared a basket this morning. It's time for lunch."

⚬~❧~⚬

Late that afternoon the train puffed into Liverpool station. Mr. Criddle claimed the baggage and arranged transport for nine children and three adults to the North Western Hotel.[2] With his wife settled, he sent for Elise. "You'll need tickets to get on the ship in the morning."

Does he need me? But she got up wearily and followed him to the Guion Office where he ordered tickets, "Two adults, four children." Elise didn't dare remind him of Isabel's age. *I know under twelve travel half fare, but can she pass as eleven?*

The ticket agent asked no questions as he squinted through the wicket over the buyer's shoulder. "Steerage, is it? That will be twice twenty-nine pounds, plus four children to a total of one hundred sixteen pounds." Adding as he counted, "You know, of course, the fare doesn't include bedding or utensils. Can be got just out, to the right."

They found the place. Mr. Criddle hesitated, "Confounded Jewish slop shop!"

Then Elise watched in astonishment as four beds[3], a water can, two tin pint cups, canteen, utensils—six knives, six spoons, and six forks appeared on the counter. *Six of us to share those four thin blankets . . . two cups!*

---

2 July 15, 1882. Percy Criddle's diary, personal copy, is used extensively for his speech and other details. Occasional passages footnoted by date. Longer quotes, obviously from the diary, are not footnoted.
3 It is not clear what Percy meant by 'beds' since the ship had bunks. I assume he meant something for warmth, thus blankets.

At the door, a scrawny little porter offered his services for the transfer of Elise's supplies to their lodgings. She smiled; her companion cursed. After considerable haggling, a few coins dropped into the desperate palm. Anxious to dine with his wife, Mr. Criddle left them collecting the supplies.

I understand now, I'm to see that the porter doesn't make off with the goods. My willingness to 'help' Mrs. Criddle has turned me into a servant. No matter that I'm exhausted after a frantic day and night of packing.

Elise learned she and her children were expected at five the next morning to prepare the Criddle family for departure. Forces beyond her control or comprehension had suddenly swept her up into his vision of becoming a wealthy landowner.

Before turning in to sleep that night there was a late night entry in the gentleman's diary.

A most officious little official-looking party in a uniform pressed his help on me most indefatigably. I resisted his advances as well as I could, though E. smiled and grinned at his sundry sallies, much to my rage. . . . much luggage, ill-labeled, on my mind. – lost my voice – to bed at 11 o'clock.

He'd worked every angle to persuade his wife to accept his dream, even disowning his own children. What he did about the 'ill-labeled luggage' would be discovered in the morning.

———————

Breakfast over, Mr. Criddle arranged the four-mile trip to the Langton Dock. For himself, his wife, and little Beatrice he engaged a cab; the rest travelled with the luggage in an omnibus. And there waiting, spewing smoke from her single stack towered the S. S. Wisconsin with two masts rigged for sail.

Edwy was busily unloading the trunks when he yelled, "Someone's stolen our trunk! Look!"

His father grabbed him by the collar, "Quiet! Can't you see it's your trunk! That's **your** name **now!**"[4] And with another shake he dropped him back to earth.

Shortly after a gentleman asked Minnie, "What's your name, young lady?"

Friendly and outgoing as usual, she answered with a smile, "Minnie Criddle."

---

4 According to Edwy's son, Rupert Vane.

Her father pounced on her, pointing to the trunk, "Can't you read? **Vane**! You're Minnie **Vane**."[5]

It stung like a whip! Minnie had always been the apple of her father's eye. Suddenly she'd lost both her name and her papa. Her mother whispered, "If we're going to get on the ship, we'll have to go along with him."

Mr. Criddle went on as if nothing had happened, "We're lucky: not too many years ago this voyage would take months instead of ten days. This ship can do eleven knots using both sail and steam. All the Guion vessels begin and end here. We've one stop to pick up some starving Irish at Queenstown (Cork) and then it's New York."

He walked away, then came back to say, "Don't leave the luggage." He paced about grumbling, "Far too late to be sailing – should have sailed in March – arrive in time to plant a garden. Not surprising the ship isn't full. What the deuce is the holdup now?"

He was not the only anxious person waiting to board. Elise heard a snippet of conversation— "You let that emigration agent talk you into this? I was happy! What's to become of us?" Elise also felt sorry for the Scandinavians: *they don't understand our language and they've already been on the way for weeks.*

Eventually their trunks were collected, hoisted up in a great sling and lowered into the ship. By morning's end people began to board. Mr. and Mrs. Criddle had a private cabin in intermediate class: a common sitting room, freedom to move about the ship and meals served at a set table.[6] By tipping the cooks he did even better, "Excellent supper for wife and children from the galley – Beef steak, hot buttered toast, baked potatoes – good, very."[7]

Meanwhile, Elise and children, laden with bags and purchases of the previous night, arrived on deck. An arm pointed, a harsh voice ordered, "Steerage, down there." The light dimmed with each step. At the bottom, they hesitated, adjusting to the darkness. Then, finding their bunks close by, they perched there, clutching their bundles and looked about.[8]

Light filtered down the stairs and ventilation hatches. They were in a long narrow space with two tiers of bunks on either side. A low board separated individual bunks from each other. They saw no dividing curtains, no chairs, or hangers, not a cupboard nor a shelf to store their bags.

"It's bloody awful! What's the stench? Phew! . . . We're sleeping with all these?"

---

5 According to Myrna Brandon Paquette Minnie's granddaughter.
6 American Guion advertisement of that time. Price of adult ticket: US $40.
7 July 18, 1882.
8 Captain responsible that his ship complied with the 1882 U. S. Passenger Act: food, sanitation, ventilation, space. Steerage accommodation must have at least a 6 ' ceiling with only 2 tiers of bunks. Each berth, 6 x 2 x 2 ½ ft., was all the space a steerage passenger could claim.

Minnie found her voice. "Must be a mistake. Steerage is for poor immigrants."

"Papa will put it straight when he finds out," Isabel said assuredly.

Their mother didn't have the heart to explain. *We're not here for lack of money. British people send their servants steerage. It keeps them in their place.*

Elise looked about for a private space. There was none. So with Cecil on her knee, she gathered her children and began, "It's been hectic . . . when your papa cleaned up his office last spring he told me he was done with business. Wouldn't need the drawing room anymore. . . . Wouldn't be paying the rent for our flat. I didn't want to upset you. I'm sorry, I should have told you. He said he was leaving for Canada, going to take up land. I thought he'd gone. But he came; wanted me to go too. Said, "I have a wife and four little children. Mrs. Criddle needs someone to help her." I was shocked and told him, "No. We are managing . . . you girls have an education and can find a position. Edwy can apprentice." I tried to resist, but he wouldn't give up. He promised you boys farms of your own. And you, Minnie and Isabel, can marry rich young farmers. Doesn't that sound like your papa? . . . He made it sound so fine. . . . I didn't know what to say. You were all at school. I wanted time to think it over. . . .

"But your papa said, "The ship is leaving in two days. It's now or never. He wouldn't wait, not even a half hour for you to come home." I broke down. "Alright, I'll do it for the children."

"I want to tell you something else. . . ." She hesitated, "You thought I was Mrs. Criddle. . . . But your papa married the Mrs. Criddle we met yesterday. I've agreed to help her . . . for your future. He doesn't want anybody to know he is your father, so you must remember **not** to call him 'Papa' . . . and you must always **obey**."

A wall separated the new Vanes from their father. Their mother was now Mrs. Vane, domestic servant.

They looked around their strange dim quarters. Elise assured her children, "Even in this dungeon, we are within God's loving care. You know your papa didn't approve of my faith, but it's a part of me. My mama prayed with us every night and God has helped me through many a tough time. I have an English prayer . . . I'd like to say it with you now before we start."

Though the children hadn't done much praying, they followed her example and bowed their heads. "Lord, God, you have called us to ventures of which we cannot see the ending, by paths as yet untrodden, through perils unknown. Give us faith to go out with good courage, not knowing where we go, but only that your hand is leading us and your love supporting us; through Jesus Christ our Lord. Amen."[9]

They were quiet until Cecil looked up at his mother's face and said, "Mama, will you sing? I feel better when you sing."[10]

She hugged him and said, "My boy, you know I love to sing . . . since I was a little girl, even smaller than you." She thought a moment and then added, "I've so many songs in my head . . . in my own language. But let me see . . . I think this one is good for today. English people sing it too.[11] She began singing—

A mighty fortress is our God, A bulwark never failing,
Our helper sure amid the flood, of mortal ills prevailing . . .

Her voice gained confidence in spite of her inward distress and the tune, also loved by the Scandinavian passengers, drew them closer. Soon their voices, singing in their own language, blended with the English.[12]

Did we in our own strength confide, our striving would be losing,
Were not the right man on our side, the man of God's own choosing . . .

As the singing died away she thought of another. "I'll tell you about Pastor Rinckart. . . . Long ago there was a war in our country. Armies fought back and forth for thirty years. They knocked down people's homes, flattened their crops and took their animals. People in Pastor Rinckart's village had nothing to eat; hope was only a faint glimmer. He spent a long weary day conducting funerals. That night he wondered, 'Why haven't I given up?' And it came to him, 'The only thing that keeps me from going crazy is having a thankful heart.' He wrote a hymn and people still love to sing it, in England too. It's always good to be thankful."

Now thank we all our God, with heart and hands and voices,
Who wondrous things has done, in whom this world rejoices,
Who from our mother's arms has blessed us on our way
With countless gifts of love and still is ours today. . .

The singing calmed her troubled spirit and brought comfort to many others below the stairs.[13]

---

9 St. George's German Lutheran Church, London, Evening Vespers.
10 Faye Young remembers Great-uncle Harry saying about his mother, "She had a beautiful voice".
11 At that time people learned by rote and would know many songs and hymns by memory. Elise, an educated woman, was an unusual steerage passenger.
12 In Scandinavian countries the state church is Lutheran. Of the 199 passengers, half were from Great Britain; the rest from Sweden and Norway.
13 Stevenson, Robert Louis. *The Amateur Emigrant*. Travelling steerage in 1879 he observed: second class passengers were 'ladies and gentlemen', those in steerage merely 'male and female'. He also noted that his companions in steerage displayed more genuine human kindness than he ever saw above the deck in the upper classes.

The landlubbers felt a strange sensation. "I think we're moving! Sure wish we could see."

Their floor shifted strangely, "Yes, indeed. I'm sure of it, our ship has cast off."

A bell rang. A dirty looking man bawled, "Dinner! Line up with your bowls!" Haggard folks got up from their bunks. The Vanes held back, watching the ladle empty once per bowl. Holding them carefully, the hungry staggered back to their bunks. But their faces soon showed disgust, some even spat it out on the floor.

"I'm not hungry," Minnie claimed.

Her mother encouraged her, "We must try . . . to keep up our strength."

The gruel gave the passengers a common bond. Elise searched faces, longing to find someone from her homeland.

Next day they watched expectantly as Mr. Criddle came down the steps and paused for his eyes to adjust. He looked about, then muttered, "How can anyone breathe this fuggy air?" Then turning abruptly, he retreated without a backward glance.

His comment stung. Elise had already looked for a mop and bucket, but to no avail and tried to smooth over their disappointment, "It's good we learned to put up with foul smells in Southwark." *But this is worse than the tannery. No wonder people die on the way to America.*

Mr. Criddle came again the next day to tell Elise he had provided the purser with her family's information. "If they question you, tell them Mr. P. Criddle reported everything already." Having delivered his message he retreated to daylight and fresh sea air and made the following notation.

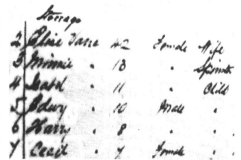

Visited the Emigrant quarters – horrified – smell enough to poison a rat – could only stand them a few moments at a time and then rush on Deck for sweet air – or lie down sick.

Not one to be idle, Elise kept her knitting needles clicking through many a tearful discussion. Her daughters had idolized their papa. They felt his betrayal terribly! They wept, talked, and sobbed again. Gradually they all came to understand that their only choice was to fit into their father's plans. It was going to be hard not to say, 'Papa'. But, from now on, he would be Mr. Criddle and the painful change would be their 'forever' family secret.

Elise's mind went in circles. *Should I have refused? We were managing and I had the 70 extra Deutschmark from my brothers for emergencies.*[14]

—————

Another day Edwy looked up to see Mr. Criddle with another man looking down on them from the railing around the hatch. "It's awful," he said to Minnie. "I feel like one of those caged dogs we used to see before the dogfights. Men looked them over trying to choose the winner."

Edwy didn't hear Mr. Criddle say, "'Tis very much the people's own stupid helpless fault. They seem to be mostly of Scandinavian origin, a wretched, dull, simple, idiotic lot. What will they do in the States?"

Or the American reply, "Oh, die, I guess. Don't much matter, I suppose – they'd be no good anywheres."[15]

—————

On Saturday morning, a distraught woman from London begged for help, "I'm taking my Mary to her daddy in America. She's got the runs bad." A call went up for the ship's doctor, "Come, see Mary O'Connor's little girl." He came, looked, and said, "Beyond hope." Then, as he walked toward the steps added, "The rest of you—no need to worry. 'Tis not catching."

Little Mary died about noon. Fellow passengers prayed for both the sobbing mother and the little soul too soon departed.[16]

The weeping mother reminded Elise of her own loss. *Fourteen years ago . . . I took my baby to the doctor.*[17] *"Hydrocephalus—water on the brain . . . no cure."* *. . . . I loved her so . . . clasped her to my heart . . . but my poor little Mabel died. Thank God, I had good friends. . . . Elizabeth went to the officials and to the grave, so I wouldn't be alone.*[18] *. . . . I was so homesick. . . . Might have returned to my family. But another was on the way. I poured out my heart in letters to Friedrich and Marie. They lost their first baby too.*[19]

Later that afternoon a sailor came below, walked straight to the grieving mother still rocking her dead child. Everyone watched as he took the tiny body from her arms, carried it up the steps and out of sight. Fearing death might call again they said, "We must not lose hope."

---

14 Harrer, Friedrich, letter from Mannheim, July 3rd, 1882, "Today Carl sent me 40, to which I have added 30, total 70 DM."

15 July 16, 1882.

16 July 22, 1882.

17 Birth Certificate: Vane, Mabel, born May 20, 1867. Father, Percy Vane; Mother, Elise Mabel Vane formerly Harrer. Lambeth Church, Surrey. Obtained from General Registrar's Office, London, October 3, 1979.

18 Death Certificate: Mabel Vane, daughter of Percy Vane, Independent Gentleman. Died March 18, 1868, 15 Palace Rd. 'Hydrocephalic Convulsions'. Informant, Elizabeth Hooper, present at death. Registration District, Lambeth, County of Surrey.

19 St. Peter and Providence Lutheran Church, Heidelberg. Birth Registration, July 5th, 1866. "Delivered here a stillborn boy to Friedrich Harrer, and his wife Marie nee Bauer. Buried by a town official, 7 AM, July 6. Evangelische Archiv, Heidelberg.

Passengers finally settled, but only to have their sleep shattered by the fog horn. No matter that it was a familiar sound to the Vanes having lived near the Thames. It was so close, so unnerving. And it was just the first in that long night. Sleep? Impossible!

Even noisy nights end, and there was Mr. Criddle once again staring down at them from his viewpoint at the hatch. Perhaps he hadn't slept well either considering what he claimed in his diary to have seen below.

Women, men, children, huddled up anyhow amid sawdust, biscuit tubs, gruel and emigration utensils. . . . But – helpless sheep in an uncommonly small and dirty fold would certainly look happier, and be better treated, I think.

Without recourse, the Vanes had to endure his upper class sport of 'steerage watching'.

The fog cleared for a while in the morning giving them a little peace, but then the blasts resumed until late afternoon. When they felt certain their ordeal was over, relief passed through steerage, "I guess we've made it safely though the icebergs."

Steerage got its cleanup that Monday morning for the health inspector.[20] Then Wednesday evening they heard shouts, "Land! Land to the starboard!" The steerage passengers began to joke among themselves. "After tonight, this nightmare will be nothing but stories for our grandchildren."

Captain Rigby checked his paperwork—readied his manifest for the American authorities.

I, Char. L Rigby, Master of the S S Wisconsin, do solemnly, sincerely and truly swear that the following List or Manifest, subscribed by me, and now delivered by me to the Collector of the Customs of the Collection District of New York, is a full and perfect list of all the passengers taken on board . . . and the names and ages of those who died.
Sworn this July 27, 1882
C L Rigby [21]

After two weeks less a day in the darkness the Vanes climbed up the stairs to daylight and stood once again on terra firma. Their fellow passengers were herded toward Castle Garden for processing while Elise and family were pulled aside to exit with the Criddles through regular customs. Wise to the ways of the world,

---

20 July 24, 1882.
21 Captain signed the legal document that all information on the manifest was correct. Within Mr. Criddle's group were several errors: Percy Criddle, age 30 instead of 38. Destination, United States. Seven-year-old Cecil is female. Isabel, almost 13, is a child of 11. Consequently Edwy and Harry's ages were both shifted younger.

Mr. Criddle handed a 'small hard package' to an official and their luggage passed unopened. In the crush, and bringing up the rear with her little boy, Elise lost some precious coins to a pickpocket.

Coming from ten days in the cold, dank hold, the ninety-seven degrees heat of New York felt good for the first half hour. Mr. Criddle got them to a hotel, while he organized the next leg of their journey. Returning later, Elise overheard him tell his wilted wife, "Beastly railway! – No first class coaches – got tickets – Your cousin's waiting in St. Thomas."[22]

That evening, squeezing into the wretched 3rd class car, they found seats among labourers, farmers, and lumberjacks. It was a raucous, jolting, and hot night followed by an endless day. Long after dark they stumbled wearily into the customs office at Niagara where another 'little hard package' saw them through. Early next morning they were rushing to catch the train for St. Thomas when a horse-drawn truck narrowly missed the tag end of the line—Cecil and his mother.

In St. Thomas, Mr. Criddle established them in another 'primitive' hotel. Norman, Harry, and Evelyn had come down with the dreaded traveller's condition—diarrhoea. Elise's servanthood began in earnest and the new nannies, Minnie and Isabel, honed their skills caring for the little Criddles. After dropping his wife off at her elderly cousin's home, Mr. Criddle took care of business—changed some money, made travel plans, and indulged in his own pleasures.

Between her sessions at the washtub, Elise sandwiched time for writing to her family—letting them know they were safe in Canada. Then, with more trust in the future than wisdom, she unstitched her brothers' money from her petticoat and slipped it into an envelope. Giving Edwy one of her few coins she sent him off to find the post office.[23]

In spite of illness, they boarded the Friday morning train—destination Chicago. Not wishing, however, to repeat their recent experience of train travel, Mr. Criddle had them detrain in Sarnia to go by water to Duluth—818-mile shipping route via the Great Lakes. Fog delayed their vessel's arrival, forcing them to lose another precious summer day. Elise saw little but the hotel laundry.

Boarding the 'propeller Quebec' the following night, all six Criddles—little Beatrice quite fevered—found themselves in a 'precious cram' of a single cabin. The Vanes, with steerage still fresh in their minds, enjoyed the fresh air, blue skies, and the clean waters of Lake Huron. Lake Superior, however, treated the Quebec to such a vicious storm that even Mr. Criddle regretted his choice of route.

---

22   Robert and Elizabeth Nicol of Scotland came 51 years earlier. Retired market gardener, visited England. Their only daughter, Jane, deceased age 18. Thoughts of another inheritance may have crossed Percy's mind. But Mrs. Nicol left her money to her housekeeper and faithful nurse. Obituary, *St. Thomas Daily Times*, June 2, 1890.
23   Harrer, Friedrich, Mannheim, Germany. Letters July 3, 1882 and August 19, 1882.

19

Fortunately, the ship's career did not end that season. They made land safely early Friday morning.

Once again Mr. Criddle joined the lineup to purchase train tickets— Duluth to Winnipeg. And also once again undertook his battle over excess baggage charges. "You want extra for every pound over 150? All the brochures in England said 300 pounds per ticket. I won't pay. . . ."

He argued, but in vain, and ended up passing another $16.25 through the wicket.

"It's an outrage. Damn everyone!"

By seven that evening, their coach was lurching along on the newly constructed tracks heading northward. Mile after miserable mile they bounced through the night chasing Mr. Criddle's dream. As Elise's head bobbed in weariness, she thought, *I'm like Sancho Panza, Don Quixote's faithful servant, who followed his knight. We have given up our world for this nightmare on wheels.*[24]

Their ride was rough indeed, but the passengers might have counted their blessings. Earlier pioneers had trekked through those forests, around lakes, over creeks and rivers to reach the prairies. Three years earlier, the Clarks (their soon-to-be neighbours in Manitoba) had travelled this route by covered wagon.[25] Among their necessities they'd packed preserved jams, jellies, and pickles. The women took flour from the barrel each night to bake bread over the campfire. Their cows provided milk, the hunters, meat. Elise's daughters, lately of the city of London, could never imagine eleven-year-old Fanny Clark, perched on a log, writing up the day in her diary. Did she envision her story someday appearing in an English publication, as indeed it did?

> Soon campfires were blazing, dishes were rattling, tents were being erected, and our camping ground presented a picturesque and busy appearance. After the evening meal we all gathered around one common fire, where talk and story passed the hours all too quickly until bedtime.[26]

The railway had soon pushed through to the Red River and settlers could board a riverboat to complete their journey downriver to Winnipeg. By 1882 the track was pushing northward by-passing the boat. The Criddles took the train for granted and were disgusted by having to transfer to another conveyance several

---

24 Cervantes, Miguel de, *Don Quixote*. In the famous Spanish novel of 1602, Sancho Panza acts as a faithful squire to his idealistic knight, Don Quixote.
25 Four families, twenty people including a baby of seven months from Cottam, Ontario.
26 Clench, Fanny Clark. *Westward Bound in '79*. Canada West Vol. IV, London, October 1908. From original. Reprinted in *Sipiweske, Light Through the Trees: 100 Years of Wawanesa and District*. pp. 186-192

times. The last straw for Mr. Criddle was to be assaulted by, "No room for your baggage. It'll reach Winnipeg in the morning."

"I'm not leaving without our luggage!"

The conductor gave him a choice, "Stay here with your baggage, or get in the van."

He chose the latter and by Saturday evening, August 12, they rumbled over the Red River and into the Winnipeg railway station. At the Golden Eagle, Mr. Criddle, still irritated, complained of 'so-so food', legions of flies, and noted in his diary:

> I failed to get any of my luggage last night, thanks to the P.C.R.C. so had to sleep minus nightshirt and with no clean clothes to put on this morning.

Monday morning he called at the Government Land Office where a kindly official told him. "Going to Brandon? Buy your supplies there—save freight charges."

Tuesday's train went without them as well—Mr. Criddle's precious watch stopped for 40 minutes during the night.[27]

Wednesday morning, Mr. Criddle slipped away. Elise suddenly realized that to catch the train, she and her children needed to gather the luggage and get everyone to the station. He turned up at the last minute and counted the baggage. "One missing! The **Vane** trunk! All you had to do – get here with the baggage. And you didn't bring your own. Just the trick for a stupid Dutchman!"

Elise couldn't believe her ears. *He's always taken charge . . . I waited, worrying we'd miss the train again. To be called a Dutchman! The Dutch! Despised by all Englishmen for attacking their navy.*[28]

She couldn't know Mr. Criddle was wrestling with her identity. Servants always go by their names, Betty or Bess or Lizzy. But he couldn't say her name, 'Elise'—too many memories. Nor, could it be Mrs. Vane—one can't have a servant of equal status to one's wife. 'Dutchman' had just slipped off his tongue. It would do. His wife wouldn't object. His British friends would smile knowingly, and for all the Canadians knew, she was Dutch. The derogatory name divorced him from the woman he once professed to love.

—◦◦◦—

The railway had been completed all the way to Brandon. They should have had an easy time of it. But that Wednesday morning was a scorcher, the coach an oven, only made bearable by a breeze from the open window. Then the train

---

27 August 16, 1882.
28 Mr. Criddle referred to Elise as 'E' in his diary until Winnipeg. From then on he referred to her as 'the Dutchman'. Several years later, he rewrote his diary for publication and referred to her initially as 'our German lady friend'. In the novel, *The Foreigner*, Ralph Connor used this common English slur, "We'll get to the mine, or I'm a Dutchman."

stopped, held up for track repair after a freight train derailment. Mr. Criddle stepped down and walked along the track counting butterflies and wild flowers while the women and children sweltered. Four and a half hours later they chugged on. Brandon appeared rather raw, having only sprung to life in the last year, but he found accommodation at the Brandon House Hotel for $10 per diem. Bedraggled and ill, Beatrice, Norman, and Elise in particular, settled in. Hordes of beastly mosquitoes added to their misery. That night a dramatic and violent prairie thunderstorm welcomed them to Manitoba.

The map at the Land Office showed the most accessible land had already been claimed. The only homesteads still available were in the Townships 8 and 9 of Ranges 14, 15, and 16. A driver was engaged and Mr. Criddle set off prospecting:

> Took gun – small hamper with canned meat, cheese, biscuits and apples – also a small flask of Brandy and a stone jug of water. In a box were tin plates, cup, wash basin camp kettle (Billie), soap, revolver, some tea – change of socks and shoes, knife, spoon, fork – Reference books, maps and papers. We (I and driver) had also some rope, a compass, a spade – 2 MacIntoshes, great coat and a rug.

Mr. Criddle felt inadequate when it came to choosing good land, yet he didn't consult anyone, pushing aside his fear that the soil was too light and sandy. He chose to see the beauty of the prairie in the warm, August sunshine and philosophized: "Is it better to have poor land with lots of wood, good shooting, and beautiful landmarks, making one remotely happy. Or rich land half drowned in wet weather which makes one wish he were dead?"

After two days he returned to Brandon and weighed the pros and cons of the land he found most attractive—NW ¼ of Section 32, Township 8, Range 16 West 1. By Monday morning he'd overcome any lingering doubts. "Of course I shall some day find I've done wrong – but it can't be helped. I've been to the Lands Office and done the trick and there's an end of the matter."

The following day he busily set about gathering the necessary supplies:

> . . . yoke of oxen $150. – everyone says they're a bargain. They are nice looking creatures and quiet – but how the D. I shall manage them, Heaven alone knows. I fear Currie's Landing – needs must, however, when the D. drives. Purchased a wagon $90. – a clumsy looking thing, but useful perhaps – also set of harness and whip $15. . . . Hope to get off tomorrow . . . Got a fairish stove (Gurney's, Ontario) and fittings (i.e. boiler, pots and pans) for $27. . . . Bought 2 second hand tents – the one 12 x 12, the other 10 x 8, with poles, ropes, etc, for $34. – as good as new.

While Norman was under a doctor's care, his father rounded up a second wagon. Then Thursday morning, the boy somewhat improved, he decided to set out. He soon discovered, however, two wagons could not take everything. Wagons were scarce, but finally he unearthed a man who said, "I'll go as far as Currie's Landing."[29]

"That's only halfway? What's your price for the whole trip?"

"I'm not fording the Assiniboine. . . .Take it or leave it."

His offer of cash didn't help this time, "Obstinate as pigs – or Canadians."[30]

Even with three wagons, there was too much cargo and the teamsters refused to overload their own teams. They discussed, lifted, rearranged, but to take everything, Mr. Criddle's oxen had a very heavy load indeed. Finally the little caravan set out. Two horse-drawn wagons followed by Mr. Criddle and his oxen, with Mrs. Criddle and little Beatrice seated beside him. The other little Criddles perched on top of the load, while Elise and her five children hiked along the trail behind.[31]

Eight miles later, at two that afternoon, the second driver pulled off the road at Currie's on the bank of the river, unloaded the stove and other utensils, and took his leave. By that time the oxen had caught up. But they scented water ahead and in spite of Mr. Criddle's "Whoa, **Whoa**!" They fairly galloped down the riverbank to quench their thirst. Taken by surprise the Criddles hung on to their perches for dear life. The cool brown water was also a great relief to the Vanes' hot feet. "Why not camp here?" they said to each other.

But the order came, "We've got a long way to go! Get your shoes on."

The oxen though, were not ready to move and paid no heed to Mr. Criddle's shouts. The driver came to his aid and after much shouting and a few sharp cracks of the whip, the team finally threw their weight into the harness. Their muscles bulged, their hooves dug into the loose earth, and up they went to the top of the bank and stopped, their sides heaving from the exertion. The driver returned to his wagon and led across the unbroken prairie following the faint trail of bent grass remaining from Mr. Criddle's prospecting trip.

Progress was slow and their ride worse by far than the train. Badger holes and molehills[32] unseen in the grass sent the wagons lurching—forward, back, and from one side to the other. Those fortunate enough to ride bounced up and down like peas on a shovel. Now they'd left the beaten trail behind, the walkers also had to step carefully over uneven ground hidden in the long grass. And sometimes,

29 Currie's Landing, eight miles southeast of Brandon.
30 August 24, 1882.
31 Vane, Harry. *Early Days at St Albans, Aweme, Manitoba, 1882-1900, Criddles and Vanes.* His name only re further footnotes for this source. Family collection.
32 Pocket gophers are commonly and incorrectly referred to as moles.

unseen by the people up front, they caught hold of the wagon box to get a little help. They slogged slowly on in the hot afternoon sun for another two hours before the oxen balked. After a consultation, the driver advised, "The oxen can't take this heat. Need a rest. Horses can make better time, let's go on ahead, unload, and come back."

The women found themselves on the open prairie with two enormous cattle beasts and no other humans or even a habitation in sight. Elise helped Mrs. Criddle down and lifted the children from their perches. Collapsing in the shadow of the cart, they waited under an endless sky on a sea of grass.

Hours later, anxious eyes spotted the returning wagon. The driver shifted some of the oxen's heavy load to his wagon and still had space to let the foot-weary ones trade off walking. He prodded the weary oxen to their feet and both outfits set out again. As evening approached, clouds of mosquitoes feasted on the slowly moving cavalcade. Eventually, in the dusk they sighted Mr. Criddle on a knoll, waving, pointing toward his chosen site.

He'd dug a shallow well and trampled down the grass for the tents. Water pails were filled until everyone's thirst had been quenched. The driver tethered his horses; Edwy and Harry learned quickly how many pails a thirsty animal could drink. The driver soon had a fire blazing, and nourished with 'tea and some grub' everyone felt better. Mrs. Criddle fretted about Norman, "Poor lad, horrid trip." She spread a blanket out on the grass for her little ones.

Nothing in the emigrant books had prepared Mr. Criddle for tent raising in the daylight, let alone by the light of a flickering fire. Luckily, their man knew about such things and cheerfully offered his expertise. Elise breathed a sigh of relief when Mr. Criddle let the Canadian take charge and everyone took care to do his bidding, attaching ropes, unrolling canvas, raising the ridgepole. When a peg slipped into the long grass, little Cecil was quick to find it. More than once the axe was misplaced, but finally, the 12 x 12 tent was up, the pegs secure and the ropes taut. Blankets were moved in and weary Mrs. Criddle settled in with her little ones for the night.

The smaller tent went up more quickly. The driver took one last check on the animals and turned in with Mr. Criddle. With her youngsters bedded down, Elise took stock of her throbbing feet. *A month's travel didn't prepare me for that walk. I'm proud of my youngsters, they've been real troopers. The driver's a fine man.* She chuckled. *Would we have ever got those tents raised without him? I'm glad he stayed; I'll not worry about wolves or bears tonight.*

Then she lifted the large tent flap and found just enough space to stretch out. *Thank God this day is over!*

Chapter Two

Tenting in the Promised Land

The moon with its backdrop of stars shone down on the little camp. Fitted into the tent like pieces of a puzzle everyone but Elise was already sleeping, breathing deeply.

She couldn't relax. Her feet ached and strange rustlings in the grass worried her. *What's on the other side of this canvas?* . . . When she heard nothing more she began to think of the future. *What will tomorrow bring?. . . I could worry until morning, but it won't help. Better be thankful . . . survived steerage . . . trains . . . sea sickness . . . diarrhoea. Like Pastor Rinckart, I should concentrate on God's blessings. Bless the Lord, oh my soul, and forget not all his benefits . . . I'll concentrate on the words . . . Bless the Lord, oh my soul . . .* Finally, she too drifted off to sleep.

Elise wakened to faint light filtering through the canvas and listened a moment to the breathing of Mrs. Criddle and nine beautiful children all peacefully sleeping. *I pray we will all get along in this strange land.* Then still in her green travel dress, she crept carefully toward the door, pulled open the tent flap, slipped out, and stood facing the dawn.

Now forty-two, she remained a striking woman, tall and slim with oval face and dark eyes. A long, dark braid was coiled around her head. There were, however, streaks of grey in her hair and weariness circled her eyes. And no wonder she felt weary, for yesterday's long walk had climaxed weeks of travel, poor diet, sickness, and many late nights doing laundry.

She took a deep breath of fresh morning air and thought of the flowers she had seen along the trail. *That cheery splash of yellow . . . must ask their names. There's plenty of empty land here for my boys. But I have to keep my side of the bargain. . . . Better stop dreaming. . . . Give me strength, dear God; I'll be needing it to get through this day.*

It's going to be hot. . . . Must go for water. Forgetting bears and Indians, she picked up the water pails and followed the faint trail in the grass to the well 400 yards away. She planned as she walked; *light a fire straightaway, the driver wants an early getaway. Percy and Mrs. Criddle expect warm water for their morning toilette. . . . Too bad the stove is sitting back there on the riverbank. What do we have? Water pails, big pot, ladle, a kettle . . . did I see the basin here last night, or is it back with the stove? However will we manage?*

Reaching the shallow well, she knelt on both knees, and bracing herself with one hand, stretched downwards to scoop some water into the pail. Pulling it up she heard herself say, "That wasn't so hard. Not full, but will have to do. Now the other one." Before returning to camp she squatted behind some low shrubs, and then cupped her hand and reached down for some more water to splash on her face. Refreshed, she smiled, thinking of home. . . . *My schooling didn't teach anything about living in this wilderness.*

Back at the tents there was still no sign of the others, so she collected some dry twigs and branches for a fire, found the matches and got it blazing. She carefully placed the pot on the burning wood. *Better watch that the sticks don't give way or I'll lose my water.*

She paused to examine her new world in the strengthening light. A sea of grass to the east and north, a wood to the south, and to the west—earth and sky blended into one. *I feel so tall . . . like a giant in the sky. How is it that I, from the Neckar Valley, come to be standing in this flat land? Will I learn to see beauty in this wild country?*

The men appeared and were soon ready for breakfast. As Elise served them porridge, she heard the driver pass on a helpful tip, "Mosquitoes are bad this year always worst in the evening. Get the youngsters to gather wood and get a good blaze going. Then pile green grass or branches on top to make lots of smoke to keep the beggars away. I didn't bother last night—too late. But, I like to make a smudge for the horses when they're not in a stable."

Getting to his feet, he said, "Well, I guess I'll be going. Thanks for breakfast. Good luck to you, Mr. Criddle."

He strode off and, out of the corner of her eye, Elise saw him throw on the harness and hitch up his team. He waved as he drove away, and she thought: *now we're really on our own.*

⋅⋅⋅❦⋅⋅⋅

The Vane youngsters began the day with delight—freedom, space—a great wide world. Then her boys got their first assignment, "There are plenty of dead branches about – make a pile for your mother's cooking. And we'll need another pile over there for a smudge." They raced to see who could make the highest.

Minnie looked after the four little Criddles while Isabel carried all the Criddle baggage to the smaller tent and laid out their beds on the ground. Mr. and Mrs. Criddle opened trunks and rummaged through their possessions, adjusting to the realities of their new home.

That evening, in his diary, Mr. Criddle wrote about his first day on his homestead:

Hard at work all day doing nothing – that is – poking about generally, opening boxes or trunks, and losing everything the moment I had found it. Shot 13 ducks in Pond to north of Tent – Cut my first tree down – a small one but it took a deuce of a lot of hacking.

Two hours before sundown when mosquitoes started biting, he got the bonfire blazing. "Now get branches."

They laid them on top and soon thick smoke was oozing out. Within its shield the family dined, joking about their day. As the breeze shifted, the smoke-sitters moved along like musical chairs. When Elise finished her chores, she joined them and soon songs of merry old England wafted with the smoke over the prairie. Accustomed to smudges, the oxen came to stand in the smoke, chewing their cud in peace.

It was not exactly fun and games for Elise, bending over the campfire and without a table. Mr. Criddle solved the pot-tipping problem with a tripod, and it worked wonderfully until one of the supports burned and the merrily boiling wild duck landed in the fire.[1] Infuriated, he lashed out, "Do you propose to feed us duck à la ash? Stupid Dutchman! Ruined my good duck!"

❧ ⸾ ❧

Six days later, the novelty of campfire food had worn off. The gentleman announced, "I'm going to Currie's Landing to fetch the stove. Be back early evening. Come along Edwy."

Any anxiety he felt for his first expedition was well hidden. But first, he had to harness the huge beasts. He held up the first collar, struggled to figure out just how to get it on and buckled up. The docile 'boys' tossed their horns, but stood patiently. Then, having finally succeeding in getting them hitched to the wagon, he climbed up and seated himself. Positioning the lines in his left hand and whip in the right, he shouted, "Get-up." Nothing happened. He slapped the reins on the broad backs, snapped the whip around their heads. They didn't move. He shouted till the air turned blue. The pair just stood there switching their tails as if he were a fly. It took sixty-pound Edwy at the front pulling on Bill's rope with all his strength, and a good deal more whooping and whipping from the rear to get the big fellows moving.[2]

All that sunny day the women dreamed of having a stove with a real oven! Their cookbook had no campfire recipes, and efforts at baking had not gone well.

---

1 Criddle, Alma, *Criddle-De-Diddle–Ensis.* p.15.
2 January, 1883. Mr. Criddle made no entries in his diary from the day after arrival until the latter part of January due to busyness and then illness. He filled in the missing months the end of January, planning to publish.

Under Mr. Criddle's guidance, Elise had dug a hole in the ground, built a fire in it, and guessed the temperature and time. Trial and error were bitter teachers; the Dutch oven unforgiving. The bread was charred on the outside, often doughy in the centre. Elise felt the sting of criticism.

Their anticipation grew as the day wore on, but having made the trip themselves, they understood the distance. They had to be patient. As the sun set, however, anxiety took over. They built up the fire hoping the light would guide the travellers home. Their camp became a small island of light in the vast dark world. First the little ones were put down and, as the hours dragged on, the older youngsters fell away one by one. In the end, only anxious Mrs. Criddle and Edwy's worried mother, kept doggedly adding fuel to their beacon.

An early morning spy spotted something on the horizon that grew into the approaching team. Excitedly the children raced out to meet them. But not until Mr. Criddle had eaten breakfast did he explain. He'd been 'benighted' in the darkness; wrapped young Edwy in his greatcoat and kept his loaded gun ready for any signs of bears. At daybreak, he retraced the wagon's tracks until he recognized a neighbour's shanty and got his bearings.

All able hands helped to slide the cook stove to the back of the wagon and then to the ground. There it stood in its white enamel glory in the great outdoors. Mouths watered for baked bread, muffins, and puddings à la Mrs. Beeton's *Book of Household Management*.

⁂

Mr. Criddle relished English callers, invited them to dine, noting, "We have to lie or sit minus chair or stool as best suits the joints."

Without concern for the cook, he expected a meal with all the trimmings and they ate circling the tablecloth spread on the grass. Mrs. Criddle presided as hostess; her young maids served in proper style. When Canadians ate with them, he imagined the guests benefiting from their example. They, in turn, humoured his hoity-toity ways, and tried to warn him of the coming winter. He didn't see an urgency to stockpile firewood, "We've plenty of wood – easily got when it's needed."

⁂

Elise might have thought more about their winter wood supply, but she had her hands full just coping. One windy day the big tent blew down and one side ripped from top to bottom. Canvas was tough material for a lady's sewing kit. The girls held the torn edges in place while the women, with the help of their thimbles, forced the thread back and forth though the canvas. Stitch by stitch, a sturdy new seam closed the gap. Instead of waiting for the wind to go down, they set about raising it immediately. Gusts of wind threatened to drag them off across the prairie in full sail, but they hung on. After a good deal of shouting, hanging onto poles, tugging, more orders, untangling ropes, they finally got the main lines fixed. From that point it was a simple matter to get their tent habitable once more.

They had learned two important lessons. Check the pegs often; adjust the ropes as necessary. Furthermore blankets had a habit of soaking up moisture, so a daily airing was added to the servants' list of duties.

Fortunately, the weather remained unusually balmy that autumn. Elise adjusted to the outdoors and filled in for a man whenever her strength was needed. Her body toughened; her hands grew rough. She watched her sons' growing skills with axe and saw. *Any mother's heart would swell with pride to see these little woodsmen.*

Following the digging of a new and deeper well, Mr. Criddle decided his permanent home should be built almost at the summit of a prairie hill 500 yards north of the tent site. He gave up the lower more protected spot for better visibility to prevent another night wandering about the prairie. He explained to the family, "The winds will be better able to blow the snow away from our doorstep."

Moving camp took two full days. In the process, the children made an unpleasant discovery about the sweet little bright-eyed pets they'd found. No one suspected that besides offering bread crumbs to the mice, they were also providing nest building materials. Their 'sweet little pets' had become **pests.** The assault began. Sticks and brooms stabbed and jabbed until every furry creature had either vanished or been exterminated. Then the children, their eyes red, faces streaked with tears, brought their damaged garments to their mothers. Once more needles and thread came to the rescue. Both women sympathized, "It's a shame. You'll see. . . . We'll fix them . . . good as new."

There were other things a needle and thread couldn't repair: pinched fingers, stubbed toes, and scraped knees. There were prickles from rosebushes and tiny cacti. Blood ran from scratched mosquito bites. After treatment Elise applied her best balm for drying up tears: a kiss, a hug, and at the appropriate time, "There you go . . . all better."

Mrs. Criddle, fortunate in having a housekeeper and two maids, escaped the exhausting labour of other pioneer women. Elise, on the other hand, was trapped. Of all her jobs, the family wash was most labourious, time consuming, exhausting, and backbreaking. But it was her duty to keep all twelve active people in clean clothes.[3]

---

3   Hall, Mrs. Cecil, *A Lady's Life on a Farm in Manitoba.* (W.H. Allen: London,1884) Mrs. Hall noted that their pioneer household assigned two women to the wash, two full days each week. p. 28.

Wash day began by fetching water from the well. She stoked the fire, heated the boilers, and after breakfast, filled the washtub. She refilled the boilers on the stove and sent the pails off for more water. On her knees, she bent over the tub beginning with the lady's white garments. Then from light to dark colours, she rubbed each sweat-soaked cuff and collar between her knuckles. It was rub and lift, suds and lift, rub and suds until she was satisfied right through to the dirtiest work shirts and pants. To wring out the garments she stood and lifted each, heavy with water. Beginning at the top, she twisted it tightly, and then flipped the top of the coil over her arm and moved downward, twisting and flipping, squeezing out the last possible drop of water. One after another she twisted and rolled until all were ready for the next step—rinsing. She dragged the tub a short distance away and dumped the dirty water. With clean water she began again with the delicate whites and worked until everything had been rinsed twice. Her hands were red from hot water, then blue from the cold; her knuckles were raw.[4]

To lighten the monotony, she would sing her favourite German songs. Sometimes cheerful, often wistful Schubert melodies floated away on the breeze.

Das wandern ist des Müllers lust, das wandern
To journey is the miller's joy, to journey!
A wretched miller he must be who never thought of journeying
Of journeying.

Other times she sang with the children:

Here we go round the mulberry bush, mulberry bush, mulberry bush . . .
so early in the morning.
This is the way we wash our clothes . . . so early Monday morning.

When the children tired of the game, she went back to her own childhood and sang:

Was sollen die Fleissigen Waschfrauen tun, . . .
And what should the busy washerwomen do? They wash; they wash, the whole
blessed day.

The clothes were spread out on the grass and ground cedar. *The 'sensitive garments' are a problem. We've no beds to hide them under. Those shrubs will have to do.*

Elise's heart leaped with joy to receive a letter. News from home! Taking a quick look around, she thought: *Work can wait. I'm going to sit down and read my letter.*

---

4 Scrub boards and clothes wringers were not in common use where money was lacking or a housekeeper did the work at no extra expense.

Mannheim, 19th August, 1882
Dear Percy and Elise!

Your precious letter from St. Thomas with post-date August 3rd arrived on the 16th of the month. We are all happy to know that you arrived safely. You have often been in our thoughts, wondering how you were making out.

Mariechen [affectionate form of Marie] went to Karlsruhe,[5] with our Anna and Elsa, to Carl's place, day before yesterday; since the girls have vacation . . . Mariechen took your letter and the money you sent along. He is also very happy to hear the good news from you and sends his warm greetings. He will also write you and took note of your address.

He shares my point of view that you do not need to send us the money: you should have used it for your children! We hope and wish fervently that you will enjoy your stay in the far away country and that your hopes will be fulfilled.

The letter dropped to her knee. . . . *It was so kind of my brothers to send me that money. . . . It was only right to give it back. Will I enjoy my stay here? I certainly am in a faraway country.*

Mother is here with us since a few weeks ago and she cried for joy when I brought your letters home. She is well and happy and enjoys the children, who are a bit wild when with her. She had difficulty walking. When she goes for a half hour walk with us she is dead tired.

She tried to imagine her mother walking slowly. *She was always so light on her feet.*

We would appreciate very much if you would, as soon as you are more or less settled, to write us again. It is very interesting for us and, of course, also for mother

---

5 The letters C and K, Carl/Karl, Carlsruhe/Karlsruhe, were interchanged in the letters and records. Although confusing, I have retained the usage of the writers.

what you do and how you live in your new and certainly strange surroundings. We are wondering if it is a good country and if it is densely populated where you live.

Pausing, she thought, *I'm sure there are people out there, but where, I do not know.*

> *I have studied the map but it isn't accurate. I found Manitoba and Lake Winnipeg and a large number of forts, so it appears to be a wilderness populated with Indians. Although the country is the same latitude as Germany, it will be much colder there than here. All this, your daily living conditions, climate, and interests, and we would like to form a picture of how you live. . . .*

> *Maybe you could, perchance, send us a newspaper from out there. You can glean a lot of information of living conditions in a country from it. In short, the more detailed accounts you write the more appreciative we will be.*

> *I shall close for today, sending heartiest greetings and best wishes for your future well being. Greet your children for all of us,*

> *mother, Mariechen and your Friedrich.*

> *[PS] Our children have started a stamp collection. They would be happy if, without causing you extra work, you could send them Canadian postage stamps, a great rarity over here. If you wish we could send you some postage stamps from here.* [6]

She lingered, savoring her news, *it's a blessing to have so loving a family. I was feeling homesick . . .* Turning back to the first page she noticed that Friedrich had written, *"Dear Percy and Elise". . . . Oh, oh! That won't do here. It was alright in England but there are other eyes here.*

How can I ask my brothers to change a habit of 14 years? . . . Do I tell them Percy is too busy here to read their letters? I'll pass on their greetings. . . . I'll think of something. They can continue to address the letters to Mr. P. Criddle; he'll skim over them anyway.

It's true, we are busy. I'll tell them all the things I have done: put up tents, help lift the stove, built fires, cook without burning myself or the food. If I had the time I could write a book.

Her boys tried hard to please, but even Edwy, her oldest, tallest, and heaviest, was still only a boy. Their efforts usually brought a good cuff on the ears.[7] When her boys didn't have the strength, Mr. Criddle shouted, "Dutchman!" She had to drop whatever she was doing and respond.

⁓⊶∞⊷⁓

Mr. Criddle dared not delay starting on a shelter. His first effort to hire help failed, so he tackled the job. Axes over his shoulder he marched off to the bush with the little boys. He selected a promising tree and with much hacking brought it down. He showed the boys how to lop off the branches while he cut down

---

6 German letters are in family collections. Translated by Helen Ens, 2001-2003. Will not be further footnoted.
7 March 7, 1883. Age and height in feet and inches: Edwy, 11, 4.2; Harry, 10, 3.10; Cecil 7, 3. 2; Norman 7, 4.

another. All too often, once the branches were gone, the trunk didn't look so promising. Still they would have to do. As the boys worked, their skill improved and before long they were also felling trees.

The house he planned would be—outside measurements, 15' x 31', with four rooms. Of the two downstairs—one, 14' x 18', on the east end for himself and his wife with a log wall separating it from the smaller kitchen-dining-family area. The walls were to be at least seven feet high, the roof pointed—eight feet at the centre. There'd be two windows downstairs and then perhaps next year he'd make a small window upstairs in each gable end.

Each day he went off to the bush with the boys. Elise looked at the hole he'd already dug for the cellar. *I'd like to see some walls going up. I can help by cooking, but logging is men's work.*

Estimating 150 logs would be sufficient; Mr. Criddle was ready to get them out of the bush and up to the building site. Elise had been wrong to think it was men's work. She and her children were drafted to drag the logs out of the 'woods'; only Minnie, Mrs. Criddle's helper, was spared.

When his wife complained at finding herself minus the cook, he explained, "Have to attach each log to a rope – we – it takes the whole lot of us – to haul it along – through a perfect jungle. Then we have to lift the deucedly heavy log onto the wagon. . . . Lots of pinched fingers! Expect the job to take at least three weeks."

They were about finished when a young neighbour happened to come by. He took in the scene and offered Mr. Criddle a lesson in the fine art of hitching an ox to a log to drag it up the hill. With relief Elise went back to the cook stove, while Mr. Lawrence conducted another lesson in ploughing. She watched them thoughtfully as she stirred the pudding. *I'm hoping that's not my next undertaking.*

The 'Canadian' looked over the pitiful supply of logs. Next day they took both teams of oxen to the tamarack swamp where there were plenty of fine straight trees. Lawrence cut a load for himself while Mr. Criddle cut down a fine fat one. Even better, he spotted another splendidly tall straight mast of a tree. This he also cut and dragged home at the tail of his wagon. Showing it off he boasted, "Measures forty two feet long—just the thing for a flag and signal staff!" He looked at the boys, "Got a job for you – need a hole deep enough for the end of this pole."

The house waited while they erected a flagpole.

Souris River flowing into the Assinoboine

Lawrence* made another discovery; Mr. Criddle had never yet ventured to their closest town. He assisted the greenhorn driver down the steep bank at Uppers' and made use of their small ferry to cross the Assiniboine River. They passed by the Souris Mouth Post Office operated by the Clarks,[8] and continued south to Millford. And there, only six miles from their camp, were lawyers, doctors, and businesses stocked with all manner of supplies, from implements to lace tablecloths.

But, having beautiful laces and fabric so near did not entice Mr. Criddle to offer either of the women the pleasure of shopping for their own sewing supplies. Elise began to lose hope of visiting other women to exchange recipes or receive tips. Nor had she learned the names of the yellow flowers. She felt a foreshadowing of suffering to come as the sun moved lower in the southern sky, the nights grew longer, and the mornings brisker.

Courtesy: Archives of Manitoba

*   2nd printing: Frederick E. Lawrence, born 1847, Richmond Hill, Ontario. Went to England at 22 seeking an inheritance for his father, Sir Charles Lawrence who had eloped and come to Canada. Frederick married Martha Ann Clay on his third trip there in 1875. He came west in 1882 to establish his homestead and went back east. Returned in 1883 with Martha, three children and her brother John G. Clay. Two more sons, Arthur and Charles, were born at Aweme. Criddles apparently shunned their high-born neighbour, for she is never mentioned in Mr. Criddle's diary. Martha suffered greatly from loneliness. Informant: David Lawrence.

8   Early settlement developed at Souris Mouth, later named, Two Rivers. During the years of riverboat transportation, Alexander Clark operated the post office on the south side. Sidney Upper had a store in his house on the north side of the river. During a Clark reunion, my mother, Ruth Clark, pointed out where it had been.

Chapter Three

If You're Not From the Prairie,
You Don't Know the Cold

Each morning Elise lit a fire in the stove and set the porridge cooking. She thought as she stirred. *What a fine food is oatmeal. Without a fuss, it replaces every fancy English breakfast. We've no milk or cream . . . no eggs, but a tummy full of warm porridge launches our day.*

Mr. Criddle returned from Brandon with his wife's list of groceries and the black cloth she wanted. She checked off the items as he unpacked the boxes, "Oatmeal, potatoes, cheese, rice (very inferior), beef—probably an aged ox, full of muscle, hams (forelegs), baking powder, salt, pepper, sugar (wretched), tea (made apparently of tea dust, poplar leaves, currant stalks, rose thorns, and grit), treacle, and canned meats—Armour Curing Co., the best, currants, raisins, caraway seeds, cocoa, coffee, onions, and a pot of marmalade, and mustard, and . . . for medicinal purposes a bottle of brandy."

Elise smiled inwardly when she heard 'a bottle of brandy'. *I wonder how many more he tucked away. . . . Is that the real reason for his two-day trip? I hear one can buy everything but spirits in Methodist Millford.*

Nothing was said about the cloth, but Elise understood she'd have to get busy with her needle and thread. *Mrs. Criddle wants me to look like a proper servant. I'll save my green dress for special occasions.*

She glanced over the bags, tins, and packages. *How can we keep all this dry and out of the reach of those filthy little thieves? Seems mice can chew their way into almost anything, even the flour barrel. At least right now we'll be able to enjoy a bowl of rice pudding with raisins and . . . cream. Well, that's where we need a good imagination.*

So, with Mrs. Beeton's recipes for roast duck and rabbit pie, their meals were elevated to the level of 'superior'. Preparation became almost a routine. The stove still stood in the open. As Elise laid the fire one cool morning and held a match to the kindling, she wondered: *how much longer will we enjoy these beautiful mornings? Visitors keep warning us about winter. I can't believe it will be so cold as they say.*

❦

One windy day, the new settlers were alarmed by great clouds of smoke billowing skyward in the distance. The red glow that night looked even more threatening. "Don't worry," Mr. Criddle assured them, "It's miles away."

Elise worried anyway. *We are surrounded by tinder-dry grass and the wind often changes.* Furthermore she'd overheard a neighbour say, "You need a fireguard. I plough around my place. There's been a fire through here before. That's why there are so many dead trees in your bush."

Mrs. Criddle had tossed and turned all night fearing the worst. So, having had a ploughing lesson, Mr. Criddle harnessed his oxen with confidence. Then Edwy, leading Billie, tried to obey his shouts of "Gee!" . . . "Haw!" The oxen probably knew the difference, but to the small boy under pressure, right and

left were easily confused. Nevertheless, they made a start, the ploughshare dug in, and the sod turned. But when the oxen straddled a scrubby ground cedar, the blade struck its root. The plough handles pitched upwards. Mr. Criddle bellowed "Whooooa!" as he flew through the air. He picked himself up, caught his breath, pulled the point free, and shouted angrily, "Getup!" Edwy leaned into Billie's rope again. But there were more roots. Before long the boy got his ears boxed. Mrs. Criddle, who stood by encouraging her husband, was pressed into duty. By the end of the day they had their fireguard.

Edwy had better success retrieving the ducks Mr. Criddle shot, spurred on by hope of duck for tea. Before long Edwy became his indispensable helper, his 'Boy'.

❦

Their built-in British pride and attitudes kept the Criddles from befriending their Canadian neighbours and the day a wife came along with her husband, Elise noticed their icy reception. Mr. Criddle made it clear to Elise and her daughters, "Mrs. Criddle is an English lady. It's not proper to mix with 'common' women. They are not the type of people we want snooping about asking questions."

She concluded, *I had friends in London, but I'm afraid, not here. I must keep my place . . . no gossiping with visitors.* Furthermore, she overheard instructions for Minnie and Isabel, "Our business is our business. You can't trust them – don't go answering their dammed impertinent questions. And don't go wandering off – the country is dangerous – bears – wolves."

❦

Mr. Criddle had all the logs he thought necessary to build his house. "I'm totally ignorant in log hut building. Lawrence tells me, he knows something of the business. I've engaged him to assist – $1.75 per day plus grub." Within a day or two, however, Mr. Criddle gave up house building entirely. It didn't suit him to be routed out of bed at an early hour to spend his day lifting 'disgustedly heavy' logs.

Lawrence offered his friend Lonsbury.[1] The two Canadians went right to work but soon ran out of suitable logs and went to Spruce Woods for more. Work was delayed again when Lawrence got called home to Ontario. Fortunately, burly Mr. Smith agreed to take his place. Joining the Criddles at dinner and tea during construction, the Canadians also made good progress in the line of better manners.[2] As the mornings became noticeably cooler, they built a small shanty to shelter the cook stove and trunks. Before the cook stove made the move, there was a disgustedly cold, snowy Sunday. As Mr. Criddle sat cross-legged and miserable in his little tent he thought of a better use for the shed.[3] Summoning help, he moved in the small parlour stove he'd bought in Brandon and told his wife, "We can make ourselves quite cozy – name it 'The Shanty'. Fetch our blankets and things from the tent."[4]

Norman, Evelyn, and Stewart expected to move with them but their Papa said, "No, the place is too small. You'll be sleeping with the big boys."

Their mother tried to help them accept their lot, echoing their papa, "It's just too small for all of us. The baby needs to be warm."

The little boys cried . . . begged . . . howled at the top of their lungs . . . but to no avail. Their father lost patience, "English boys are tough."

"I don't want to be tough. I'm cold," they cried, but the door remained closed.

Elise gathered the little orphans into her tent and set about comforting them. "I'll be your Mama Dutcheen. Norman and Evelyn, go with Minnie and Isabel to get your blankets. Bring Stewart's too, we'll be nice and cozy." She settled five-year-old Stewart on her knee along with her own Cecil. Minnie took in Norman. Isabel's blanket encircled Evelyn. Harry and Edwy wrapped themselves together in their blanket to complete their circle. Elise's heritage of Black Forest stories was going to come in handy as three teary faces peered out. She plunged right in—

"Once upon a time there was an old goat who lived in a house with her seven little kids. She loved them all dearly. One day she had to get some food. So she

---

1 Various spellings used for the name but on the homestead document, he signed 'Lonsbury'.
2   January, 1883. ". . . got so far as saying Good-morning or Good-night to my females which is the more extraordinary as Canadians appear to deem and think women utterly beneath their notice, excepting for purposes of drudgery. . . "
3   Vane, Harry. "Lonsbury, Pete Smith and Bruner built the shanty for Mr. Criddle and Alice before they began work on the big house. Mr. and Mrs. Criddle and their young ones lived in that for the first winter."
4   January, 1883. "A. [Alice] I and Bobo lived therein till 2 days after Xmas when I moved up into the House. . . ."

gathered her children around her and said, 'I have to go into town for food today. Please be on the lookout for the wolf. If he gets into our house, he'll gobble you up, skin, hair, bones, and all. He'll pretend to be friendly, but whatever he says, don't open the door and let him in. If he changes his looks, listen carefully. The wolf has a gruff voice. And don't just look at the face, the wolf has black feet.' Then, she kissed them and waved goodbye."

The little boys forgot about their own difficulties as Mama Dutcheen's story unfolded. At last they succumbed to the sand-man and were rolled up in their blankets for the night. She said to herself, *no doubt their parents will let them in during the day. They'll get used to sleeping with us. I'd better have lots of stories up my sleeve.*

⸺❧⸺

Elise now had seven youngsters in the 12' x 12' tent with no heat but their own bodies.[5] Minnie continued her role of looking after the three little boys as well as taking the hot food her mother prepared to The Shanty. She also looked after such personal needs as emptying their chamber pot. Harry did their chores – wood in, ashes out, water in and slop out. One day he was holding Mr. Criddle's white cricket pants to warm at the stove in preparation for the gentleman's dressing. Seeing a wisp of smoke, he jerked the pants away, but it was too late. Harry got the worst bawling out in his ten year life.[6] His mother tried to comfort him and did the best she could with the scorched pants.

Elise's other children had jobs in addition to gathering fuel. Edwy, as the oldest lad, carried up the water. Then, helped by his little brothers, he prepared the piles of kindling and sticks from larger branches, broken or sawed to fit into the stoves. Isabel looked after the blankets, shook off the frost that had formed each night from their breath and tried to get them dry. After the well froze solid, Cecil was in charge of filling the snow-pot on the stove. It took many buckets to get enough water for drinking, his mother's cooking, and washing. The Shanty had its own snow-pot which Harry filled and refilled. The cook-stove's little firebox needed constant feeding, the more so because its warmth was quickly lost to the cold prairie air. And so throughout the hours and days, Elise mothered as she worked.

Living outdoors had some advantages for Elise as she had a view of all activities in the camp. Mr. Bruner unloaded boards for the roof, floor, window frames, and doors. She saw the precious flagpole come down to be converted into a ridge pole for the house. She was pleased to see the roof boards nailed in place; short logs fitted to stabilize the openings for the door and windows and at last the door

---

5   Stoves set up in a tent with snow banked about the walls, could be reasonably warm. There is, however, no mention in the diary of the cook stove being moved to the tent. Also, Harry writes of the severe cold.
6   Vane, Harry.

set in its place. She observed the men slice slivers off logs and fit them into spaces in the walls. The day finally came when their work was done. Mr. Criddle told them, "I will make the place windproof – still hundreds of tiny cracks, but mortar will do that trick."

Elise knew her mother would be pining for news. Wrapping herself in a blanket, she tried to explain as gently as she could how she was managing to keep warm. To explain why she hadn't written she told some white lies about the long distances to neighbours and the post office.

As the thermometer dipped lower, Elise's knitting needles clicked steadily, turning out mitts. *I'm glad we have wool, but I didn't realize we'd need something for our hands. Surely it won't get too much colder. We haven't any greatcoats.*

But it did get colder. Every ounce of Elise's creative abilities went into helping her children cope. The Vane family's days were overshadowed by the cold and the need for firewood for both cooking and The Shanty.

In the bitter 25-below cold of December and without proper clothing, Elise led her troupe of gatherers heroically into the bush for wood. The cold pinched ears, noses, and chins. It slipped through their mittens to fingers, through footwear to toes. They hurried to the bush; worked like Trojans to keep warm; shouted encouragement to each other.[7] The boys became handy with their axes, chopped down dead trees and quickly lopped off the branches for the others to drag out of the bush. Within the bush they were sheltered from the wind and the hard work helped them keep warm. Carrying and dragging the branches home was the worst, and they cried with pain as warmth returned to their hands and feet. Elise wrapped them together for warmth, praising them for their courage. "You have done well. We have to have wood, or we'll perish." She even imagined a headline in *The Brandon Daily Mail:* FAMILY OF HOMESTEADERS LOST TO A MANITOBA WINTER. But, from somewhere in her past, came the will to survive; every ounce of her faith in a caring God kept her going.

The weather became unbelievably cold. Mr. Criddle sheeted over the openings still waiting for windows in the new house and moved in the stove. At last the cook was sheltered from the wind. And with the stove set up, she and the children moved in.

The roof was not shingled. Daylight also showed through the walls still waiting to be chinked. Elise closed the door to the Criddles' big empty room, piled wood near the stove, and laid their blankets on the floor. She and her girls

---

7   Vane, Harry. "The snow was deep and it was cold. We were not dressed for cold weather – no overcoats or sweaters in those days. That first winter it all had to be carried up by hand since there was no sleigh."

wrapped themselves together; the six boys, without undressing, combined their blankets and body heat.[8] The stove tried its best, but it was no match for the challenge. "Is this warmer than the tent?" they asked their mother.

One morning not long after their move, she set the kindling in the cook stove, carefully laid the wood on top, struck the match and held it to the kindling. A tiny wisp of smoke curled upward, but it was not drawing as usual toward the stovepipe. She replaced the lid, but the smoke simply seeped out around it. When the wood caught fire, more smoke poured out through every crack on the stove top. The children started coughing. The little Criddles rushed out and banged on their parents' door. Elise and her children grabbed their blankets trying to wave the smoke out the door. Once the stove really got going, its heat forced the smoke up the stovepipe and the door could be shut. The porridge pot began to boil. Breakfast was on its way.

Although no real harm was done, it was a horrid bother. Elise was puzzled: *it can't be all my fault. Why does it happen? I hope he'll ask someone. . . . Their boys don't mind though, gives them an excuse to get into their parents' warm bed.* She chuckled. *A rather rude awakening for them.*

An Indian on horseback came by one day and Elise pointed him to Mr. Criddle. There was a deer slung over his pony and through gestures and nods, they struck a deal. Elise was delighted to have fresh meat, but she would have been surprised had she read the exaggerated account of the event in the diary.

Of him I bought about 216 lb of venison after some bargaining for $1.50, from a deer he had that morning shot and was carrying home to camp, slung across his pony's shoulder.

Mr. Criddle's chinking job, he soon discovered, was a very messy, tiresome task. He began with hot water to 'slack the lime' and mixed it with sand the boys brought to him. He managed fine with the inside walls. But, when he ventured outside with his bucket and trowel, trying to force the mixture into countless cracks, the cold attacked. Between constant warm-up breaks, he doggedly forced the stuff in as far as he could before it solidified. Finally, feeling very proud of his accomplishment, he announced, "Got the job done – very windproof and snug."

Elise had doubts, remembering that her brother Wilhelm didn't do such work in freezing weather. *It's frozen in place now, but if we ever warm up . . . will it stay in place?*

---

8 Vane, Harry. "The rest of us lived in the big tent until Christmas, by that time Lonsbury and Co. had partly built the house and we moved in to that. The roof not yet shingled, we could see daylight through it."

Just before Christmas Mr. Criddle said, "There'll be mail – I'll walk – Bruner's place is on the way – he might drive me."

He returned, riding on Billie. Jumping down, he immediately doubled over clutching his leg. "Got a deuce of a cramp!" He managed to get out some bad news, "Two homesteaders close by – found frozen. An old homesteader – sawing firewood. And Joe Robinson inside his shanty."[9]

That said, he shivered and as fast as he could hobble, made for the Shanty and his warm chair by the stove. His wife wrapped him in blankets and dug out his brandy. Billie, on the other hand, couldn't stay, since there was neither barn nor hay. Edwy and Harry had to lead the big ox back three miles to Bruner's, his winter boarding home.

Even though Mr. Criddle complained of pains, he managed to down a real English Christmas dinner with its cherished plum pudding and mince pies, while imagining the goose, chestnuts, celery, Stilton cheese, and wine. That night Elise did her best to write her family a positive letter.

She was about to learn the Criddles would be dependent on her resourcefulness and courage.

Mr. Criddle had taken to bed, "Got Rheumatic Fever, and there isn't a decent doctor to be had." His wife wrapped him up and for days they were both constantly on the move. She hoisted him up from their blankets on the floor to his chair, and then had to help him down again while he moaned, "The first thing I'm going to do when I recover is to make myself a bed."

Two days after Christmas, thinking the new house, he had dubbed St. Albans would be warmer than the thin walled shanty, they moved the invalid. Now, at least, both stoves would be heating one building. Still, survival depended on their servant. Elise inspired her children and with their help kept the fires burning. *I must not say anything*, she worried, *but, what if . . . ?*

January's weather continued bitterly cold; and she, with her little wood-crew ventured forth every day no matter how bitter the weather.[10] The truth was that the stronger the wind, the lower the temperature, the more wood they needed. And each day their wood supply became ever more distant, their journey longer.

Elise's heart skipped with joy to receive a letter from Friedrich and she stood leaning over the warm stove to read it.

---

9   *Brandon Daily Mail.* Dec 23, 1882.
10   Jan, 1883.Wood-crew with Mr. Criddle's nicknames—Elise/Dutchman; Isabel/Dico; Edwy/Boy; Cecil/Shrimp.

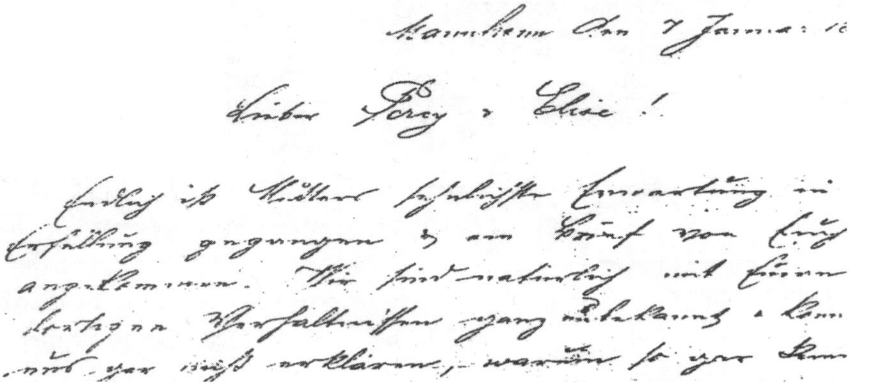

[handwritten letter in German script]

Mannheim, 1883 Jan. 7

Dear Percy and Elise,

Finally mother's most longed for desire is fulfilled and a letter from you has arrived. Naturally we are totally ignorant of your living conditions over there and we could not explain to ourselves why no news whatsoever from you made its way here. But now we know your isolation and long distance from the Post Office, we understand.

Praise God you are well and we hope that you don't suffer too many hardships and we join you in wishing that the winter will pass by in good time and the better season will ease your living conditions.

What really your work is, and how you plan to earn a living, you have not written us and yet we are very much interested. If my guess is correct you plan to build up a farm and you want to cultivate the land or something similar.

What does Souris Mouth mean? Is it a village, a valley or a mountain? We do not know, or is it the name of your Post Office?

Please write us about it. Mother longs so much for some news. Mother enjoys it a lot at Carl and his wife's place. As long as she lived in Heidelberg, we always feared she would become sick and would have no one to help her. In all cases this is a better arrangement.

In this area all along the Rhine there have been floods. Villages half an hour from here have been inundated as a result of breaks in the dykes and more than 100 houses have collapsed. The people barely escaped with their lives and lots of cattle drowned. . . . three nights the water was so high that they feared it might go over the dykes, so that the military and firemen kept watch and built emergency dykes, so they were successful in saving the city from a flood.

On the whole we are fine. We could use more money, now that the children need so much more for their education . . . Main thing is we are healthy and that is our wish for you as well. May the New Year be a blessed one and may you be happy in it.

With this wish and the heartiest greetings from all of us, I remain your brother,
Friedrich

She looked it over again. *He wrote this in response to the letter I posted before the winter really began. I **thought** I knew about the cold. I'm wiser now, but I can't tell them. It would kill my mother.*

The cold eats into my bones . . . the pain of my swollen feet. Frozen too many times . . . . Servanthood sounded so easy. Can I carry on or should I give up? Are we all going to perish? Should I send the boys for help? We have kind neighbours. . . .

There was a moment of hesitation and then, *No, I can't quit, not yet. I am breathing. . . . I can still stand and walk. I came for my children, **their future**. . . .*

I can't do this alone, but God has not abandoned me. Like Pastor Eckert, when all seemed lost, he kept loving, kept being thankful for what he had, and that got him through. God in Heaven, please I beg of you, give me strength to prepare one more breakfast, one more trip with the children for wood, one more cold night. Percy will recover, this cold has to end.

Elise also drew courage from her past. *My ancestors saved their lives by hiding in the forest and had to start over. My grandfather kept on teaching even after all his Austrian textbooks had been burned.[11] My grandmother's courage. . . . My Papa and his little brother, only boys, started with the postal service. My mother's people had to rebuild after the French attacked and blew up our castle. Herr Erhardt's school was in ruins after the '49 revolution. He rebuilt. And I benefited.[12] They didn't give up. Nor will I. And my dear children, bless them, will help me through this, and we will all survive.*

Elise's resolve faced a good many tests through the early weeks of that frigid January while Mr. Criddle lay ill. The struggle to survive overshadowed every part of her being, while despair claimed Mr. Criddle. In time, the invalid began to show improvement, taking an interest in those about him.

Near the end of January, he asked for his diary, saying, "I vowed to keep a daily account of our life here. But failed. Never mind – can't be helped – as I

11 Fenner, Achim, *Schule in Badischer Zeit: 1810-1818.* Andreas Harrer, Latin teacher in Radolfzell 1803-1812. (Primo-Verlag Stockach) Stadtmuseum, Radolfzell, DE.

12 Institut Erhardt, *Erhardt'schen Lehr–u. Erziehungs-Anstalt für Mädchen.* She studied: German, (spoken, grammar, composition, literature); French, the same; English, (speaking and writing); History, Geography, Drawing, Music, Bookkeeping, and Deportment. School Report, Elise Harrer. Family collection.

have at present nothing to do but sit and read or write. I will endeavour to do so now. Five momentous months – the most exciting time of my earthly existence. I'm going to get my story published. " [13]

The exertion overtaxed his strength and he had to rest. But in the following days he scribbled away, filling page after page, recalling the events that filled the time since the day after their arrival.

⌘

Letters arrived and among them was one from Karlsruhe. Elise took it eagerly, *Carl's handwriting! I hope there's nothing wrong.*

Karlsruhe, 16ᵗʰ January, 1883

Liebe Elise!

> *Finally we have received your much awaited letter from the first Christmas Day, giving much joy to all. On Christmas Eve Mother, my wife and I thought of you especially and especially mother emphasized, that her greatest Christmas joy would be to receive news from you and your family. Her greatest desire has been fulfilled. In order that Friedrich and his loved ones could partake of this joy, we sent the letter to Mannheim that same day.*

> *We were happy to read in your dear lines that you are all healthy and up-beat, which is really the greatest good here on earth. May God grant you happiness and contentment in other respects as well! May you enjoy life in your new home, that is our sincere wish for you.*

> *. . .*

> *Your misfortune had depressed her so that she couldn't sleep anymore and sat all day on an easy chair and in her mind occupied herself with you. Thank God, that has changed now, especially your letter has freed her of this worry; she has again received a will to live.*

> *Yesterday she attended a beautiful Concert in the Concert Hall, today she wants to go with my wife to the theatre where the "Meistersinger von Nuernberg" by Richard Wagner are being presented. Only three weeks ago she could not have been persuaded to attend such entertainment.*

[He wrote that Friedrich and his daughters had been ill with Scarlet Fever]

> *In closing I beg you and Percy, whom I greet most heartily, not to let us wait so long for some news about you. So live happily, greet your lovely children from mother, my dear wife and me. Mother and my wife greet you and Percy many thousand times.*

> *May God take care of you.*

> *Your brother Carl.*

Elise stood thinking. *I'm glad I wrote. Christmas was always such a special time for our family. My Mama is happy to be at Carl's. . . . Amalie is looking after her like a daughter. But, I should never have written about the cold; it was cruel.*

⌘

---

13   January, 1883.

They had a mild spell the last week of January which gave the wood-crew a little respite. But, the cold returned with a vengeance. Edwy came in from sawing wood. "I can't stay out, even a few minutes."

By early February Mr. Criddle, although still hobbling about the house, took over the command of his estate and hired Mr. Smith to fetch a load of wood.

"I'll go to the Tamarack, get you some hardwood. Holds the fire better than poplar."

Unloading later, he came in to warm up, "It's a brute of a day. Thermometer went down to 40 below yesterday."

Mr. Criddle responded from his chair beside the stove, "I should have hardly thought it so cold."

That load ended Elise's wood gathering adventures, but the hardwood was tougher for the little boys to saw. And splitting the logs was another challenge. The wood also unleashed an entirely new foe in the form of a horrid black liquid that oozed from the joints of the stove pipes and dripped to the floor. Elise was still assessing the mess when she heard a whooshing sound in the stovepipe. It turned from black to orange, then red, and the glow spread up the pipe to the ceiling.

"*Lieber Gott!* . . . Oh, dear God, help us, our house is on fire!"

Terrified, she ran upstairs. The wood around the stovepipe was darkening. "Get some water and wet towels, in case it catches fire," she told the girls. Then she thought of the roof, "What if sparks land on the tar paper?"

She ran outside and looked up. Masses of smoke and sparks spewed from the stovepipe. Fortunately, as the glowing sparks arched through the frosty air, they turned black and fell lifeless to the snowy roof.

Mr. Criddle shouted from his room for water. Receiving a pail, Mrs. Criddle panicked. She heaved the water as high as she could at the red-hot pipe. The spitting and steam sent her reeling backwards. As the roar died away, the only remaining problem was to mop up the mess.

They learned to tolerate the fires, the smoke and creosote, and took the clean-up in stride.[14] When Mrs. Criddle took ill, her husband studied *Watson's Practice of Physic* until he was 'black in the face,' but couldn't decide what ailed her. Meanwhile, Elise, stretched to her limit, thought: *I'd like to be sick too, for awhile.*

⤶⤷

As winter's grip relaxed, the stoves finally succeeded in heating the house to a livable temperature. But that blessed comfort actually added to Elise's stress as mortar loosened and fell from the spaces between the logs. And even more

---

14 Feb. 16, 1883. "Had the chimney on fire only twice within 2 hours this morning. It had been dripping like mad."

troublesome, the icy coating on the walls, gradually built up during the winter, began to melt. Water ran down soaking everything on its way to the ground. And upstairs, as the sun's rays warmed the tar-paper roof, the frost, suspended on its underside, began to let go. And, not content to soak everything upstairs, the water seeped through the boards and dripped to the dirt floor below.

The days lengthened, the Governor's energy returned and he engaged Smith to lay a floor in the house. Then he rehired both former workmen to draw logs, build a barn and fowl house. The hay he'd bought the previous fall, not realizing it was on the other side of the river, had to be fetched so his oxen could come home from Bruner's. And the seed wheat and potatoes he'd purchased from Clark's had to come across before the ice on the Assiniboine broke up. Lonsbury also agreed to plough twelve acres by May 10, at five dollars an acre. Mr. Criddle had everything in hand. He was all optimism, "This will be a good year."

March brought marvelous bright warm days when snow can be formed into snowballs. The youngsters at St Albans started rolling and lining up their huge balls into what grew into a great snow castle. It had five-foot walls, a ten-foot tower, passages, and chambers. Mr. Criddle was a boy again.

Elise managed to get away from the stove. The children, their faces glowing with pride, gave her a tour. She felt so encouraged by their enthusiasm that she was more optimistic than she had been since the coming of the cold. *How wonderful to enjoy the outdoors like this . . . spring must surely be on its way.*

Chapter Four

Forty Bushels an Acre

When the snow retreated from the open spaces, Cecil found some little purplish flowers with fuzzy stems and brought them to his mother, "Found them over there, Mama, come and see." But such rambles were not to be. Instead, they went with shovels and an axe to the hill behind the house where the smudges had burned off the ground cedar the previous fall. Mr. Criddle pointed out the area "The tops are gone, now we have to get rid of the roots – make way for the plough. Five acres – ten days should do it."

At first Elise found working in the cool, misty morning a pleasant change. She yanked on the end of a root while Isabel dug to loosen it with the shovel. Harry and Edwy also worked together. Little Cecil and Norman carried the pieces to a central pile. Mr. Criddle didn't care for the backbreaking job and by noon had another plan, "I've got to make a proper well. I'll need the Boy. Carry on. "

Edwy had done some digging on a well the previous fall, but the sides had caved in. This time Mr. Criddle began with a 4' x 4' x 10' crib of tamarack poles. He set Edwy digging while he finished and nailed steps to the inside. They dragged it to Edwy's hole and lowered it into the pit. Edwy kept digging, filling pail after pail for Mr. Criddle to lift to the surface. As Edwy dug himself down, the crib went too. There was no water at ten feet, so they added another and by seventeen feet they had a good supply of drinking water.

One afternoon a root picker noticed something coming from the west. Elise stood to rest her back and made out a team of horses. They all pretended to keep digging, but they soon knew there were two people on the wagon. Before long they saw more heads on a rather bulky load, and then two dogs trotting alongside. The wagon even had crates hanging outside the wagon-box. Harry said, "Don't know the horses."

The man waved and pulled up. "Hello! I'm Fred, Fred Blaine. Got off the train at Chater. On our way to homestead 32.7.15, about a dozen miles further on."

He saw Mr. Criddle hurrying toward him and climbed down. Before long they were invited for tea. Mrs. Blaine, who also seemed pleasant, handed down her little one, and then clambered down herself. "We'll all appreciate a rest. Our team too . . . such a heavy load."

A tousle-haired girl Isabel's age and four younger ones found their own way to the ground. Elise wiped her grimy forehead and thought, *Mrs. Criddle will need to receive her guests . . . I'd better clean up and help Minnie with tea.* She told her young helpers, "Your first visitors, make them welcome."

The Blaine kids were as outgoing as their parents. The oldest introduced herself with a friendly smile, "My name is Harriet." Appreciating such a big audience, she held their interest by carefully cracking open a box on the side of the wagon. Curious, the city children moved closer. Two noses appeared in the opening. She pointed, "This is Tiger. This is Ginger. We don't want them to get out till we get to our new place. Cats keep the mice away. . . ."

Harriet had more to show them, "Climb up on the wheel, like this." And she nimbly stepped, via spokes, to the hub of the wheel and to the top where she stood looking down, "This is Dad's big pet." In turn they all clambered up, heard deep guttural grunts and saw a strange smooth round snout pressed between the slats of its crate. "That's Berky," she giggled, "You can feel her nice pink nose. She's going to have babies." They timidly touched the snout's smooth surface and giggled too. The tour moved on: four ducks, two turkeys, twenty-nine chickens, and five cattle beasts. Then Harriet took a pail and a three-legged stool from the back of the wagon and sat down beside the cow. In a very short time she had some foamy white milk for tea.

But the Blaines had a long way to go and departed directly after the meal. From then on the Criddle boys begged their papa to get them a cat, a dog, and, especially, a cow.

The lingering snowdrifts retreated into the bush and green blades began to show through the brown of last year's grass. Elise overheard Mrs. Criddle tell her husband, "There will soon be grass for a cow. It would be wonderful to have milk for the children and butter for our bread."

Elise wondered *who's going to milk her? Farms have milkmaids . . . Minnie and Isabel are maids. I expect Isabel will have this honour.*

Assuming his Canadian workmen knew something about the makeup of a good cow, Mr. Criddle set off for Brandon with Lonsbury and Smith. Finding no livestock for sale that afternoon, they decided to enjoy themselves and made for the residence of Woollhead, his boyhood friend from England, also planning to homestead. Albert hadn't changed over the years, and the festivities began as Mrs. Woollhead served them the last of her mutton and bread pudding. She also dished out a good portion of hatred for all things Canadian. The men laughed at the poor woman and then retreated to the hotel with her husband to continue their festivities with the excuse that there was nothing else to amuse themselves with.

After another day's holiday the purpose of the trip resurfaced, and Mr. Criddle made his purchases: a promising Collie, five weeks old for five dollars, a Spanish cock for a dollar, and a pretty little cow for seventy dollars. Her seller claimed, as he patted her back, "My Nellie here, is three years old. Going to calve in eight days—her first."

It didn't register with the buyer that the farmer might be selling the cow for kicking or low production. Nor did he consider that a first calf would be its mother's introduction to a milk pail. Happy to have accomplished his mission, he and Lonsbury 'tooled' on home – their feet high and dry in the wagon. Smith, leading Nellie, picked his way home through the spring slush and mud.

A very different drama was unfolding on the home front. The root-crew looked up from their work to see a fire bearing down on them. They raced into the house shrieking, "Fire!"

Terrified, the women grabbed every pot, kettle, and pail they could lay their hands on. The boys fetched water from the well. Then with vessels in place, the defense courageously took up positions along the edge of the fireguard ready to douse sparks that jumped across. The flames came leaping toward them. They braced for action. But suddenly, the wind shifted. Like a miracle, the fire turned back on itself. By the time the men arrived on the scene only a few smoldering pockets showed their narrow escape. When the children saw the pup, they forgot the fire. The wiggly little fellow made such a hit; they cared nothing for the cock and didn't ask about the cow. When Smith and Nellie arrived, however, the children wanted their drink of milk. "No, Nellie doesn't have any milk. She's going to have a calf. Then we'll have milk." Nellie went uncelebrated to her stall.

Confident that a cow would solve the need for milk, the next step toward self-sufficiency was to have their own eggs. Mr. Blaine had agreed to exchange a roll of brown paper for a brace of hens. So on a fine spring day Mr. Criddle set off southeast to collect them. The walk was worth the effort, for he retuned with a pocketful of eggs for his wife and two hens in an old basket.

"These will be fine hens," he told them. "Their pedigree is a mile long – Hamburg, Spanish, Dorking, Poland, Brahms – maybe more. He'll have two little pigs from his Berkshire sow to sell us."

Mr. Criddle set his hand to the plough by hiring Lonsbury to break two acres for wheat and Lawrence to broadcast the seed by hand—six and a quarter bushels in two hours. After two passes over the seed with the harrows, he told his wife, "Feel confident I can expect a fairish crop."

Mr. Smith finished the siding on the east gable of the house, then ploughed a second garden nearer the wood where the soil looked richer. Lonsbury took over the plough while Smith rigged up new stable stalls.

The unpaid labour force prepared the earth and had two rows each of peas and onions in the ground by April 26. The gardening operations were interrupted by a settler from Blaine's district travelling to Brandon. Invited for dinner, the man failed to properly acknowledge the lady of the house or express his appreciation. Mrs. Criddle hadn't been so pleased to have extra work and wanted her hospitality acknowledged.

> . . . mortally offended Alice by marching off without taking the smallest notice of her. I really should like to discover the secret of so many Canadians treating females with such extraordinary disrespect. Every male – bird, animal bar insect, and every man in the world bar these People out here, seems universally to display gallantry to the gentler sex – and – why the Canadian should prove the exception to prove the rule is – to say the least – a nuisance.

Their first fire had frightened them, but a few days later another from the southwest threatened their precious bush. This time Mr. Criddle was home to lead the charge with Elise and her five children. He and the boys beat the edges of the advancing fire with spades. The others ran back and forth scraping snow—still lingering under bushes—into pails and threw it at the flaming grass and cedars. It took two frantic hours, but they saved their bush. Triumphant and exhausted, the firefighters dragged themselves home. Mr. Criddle spoke for them all, "Need a drink – pretty badly knocked up."

Mr. Criddle's next project involved planting potatoes. He'd bought over eighty bags from the Clarks at a cost of $61.75 including transportation. Elise and Isabel were instructed to cut the potatoes so that each small piece had three eyes. By the end of the day, when they closed their own eyes, they still saw potatoes. As they continued cutting next morning, the planting began in the little field where they had been digging out the roots. Edwy led the oxen; Mr. Criddle gripped the handles on the plough hollering, "Keep straight!" Harry followed, picking up roots loosened by the ploughshare. In turn, the small boys dropped the cuttings—eyes up, every second small step, along the inside edge of the furrow. When Cecil's pot ran out, Norman took over. By the time his pot was empty, Cecil was back. There was no time to lose because the next pass of the plough would fill in the furrow. The plough made two more furrows before they planted another row. Within two hours, the first two bushels had been planted.[1]   Isabel and her mother noted the bags yet to cut and knew their hands would be stained and sore for many days to come.

Mr. Criddle claimed, "All work and no play makes Jack a dull boy." So on a lovely May Sunday, the first crack of the cricket bat sounded at St. Albans. Mrs. Criddle—pleased to see a good English game—was more than a little proud when her husband scored thirty-five in a single inning over his greenhorn opponents. But Sunday's leisure was not for servants; the Vane boys fetched stray balls, while the 'fairer sex' prepared the food.

On May 24, the birthday of Her Gracious Majesty Queen Victoria, Mr. Upper of Souris Mouth organized a basket picnic and invited all his neighbours to enjoy a day away from their usual grind. He made a huge swing for the children and raised the Union Jack. The day dawned bright and warm. Mr. Criddle dallied at home keeping his family working until mid-afternoon and then he set off alone.

When he returned Elise served Mr. and Mrs. a late cup of tea and overheard, "Was a dull affair – gathering of country clowns. Had a race between two local crocks. Was a disgrace to call it a horse race." He sighed, "Oh, for the glories of Epsom Downs. I entertained on Upper's piano. Sang that little recitative that I used to sing in your Uncle's drawing room. Remember?"

Mrs. Criddle looked doubtful, so he sang, *"Oh flower wasting in the wilds, Oh flower stricken by the storm, Come to my home be tended by my care, For I have love in store. . . .*[2]

She nodded politely. "They applauded – but then – some clown asked, 'Can you play dance music?' Such is the culture in these parts. . . . Lots of talk about an accident on their ferry the night before – it's a dammed dangerous crossing – the Assiniboine is high. Couldn't make out what went wrong. Anyway McVey nearly drowned – lost one of his horses."

Later that night, still nostalgic for his old life, he mused in his diary "Pity McVey didn't quite succeed in drowning himself. There's a graveyard[3] about forty yards from the swing – a funeral after the day's doings would have been exceedingly apposite – undoubtedly added interest to the occasion."

---

1   May 12, 1883. ". . . cleared ground as we went of a considerable amount of dead poplar scrub, some ground cedar"
2   Recitative in family collection.
3   Uppers had lost a child.

Gardening was the area in which Mr. Criddle felt most confident. With plans in hand, he gathered his gardeners at the new site. "Use the rake like this – get the ground smooth." He looked at Edwy, "Go cut some stakes for row markers." Taking a hoe, he continued, "Make a little ditch for the seeds – not too deep. We'll start with big seeds – beans and peas every so far, like this." He dropped a few. "Fill it in – pack the dirt with your feet." He showed them how. "That will do the trick. Remember you'll have to water them every day. . . . We'll soon be eating your fresh vegetables."

Elise had no experience gardening, but she found ways to help the children get through a great deal of boring work. They raked the earth "smooth as a bed for a princess", and "banished evil weeds to keep their kingdom safe." One afternoon, six-year-old Stuart accidentally put his head in the path of Evelyn's hoe. One look at the blood and both boys fled to their mother. Elise stayed with the rest of her crew. *I'm afraid there'll be trouble for the Dutchman for not watching the children more carefully.*

To Pioneer Women, Mennonite Heritage Village. Steinbach, Manitoba. Alvin Pauls

The childrens' vegetables flourished until they were 'cooked' by a killing frost on June 2. That disappointment was overcome, by the still unhappy Mrs. Woollhead. Now living on a homestead a mile east, she wanted a break and sent her cows to Criddle's paddock. Isabel knew nothing of cows, but she had watched Harriet and soon had frothy white milk in her pail. The little Criddles wanted a drink, but adults had priority. Isabel told them, "You'll have to wait till morning. Your mama and papa want butter. Tomorrow morning after Mama Dutcheen skims off the cream you can have milk."

Isabel's career as a milkmaid had begun.

The butter churn had been in the corner since March, so after several more milkings Elise washed it out and poured in the cream. Taking turns, the children lifted the dasher up, then pushed it down—up—down. After what seemed like a very long time and a great deal of effort, they had butter and fresh buttermilk.

But, Mrs. Woollhead's holiday was over and the cows went home. Watching them go, the little Criddles asked, "Papa, when is Nellie going to have a calf?"

❧

For days Mrs. Criddle was laid up with toothache. Completely fed up, she moaned, "I can't take it anymore. These teeth have to be pulled."

They set out for Millford. That evening she told Elise how her day had gone. "We got as far as Souris Mouth. The Clarks told us, "You'll be sorry if you have a tooth pulled there". They invited us in. Met the young Misses Clarks. Mr. Criddle tried to entertain, but their harmonium! He wasn't used to pumping the bellows while he played. Came back across the river and stopped at Upper's. Entertained there—*Charlie Is My Darling* and other such songs. Stopped at Woollhead's for tea." She put her hand to her jaw, "I'm still suffering."[4]

After Mrs. Criddle spent another two weeks in misery they went to Brandon. This time she came home well pleased with both dentist and bargains. "A bankruptcy sale . . . look at this, half a chest of tea only twenty-six cents a pound, and these," as she lifted them from the box, "pickles, marmalade, currants, raisins . . . sugar at ten cents a pound." Mr. Criddle bragged about his own good luck, "Eighteen plugs of Myrtle Navy tobacco at fifteen cents per plug."

⁕

Fresh radishes finally arrived at their table. Elise thought she had never tasted anything so fine. *Porridge, bread, tinned meat, potatoes—everything tastes better with radishes.*

A government official made his way through the countryside gathering assessment information and filled out his form with information resentfully supplied at the Criddle table. Elise felt his questioning gaze when Mr. Criddle asserted that "Mrs. Vane is not a servant, no wages for your records." He managed to get a glimpse of the gentleman's notations:

> Tax Collector proceeded to assess me – sum me up – I don't know which – but he filled in a large printed form in a mysterious manner – wherefrom I afterwards gleaned that I was married – had two wives – am Protestant in Religion – a Farmer by Profession – and – 38 years of age. The 1st and last items are true – the rest – near enough for Brandon statisticians.

Meanwhile, Nellie's eight days stretched through April, May, and most of June. Finally the birth appeared imminent and she was confined to the paddock. But the cow had a better idea. Gone all day, she returned in the evening without a calf. They locked her in the stable thinking the calf had died and went in search of the remains. Trekking through bush and swamp they suddenly came upon a beautiful brown and white calf standing motionless in a tangle. Mr. Criddle, rope in hand, approached it and was about to slip the noose over its head when the little critter bolted. The chase was on. Catching him at last, Mr. Criddle wrestled it to the ground. No longer silent, the calf bawled desperately for his mama.

While Elise was serving Mr. Bellhouse tea, they heard a loud call for help. They rushed out to help Mr. Criddle drag the 'little villain, skittish as his ma and strong as a little elephant' out of the bush. Then holding it down, he hollered, "Fetch the buckboard." Elise and the children ran home to fetch the wagon. Un-

4 June 14, 1883.

fortunately, the wagon tongue had been removed and their fetching took time and ingenuity. The rig got to the scene, the calf was hoisted up and Mr. Criddle held it down. They journeyed home in triumph; the slow moving rig accompanied by Turk's excited bark. The dream of milk and butter danced in everyone's mind.

As Elise expected, Isabel found herself in charge of all matters to do with Nellie and her milk supply. She worried for Isabel's safety, *that cow is so skittish.* Next morning, when the milkmaid approached her victim with a pail, Nellie showed every intention of keeping her milk for her own newborn. At Isabel's first timid touch to her swollen and tender udder; Nellie let fly with her hind leg. Patience was not one of Mr. Criddle's virtues. When a walloping didn't convince the cow to stand quietly, he bound her hind legs together so she couldn't kick. Her milk was then divided between Isabel on one side and the sucking calf on the other. Unfortunately, the gentleman had to get out of bed at a miserable hour, even on Sundays, to truss Nellie's hind legs for the privilege of having milk. Poor Nellie was so terribly riled up by the time Mr. Criddle got done beating her into submission, that, were it not for the calf, she wouldn't have let her milk down at all.

Meanwhile he wrote an account of the situation for his prospective readers in England:

> Keeping a cow reads very well in books and is very well in practice if one has nothing to do with the matter but drink the milk and eat the butter – otherwise – 'tis an unmitigated nuisance. At present our supply of milk seems likely to amount to about 2 qts a day (Mr. Calf getting all the rest) – and – how the deuce we are going to make unlimited butter and have a like proportion of buttermilk from that quantity for the pigs I have yet to discover.

In the fine tradition of farmers Mr. Criddle walked out to check his crop. To his horror he found 'cockles' growing among his wheat.[5] He rallied his work force, pointed out the weeds and said, "Got to get rid of these – every one."

Once again, drudgery did not suit Mr. Criddle's temperament. He saw it as "an innocent recreation, much suited to persons of a quiet, contented mind – and – not subject to sunstroke." Elise found herself in the field managing the cockle pulling crew.

Meanwhile Nellie's resistance continued unabated. Twice a day she struggled, was whacked, often severely beaten, but remained defiant. Although Elise worried about her daughter, she cringed at poor Nellie's beatings and Mr. Criddle's threat. "I'll turn you into beef."

Seeing the cow tremble as Isabel sat down to milk, her mother thought; *there must be other ways to train a cow . . . Mrs. Woollhead's cows were so content.*

5 Cockle: Middle English: Several of the weedy plants of the pink family.

Anxious to have more milk for her own children, Mrs. Criddle took the first step in weaning the calf. Returning to the house, she told Elise, "My plan worked. With warm milk on my fingers I put them into the calf's mouth. He was hungry and started sucking. I held my fingers under the milk and he sucked up two bowls in no time. We can soon wean the calf completely and have all the milk for the house."

Without her calf, Nellie fought on. Mr. Criddle tied her hind legs to the stable wall so she could kick neither milkmaid nor pail. One day the little cow got her revenge by getting out of the paddock and dined to her heart's content on iron-rich Brussels sprouts and broccoli. Furious, Mr. Criddle sent for expensive, newly invented barbed wire fencing which, unfortunately, stretched only half the distance. Rails, free for the cutting, completed the job. Elise shook her head and told Isabel, "I don't think we can ever build a fence to keep our Nellie from getting where she wants to go."

Through many a scrimmage, Nellie lived, Isabel persevered, and butter graced the Criddle table. In the meantime they had good luck with the setting hens. To the delight of the children, seventeen baby chicks pecked their way into the light of day.

One hot afternoon Mr. Criddle took the boys for a refreshing bath in Woollhead's pond. The water was not deep, nonetheless deep enough for Cecil to disappear under the surface. Norman hollered. Mr. Criddle fished him out. Cecil coughed and sputtered back to life.

July's hot sunny days stretched on and on. The children watered the gardens, but the potatoes and crops wilted. A splendid rainfall on the July 23rd changed all that. To celebrate, Mr. Criddle sent his forces collecting butterflies. He mounted the resulting twenty-two specimens and noted several new varieties.

Summer was so enjoyable, but nagging thoughts of winter lurked beneath the pleasures. Their animals grazed for free during the summer, but they would need, he calculated, five or six loads of hay, over and above the mangels[6] and oat straw. So in early August grass cutting began. When the scythe blade kept catching on old dry grass, he resolved to burn fifteen or more acres before next summer. Elise and the youngsters were dead beat by the end of each sweltering day. Mr. Criddle saw the exercise in a different light.

> 1st, one looks out for a bit of swamp - then one finds it – then one mows the best of the grass growing round about – then one goes away – then one comes back again – next day – to pile the stuff up into cocks – loads it onto a wagon – provided always that wagons can get through the swamp in summer

6 Mangels: large reddish orange beets grown for cattle feed. Their crop: 10 bushels.

time – and carts it home to be made into a stack or heap close to the stable. And – here again the superiority of Canadian farming over English asserts itself - the stack requires no thatching nor shaping.

His romantic account collided with reality as gale-force winds tore at his tar-paper roofing and whipped the vegetables and crop without mercy. By the end of July nerves had reached the breaking point. Mr. Criddle began the day by whopping the oxen for straying and hobbling Miss Nellie for kicking. The hay makers fought the wind all morning and finally got a load on the stack and went in for dinner leaving the empty wagon by the door. While they ate, a severe gust swept the buckboard down the hill twisting it so badly haying was left off for the rest of that miserable day. The alternative—butterfly catching. That decision revealed a broken net. During the fuss over that, Mrs. Criddle shrieked, "Oh-o-o-o! Mice! Mama! Babies!"

Further investigation of their room turned up a multitude of aunts, uncles, and cousins. Later that afternoon, Isabel took the butter to cool in the well. It slipped from her hands and fell. She retrieved it from the bottom, but the water was milky. Busy with the water, no one noticed Billie eating cabbages and turnips in the children's garden. When Mr. Criddle tried to repair the wagon, the peg came out of his grindstone handle. All the while he struggled with the *** thing, the clouds that promised rain, dropped their moisture on other people's fields. The final blow—Minnie made a mess of the evening meal!

Neighbours said, "I can't remember such a dry summer."

Other districts had rain, but day after day clouds circumnavigated the Criddle homestead. Still, potatoes and turnips, a few peas were growing and the calf and little pigs from Blaine's were doing well. Clouds kept promising; there was still hope. Fortunately, two wild-looking men dropped in and eased the tension.[7] They received a cool reception until the Canadian introduced himself, "I'm Seton from Carberry. My friend, Mr. Christie, is from England. He's not feeling at all well."

At that Mr. Criddle invited them in and 'physicked' Christie. The conversation expanded to all things natural and the new butterfly collection came out. The visitors impressed their host by providing identification, both common names

7 Seton came with family from Scotland to Ontario. Loved nature, studied art in Toronto, then on scholarship to the Royal Academy of Art in London. Came west to brother Arthur's farm near Carberry. Published *Birds of Manitoba* in 1891 and became Provincial Naturalist in 1892. Both naturalist and writer, he was an early practitioner of the modern school of animal-fiction e.g., *Wild Animals I Have Known*.

and Latin, for every one of his specimens. Leaving for Souris Mouth, the men wished Mr. Criddle luck in discovering a new species to be known as 'Criddle-de-diddle-ensis.'[8]

Next morning, still without rain and everyone on edge, Minnie suggested that news might help Mr. Criddle's depression. In spite of threatening clouds, she set off for Souris Mouth. She arrived at the post office just as the rain began.[9] The Clarks said, "Wait here 'till it's over."

Minnie accepted their offer and soon forgot to watch the time.

"Stay for supper! We'll drive you home."

When Minnie didn't return as expected a big bonfire was lit. The boys shouted to no avail. Elise, thinking of bears and other terrors, was worried sick. When the Clarks finally delivered their guest, she was welcomed with joy. Then Mr. Criddle tore into her, "See how selfish you've been. Look at your poor mother. She's been in tears all evening. **Never**, do this again!"

For a time at least, Minnie's strong independent spirit was subdued.

Christie and Seton returned late that night and there was more sharing of natural science before the men retired to The Shanty.

Listening to the naturalists helped the children appreciate how much there was to learn about the world around them. They brought their papa an interesting green caterpillar and to teach proper observation skills, he examined it and wrote down his findings, "Three to four inches – unusually thick and deep – no horn – yellow slashes down the sides, terminated with spots – six rows – scarlet and pearl hue – breathing vents also scarlet. Covered with numerous undoubted spines – similar to what one would expect a moulting porcupine to possess."

The homestead agreement required more ploughing, so Mr. Criddle harnessed his oxen. Before long though, he was back muttering, "Rough ground – obstinate oxen – stupid Boy – blunt share – drought. The game isn't worth the candle – so adieu to the fascinations of the plough till – next June." A few days later he needed another distraction and envisioned a tennis court—smooth and green—in front of his house. As a first step toward the dream, he thought of the plough, "I'll use the sods to bank up the house for winter." The boys carried out his plan.

They'd been longing for rain. Without warning, on August 19, a strange, ominous darkness enveloped the farmstead. A moment later all hell broke loose. The racket was deafening, the house deluged. In ten minutes, the sun was shining again. Venturing out they found hailstones as big as hazelnuts, hard as adamant, an inch deep. The tar-paper roofing had vanished along with a third of the hay-

8 Aug. 8, 1882. The same occasion is also mentioned by Seton in his diary. "Aug. 9, 1893. Crossed the Assiniboine River . . . slept that night under a binder." Diary in Seton House, Carberry, MB.
9 Vane, Harry.

stack. Plants were cut to pieces, the cabbages hacked and perforated. Wheat and oats thrashed out on the ground, barley beaten flat, mangels torn to shreds. Mr. Criddle moaned, "All the poetry has gone out of farming."

Recovering, he decided to salvage as much as possible and hired Upper with his self-tying binder to cut his wheat. Due to the drought, the stalks remaining after the hail were barely tall enough to catch the knives. But they gathered what they could, including the rakings and gleanings, and got seven miserable little loads in a stack to await the threshing machine.

Gophers feasted on the shelled-out grain until Mr. Criddle went shooting. Twelve dead hardly turned the tide. In fact, his gun missed so many of the targets that Mrs. Criddle spent all Sunday morning cleaning congealed oil from the gun stock.

Monday morning Elise joined the crew carrying sods from the future tennis court to place against the base of their house. She told the children, "If the floor is warmer; maybe our feet won't have such painful itchy swellings from chilblains this winter."

On a golden September Sunday, Mr. Criddle took his wife on an exploratory excursion to the tree he had nicknamed 'the Preacher' She told Elise that evening, "Wonderfully wild, romantic spot. Papa's tree is smallish, too ancient to be pleasing. Fine view. On the far side we looked down into a great sandy punch bowl." Elise was enchanted. *Oh, to see it myself.*

Beatrice enjoyed her pets. The rabbit, now grown, had turned white and began gnawing on table and chair legs. Her Papa threatened it, "Take care! You'll be our next rabbit pie." Her saucy squirrel, enticed with handouts of bread came right into the house for crusts. Growing more aggressive, he climbed up the screen door and scolded to get in. His boldness became too troublesome, but he wasn't made into a pie.

Mr. Criddle couldn't wait for his smooth green tennis court and in the interim selected another grassy area. A scythe couldn't cut the grass short enough, so he handed the boys knives. Down on their knees, they cut it blade by blade; a tedious job even though prairie grasses grew sparsely on the sandy land. Elise heard as they came in, "Easier than haying."

With the grass cut, he got Smith's help "beating out the nubbles and leveling up holes per beater, spade, water, dirt." When the English Owens dropped by the following Sunday, Mr. Criddle took them on with his homemade racket and single-handedly won six straight sets.[10]

<hr/>

Harvesting filled their weekdays; first the mangels, then the potatoes. Mr. Criddle tried to plough them out, but failing that, he set the crew to work. Elise found herself lifting and breaking apart the sods with the shovel, one hill at a time, days on end. Each night she crept up the stairs to bed. *My poor back. It's hard for the children too.*

A threshing outfit from Ontario charged farmers eight dollars a pitch, so to split the cost Mr. Bellhouse moved his stack to Criddle's. They also charged five cents a bushel for wheat—three and a half cents for oats. Farmers also had to feed the gang and their horses. Preparing for nine extra men for the expected two or three meals kept the women hustling. Actually they were threshed in only two hours: seventeen bushels from the two acres of wheat and twenty-seven of oats. "So much for my harvest," Mr. Criddle rationalized, "the next can hardly be worse. Will probably be a great deal better – the British pamphlets promised forty bushels to the acre."

Elise and her crew went back to digging potatoes. On October 6 the plough returned. Although it missed some and cut some, it was faster and got the 'back setting' done at the same time. Furthermore, some of the crew were free to harvest the carrots, turnips, beets and onions. Smith came to walk Nellie for a second visit to Owen's bull. Elise wished he'd taken Billie too; *it would have kept him from getting into the garden and eating the last of our cabbages.*

When Mr. Criddle took a load of potatoes to sell in Brandon, he met Woollhead in need of cash. Home again at tea, he told his wife, "I've purchased Woollhead's house and lot – $300. Eighty dollars off the price – will do his ploughing next spring. I'll sell it for a good profit." When ice began forming on the water pails at night, Elise told her girls, "Remind me to empty everything. Last winter, remember Mrs. Criddle's ink bottle froze and spoiled her lovely paper . . . made such a mess of her little writing desk. Perhaps we should sleep with the bottles; only way I can think to keep them warm."

As soon as all the vegetables had been carried to the root cellar, the crew started cutting firewood. They were all handier with the ax and used the oxen to haul the logs home. Elise thought as she worked, *this is hard work, but I don't mind. So long as we won't have to repeat last year's treks to the woods.*

<hr/>

10 Trevor R. Owen, NE 4.9.16.

Up until then Elise had worried about bears. One clear cold night, a new sound, impossible to describe, sent shivers up and down her spine. Every twenty seconds, another series of yells or short screams were very resonant. Mr. Criddle peered out the window, "Some bird perhaps – but what at this time of year?"

He shouted out the door and the noise stopped. "Wonder if it's a lynx'.

A few minutes later they heard it again, but too tired to stay awake worrying: Elise retreated up the stairs to the safety of her bed and pulled the covers around her ears.

Sunday, November 24, they celebrated Mrs. Criddle's natal day. Elise and her daughters prepared a special meal, topped off with cake. They felt rather awkward though, knowing both mothers were born on the same date. Elise fought to keep smiling; *it's hard not to think of the olden days . . . . Percy's secret kisses, his expensive gifts . . .*

Mrs. Criddle enjoyed the treat and didn't ask the date of Mama Dutcheen's birthday.

Six days later Edwy confessed, "Nellie's calf is sick."

Striding off to the barn, Mr. Criddle found the little fellow near death and yelled at the frightened boys. "You've starved him! Expect a calf to live on marsh grass? I told you to feed it oatmeal gruel at least once a day. I trusted you – now I have lost a fine calf. You expect me to look after **everything**!"

Their wood pile grew while their stock of food stuffs decreased: Mr. Criddle's tobacco supply ran low and the oatmeal gave out completely. Elise didn't understand and tried to puzzle out the situation. *Why does he say, "We're a beleaguered city on half-rations" as if it is something of which to be proud? We find it hard to work on empty stomachs. Upper's store is only three miles away. Are we so short of money?*

On December 6 Upper 'raised the siege' by delivering a whole load of foodstuffs, including tobacco. The woodcutters, anxious to have enough wood, went out again, strengthened by a hearty bowl of oatmeal.

But Elise's worry about a money shortage came closer. Tinned meat was too expensive for regular meals. The gun was put away and the boys tried to snare rabbits, cheaper, more sure.

Once Elise and the girls were not needed outdoors, Mrs. Criddle was free to begin lessons with her children every afternoon: reading, spelling, arithmetic, and geography. Her husband kept the Vanes busy. "The temperature in the root cellar is getting low. See how the tops of these mangels are spoiling – got frozen. Make a fire here when it gets close to freezing." He picked one up, "The lower half is still sound – amuse yourselves by chopping off those spoiled tops."

Later in December Elise opened a letter from her brother. Noticing the date, her heart leaped in anticipation; *Friedrich remembered my birthday!*

Mannheim, November 24, 1883

Liebe Elise,

I have received your letter of August 15 and we were happy that the news was favorable. We believe that you have a lot of hard work, yet it must give you some satisfaction to know you are your own boss and that you can see improvements as time goes along.

We certainly could empathize with your fear and worry over Minnie, more so because we are worried whenever one of ours does not come home from school on time.

What do you do for an education for your children? Do you teach them yourself? Surely there is no school in your proximity yet?

Hearty greetings to Percy and your children from Mariechen and our children and hearty greetings to you from your Brother, Friedrich.

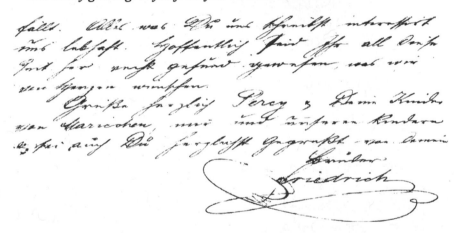

She choked back disappointment. *My loving brother forgot . . . didn't even mention my birthday. . . .* Then, recovering she looked it over again. *. . . . I wrote just before the hailstorm. So much has happened since, and I haven't had the heart to write about it.*

Christmas was approaching and Mrs. Criddle laid out her plans, "We can't have Christmas dinner without plum pudding." She opened her cookbook, "Let's see. We don't have brandy. We'll use the children's recipe: 1 pound flour, 1 of bread crumbs, ¾ pound stoned raisins, the same of ¾ currants and suet—get suet from Mr. Upper. Three or four eggs, milk, 2 ounces candied peal, 1 teaspoon of powdered allspice and salt."

Elise nodded.

Mrs. Criddle continued, "We'll chop the suet and de-stone the raisins one night, mix it the next. Tie it all up in a cotton bag ready to put on as soon as the porridge is served. Five hours of steaming.[11]

"For a vegetable—we'll treat ourselves to turnip sprouts from the root cellar. Isabel, you can cut them and put them on to cook just as the potatoes are done. They cook quickly."

And so their second Christmas in the frigid Northwest,[12] far from their native lands, went smoothly, every tummy satisfied. The pet hare got into the tea leaves, and finally crossed his finish line by chewing on Mr. Criddle's door during the night.

On New Year's Day, Mr. Criddle started building a partition upstairs. Elise was surprised and pleased; *we've had no privacy since London. It will be lovely to have a room apart from the boys. I wonder, did Minnie speak to Mrs. Criddle? But it doesn't matter, I'm thankful it's under construction.*

Elise drank in the loveliness of a rare mirage one morning. Mystical mountains danced in the shimmering light on the skyline. Trees looked taller; distant objects, usually not visible, appeared distinctly. *Is this beauty a herald of cold weather?*

Next day their house began cracking like gunfire, a sure sign of cold. Elise kept the stoves roaring, but couldn't even make the kitchen comfortable. *Frost is building up on the walls; it looks like last year's mortar has disappeared. I'm afraid the sods around the walls won't be enough to keep the chilblains away.*

Upper stopped by—electioneering, but didn't bring the mail. "He'll not get my vote."

Dispatched to Two Rivers, Edwy returned laden with letters for the Criddles. "I'm sorry Mama, there's nothing for you."

She smiled, gave him a little hug, and said wistfully, "It's alright . . . I'll read my old ones again."

‎‎‎‎‎‎‎‎‎‎‎‎‎‎‎‎————❧❧————

---

11 Beeton. p. 666.
12 All-time record cold for Brandon: - 41 Celsius, December 24, 1883. *Manitoba Co-operator*, December 15, 2011.

Chapter Five

The Inheritance Runs Out

In early January the temperatures went to minus thirty-nine with winds that pierced through their meagre clothing. Nor was the suffering limited to the chore boys, for every unfilled crack was like an open window. Elise had the kitchen stove roaring for an hour before Mr. Criddle came from his room complaining, "Mercury in my thermometer is plumb out of sight."

Hovering near the stove, she marveled. *If they have more than thirty-two degrees of frost in their room, he might take pity on the rest of us. Way back in November he complained of winds coming through the cracks with 'more than life-giving freshness'. He got busy and chinked the walls around **their** room, but didn't get to the rest of the house. He's done the partition upstairs. It would have been better to have our walls rechinked.*

The girls' room above the kitchen had its stovepipe giving off heat as it passed through from the floor to the roof. The boys had the larger space above Mr. and Mrs. Criddle's room. Once again they slept fully clothed between two straw mattresses. Harry told their mother, "I know we're supposed to be tough, but I'm on the outside. I'm cold all night. The wind finds every crack. Lots of holes in the roof from that hailstorm."

He looked at Edwy, "Do we have more tar paper?"

Edwy winced, "It's too deuced cold to go up on the roof these days!"

Mortaring got underway, but due to the necessity of warm-up breaks and the digging out of drifted doorways, progress was very slow. Mrs. Criddle, being in a delicate way that winter, stayed close by her fire, sewed a pair of very 'respectable' trousers for her husband, and gave lessons to the 'infants'.[1]

The hens also suffered from the cold and stopped laying. Isabel brought in three seedy ones, "Duchess can't walk."

Checking her feet, Mr. Criddle pointed out, "Scaly warty legs. What's wrong with old Speckles?"

"She doesn't eat, She just sits on the floor and doesn't fly up to roost with the others."

---

1 British Infant Schools corresponded to Canadian primary grades.

"Old age – give her an emetic – Ipecacuanha."[2]

"Blackie has a bad cough."

Watching her for a moment, he agreed, "Indeed – croupy cough. Give her the same."

After a day or two in the house, Duchess could walk. He explained, "I've scraped her warts off with my fingernail. The scaly excrescences had stopped the circulation."

Neither Speckles nor Blackie improved, so he changed their treatment, "Mix paraffin and water fifty-fifty. They won't like it, but use a feather to ram it down their throats."

The chickens were not too sick to struggle. Elise held the hen, looked her in the eye and said, "Now, Blackie, we're not going to hurt you. Just doing our best to make you well. It won't take long and you'll feel better. . . ." Isabel took the bird and held its wings and legs, Minnie the head, and their mother pried open an unwilling beak with one hand and stuffed the medicine-soaked feather down the throat with the other. Elise enjoyed playing veterinarian. *What a turn my life has taken. Mama wouldn't imagine me doctoring sick hens in the kitchen. I could make a good story out of this for her—'Nurse Harrer and the Hens'; 'Schwester Elise und die Hühne'.*

Sick hens were only a fraction of Elise's concerns. Her Edwy, still poorly dressed for the cold, tried valiantly to do everything asked of him. *Only a lad of twelve,* she thought, *but he's out there in the freezing cold trying to do a man's work. He says the snow is very deep in the woods and it's hard just getting to the trees. Once they're down he has to drag them to the pile.* At tea one night, Mr. Criddle boasted, "Cut and carried out twenty-four logs from the West Wood today with the Boy. Going to build a larger pigsty and paddock. Cut down two big trees to make sledge runners."

Then he proclaimed a half holiday. "The Boy's about knocked up. Good excuse for a rest. We'll go down to the pond and clear off some ice. Have a little skate – give him and Minnie lessons on my old pair."

The mortaring, sandwiched between logging and various other interruptions, moved as slowly as molasses in January. One of the intrusions was Woollhead who had apparently reached the limit of storekeeper Upper's willingness to accept promissory notes. He promised sixty cents a pound for seventy-five pounds of potatoes and went home happily. To celebrate the sale Mr. Criddle took another skating break and ended the afternoon with a hockey game on the snow. He came in crowing, "Scored a brilliant victory – took on all the kids."

---

2 Ipi-kak-yoo-**an**-ă. Dried root of a South American plant used as an emetic or purgative.

Winter kept the Vanes busy. The boys fed the animals, cleaned out the barn, and twice a day Isabel milked Nellie. Edwy went to the bush. His little brothers sawed throughout the days to keep the fires fed. Their feet built up a packed path to the well, another to the outhouse, and still another to the ash heap. As their mother handed them the pail of ashes she always warned, "Watch out for live coals, we don't want a fire." An equally well-beaten path led to the root cellar where they kept a fire going so the vegetables wouldn't freeze. They brought potatoes to the house and later the cooked peelings went out to the fowls. There were meals, dishes, washing and through it all Mama Dutcheen encouraged the youngsters and offered sympathy for every hardship from frostbite to hunger pangs.

Mr. Criddle couldn't believe the speed at which the woodpile vanished and congratulated himself on choosing a homestead with trees. "The amount of wood we go through — utterly astounding. Been calculating the fuel burned in both stoves — average 200 pounds per diem."

He hadn't done so well calculating how much hay his cattle would need to get through the winter. Prying the last of his hay from under the snow in late January, he realized the supply was about done. That evening Elise heard, "Must buy hay, confound it — Bellhouse will sell . . . but I have to fetch it. Have logs for sledge runners — just need to be trimmed and pinned together with a rod."

Elise thought *I hope it doesn't take long. Nellie's all bones. How can the poor creature give milk?*

Resting her feet beside the warm stove at the end of each long day, Elise had plenty of work for her fingers. Eleven people wore through the heels and toes of their woolen socks and stockings with alarming regularity. She could darn small holes, but when heels disappeared entirely she had to pick up the stitches and knit new ones. And patching knees kept her stitching late into the night. *I could put it off, if only they had another pair.*

Isabel and Minnie washed up the dishes after tea, tidied the cooking area, and helped with the children's lessons before taking the little boys to bed. Elise reminded them, "Put another big stick on the fire. It saves me from getting up."

One day in February, Upper brought them another load of foodstuffs and had what he thought to be good news. "We're planning to open a school. Have more than twenty children round about. Sent a petition to the South Cypress Municipality. You have school-age children. I expect you're interested."

Elise thought, *Good news, indeed!* But as soon the door closed, she heard otherwise. "They didn't consult me. Tax us eight dollars an acre for a wretched school! I'll look after **my** children. They can do the same."

Maria Theresia, Empress
of Habsburg Dominions

He's upset, Elise thought. *Taxes can't be that high! My goodness! In my homeland every village had a school. Even the poorest child had a chance to learn to read and write. Maria Theresia saw to that away back in the seventeen hundreds! I know things were different in England. Only the well-to-do children had the opportunity. I remember the commotion just after Isabel was born. Many said national schools were going to be the ruin of the country; the poor wouldn't know their place if they learned to read. I was happy when the law prevailed, but I guess the family at St. Albans is going back to the old English ways.*

Mr. Criddle proceeded to alert his friends to get the ball rolling on an unpleasant surprise for the Two Rivers' people at their school meeting.[3] He put the mortaring and sledge building on hold and trudged from farm to farm. To his great surprise they thought a school was a good idea. They would vote down the Two Rivers School and build Poplar School further west. He chaired a meeting at Lonsbury's and wrote up the petition. While there, they also wrote out a petition and signed it requesting a post office.

Elise saw him come and go. *Schools are important, but I wish he would finish stuffing our walls. Seems like the wind never ceases to whistle around my ears. He complains of eighteen degrees of frost in their room, but it's much colder for the rest of us. The boys can get warm in the daytime, shoveling, chopping, and sawing. The girls and I have the stove. . . . It's the nights! . . . This will be a long winter.*

When Upper delivered another load of groceries he said cheerfully, "I'm pleased to tell you our school is in the works. We're holding a meeting on February 28 to finalize it."

Mr. Criddle finished up the chinking and travelled about mobilizing his supporters to attend the meeting and outvote the Two Rivers people. The day before the meeting he returned from Woollhead's, "Damn the snow and everlasting winds. . . . Damn Woollhead, he's entrenched in the enemy's camp. But we'll vote them down even without him."

The scheme swirled about in his mind while he contended with mundane matters on the home front. "Give Beatrice Ipecacuanha for her croupy cough. And the hen, Whistler – equal parts castor oil – rhubarb and two parts bread crumbs. No hay for the oxen – let them out – find their own feed."

The day before the big meeting, Edwy helped bolt the sledge together. They hitched up Billie and set off to Bellhouse's to fetch a small load of hay. Sometime later Mr. Criddle stomped in, but didn't stop to talk—went straight to his room. *That's curious,* Elise thought, *I expected he'd be telling us how well his new sledge*

---

3 February 25, 1884.

worked. When the boys came in, Edwy, with one eye on the gentleman's door, told her slyly; "We got over there alright. Forked on a jag of hay and started home. Mr. C jumped on the sledge. And crack! The thing collapsed. Got in a real funk—left it right in the middle of the trail. Took off in a huff. Harry helped me. Guess we'll put it back together after his big meeting tomorrow."

Next morning Mr. Criddle's 'claque' assembled and, confident they were going to put an end to Two Rivers School, knocked at the door. Upper welcomed them, "Good morning gentlemen! You're most welcome. But, if you came for the meeting, you're too late. We waited three quarters of an hour. You didn't turn up. Everything is signed. The meeting's adjourned."

Protesting didn't help. Retreating to Palmer's place, they wrote the Municipal Council to declare the meeting 'null and void'. That evening he told the family sarcastically, "Just as they do in eating, Canadians must be far superior to Britishers in getting through business – fancy an English public meeting taking but 15 minutes to open – pass half a dozen resolutions, get the minutes put in order, copied out and signed – yet, according to those six individuals – that was all they took."

Elise dared not comment even to her children, but she smiled inwardly. *They wanted a school and weren't going to let outsiders stand in their way. Mr. Upper is a good man; he could have charged to bring our foodstuff. I'd like to ask if his family gets pale, round reddish patches like Minnie and Beatrice. Is it scurvy? If they don't have the problem I'd like to ask what they eat.*

Having reinforced the sledge, Edwy and Mr. Criddle went back to rescue the hay. The starving ox spotted the pile of straw lying in his path. Temptation ruled and he stopped to eat. His master had other plans. When shouting the choicest of words had no effect, he used his pitchfork until Billie gave in and hauled the loaded sledge home on his still empty stomach.

Two days later when Edwy harnessed Billie he asked innocently, "What happened? There's a lot of blood caked on his side."

Mr. Criddle looked, "Frozen. Can't wash it – might catch cold. Probably hurt it on a tree branch in the wood."[4]

❧❦❧

There were a few days when the cattle could forage for their own fodder, but mostly the weather stayed bitterly cold and stormy. Edwy's cheek froze just digging a path to the rootcellar. Temperatures in the house dipped well below freezing by morning. In the fowl house, the black pullet, having laid four beautiful eggs, died without explanation—another egg producer soon followed suit. Nellie's milk supply ran out, and Norman had a fever.

---

4 March 3, 1884.

Into that depressed house walked the tax assessor, opened 'Schedule C' and proceeded to ask the usual questions regarding religion, income, value of furniture, and bad debts. Was he solvent? At that Mr. Criddle took the form and instead of answering, drew solid lines through the rest of the spaces. The fellow left, shaking his head.

⚬⚬⚬

The Municipal Council agreed to hear the school case on March 11. So in spite of a blizzard, the spokesman joined Lonsbury, Smith, Lawrence, Bellhouse, and McManes for the drive to Millford. Drifts on the trail had the sleigh box teetering to the flipping point so often that Mr. Criddle chose to walk behind. They were going down the steep cut in the bank of the Souris River at Millford when a large overhang of snow timed its fall such that it missed the sleigh but half smothered the man behind. Pulling himself free, he brushed himself off and carried on. Council listened patiently to Calverley and Upper's pitch, and then to the opposition. In the end, it pronounced 'the late meeting null and void'. The Criddle team's jubilation cooled off quickly on the way home, for the wind was 'full in their teeth'. Not wanting their horses to take them all over the 'semi-precipice' on the hill, they had to tramp down the snow left by the morning's avalanche. By the time they reached their respective abodes, each man was suffering some form of frost-inflicted injury.

Warming up by the fire, Mr. Criddle shared his highlights. "Dreadful day – heavy snow – blizzarding – could hardly see two hundred yards. Worst day perhaps, that I have ever been out. Met the Reeve, Mr. Burnett and Major Rogers – who found me a good glass of beer. Had the best meal since I arrived in Canada – excellent soup – beefsteak – potatoes – turnips, pickled beet – pie – tea. Only twenty-five cents."

For a household on a diet of potatoes, his meal sounded so good they would willingly have braved the weather, but he didn't seem to notice. "Of course, our side won – enemy looked pretty downcast. But the war is not over yet. There will be a grand battle on the third – nearly equal forces. How it will terminate I can't say – Upper is sure he'll get his Two Rivers School – I'm equally certain we'll get ours."

⚬⚬⚬

One March morning, on Elise's usual trip outdoors with the chamber pots, the air was unusually sweet and calm. Hoarfrost bejeweled the shrubs, the barbed wire fence, even the straw on the roofs of the fowl house and barn. And far away to the south, clearly visible over a grey horizon, she could make out the 'summits' of the Cypress Hills. *So beautiful, so very beautiful. . .*

When the hay ran out again, Nellie and the oxen were expected to scrounge 'goose grass' on the prairie. But, the pickings were sparse. They'd pulled out and eaten as much of the straw on their own roof as they could reach. Now they wanted to satisfy their hunger with straw from the fowl house roof. One night Mr. Criddle had to turn out twice to drive them away, "Confound 'em. Next summer I must lay in a decidedly larger stock of hay."

—❧—

Meanwhile the Department of Education studied both school petitions and sent a directive. Each side must choose a committee of three to reach a solution. There were meetings and politicking, but neither side budged. Finally on April 1, the committees came together with an official from the Department to choose the location and three trustees. The first item on the agenda was to appoint a chairman from the six to conduct the business. After a great deal of jostling, Mr. Criddle reluctantly took the chair. But, without his sharp tongue, his supporters floundered. Within the hour he had the honour and privilege to sign the minutes and swear in trustees, Upper, Calverley and McManes. Two Rivers School # 299 came into being under the signature of 'Percy Criddle, Esquire'.

Disappointed in politics, he turned his energy to organizing his own work-force for the coming season until a blizzard on April 7 kept everyone but the chore boys indoors. And someone had to chase away the hungry oxen still trying for the straw on the fowl house. Elise felt sorry for the beasts. *We may soon be just as hungry. One bag of flour goes quickly with so many mouths to fill.*

Clearly, money had to be found somewhere and since he planned to publish his diary, the time was now. "Don't worry," Mr. Criddle assured them, "shortage in the food line won't last long. I'll start rewriting my diary – send it to England. Lots of helpful advice for immigrants – be published anon."

That evening he penned the closing, "As I can never hope to write anything of interest after this, I close my diary." And the next morning with a fresh supply of paper he revisited the pages and repenned the account of their departure from London:

> July 14, 1882 - 5 P.M. This day I arrived at Liverpool in conjunction with my wife, A. the Dutchman, our German lady friend, and nine youngsters en route for New York, St. Thomas and thence, Winnipeg and the Great North West. Class Intermediate as far as self and infants are concerned – the rest 'steerage'. . . .[5]

He wrote diligently, between such activities as raising a new flagpole, tennis on Sundays, and noting the returning birds. Without funds to hire help, he had to put down the pen to plant his crop. "Miserable occupation," he grumbled after a day of casting wheat by hand.

5 Criddle, Percy. *A Settlers* [sic] *Diary in Manitoba, 1882-4.* Unpublished. Archives of Manitoba. MG8 B80 M19.

Then Woollhead landed on his doorstep, "You didn't pay me all three hundred dollars for my house. Remember my ploughing in exchange for eighty dollars?"

Mr. Criddle remembered alright, but he planned to buy himself out of the pickle by selling the Brandon house. Hitching a ride to town, he discovered a terribly depressed economy. No one wanted to buy a house at any price. Like the prairie horizon, making his fortune in Canada kept fading into the distance. "Wish most heartily that we had left the 'Great Lone Land' alone – there seems to be a curse upon it and nothing thrives."

One April morning, Mr. Criddle was up at four to broadcast some wheat before the wind got up. Edwy was to harrow in the seed and was told, "I'm off to Upper's for groceries and seed from Clark. Finish this – meet me at the ferry with the wagon – need it to fetch the stuff home."

At the store, Mr. Criddle met Miss Upper just out from the East. Delighted by the way she held her hands on the keyboard he had to tear himself away to cross the river for the seed. It was evening when he returned to his team waiting at the top of the hill. He told the boy, "This approach to the ferry looks worse than it is. Lock up the two hind wheels."

With ten bushels of oats and a few of barley, they returned for the groceries. Edwy loaded while Mr. Criddle admired two beautiful Brahma eggs, 3¾ and 3½ ounces. By the time they headed for home, the sun was down. "I told your mother to hoist the lantern up the flagpole – should see it," and they headed out.

"Can't see the bloody light – just have to steer as I think proper – gave your mother instructions – but just like a Dutchman – probably let it blow out – or failed to light it before hoisting it up, or failed to hoist at all."

Edwy was puzzled. *I've worked all afternoon in this gale. How is Mama going to hang out the lantern? Even if she does, the halyard is on the north and the wind will keep it there. . . . Isn't it dangerous to hang a lantern on a rope in a gale like this? Poor Mama! Anyway, the oxen know their way home.*

Reaching home they found the lantern on the lanyard, its wick turned down, bumping against the pole's lee side. He thundered into the house, "Why didn't you put the light in the cellar and shut the door? You're the arch empress of muddlers! Had nature but given your mind but one more twist you might have been a Newton or a Shakespeare – as it is – why – you're exactly the converse."

No one came to Elise's defense. *At least he didn't use his stick. . . . I'm stretched to the limit . . . extra with the mother-to-be. . . . I know something about empresses; Maria Teresia was a wise ruler.* She sighed. *It was an easy order to give, impossible to carry out. . . . I was afraid the glass would break banging in the wind. Didn't want to burn the house down. . . .* She was puzzled by his violent outburst. *Did something go wrong? . . . He didn't bring everything we asked for. . . . Has Mr. Upper cut off his credit?*

⌘

On the morning of May 2nd Minnie returned to the kitchen after taking Mrs. Criddle's breakfast. "She wants you to stay nearby. Have everything ready. Says the time has come. Don't send for Mrs. Bellhouse. She has every confidence in you."

Mr. Criddle went out saying, "Wretched weather through April – behind in ploughing."

A healthy baby girl was born that afternoon.[6] When the Papa heard the news, he left Edwy in charge of the ploughing to check out the new arrival. On his return he told Edwy, "A hardy little animal apparently – see you managed without me – appears you'll soon be able to take over the business."

Mrs. Bellhouse came the following Sunday to congratulate the new mother. Minnie served tea to the Criddles and their guest in their room; everyone else ate their allotted helping of plain boiled potatoes. Alone with the children, Mama Dutcheen suggested, "Let's pretend we are eating our favourite food. . . ."

She didn't need to prod; they had lots of ideas, "Plum pudding, mince pie, apple trifle . . ." *What wonderful children! It's come to this . . . They are so thin. What is to become of us?* While the girls cleared away the dishes she took up the mending basket. *I shouldn't do this on Sunday, but the girls are free to do the dishes and the boys need these socks.* Her needle was barely threaded when the new Papa appeared. "The women are cooing over the baby."

Susanna Harrer

Handing her some pages he said, "I have written a letter for you to send to your family."

She skimmed down the page . . . " drought and hail . . . nothing to eat . . . need cash to tie us over." She was mortified.

Dear God. . . I've tried to protect my mother. She looked up pleadingly. He impatiently held out pencil and paper and said sharply, "Short of food. Do you want your children to starve?"

---

6   Maida Criddle born May 2, 1884. Registered by Percy Criddle, Gentleman, 12th June, 1884.

7   March 17, 1884. Name, age, height in feet and inches, weight in pounds: Edwy: 12, 4.4, 66; Harry: 11, 3.11, 51; Cecil: 9, 3.4, 41; Norman: 9, 4.2, 55; Evelyn: 8, 3.8; 42; Stuart: 7, 3.7, 44; Beatrice: 4, 3.3, 35. Minnie: 15, 4.10, 133; Isabel: 14, 4.6, 92.

No, I don't, she thought; she began writing the letter. *Meine liebe Brüder,* and wrote steadily until signing, *Ihre Schwester, Elise.* Mr. Criddle took the letter. She cried silently, keeping her head down to hide her tears.

※

As they gardened and cleared two more acres of scrub, Elise thought of her brothers. *Things are tough there too. Will they be able to help?.. These roots are so stubborn! I haven't the strength I had last year, when we had enough to eat. Wish we could rest. . . . At least Minnie is spared . . . Mrs. Criddle likes her help.*

Thanks to diligent watering, their vegetables were doing well; everyone longed for greens to eat with their potatoes. A June 9th frost cut off that hope.

When Elise heard that their petition for a new post office had been granted, she thought Mr. Criddle would be happy. She learned otherwise as he railed, "Some idiot named it Aweme. I've not the remotest notion how it's pronounced – Indian, I presume. But – we're an English colony. Wish both personally and by our distant friends to have an appellation suitable for white men."[8]

※

Without rain, everything remained tinder dry and one windy day they looked up to see smoke billowing from the Bellhouse's. Mr. Criddle and Edwy rushed off, but the house was already engulfed in flames. The family was in shock. A coal in the ashes dumped outside started the blaze and when their daughter tried to stamp out the flames she was badly burned. Their neighbours offered flour, carrots, potatoes, a place to stay, and help getting logs to rebuild their home. Mr. Criddle returned to the scene next morning and digging through the ashes found a melted blob that was their silver spoons but Bellhouse's precious gold watch was still intact. He didn't notice any living embers, but should have. Fanned by the afternoon wind a new fire swept eastward toward his own property. In no time at all, his beautiful green West Wood was smoldering.

※

Poor old Speckles departed the world as Blackie's brood of ten chicks pecked their way into it, making fifty-three chicks. The children carried water to their gardens every morning before planting potatoes. Satisfied, their overseer wrote in his diary:

> All the kids work the entire day bar Bobby [Beatrice] – who makes herself very useful however carrying potatoes and helping me. By the bye, the baby [Maida] doesn't help – but takes care of her Ma at home. Of course all is getting on as well as can be expected.

He allowed a half holiday on the Queen's birthday for the children to walk out with him to catch butterflies and moths. Next morning they were back at

---

8 Aweme PO opened 1884-08-01. Postmaster, T. Carscaden on 17.8.16 , named after a village in England.

work while he joined the neighbours at Bellhouse's building bee: three scorers, two hewers, four corner men and two extras—Bellhouse and Criddle. By the second evening the family had a new home.

Meanwhile the boys rescued 62 blackened but usable posts in the wood and dragged them home for the new paddock. Mr. Criddle spaced them out, marked their positions and began digging. But he soon left it to the boys, "Cabbages need to be transplanted."

Next morning when he went to check his work he found the poor little plants shrunken and brown. "Encouraging country! Last season we were badly enough off. This year starvation stares every settler in the face."

While Edwy and Harry were working on the fence, Elise and crew were told to soak bags of straw and fill water pails. "We've got to burn off the old grass and scrub in the swamp. Be easier for the scythe." He gave instructions and left saying, "Take care – don't let the fire get away."[9]

While she worked Elise reminded herself, *we do need more hay. Nellie must eat if we want milk. Billie and Lazy's bones look like they're coming right through their hides. Burning should make haying easier. I'm feeling weak; I hope we'll soon have more to eat.*

The drought ended dramatically on June 15. Hurricane force winds and torrents of rain soaked the house from roof to floor. *What a mess! It's not just cold that finds cracks. Still a flood is better than a fire.* Mr. Criddle came in from checking the rain gauge, "Can't measure – the cup blew away. I'd say eight inches. Had this precious storm divided itself into moderate rains – one, three weeks since, one, ten days since and some today; we might perhaps, have had a crop. As it is – it comes too late; has done a lot of beating down and swamping – such is Manitoba."

Moistened by the rain, the wheat and vegetable seeds sprouted and hopes revived for something to eat besides potatoes. Elise tied her apron strings a little tighter. *But for that frost, we might have had fresh green vegetables. They will come along now.*

❦

Hearing a dreadful commotion in the yard one morning Elise went out. Billie had apparently objected to Edwy putting on his harness and hit Edwy's eye with one of his horns. Furious, Mr. Criddle grabbed his whacking stick and began beating the living daylights out of the beast. Elise watched in horror. *Please God spare our Billie. Surely he has learned his lesson.* By the time the man had run out of sticks and his fury spent, the harness was in pieces. Mr. Criddle stormed back into the house while Harry let the ox go and picked up the pieces. Elise led

---

9 May 29. 1884. "The Dutchman and Co. employed clearing part of swamp for haying purposes . . ."

Edwy to the well and washed his face with clean cold water. "It's swollen . . . but your eye looks alright. Is it painful?"

Edwy blinked, "Not too bad."

"We're all getting short tempered. Being hungry affects our nerves."

Once Mr. Criddle had cooled off he told her, "We haven't had meat for weeks. Cook old Whistler . . . her egg laying days are over."[10]

◦◦◦

When another envelope from Germany arrived Mr. Criddle opened it at the post office and cashed the money order. Back home he skimmed through the letter, then handed it to Elise. Her hands trembled as she held the thin pages to the light to read.

Mannheim, June 3, 1884

Dear Elise!

> *Your dear letter that I received yesterday has caused me a lot of pain, and I can't tell you how sorry I am, that bad luck seems to pursue you. Karl was here yesterday; he brought mother over to our place, where she will stay a couple of weeks. He also was quite alarmed at your news, since we always believed, that even though you had to work very hard, you still were not suffering want.*

> *We regret that we cannot send as much as we would like to since we also do not have much, and we have no accumulated savings. We have to be very frugal and are happy if we can make it without going into debts.*

> *Today we sent under the Address <u>Percy Criddle Posterestante Brandon per Postanweisung (money order) DM 99.96 = Dollars 23.52</u> to you and hope and wish that this, although small amount could ease your situation somewhat. Excuse us, that it isn't more, but much as we regret it, this was all we could do.*

Dear Friedrich, almost 100 DM. I'm so sorry . . . you need it for your own children. But twenty-five dollars will go a long way towards flour and oatmeal. We have vegetables from the garden. . . . We'll surely make it until we have our own wheat for flour.

> *That you didn't write mother anything of your deplorable situation Carl and I appreciate very much, because she would have been so alarmed and excited and it would have been a week before she would have calmed down. When you write, don't mention anything in the letter about the money, just write on a separate piece of paper, that you can put into the envelope, if you have received the money, so that I can let mother and Mariechen read the letter. I haven't told Mariechen anything so that she won't by accident tell mother about it. Also if you write Carl, don't mention your bad luck, for mother could easily open the letter and I would like to save her from the worries. I will inform Carl as seems fit and the opportunity arises.*

---

10   June 3, 1884. "I am not very well – weak – thin – half-starved – no flour for a week past – hardly any meat for a long time."

Mother has become quite old and unsteady on her feet. If we go for a short walk with her, we have to guide her, alone she cannot walk very well, but apart from that she is in a good mood and has a good appetite.

Lamentably, I have no experience in farming, so that I cannot give you any good advice and perhaps conditions in your country are so different that it wouldn't be applicable. Here the farmer can get insurance against hail damage with any company, so that when your crop gets hailed out, you are reimbursed. Do you not raise any peas? I have been told peas do very well in Canada and are grown in large quantities and get exported even to us here. Here farmers plant enough for their own consumption, also beans and lentils, since they make for very nutritious food. Also oats for oatmeal porridge, which also produces a lot of energy for heavy work. Then also every farmer raises a few pigs in summer and slaughters them in fall so that there is a meat supply for the winter. Also geese and chickens are on the farmyard, they eat all the refuse, grow fast and do not require a lot of care. But as I said, I don't know whether this is suitable to your environment, but I should think so.

My dear brother, I'm surprised you know so much about farming. Good suggestions. I agree oatmeal is a fine food. I hope with your money, we will have porridge for breakfast again . . .

Your letters to me send to the same address to F.H. Address Mr. Salomon Maas, Banker, Mannheim. I heartily wish that this year you could have a good harvest and that soon your conditions will improve. All business has its difficulties and every beginning is difficult. Do not lose your courage, better times are sure to come.

All of you stay real healthy and receive my warmest greetings from your brother Friedrich

That evening Mr. Criddle walked with Edwy to Clays and bought a bushel of wheat. They ground some in the little coffee grinder and Mrs. Criddle treated them all to rolls.[11] When the boys discovered wild strawberries the children went picking with pots and pails, "Mind you don't eat any. Need every berry for jam." No one admitted to disobeying the order.

Woollhead came again, anxious about his ploughing. Since Edwy had mastered the art, Mr. Criddle took him over and agreed on the area the lad was to plough. Walking home he picked a bouquet of flowers for Mrs. Criddle, "June flowers, twenty-three varieties!"

That evening Edwy boasted, "I made twenty-two rounds."

His mother smiled; "That plough weighs as much you do; I wish you didn't work so hard."

"Don't worry Mama . . . I'll soon be thirteen."

❧ ⁂ ❧

---

11 Vane, Harry.

From then on all the talk and work centred on being ready for the arrival of a friend from England. Elise and her family remembered Mr. Tulk's visits to their home in England. "It will be different now," their mother said, "our situation has changed. He is coming to visit the Criddles. Don't count on gifts now. I feel sure he will still be the same thoughtful gentleman, but he does have to maintain their station."

As letters went back and forth across the ocean, she gathered some details. "J.A.[12] doesn't want us to fuss. Will sleep in the same hammock he used in the woods of Guiana. He's purchased everything on my list: a weather station, tennis balls – racquets, a thermometer capable of going low enough to measure – seventy-five below, Mason's hygrometer and a fine double breech loader, two hundred empty cartridges with caps. He'll purchase powder in Brandon. There'll be hunting and feasting – ducks and geese – venison."

John A. Tulk

He told his wife, "J.A. is willing to pick up foodstuffs. We're to write him in Montreal to let him know what's wanted."

Elise would learn those specialties would be served only at the table with the guest. Nellie solved their milk and butter problem by giving birth to a beautiful bull calf. "What is butter without bread?" Mrs. Criddle cried.

Her husband went for flour to the mill in Millford and came home with none. "The place shut down till harvest – no flour. But we'll have potatoes," and he took a pail out to the patch.

He was soon back with some beauties, "Dug these from Seven Sisters Field – six consecutive roots – 53 taters."

The Vanes dug a load for Brandon and next day Edwy drove up and down the streets hawking, "Fine new potatoes – two dollars a bushel!"

Sales were brisk until competition cut into the price. They took the rest of his load to the grocer to swap for flour. Home again in exceedingly good humour Mr. Criddle took his wife visiting. In their absence Elise wrote letters. For her nieces, she described their baby chicks. For her mother she enclosed pressed flowers. So they wouldn't worry, she told them about wonderful broad-beans, carrots, and potatoes. And that the crops looked promising.

Mrs. Criddle came in from her outing quite excited; "Found a marvellous patch of wild raspberries. Had a good feed. The children will go there tomorrow to gather more for jam."

———

12 'J. A.' was Percy's nickname for Mr. Tulk, also 'J.A.T'.

Mr. Tulk boarded the *Vancouver* for Canada on Edwy's thirteenth birthday, July 31. His arrival 17 days later meant Mr. Criddle had lots to do if he was going to holiday with his guest. With no money to hire help, Elise and the youngsters worked from dawn till dark: ploughing, haying, and harvesting. The Shanty, still deplorably wet from the deluge, was turned out and the old tent rescued.

The gentleman arrived two days earlier than expected, laden with treasures: clothing for Mr. Criddle, the all important thermometer, weather station, and foodstuffs.

Henry Alabaster

In the midst of the celebrations, a sad letter broke the news that Mr. Criddle's cousin, Henry Alabaster, had died suddenly in Siam.[13]

Elise's heart went out to his wife, Palacia. *What a long, sad journey home for her. Henry was a kind, thoughtful man. Always generous to Percy, paid good commissions on his orders for the King of Siam: scientific books, the very best surveying instruments, and microscopes. Percy claimed Germans made the highest quality and used the purchases to visit me in Heidelberg. After I went to London, Henry kept us going for another ten years. I used to walk to the Thames with the children to watch Mason's ships pass by, heavily laden with goods for the East.*

---

13 · Alabaster, Adrian, *A Quintet of Alabasters. (Able Publishing, UK., 1997) pp. 187-210.* Henry Alabaster died August 8, 1884. Survived by wife and sons, Percy, Charles and Ernest. The King of Siam granted her a pension of £300 per annum for life. Signed by King Chulalonkorn.

In Elise's next letter she found a sprig of heather. *Oh, the woods . . . our walks together.* Then a lovely blue ribbon slithered from the pages. She ran her roughened fingers along its silky surface; *Mama remembers. I loved blue, the colour of the sky and forget-me-nots. But I can't wear it . . . wouldn't be proper. I'm getting used to black, though I'm not fond of it.*

Mannheim, September 14, 1884

Liebe Schwester!

Your last letter I received on the 27th of July. I thank you and your dear children greatly for the dried flowers you included, which gave me great pleasure. I sent the part meant for mother and Karl to them and they too were very happy to receive them

Fourteen days ago I together with Elsa, went to Karlsruhe in order to congratulate mother on her 75th birthday which she celebrated on the 31st of August. Mother is, thank God, well and has given me the enclosed ribbon for you. We had never thought that we could give you joy with something like this, for we could have done that sooner.

. . . We read in the newspaper that some weeks ago a big storm hit Winnipeg and surrounding area and caused a lot of damage to buildings and fields. We thought of you and fervently hope you suffered no damage from that storm.

Mariechen was in Heidelberg together with our children at her mother's place for fourteen days. Sunday I was there as well and we made several hikes. The children send the enclosed flowers together with their best wishes. The flowers are from the Heidelberger woods and are called Ericka- heather- or also Heidekraut (heath plants).

A club of German Architects has been formed, in order to collect money in all of Germany for the renovation of the Heidelberger Castle, to prevent its complete ruin.

Can one of your children do some sketching? We would like to see what your house and your immediate surroundings look like. . . . .

. . . . from your brother, Friedrich

She looked it over again. *I'm happy about our castle. Friedrich brings my homeland close.* She thought about the sketch, but instead of a pencil, she picked up the mending.

⋙⋘

With Mr. Tulk in residence, Elise's days were far too busy to write letters or sketch. She got her orders before the men went off to enjoy the day: hunting, fishing, or calling on neighbours. The children said, "We like it when they hunt. Hope for good luck."

A wretchedly wet season made it hard to make more hay and get the grain cut and stacked. Finally, though, the threshing was done—178 bushels of wheat, and

22 of barley. The oats were so poor they stayed in the stack unthreshed. Elise and crew then turned to digging potatoes until a wintry October 25 ended the operation. Facing another winter of chilblains, Edwy ploughed more sods to bank their walls. The chinking of the previous winter, although acknowledged as missing, did not yet appear on any list.

After Mr. Tulk departed November 6, Mr. Criddle tried to sort out his situation. He had no problem finding work to keep everyone busy, but in order to work, they had to eat. Wheat sold for forty-five cents a bushel, potatoes for thirty cents, if at all. The cost of a 100-pound sack of flour was $2.50 and disappeared in no time. His book had not yet been accepted for publishing. His house in Brandon hadn't sold. His purse was empty. Hunger was at the door. [14]

He announced at tea, "Mrs. Criddle has agreed to let Minnie go to Brandon and find a position. She's 16 now – so along with her keep she can earn five to ten dollars a month – keep half the cash – send the rest home to keep our fires burning. Lonsbury will give us a ride tomorrow." He looked at Minnie, "Get your things ready – have to be at Lonsbury's early."

Elise was shocked. *My Minnie! . . . A domestic! He wants her to be a common servant? . . .* She looked at her daughter, watched her face flush with excitement. *Minnie's always one for adventure. . . . If she wants to go . . . it doesn't do for me to be selfish.*

And Minnie wanted to go. "Don't worry Mama, remember the crowds in London. I managed there. I'm two years older now. You can have my share of food. . . . I'll write."

Up she went to gather her few possessions. Her mother and Isabel, hearts heavy, finished up in the kitchen. Elise needed every ounce of her faith in a loving God to face the morning.

---

14   Mrs. Criddle had inherited her brother, Henry Nicol's estate. He died January 30, 1881, in Algiers, Africa, where he had gone hoping to improve his health. The will was proved 22nd of February, 1881. Alice Criddle, formerly Nicol, sole executrix, "**for her sole and separate use free of marital control**". Personal Estate under £1500. The money saved Percy from bankruptcy. Assured that £800 was sufficient to get established in Canada, he emigrated.

Chapter Six

How Bad Can It Get

Elise found the first few days of Minnie's absence difficult. The mistress of the house missed her too. Minnie knew and understood all Mrs. Criddle's needs and no matter how Isabel tried to fill her sister's shoes; the fit was not comfortable for either of them. Minnie's tasks were divided and added to mother and daughter's duties, while one less plate on the table didn't increase their helping of potatoes. Elise consoled herself, *Minnie must be eating better.*

She received a letter postmarked Karlsruhe and hoped for cheery news.

Karlsruhe, November 6, 1884

Dear Elise!

I have received your dear letter and forwarded it to Friedrich in Mannheim, Lit.O.6 No.3/4. Too bad that we learned very little that is uplifting from your dear lines. Hopefully you are fully recovered and you can fulfill your difficult vocation. If only once good fortune could make its entrance at your place! Faith in God, who has always helped, one must not lose hope!

Dear Karl, uplifting news will not reach you any time soon. Just when I think it cannot get worse, it does. But what has happened to Friedrich that he is receiving his mail at home. His banker went bankrupt. Has he not found another position? Has England's bad economy reached Baden?

With Friedrich it is not going so well either. Lamentably, he has not found employment. He is presently occupied at the Gantmasse. But how long will that be possible! The prospects are too sad. For a man the age of Friedrich it is very difficult to get employment. It is fortunate that his health is much improved. Let us hope to God, that with his help everything will turn out well.

Amalie and I are fine. I get these coughing spells from time to time which necessitates that I am housebound for a few days. For today, farewell, and to-gether with Percy and the children receive my warmest greetings.

our brother Karl

I beg for early news!

81

Elise hoped for flour the day Mr. Criddle left with a few bushels of wheat for the mill in Millford. He returned without it. He had called at the post office. Two letters were for her—a short upbeat one from Minnie and Friedrich's with a picture. *One of his daughters . . . reminds me of myself at that age. . . . Is it Elsa?*

Mannheim, November 29, 1884

Liebe Elise!

I wrote you about two months ago and I enclosed a piece of blue ribbon, which mother had given to me for this purpose. Since we have not received any news from you, I don't know whether my letter got lost. We would be very happy to hear from you again. Hopefully you are all well and have received better results from your harvest.

She paused, *I should have written . . . haven't thanked him for the gifts . . . I'm glad I had a ribbon to give Minnie when she left . . . helped me hold back the tears. I didn't want to weep like Mama, when I left home. Minnie didn't have a worry in the world. Nor did I. Percy came to visit us so often I truly expected we'd be back in the summer with her first grandchild . . . .*

Mariechen is suffering from her usual winter cough. Also Anna was not well; she had the so called wintertoelpel, but is again feeling better. While organizing old papers I found a photograph of our Elsa, which was taken about three years ago, but she still looks like it, only she has grown taller. I enclose this picture, hoping it will give you pleasure. We have not had our children photographed since then, because we too have to avoid unnecessary expenses.

Eight days ago mother was here together with Carl's wife; she had heard via Heidelberg that Mariechen was sick and she came to look her up. Mother looks well and is cheerful but still she is stooped and walks slowly.

My goodness! Dear Mama, taking a trip like that! . . . How good of Amalie to go with her. Must have been a good tonic for Marie, Mama's always upbeat.

At the end of September Georg Fahrbach, an uncle of Mariechen, who lives in Riga, Russia, was here. He invited me to go with him to the Niederwald on the Rhein, to see the monument commemorating the unification of Germany. It really was great and wonderful, the panorama seen from there looking towards Ruedesheim, Bingen, Castle Ehrenfels the Maeuseturm (Mousetower). I had never been there, even though one can make the whole tour, there and back in one day.

. . . . all the forestry men of Germany made the same excursion, several hundred men. Patriotic

speeches were given and enthusiastic highs were delivered to the emperor, Germany and Bismark. In closing they sang Die Wacht am Rhein [The Watch at the Rhine]. All people present were delighted and I count this day as one of the loveliest ones that I have experienced.

She closed her eyes, *that song! The French would never leave us in peace. We students loved to sing it. Imagine the sound of three hundred men singing together. What a treat for Friedrich!*

I shall close now and I hope to receive good news from you very soon. Mariechen and our children send hearty greetings. You, your children and Percy receive the heartiest greetings from your brother, Friedrich.

Elise tucked the letter into her pocket, but the voices sang on:

Es braust ein Ruf wie Donnerhall,	*The cry resounds like thunder's peal,*
Wie Schwertgeklirr und Wogenprall:	*Like crashing waves and clang of steel:*
Zum Rhein, zum Rhein,	*The Rhine, the Rhine,*
Zum deutschen Rhein,	*Our German Rhine,*
Wer will des Stromes Hüter sein?	*Who will defend our stream, divine?* [1]

She wanted to respond right away. Yet, she couldn't get up the nerve to ask for paper. And then her enthusiasm collided with reality: *Dear Friedrich . . . I appreciate your letter. I'm still your loving sister, but after I say thank you . . . what else can I say? . . . You remember how my young Englishman came bearing extravagant gifts and showered me with attention. You, my brothers, weren't surprised that he loved me; you praised me too. Told*

Friedrich Harrer

Elise Harrer

me, "Sister, what a marvel you are! Nothing gets you down. You take after your Uncle Friedrich, always spinning stories. You'd even have one for Wilhelm while he waited for his porridge." When Percy left, and I was lonely, you would try to cheer me up by singing something romantic like 'The Last Rose of Summer'. She recalled it so clearly: *Letzte Rose, wie magst du so einsam hier blühn? Deine freundlichen Schwestern sind längst, schon längst dahin . . ./ Tis the last rose of summer, left blooming alone. All her lovely companions are faded and gone. . . You teased me saying, "Your lover is just across the channel; he'll not forget his lonely rose. . . ."*

1 The song was rooted in conflicts with France calling on all Germans to unite to defend 'their' Rhine.

Friedrich expects our financial problems to end soon. . . . He can't begin to imagine my life; the primitive conditions, our meagre diet of potatoes, and my lack of freedom. I have to hide any hint of the other family. Oh dear brother, what can I write?

Longing to have bread for Christmas, Mrs. Criddle pleaded for flour. Her husband consented to return to Millford with the same thirteen bushels of wheat. Part way, a team of horses overtook the plodding oxen and Taylor offered him a lift to Millford. Oxen, sledge, and Edwy were left at the closest farm. He told his mother that evening, "Wind cut right through my coat. Sure glad I didn't have to go all the way. Mr. C left me at McDougal's. They invited me in, had bread with both butter and jam! Imagine! Wished I could have brought you some. Anyway, Mr. C had success . . . 450 pounds of flour and 300 pounds of shorts. Shorts were left over from the milling, real cheap. I guess we'll not be having oatmeal for breakfast for awhile."

A bitter cold night followed and next morning, Mr. Criddle was close to needing his new thermometer. "Another rasper," he reported, "temperature in our room at dawn down to two degrees." Checking outdoors he added, "Minus thirty-six but no wind. I'll walk to Two Rivers after dinner – want the last mail before Christmas."

He returned just before dark, laden with mail. In due course, little Beatrice came out of her parents' room with a letter for Elise.

Mannheim, 16 December, 1884

Liebe Elise!

I wrote you December 3rd and enclosed in the letter a piece of ribbon. On the whole I have now written you 4 letters (this one included) of which I do not know if they have arrived. Under separate cover, I sent you two scarves or shawls for Christmas and I hope they got into your hands.

She winced. *I should have written. What has happened to me that I leave them to worry?*

Hopefully all is well with you. We hope to hear from you soon since quite a long time had elapsed since your last letter. We wish you all happy entertaining Christmas days and much prosperity for the New Year, that it may bring success in all your undertakings.

We all send our heartiest greetings and best wishes for your well-being.
Dein Bruder,
Friedrich

She glanced toward the flour barrel. *To have enough to eat would be blessing enough. But, "happy entertaining Christmas days?"... Without our Minnie? That is just not possible. We all miss her.... But I must do my best to keep upbeat.*

When she opened her trunk on the landing that night to stow Friedrich's letter away, she took out his scarf. Wrapping it around her shoulders, she dreamed of happier Christmases.... *Mama and I had been setting out all our special baking. When she was satisfied that everything was ready, she hung her apron on a hook and smoothed her skirt. On the way past the little mirror in the hall, she paused to pat her hair.... Then we joined the boys in the front room and soon we were happily greeting Grossmutter and Grossvater Haarbarth, aunts, uncles, and cousins. What chatter ... hearty laughter! And we always ended around the piano singing, Stille Nacht! Heilige Nacht! All is calm, all is bright....* For a few moments she was part of the revelry and reverence of that holy night....

Then, she stowed away the scarf. *There's never a mention of Christmas music here.*

Christmas day was one Elise hoped never to repeat.[2] Mr. Criddle didn't admit to his family that they were close to the edge. The dinner was meagre. Three days later he wrote in his diary, "Christmas over – no pudding this year – couldn't afford one – no money – no nothing – better next season I hope. One gets rather sick of bread made of musty flour and potatoes."

The weather had been kind, except for a few brutal days leading up to Christmas. By mid-January the temperature dropped to thirty below and Mr. Criddle emerged for breakfast grumbling, "Bloody cold – three below in our room by the new thermometer."[3]

Elise was trying to warm up over the fire after a cold night in bed. *He hasn't mentioned filling any cracks this winter.... Surely there's a way to plug them upstairs ... with something.... Rags would do. I should have thought of it before ... rip up some of my worn garments and stuff the biggest ones at least. They shouldn't object, and it will cut down on the drafts.... I'll get the youngsters to help.... If we're warmer, we'll sleep better.*

Nellie, also cold and poorly nourished, had given up on milk production. "Confound her," Mr. Criddle said.

---

2   Vane, Harry. "I remember one Xmas day Mrs. Criddle made three custard pies and bread, made of shorts and bran, and no yeast. No candies or oranges. The Indian brought us a piece of venison. That was our meat for eleven or twelve people."
3   Minus 3° Fahrenheit is -19° Celsius.

Mr. Clay had given permission to cut wood on his homestead a mile and a half south. Logging had begun right after Christmas. When Cecil could manage sawing enough firewood on milder days, Harry went with Edwy—Mr. Criddle's number one assistant.[4] But on extremely cold days, Harry had to stay back to help Cecil, and then Norman took Harry's place. Once the trees were down, the boys trimmed, dragged, and sorted—small trees for posts, large ones for logs, and all the larger branches and sticks for the stoves. Not having whiskers to protect their faces, the boys' often returned home with frostbitten chins, cheeks, and noses. They dared not complain for Mr. Criddle often warned, "We'll soon be travelling much further. This area will soon be cleaned out – wretched Canadian stoves burning up all the wood. I say in two years, the supply will give out in this neigbourhood, and then a couple more years will bring us pretty near to coal at seven dollars and a twenty-five mile journey for it."

Elise wondered, *Gracious! More long cold drives to Brandon for Edwy. . . Will we have the money for coal?* She had not yet asked for paper to write her family. *The children need food more than I need a stamp. I just worry about Mama. Is she fretting herself sick? I told them we are a long way from a post office. . . . How can I be so cruel?* But, overcome by weariness, night after night, she confessed, *I had good intentions to write that letter, but I've failed again.*

⌾⌾⌾

Back in London, Mr. Tulk had been peddling Mr. Criddle's, *The Settler's Diary* from one publisher to another with no success. The manuscript returned to its author in Manitoba. It landed with a thud on the kitchen table; "Damned publishers! They've praised it, called it vivid and real – but they won't publish it. Damn them all." The rejection letter followed, "Read it for yourself!" He stomped off to his room and the door banged behind him.

A SETTLERS

DIARY

IN

MANITOBA

1882 – 4

Per John Augustus Tulk
Addlestone
Weybridge
Surrey

214 Piccadilly,
London W. 30 January, 1885

Dear Sir,
    We return our best thanks for the favour of the perusal of your manuscript entitled "A Settler's Diary in Manitoba" to which we have given careful consideration.

---

4 February 24, 1885. "Of course the Boy accompanies me always, Harry too very often, or Norman and they do the logging while I cut."

We regret to say however that on consequence of the large number of new works which we have at present in preparation, we find we are compelled to withhold from making a proposal for the publication of it. We return the MMS herewith again thanking you for the offer of it.

Yours faithfully,
Chatto

A few days later his spirit rebounded and he announced, "Am going to write a new book – *Manitoba the Great North-West* – its geography, political parties, agricultural prospects, hunting, field for immigration, climate, etc, etc, etc. I mean to make ten thousand by its sale at least and – then live happily ever after. Going to start immediately."

Elise thought, *I'd better take this opportunity to ask for a few sheets of paper to write my mother.* He gave her a postcard, "Tell Friedrich you received his letters."

With tiny writing, she managed thanks for his letters and gifts, and promised to write more soon. *That's the best I can do. At least they will know I am still alive.*

As the winter wore on, Mr. and Mrs. Criddle went visiting. Their children, sensing they were missing a good dinner, wanted to go along. Mama Dutcheen came up with another idea to deflect attention from their dry potatoes.[5]

Mrs. Criddle paid dearly for her dinner, "It looked like a nice day, but such a wind! And the snow was mushy . . . slipped every step! He was in such a hurry, bustled me along. Mr. McElroy drove us home thank goodness: I'm not going anywhere again . . . unless I ride." But, she did go again on the sledge. Elise watched them leave, and didn't envy the ride. *It's such a tipsy lurching thing, and nothing to hold on to.*[6]

When their flour gave out, McManes took their calf in exchange for two dollars and eight sacks of flour. To get the cash, Mr. Criddle got a lift to Brandon, and stopped in at the Langham Hotel, where Minnie slipped him half her wages.

He brought home alarming news, "Brandon is full of fright, patrols every night for protection. Twelve settlers are dead and 40 Indians killed. What the cause of the outbreak may be I know not, but a half-breed named Louis Riel, a well-known character, is the Indian leader and he **says** he intends to throw over allegiance to the Queen entirely. Let's hope that for once we shall follow the example of our American cousins and shoot as many of the beggars as we can catch. We don't want any humanitarian humbug out here, though it may be all very well for people who can put their toes on the fender in safety at home. Either **we** or the Indians must go out and – it will have to be the Indians sooner or later – so – let's

---

5 February 12, 1885. ". . . reduced to potatoes once more . . . the children are already quite thin enough. When I get some cash I shall be able to take 2 more grists to Millford and then we shall be able to hold out till next harvest."
6 Commonly called 'stone boat'—a low flat platform on two solid runners.

save time and money and say – sooner. As for the half-breeds – why – they combine the worst qualities of both French and Indian without any of their virtues."[7]

Elise tried to understand, *the few that have stopped here . . . I can't think of them as killers. The children still mention the fellow giving us venison for Christmas. We were hungry. Maybe they are hungry now. They say the buffalo have all disappeared.*[8]

Situated on a hill, St. Albans was to be the strategic location to gather if danger threatened. Mr. Criddle added his rifle, revolver and shotgun to their arsenal. "My homemade gunpowder – makes lots of smoke and will kill at close range."

Amidst all the tension, Susannah Bellhouse departed this life. Her parents wanted to give her a proper burial in Millford Cemetery, but a spring blizzard shut down their efforts to reach Rev. Rounthwaite. Four days later they were able to reach the cemetery where Mr. Criddle, rather nervously, read the burial service.

All the snow left by the blizzard soon melted in the warm spring sunshine. Long strings of migrating geese honked overhead and the prairie burst forth into new life. To Elise's delight, the early morning air was filled with the joyful songs of the killdeer, meadowlark, and a whole orchestra of blackbirds. Mr. Criddle strolled out with his shotgun and in no time at all was back carrying a pail, "Eight shots, seventy-nine blackbirds – might get any amount more if I wanted. Will make a tasty pie for tea."

Elise couldn't believe it. *Is he serious?* She looked in the pail. *Poor little things! Hardly a mouthful from each little musician. . . . The nursery rhyme, "Sing a song of sixpence, a pocket full of rye, four and twenty blackbirds, baked in a pie.". . . Never thought about it.* She sang on, *"When the pie was opened the birds began to sing, wasn't that a dainty dish to set before the king!" These poor little birds will never again sing.*

Elise began cutting out tiny breasts to make his pie, while Mr. Criddle tacked a new certificate on the wall. Standing back he said proudly, "My commission as Game Guardian."

Mr. Criddle's three years on his homestead ended August 23rd and he was already thinking of more land to make use of his growing workforce.[9] He had a pre-emption on his southern border, but he decided to check out the unclaimed section kitty-corner to the north east, still available for homesteading. The first quarter, he decided, was only fit for grazing livestock. But the next quarter north looked promising and he mumbled, "The Boy is only fourteen, but, there's more

---

7 April 1, 1885.
8 McClung, Nellie, *Clearing in the West: My Own Story*. Her teacher explained the uprising; consequently the Northfield community sympathized with the dispossessed striving for their rights. Northfield School was south of Millford. (Toronto, Thomas Allen Ltd. 1935), p p.183-195.
9 Ages of workforce as of April: Isabel 15, Edwy 13, Harry 11, Cecil 10, Norman 10, Evelyn 9, Stewart 8.

than one way to skin a cat. Widows can homestead if they have a son. I'd say the Dutchman qualifies – old enough." He chuckled. "If things work out my demesne[10] will presently be two miles long and mostly half a mile broad in a zigzag.[11] He walked home feeling very smug.

Elise had no time to dream about the future. She had more work, both inside and outside the house, now that Mrs. Criddle needed Isabel's assistance. There was always something extra for her busy routine and that day it was preparing their little pig's carcass for the family table. The bristles had to be scraped off and the pork cut into family sized portions.

As soon as the weather permitted, Mr. Criddle took a few bags of potatoes plus a crate of eggs and joined up with friends driving to Brandon. Combining Minnie's contribution with his sales, he bought drinks for the fellows and stores for home. Discussing the trouble in the Northwest and what the government should do about it helped shorten the journey.

It had been months since Elise had written Friedrich that postcard, so when a letter arrived, she felt guilty. *I'm glad Friedrich hasn't given up on me, but I've not kept my promise.*

Mannheim, April 18ᵗʰ, 1885

Liebe Elise!

Your postcard of February 18ᵗʰ, '85 I received a few weeks ago. I was happy to receive a sign of life from you again and to hear that you had received letters with enclosures from November and December. Your long silence had us worrying. We are looking forward to the promised letter; I expected it from day to day, that is why I did not write sooner. Hopefully you are all well.

Very worried we have been lately reading newspaper reports about the Rebellion taking place in Canada. For we fear that you too must be suffering under it. Hopefully our worries will prove to be groundless and the whole thing will die down. . . .

You will now have a lot of work to do but if you find time, write to us again and tell us how you survived the winter.

With heartiest greetings from us to you and Percy, and the children, I remain

Your faithful brother, Friedrich

She sighed; *I just have to write something . . . but what? There's so much I can't describe of my life here as Widow Vane, of the Great North-West. A farmer's all-round-servant far from my family, my church, friends, music, books . . . even the freedom to*

---

10 Demesne in feudal system: all the land maintained by the Lord of the manor.
11 April 16, 1885.

walk in the woods. It's a chore to write a letter without a hint of the other family. The truth would kill my mother!

They know life is hard in this new land. Should I tell them about the accident? Edwy, Isabel, and Harry had been bringing home firewood. Percy asked them to stand the long poles upright, leaning inward. Percy admired the effect and told them, "We'll call it a chapel." They were raising a big 28 foot one, had it up and almost in place, when it toppled backwards right onto them. Edwy's head was cut, and his leg scraped and twisted badly. He's fine now. Luckily, the others escaped serious injury.

Or, Edwy's adventure taking wheat to the mill in Millford? That steep descent to Upper's ferry . . . Edwy locked the hind wheels with a rope, to hold back the wagon and keep the oxen from rushing down into the river. That day the rope broke and the oxen barely stopped in time. Then they started up the other, even steeper bank. The oxen were pulling hard and Lazy's collar broke! . . .

She shook her head, *No; I think not, it would worry Mama. . . . I'll tell them about that bitter day last January when Percy planned to take the oxen to the bush for a load of wood. They gave him trouble getting the harness on, but then, lumbered nicely all the way to the bush. He was busily chopping, when the team decided they had waited long enough in the cold, and started for home. He hollered, "Whoa!" But they kept going. Percy had to trot home on his own two legs.*

And something for my brothers: Percy ran out of tobacco and brought home some bark, he called kinnikinnick. He said it smelled like smoldering wood. That should bring a smile. And, I'll tell them that, to help the farm, Minnie went to Brandon to work.

She handed her letter to Mr. Criddle. *I hope it passes inspection and gets mailed.*

⁃•⦿⟋⟍⦿•⁃

Spring was even busier, everyone rushing to get the crops in and planting the vegetables. The eggs were gathered and given to broody hens to hatch. For the first time they had two turkey hens whose instinct told them to make a nest in a secret spot. To keep that daily egg from skunks and weasels, Beatrice spied out their location, marked the first eggs with an X and stole away each new egg until she had enough for a sitting. Then all the eggs were returned and both turkey hens hatched fifteen eggs. Next Christmas dinner would boast roast turkey.

Although the roads were scarcely passable, Mr. Criddle and Edwy set out for Brandon with little pig Jack, 36 pounds of rhubarb, and several dozen eggs. Reaching Currie's crossing, they found his ferry had not yet been launched for the summer season, so the oxen had to plod 11 extra miles, postponing Edwy's hawking until one o'clock. Later Mr. Criddle collected Edwy's $2.80, added Minnie's $5, and bought the most essential supplies. Young Jack didn't sell and after a long day's travel there and back, he was more than happy to rejoin Jill in the pigpen.

Mrs. Criddle was delighted to get her sugar. Mr. Criddle, with tobacco pouch full, went visiting. He returned rather late that night, fully energized, "We had a grand musical evening – going to start a Choral Society – I to be conductor."

He was happy, the crop was flourishing, and everyone looked forward to fresh vegetables. Elise also was encouraged to see a letter from home. *My goodness! Doesn't seem long since I wrote my brother.*

Mannheim, 30 Mai, 1885

Liebe Schwester,

I last wrote you on April 18 and I hope you received my letter. Your dear letter postdated May 2 has been received these days. It was strange, that no news had come from you, but then I thought probably none of you had been to the Post Office recently.

We were very sorry to learn that you experienced such a very harsh winter. Believe me, dear Elise, that's how farmers are faring here, and some even worse. Land is very expensive and the produce is cheap, due to the enormous imports from America and Russia . . . which is the reason so many small farmers sell their land and emigrate because in America they can buy ten times as much land as they have here with the sale of their land. . . .

You at least have the advantage of being your own boss and can live as you like. . . .

The words jumped at her, "you are your own boss and can live as you like." She swallowed hard, trying to regain her composure. *If you only knew, dear brother, but I still dream. . . . My boys built a fine new calf pen . . . will soon be men. There is still land to homestead . . . after working so hard, surely Percy will help them start up their own farm.*

Here we have to take into account the society in which we live, we have to keep up in dress, customs and luxury if we don't want to be regarded with looks and shrugged shoulders. So I have to, in consideration of society, let my girls take piano lessons, because it is deemed absolutely necessary that young girls learn music. I have fought this for a long time because often I observed in my circle of acquaintances, that girls took lessons for many years and wasted the money. As soon as they were married they neglected piano and music altogether. The money was just thrown away. Now I have to buy a piano, pay for lessons. . . .

She gasped, *Oh, that's just what I have done! Thrown away my music.*

Main thing is that we are in good health, then everything can be conquered. I think mother will come in a few days to spend several weeks with us.

She felt relieved; *Mama must be feeling well to plan another big trip to Mannheim.*

I have been following the reports of the rebellion in Canada in the papers, and I recently sent you a Mannheim paper in which the capture of the leader

Louis Riel was described. Well, thank God! That spectacle has an end and you are free of that worry. A few days ago I read that the Indian chief Pound-maker has surrendered with his people. Only Big Bear with 700 men want to oppose. . . . I am glad for you, that you don't have to fear.

Gracious! Friedrich knows more than I do. . . .

> *Yesterday we had a visit from one of your former acquaintances, Elise Schmidt. She has had hard times, has made her living as a servant girl for years. She wanted Mariechen to hire her, but that is not possible . . . . We don't plan to keep a maid as soon as our girls are more grown-up. We would have gone without one earlier if Mariechen's health would have been up to it. Even now she is busy all day, the girls are real daredevils and so there is always something that needs to be washed or mended. . . .*
>
> *As far as I know Karl and Amalie are doing fine. We haven't heard from them for weeks.*
>
> *I shall write again in the next weeks. If you can, let us hear from you again. Greet Percy and your children and yourself, from your brother, Friedrich.*

Elise tucked the letter away thinking everyone was well. Her happiness lasted until the next mail. Mr. Criddle dropped an envelope on the kitchen table as he went to his room. She eagerly picked it up. *It's from Karl. . . . He's sent a card.* She unfolded it and gasped . . . *a black border. Who? Marie?* And then she saw, *Susanna Harrer. Oh dear God! . . . Not my beloved Mama!* She sank to a chair; and forced herself to read the words:

God Almighty has had the pleasure to call our Mother, Mother-in-Law and Grandmother

Mrs. Susanna Harrer
Postmaster's widow

Today early at 3:15 A.M. after a short suffering into a better place.
Karlsruhe, June 9, 1885

From the grieving family.

The interment will take place June 11, 10 AM from the funeral home, Luisenstrasse No. 27

My dear brave mother . . . Friedrich said you were planning to visit him in Mannheim. I can't believe it . . . . She sat transfixed, too shocked for tears.

Mr. Criddle opened his door and handed Isabel a letter, "Here's another . . . Friedrich."

Isabel drew out the letter. It was folded around a sprig of pressed ivy leaves. Her mother took them crying, "Oh . . . from Mama's grave! Mama is really gone!"

She buried her face in her hands and sobbed.

The one who tended other's tears now needed to be consoled. Isabel brought another handkerchief and with her arm on her mother's shoulder said, "I wish I could read Uncle's letter to you . . . will you read it and tell me?"

As soon as she could see through the tears, Elise stumbled through the first paragraph and told Isabel: "These ivy leaves are from Mama's grave to comfort me weeping alone over our common loss . . . in a far distant land."

She grasped her daughter's hand and, after a few more tears, exclaimed, "I'm a long way from my brothers. Thank God you are here."

She skimmed the next page.

The notary public, who has to regulate mother's financial affairs officially, requests an attested authorization from you and Percy. This is necessary in order to draw the pension that mother still had coming from April 1 to June 10, which is needed in order to pay expenses. Karl is going to send the instructions. I would beg you to draw up this authorization according to Karl's directions, for which you needs must wait, as soon as possible and send it to us. If not, Karl and I will have to pay the bills out of our pocket.

"That's all legal business, I'll tell you later."

It went slowly. Elise read a sentence or two and then translated. . . . "Marie is sad and affected by mother's death. They always got along very well. . . . All mother's friends assured him, that even during the last weeks, mother had, with obvious pleasure, spoken of visiting again. . . . . But she stopped during the last days, realizing it would be impossible." Elise spent another few moments with her handkerchief. . . . "Friedrich went to see her on Sunday. She spoke very little, barely yes and no, when he asked something." Imagining him at her mother's bedside Elise needed another handkerchief. " Be comforted, dear sister, at this loss and count it as grace from God . . . that we could have her with us for so long. She would have, had she lived until August 29th, been 77 years old. And her end was an easy one. . . . We shall always remember her fondly and with respect, and we siblings want to remain in a loving relationship, as was her wish. . . . Friedrich sends his heartfelt greetings."

Elise folded the pages of his letter around the ivy, and with the envelope safe in her pocket, looked up at her daughter and said, "We had better tend to tea."

Chapter Seven

Who Would Have Guessed?

The prospect of cash from Germany reinforced Mr. Criddle's desire for more land. He'd buy another team of oxen, harness, and plough. Edwy was able to put in a full day's ploughing and by next summer Harry would be strong enough to handle the second one. The quarter to his north seemed ideal, but he couldn't apply for it until he completed his first, the end of August. In order to ward off other would-be homesteaders he staked out a few acres to plough right away. Next morning he went back with Edwy, did a round, and left the boy to finish.

Walking north he found the Owens busily adding a kitchen to their house. "We need extra hands. We'll pay any number of workers you can bring. Remind you though, we don't feed."

As Edwy emptied his plate three nights later, he told his mother, "I think Mr. C likes to take me with him." Then in an even lower voice added, "He made sure I got the heavy end of the log. We earned thirty-one dollars in three days. Guess that wasn't too hard to carry. But, I'd rather help the neighbours around here. They always give us a good meal."

None of the other youngsters enjoyed the likes of Edwy's travels. They and Mama Dutcheen did get as far as the berry patch in the bluff.[1] And, after Nellie calved, Isabel took her twice daily walk to the barn with the milk pail.

After the German notary's form arrived, Mr. Criddle wanted more than a signature from Elise. Holding out some scribbled pages, he told her, "I want you to translate this letter to send along with the form."

She skimmed the pages, expecting to read an expression of sympathy. She saw, 'poor crop', 'cold winter', 'everyone hungry', 'need money to tide us over', and 'life insurance'. Her stomach tightened . . . *My poor brother. It seems as if I don't care about Mama . . . just want her money.* Did he not read that she had very little? But Mr. Criddle stood over her. She did his bidding.

Later that evening, tears of grief and regret mingled with her prayers.

※

Lonsbury dropped in and bragged, "I got seventy-five cents a pail for new potatoes in Brandon." The crew was sent immediately to the field. Before dawn next

---

1 Clump of trees on the prairie.

morning the loaded wagon was on the road. Edwy turned hawker. Mr. Criddle went straight to the post office to mail the letter to Germany. Dreaming of another inheritance he dropped in at the hotel to collect Minnie's wages. Luck was going to smile at last!

Regrettably Lonsbury's potatoes had flooded the market. Edwy had half a load unsold which limited the groceries, although a dollar went for a pair of Aylesbury ducklings Mr. Criddle couldn't resist. He elaborated on their expedition, "So much for the city of Brandon with its riches – three-quarters of the people too poor to buy a pail of potatoes. The Boy, oxen and I – had had enough of it after the first afternoon's work, spent a night on the Prairie – returned to the town next morning to continue our labour – we have had _more_ than enough."

He placed a duckling in each of Beatrice and Maida's cupped hands, "What will you call them?"

It was already August and the low-lying land cleared and burned the previous summer was still ankle deep in water. They needed to put up some hay, if they didn't want their oxen stealing all the straw off the roofs again next winter. Mr. Criddle and Edwy waded in with scythes. Elise and crew gathered up the tall coarse grass in their arms, splashed out to dry land, and spread it out to dry. The women had great difficulty wading back and forth in their long wet skirts. Elise said, "Isabel, you might tuck your skirt up a little at the front. Be much easier. I don't dare."

Exhausting and miserably dirty work it was, nevertheless they managed to get three loads dried and stacked. Their taskmaster had had enough; "I'm giving up the business for this season. I'll get Harry started on the plough."

Next night Harry reported proudly, "Did my first full day, twenty-five rounds. I guess I could say, I'm a man. You can be proud of me."

In the lull between haying and harvest there were other projects. Mr. Criddle's "wood chapel" had blown down several times. "We'll try two uprights and a cross piece. Lean all the poles against that – perchance this time I may expect success."

While the boys organized the poles, Mr. Criddle noticed his little ducks waddling across the yard. Having measured out an area near the fowl house, two and a half by six feet he called the little boys. "Ducks like water. Let's make them a pond. Dig it down a foot, and then we'll line it with clay. Harry will know where to find it."

When that passed inspection he said, "Now, get some of that old straw off the stable roof and fill the hole. We'll set it ablaze this evening – see if it holds water in the morning."

The early wheat had turned golden in the hot August sun. He sent for the man engaged to cut it, but got only a message in return. "Sorry, my binder broke down."

In desperation, Mr. Criddle remembered McVey Jr. had one and walked over.

"I don't think you will like my machine. It cuts and ties the sheaves just fine, but it needs a hand to turn the sheaver."

It didn't sound like a big problem to Mr. Criddle, until he had to walk alongside the binder all day tripping the 'blessed thing'. Still, they managed to finish the three and a half acres of Prairie Field. The prospect of a bumper crop of fine, well-filled kernels set his spirits soaring. There were more signs of plenty: young Brownie just hatched a third brood of chicks, and the garden showed great promise. "Pumpkins – one is three times as big as my head – several citrons are progressing towards visibility, lots of cabbages, peas, citrons, tomatoes."

On August 25, as if to punish Harry for choosing that birth date, frost stole silently across the fields and gardens. By morning the thermometer showed six degrees of frost. All their promising vegetables sparkled in the bright sunshine. Their beauty was short-lived, by evening the leaves drooped, and after another equally cold night, their fate was sealed.

Elise, unhappy about having to return to a diet of potatoes, tried not to attract attention from the unhappy farmer. The youngsters escaped to a grove of oak trees to gather acorns for Christmas. Harry went to McVey's to work for a week in return for the use of the binder. Edwy and Cecil banked up the fowl house to make it warmer for the coming winter.

With the exception of the already stooked wheat, the rest of the crop was damaged. The year 1885 would be remembered for both the Riel Rebellion and the devastating early frost. Some claimed the country was good for nothing but poplar trees and weeds. Mr. Criddle heaped blame at the feet of the "idiotic Government and a one-horse railway". Many talked of leaving; some decided to do just that. Connell was departing for New Zealand, Taylor and Carscaden to Dakota.

Cook hadn't ploughed a furrow, but he was rumoured to be canceling his homestead application because of the indifferent quality of the land. Its location kitty-corner to southeast, made it a desirable piece of land for Mr. Criddle.

Trail to Two Rivers crossed 28.8.16

Am contemplating letting the Dutchman homestead the NW ¼ of 28 (late Cook's). 'Tis apparently good ground and practically clear bar perhaps 5 acres. . . . I shall get about 125 acres of clear land in addition to my present holding - with 115 acres brush, swamp and wood.

He wrote Cook, suggesting that if he were going to withdraw, he should do it formally so another homesteader could settle there.

Mr. Bellhouse, their closest neighbour, hadn't been beaten. On hearing Carscaden was giving up the Aweme Post Office, he considered taking it over. In very short order, he and Mr. Criddle had a petition written, signed, and sent to the postal authorities. To have weekly mail service within a half mile of St. Albans would be fortunate indeed for the Criddles.

Then, reminded by Mrs. Criddle of the need for meat, he went hunting. Providence was with him, "Finally put a bullet bang through the middle of a Sandhill Crane. Young bird, tell by the colour – lovely brown and dove." He weighed it: "Seven pounds!" Measured its wing-spread tip to tip: "Five feet seven inches!" Then he handed it over to Elise: "Cook it for Sunday dinner."

As soon as the crop was stacked ready for threshing, Mr. Criddle hustled off to Brandon to finalize his homestead. While Edwy worked the streets hawking another load of freshly dug potatoes, Mr. Criddle met up with two friends who had agreed to act as his witnesses. Aware of the requirement that every witness must have known the applicant for three years, they agreed that their arrival in the spring of '83 was close enough. Thus, when the commissioner began, "Have you known Mr. Criddle for the three years of his residency on his homestead?" they nodded. "And do you swear to the truth of this statement?" They nodded again.

He turned to Mr. Criddle and placed the form on the counter. Confidently he took the pen and filled in the improvements he had made: built a log house 32 by 16 feet in October, 1882, and prior to that date, lived in a tent and shanty; had a log stable and granary; a well, and 38 acres under cultivation. Then with a flourish, he signed that all was true in every particular.

The commissioner asked Connell and Taylor to state the duration of their acquaintance. Both asserted, "We have known Percy Criddle since he perfected his entry in the month of August, 1882, the date he began to reside and cultivate his homestead up to the present time." Each in turn proceeded down the page, "Has raised crops upon 20, 30, 36 acres of the said homestead for the past three seasons. The size of his house, and the nature and extent of the other improvements were correct." And lastly, "We believe he has in good faith fulfilled the duties of his

Homestead prescribed by the Dominion Lands Act, in order for him to receive patent therefor [sic]". As neither man had a personal interest in the lands, everything was subscribed, sworn, and duly signed, September 15th, 1885.[2]

The three proceeded to the hotel; Mr. Criddle ordered a round of drinks. After a sip or two he excused himself. Then with Minnie's monthly contribution in his pocket, he drank to their future. "May you enjoy health and wealth far from the troubles of this blessed country!"

His friends took their leave. But not anxious to check on Edwy's progress, Mr. Criddle hoped for another pleasant chat with the matron.

Mrs. Sharpe, however, was in a serious mood. "Brandon people are terrible bigots, full of prejudice, especially toward niggers. I have a Mr. and Mrs. Allaman[3] of that race here. She tells me her husband has to go out of town. She's very unhappy, says people are cruel." She paused a moment for effect. "She's afraid to stay alone. Her husband is looking for a good boarding place out of town. Minnie has befriended the young woman and suggested I talk to you. Tells me you are very much opposed to all hypocrites, no matter what their stripes. Would you consider taking in the young woman for a month?"

Mr. Criddle was flattered.

She pressed on, "I'll let Minnie go for a few weeks to look after Mrs. Allaman just as she does here at the hotel. Mr. Allaman will pay you the same rate."

That settled it. He asked, "How soon is Mr. Allaman leaving?"

They arranged everything very quickly, and he agreed to return for them on the twenty-seventh.

Edwy's day was not so profitable, only three dollars for seven sacks of potatoes. But, that didn't matter so much now. Although Mr. Tulk wasn't coming that fall, they would have another paying guest.

⁕⁕⁕

Elise was excited to have Minnie coming home. *But with a black woman? We had black colonials in Southwark, but I don't recall that they were of the class to stay in hotels. I think Minnie has something up her sleeve.*

Elise prepared to move out of her bed to sleep with her daughters. They constructed a makeshift partition in the girls' rooms to give their guest a semblance of privacy.

With an advance payment toward her stay, the stop at the grocery store was a pleasure. Then the young women made themselves comfortable in the wagon for the long, slow, eighteen miles to St. Albans. Mrs. Allaman had never been to the

---

2 September 17, 1885. Archives of Manitoba, Homestead files GR 2060.
3 I retained Allaman, the spelling in Mr. Criddle's diary. The census records spelled the name, Allaeman.

country. She plied Minnie with a constant stream of questions about the houses, the families, the animals. Since this was only Minnie's third trip, she had to call on the men up front for answers. The hours passed very pleasantly.

The youngsters were on the lookout and ran to welcome Minnie, nearly choking her with hugs. She broke into the merriment and introduced their visitor. Any friend of Minnie's was welcome, and five-year-old Beatrice led the way into the house. Elise warmed to the young woman, *I can see why Minnie likes her . . . she's very amiable. I have a suspicion, though, that Minnie has a reason for bringing her way out here. If I'm not mistaken we're going to need some things she has packed in that big trunk she brought along.*

The next day Minnie showed her guest around the farm. The smallest chickens delighted her, even if they had lost their delightful yellow fuzz. Nellie's calf charmed her, too. Everyone enjoyed more variety of food and her stay seemed to be going well. It was smooth sailing, until early one morning Mrs. Allaman called plaintively, "Minnie, I need you. Can you come?"

Within minutes, Minnie was in the kitchen having an urgent 'one on one' with her mother. Mother and daughter locked eyes for a moment and enjoyed a silent laugh. Minnie went back to her patient. *So, my suspicions are correct. Minnie couldn't tell for fear Mrs. Allaman be sent back to Brandon. . . . Knew she could count on me. I'll go up straightaway. I need to open her trunk and see what else we might need.*

She put another stick in the stove and told Isabel, "I'm needed upstairs."

On the way up she had just enough time to collect her thoughts. *That Minnie! Who else would have thought up something like this! If all goes well I'll have a little one to take my mind off losing my dear Mama . . . and that dreadful letter I wrote to my brothers.*

Mrs. Allaman's labour was short for a first birth. The tiny infant slipped into Elise's capable hands without complications. Its first cries carried throughout the house taking all the others completely by surprise. Mr. Criddle had been out with the dog chasing down a mink. For once, he was so completely flabbergasted by the news that he had nothing to say, appropriate or otherwise. That night he told his diary, "Really – life is full of surprises and excitement out here after all. Who the devil could have guessed that the Criddle mansion would ever prove the first home of a little nigger."[4]

---

4 October 9, 1885.

Elise was too busy with the new mother and her infant to think about Karl's reaction to her letter. Until, that is, she saw a letter from him on the table a few days later. Apprehension swept over her again.

Karlsruhe, September 20, 1885

Dear Elise!

Your letter and your authorization I have received and I thank you for the promptness. Lamentably it won't do much good, since the inheritance from our dear mother, as remarked in the previous letter, is small. What is left of cash money will not suffice to pay the expenses incurred by her sickness and funeral. The total including doctor's fees, will add up to about 250 M. I got from the Post 90 M. From the care institute I will, if they pay at all, receive, according to my calculations, about 70 M. which I would not receive before October. I am sorry, that you were under the wrong impressions, concerning money from the care institute. That was not a life insurance, for then mother would have had to pay in every year, but what happened is that she received money every October.

Elise closed her eyes for a moment. *My poor brother, I knew that.*

Concerning the other property, there are: one bed, an old dining room suite with six chairs, a chest of drawers, a wall clock, some white garments, dresses, etc. . . . People do not want to pay anything for that kind of stuff.

*Our dining room table. . . . So many happy times around it . . . . Papa's Black Forest clock still ticking? Mama's under-garments . . . now **they** would be nice to have. . . .*

Oh, if only you did not live so far away, so that we could send you some things. But the transport costs would be greater than what the things are worth.
She sighed. *It's no use. . . . If wishes were horses then beggars would ride.*

As soon as I have received the money from the institute, I shall send it to you and I shall see what else I can do. You ask about a will. I have not found any. And even so, it would only be valid, if conditions would have remained unchanged as they were 30 years ago and in the case of a life insurance.

Concluding from your letter, you believed our dear mother could have lived tranquilly, depending on her pension. That would have been the case, if the debt account had not been so great, she was still paying when she left Heidelberg.

Elise looked off into space. *Mama, I keep thinking of all you did for us. We lost our papa and you tried to make up for him. Gave us the best you could on your little postal pension. We overstretched your means . . . thought we could pay it back. Wilhelm was well on the way to success when he left you so suddenly.*[5]

Wilhelm Harrer

---

5   Harrer, Wilhelm Jacob: unmarried architect, born Feb. 10, 1846. Baptized Feb. 22, 1846. Died 1872: Heidelberg. Index of Probate Records, File H 11070. Actual file is missing.

Papa was too young to die. You always said, "We had only 13 years, but they were very happy ones." How long did you live as a widow, 1849 to 1885? . . . 36 years! Dear God! My dear brave Mama.

Only when she came to live with me, she could live free of worries. That is the reason I took her to live with us, because I found it difficult to give her 2-300 M. annually, which I have done the past twelve years.

Dear Sister! Your description of your life, the privations etc. has touched us deeply and it hurts us, that we are not in the position to help you.

For today, farewell and receive, together with Percy and your dear children the heartiest greetings from my wife and your brother, Karl.

She folded up the letter thinking wistfully: *He took it better than I expected. I wouldn't want them to sacrifice for us. . . .* She turned her attention back to the baby. *He's such a little mite. I am going to do all I can to give him a good start in life.*

Two weeks later, Mr. Allaman came and gave the Criddles several small presents to show appreciation for his wife's care. But Elise wouldn't let her leave, "It's too soon to travel all that way, I think your little one needs at least another week with us."

The head of the household was away threshing when the guests departed. Elise had washed out every last diaper, all was folded and packed. She held the wee bundle in her arms, sang him a little lullaby, kissed his tiny black forehead, and handed him up to his Mama in the buggy. Minnie hugged her mother saying quietly, "It was good to get home. I counted on you, and you didn't let me down. The Allamans have a tough time in Brandon. I don't think they will stay very long."

With another hug she stepped up and into the buggy and the wheels carried them away. Elise's prayers went with them.[6]

❧⸻⸺⸻☙

Threshing was dusty, disgusting work for an English gentleman, but he knew that in order to receive help he had to be willing to help others. He couldn't send the Vane boys in his place, for to the neighbours, they were still boys. Elise heard him grumble, "The more I come in contact with these Canadians, the less I think of 'em and the more degraded I feel in having to mix with them."

The stressful harvest season ended with their best crop yet, almost 300 bushels of wheat. Tragically, only 50 of them were first grade selling at 65¢ a bushel. His optimism was rekindled by the arrival of an envelope. His chest swelled in pride as he pulled out the 'Homestead Patent.' He tacked the patent up on the wall and said proudly, "If only my *Mutter* could see this." [7]

6 United States Census, Alameda, California, 1900. Allaeman, Charles, born, New York, head cook, and Mary, born Canada, married in Toronto, 1883. Five children, four living. Emigrated in 1889. Rented house. Both adults could read, write and speak English. Familysearch.org. Viewed, May, 2011.

7 Percy used German for 'mother' in all his letters, e.g. "Well my dear Mutter, At last you've condescended to write to me again . . . . I can wait very well for the other £14 - I've got plenty to tell you but have no time so I'll wait till the receipt of the other half of the £20 note." January 1863. Family collection.

Percy Criddle was now a landowner; far beyond his reach in England. Given that landowners could borrow against their land, he took immediate steps to arrange a $500 loan through Mr. Burnett of Millford. Not waiting for the cash to come through, he set the wheels of expansion in motion. With a down payment and a promise to McVey Jr., he bought a cow for $35, plus 100 bushels of oats for 14¢ a bushel. For $110 he purchased Bruner's oxen. Then, since they would need a stable, it was off to the Spruce for logs. As he chopped down average sized trees, he noticed some fine large ones. They would do for a larger building and the seed was sown. At tea Elise heard him say, "If I add two rooms to the house we could have a living room for company – a private room for Tulk. Tents might do in Africa, but it still irks me that he didn't come this year. Want to make sure he comes next fall."

So, as they cut the stable logs they also cut large ones. One evening coming home they spotted a beautiful owl in the south bush. While the boys unloaded, he went off with his gun and soon returned with his prey and proceeded to write up his observations:

> About 3 ft across wing tip to tip – grey beak and claws – light fawn legs – grey and brown feathers generally ticked with white and black – brown crescent at outer sides of eyes – light grey or white inner side of ditto and below beak – black and yellow eyes – crest or horn 1½" long on either side of head (black, brown and grey) – Tail feathers barred, face surrounded by a pepper-and-salt ring ¼" tiger fashion.

The price per bushel of wheat had fallen ten cents, but he had to sell. From the proceeds, he came home with several rolls of brown paper. Carrying them through the kitchen, he announced, "Covering the walls in our room – cut down on drafts – give it a fresh and clean appearance."

The paper also made a splendid background to display his trophies—wings, heads, and claws. He stood back, "Twill look quite charming when finished, I verily believe."

Called in to admire, Elise thought, *At least he displays them in their own room.*

Edwy was trusted for the first time to go alone that November with wheat to Brandon. From its sale he purchased a barrel of salt, boots for his master and boys, a new lamp, and 'stores' for the house. Elise felt very proud of her lad's good management, and more so, as she watched him hand over the remaining $5.45. That money went immediately to McVey Jr. on delivery of an 'almost' pedigree Berkshire boar. McVey brought along two little pigs for Edwy and Harry in exchange for their help during harvest.

Another grain-selling trip solved the problem of what to feed the builders of their new stable. With both senior and junior McVeys, and McElroy's help, it went up in a day. Lazy and Bill, and newcomers, Lion and Lamb, had a temporary home until a larger one could be built.

❧ ⬥ ☙

Friday the 13th lived up to its bad reputation. Fearfully the Vane boys broke the news at breakfast. "The calf died in the night."

They were lucky because Mr. Criddle had more pressing things on his mind and responded absentmindedly, "Nice luck!"

In that evening's mail Minnie sent sad news, "Mrs. Allaman lost her baby." Elise blinked away a few tears, *Poor girl, she loved that baby! Such a blow for a mother. . . .* Elise was still remembering her last moments with the sweet little black boy, when Beatrice came out of her parent's room to give her another letter.

Karlsruhe, October 24, 1885

Dear sister!

This week I have received the overdue account of our dear mother's assets from the care institute and have sent the little, which amounted to 23 dollars, to you by mail today under the address of Mr. Percy Criddle Esq. Aweme, Manitoba, Canada, North America

Hopefully you are all well and will soon receive the money.

Fresh tears welled up in Elise's eyes. *My dear Mama, twenty-three dollars! I haven't seen it; but thank you. I am rich in memories.*[8]

I am sorry I couldn't send more. But the assets of what she left behind hardly covers the cost of her illness and the funeral, which amounted to more than 300 DM.

Friedrich, who now has his mother-in-law living with him and the children, also my wife, send heartiest greetings to all of you. Winter is at the door again; with God's help this one will be better than the previous one for you.

Write soon and tell us how you are doing and if you have received the money. From your brother, Karl

❧ ⬥ ☙

---

8 November 1, 1885. "Received $23 from Germany."

Once the stable was up, it was full speed ahead with the logging before winter set in. There were big plans, "Need 53 logs for granary bins and duck house – 72 for the house – 35 for another stable. Wood supply is drying up – get all we can to dry out for next winter."

While Harry, Cecil, and Norman went to the bush, Mr. Criddle had Edwy hauling wheat. Weed seeds made good chicken feed, and clean wheat brought a better price so the grain needed to go through the fanning mill before Monday morning. Elise was already busy, so Mrs. Criddle found herself organizing the younger ones to keep the handle turning. It was good they had the chicken feed for Monday night's news was discouraging, "Frozen! Bad business – only fifty cents – but such is my luck."

Jack and Jill were the next to be sold. Elise and Isabel were busy long into the night preparing the pork. While Edwy was collecting $24.55 for the meat, Mr. Criddle chased down the loan agent to collect the loan he had arranged. He got only $200. It was a start: $10 for a homestead entry for NW ¼ 4.9.16, a plough, harnesses for the new oxen, and finally 25¢ for vaccine for Maida, stores, and clothes. Then after joining McElroy, McVey Jr., and Bruner at the hotel, his Boy transported him safely back to St. Albans.

Mrs. Criddle's wardrobe didn't depend on her husband's choices. She un-packed a two-foot square box from her cousin: six new dresses, an opera cloak, riding-habit, 29 pairs of stockings, shoes, and more.[9] Rejects ended up with Mama Dutcheen to make over for the little ones, or patches.

Annual school board meetings were held all across Manitoba every Decem-ber. While the Western ratepayers organized to open another school, Elise was almost afraid to open the door. Two Rivers School had been operating for two years and several ratepayers were dead-opposed to another one cutting into their tax base and operating funds.[10] Those living further west came with equally strong feelings. Finally the latter group received the go-ahead, although 'Poplar', their choice of name, was lost. Aweme Union School # 454 would have children and be supported by taxes from the three adjoining municipalities of Oakland, Cornwal-lis, and South Cypress.[11] Elise hoped the hostilities would end. *I never dreamed children's education could cause so much trouble. . . .*

---

9   December 10, 1885. "Box from Louisa Nicol brought home – great rejoicings."
10   Two Rivers School # 299, located on the NW corner of 22.8.16, land donated by John Martin.
11   Built in 1886 on Peter Smith's land, NE ¼ 12. 9. 17. Closed in early 1900s, moved east in the 1920s, reopened. Closed, 1944. *Echoes of a Century Douglas Centennial 1882-1892.* p. 434. Douglas History Book Club, 1982.

With the school issue settled, Mr. Criddle was reminded of the lack of food on his table. Hiring McElroy to take 42 bushels of wheat to the mill in Millford, they had in return 956 pounds of flour and almost as many of shorts. In order to obtain raisins for Mrs. Criddle's pudding and mince pies, 12 turkeys lost their young heads. Elise plucked them, pulled the pinfeathers, and helped Edwy get away early next morning to reach the housewives of Brandon.

With Christmas dinner on the horizon it was time for the young folks' semi-annual weigh-in. Elise watched as she washed the tea dishes. Mr. Criddle moved the weight along the arm until it balanced and carefully recorded the weights. They were all gaining, not much, but they were gaining! She marveled. *With so little on their plates, how can they? Fortunately, he doesn't include me. I don't want to know how thin I have become.*

On November 24 Evelyn chased down one of the remaining turkeys. His father lopped off its head and carried it to the scales. "Ten pounds', he said, and handed it to Elise.

I had hoped for a larger bird. We'll make short work of this.

Next morning Elise was early in the kitchen; her boys began their Christmas with a run to Clay's bush a mile south to fetch the cows for Isabel to milk. By noon, the aromas of roast turkey and plum pudding brought everyone to the dinner table. They did, indeed, enjoy a feast, though scanty. The senior Criddle topped off his meal with his usual rum and hot water. The youngsters went sleigh-ing in the afternoon. It was a good day!

Mild weather during the holiday season enabled Mr. and Mrs. Criddle to go visiting. The children looked to Mama Dutcheen for another story from her mag-ical land of talking bears, evil witches, and fairy godmothers. With little Maida on her knee, she began.

"Once upon a time there was a miller who had no sons. Three young men helped him grind the grain into flour. As he got older, he began to worry, 'Who will look after me, when I am too old and weak to work? These fellows have been helping me. I'll give my mill to one of them. But of the three, how do I decide?' He asked each of them, 'I am going to give my mill to the one who promises to look after me when I am too old to work.' Each one said, 'I will.' The miller had to think of another plan. At last he called them together. 'I have a test for you: Go out into the world and find me a fine horse. I will give my mill to the one who brings me the finest horse. I don't want you arguing about which direction to go. I have three feathers here. I'll blow and you must follow your feather.' The young fellows each choose a feather. The miller took a big breath. He blew very hard.

"One of the feathers went west. The second was carried east in a gust of wind. The third feather, the one the youngest boy had chosen, stayed afloat only a short distance and landed on the ground. Now the two older lads often teased the youngest—calling him 'Simpleton'. They laughed, 'Well, Simpleton, are you going to find a horse right here? We don't see any.' And with that, they set off in great good humour, one to the west, the other to the east.

"Simpleton walked sadly toward his feather. When he bent down to pick it up, he discovered a sturdy ring in the ground. Scraping away the dirt, he uncovered a trap door." Mama Dutcheen told her wide-eyed audience, "Must have been a door like ours to the cellar, do you think? Anyway, Simpleton lifted it up. There were steps going down, and down, and he said to himself, 'I wonder where they go.' He wanted to find out, so down he went; down and down, until he came to a door at the bottom. 'Should I turn around while I still can?' he thought, 'No, if I go back now, I'll not find out what's on the other side of this door. I'll knock.'

"He struck the big door with his knuckles three times, knock, knock, knock."

Elise's tale spun on. One adventure followed another with only short breaks to add wood to the fires. "Eventually the older fellows returned with their horses: one blind, the other lame. Impatient for Simpleton; the miller was about to give up and choose between them when a horseman came galloping toward them along the river road. The rider reigned in his splendid steed and young Simpleton

jumped down. 'This is my horse.'"

Elise's audience clapped their hands with pleasure and agreed with the miller to give Simpleton the mill. Her story ended happily. "Simpleton cared for the old miller with great kindness as long as he lived."

The youngsters missed a good dinner, but had nourishment for their minds.

Chapter Eight

Land of Her Own

December 31, 1885

After lighting the kitchen stove early that morning, Elise went out for her usual excursion and paused to take in the beauty of the morning sun, encased in an awe-inspiring, shimmering white halo. *How extraordinary! It's ever so much brighter than usual. I'm afraid we may be in for some very cold weather.*

Her prediction was correct. By the end of January, Mr. Criddle's thermometer showed -5 degrees Fahrenheit in his bedroom at dawn. Outside, the temperature at the front of the house was -44 F, and at the back even colder at -48.[1] Cecil and Harry were kept busy at the saw-horse from dawn to dark, supplying the entire household with wood. Elise kept her shawl and mitts on while she stoked the fires in the morning and thought of the buffalo greatcoats the Canadians wore. *If I had such a coat, Isabel and I could use it at night as a blanket.* Cold as they were, the scarcity of food was an even greater concern. Although Mr. Criddle took his gun on every logging excursion and each time promised a rabbit or two, he hunted without success.

Burrough of the Gleann Museum and Archives, Glenboro, Manitoba

In an effort to save the chickens that were squatting helplessly on the floor of the fowl house, the boys carried the flock to the house. Once the birds were warm, they were soon eating, drinking, and investigating the premises. Before long, a hen perched on the wash basin and sent it crashing to the floor. It became clear that sharing space with the chickens was intolerable and so they were put through the trap door in the kitchen to the cellar below. Although an unpleasant odor wafted up through the floor, it couldn't be helped. Only 33 hens and 13 cocks survived, many of them without combs and missing toes.

Elise worried how the skimpy rations would affect the youngsters' health. Cecil admitted to feeling light-headed when he couldn't keep pulling his end of the saw. Harry took him in to see Mr. Criddle who gave him a dose of quinine and

---

1 -5° Fahrenheit is -22° Celsius; -44° Fahrenheit is -44° Celsius; -48.5° Fahrenheit is -47° Celsius.

sent him back to work. Norman developed the same symptoms and he also was given quinine. Evelyn received the same treatment for a painful swelling under his left arm.

Feeling faint herself, Elise managed to keep steadfastly at her post and she found it trying when Mr. Criddle complained of living without a decent doctor. *I'm quite sure I heard Mr. Bellhouse mention how much he liked Dr. Husband. He said there are two other doctors in Millford. If we had proper food we wouldn't need a doctor. With no money for food, how can we pay?*

Most of Isabel's time went to care for Mrs. Criddle, who also became unwell. Elise soldiered on through February faithfully applying hot cloths to Evelyn's swelling until it grew so large the boy couldn't hold his head properly. His father muttered, "If I did send for a doctor – where would the ten dollars come from? And if it's cancer, the doctor can't help."

An invitation to Mrs. Bruner's 'February Ball' gave Mr. Criddle a chance to escape the discontent at home and enjoy a little levity. His family learned the next day that the party was enjoyed by all. "Lots of neighbours – dancing on the first floor – cards on the second, and the men of course, had to go to check out the horses. Saw some interesting bottles going the rounds."

As Mrs. Criddle's condition worsened, her husband couldn't decide if it was an abscess or a hernia. He talked again about sending for the doctor. But when her pain gradually centred in her side and then began to swell, the question was settled, "A boil – not something requiring the doctor."

Elise carried on supplying hot poultices. When the boils finally broke, both invalids gradually convalesced.

<hr />

At the end of March, Harry's piglet was deemed large enough for butchering. The ninety pounds of fresh pork helped everyone feel better and they began to think about spring and new beginnings. Winter, though, wasn't over. A raging blizzard swept in from the northwest and swept away everything not firmly fastened down. Mr. Criddle peeked outside and reported, "The straw from the roofs now adorns the prairie between here and Woollhead's – the soil from top of the hill is on its road to Newfoundland."

The storm gradually blew itself out and afterwards Mr. Bellhouse walked over. "We've scored success in our letter writing blitz. I will be appointed post master April 3. Though the western settlers are enraged! Delivery will be but once a week. Must keep up the pressure for twice."

The family was also encouraged when Cherie, the new cow, had the good sense to deliver a heifer calf. Blessed with fresh milk, the calf also gave hope they'd have another milk producer in the future.

There was more good news. Mr. Tulk sent an eleven-pound note to cover the charges on freight he was packing for Manitoba. The roads were hardly clear of snow when notice arrived that Tulk's boxes were in Brandon. Mr. Criddle ordered, "Load the wagon with potatoes. Have it at the door by eight."

Mr. Criddle set out with Edwy. It was a tough trip, especially through one flooded stretch. Mr. Criddle abandoned the load and walked across higher ground, waving his stick and yelling. Edwy, his rubber boots full of water, slugged through with the oxen that were up to their bellies in mud. Fortunately Currie's ferry was operating. Still it had taken eight hours to reach Brandon—too late for Customs. The hotel owner bought their 20 bushels of potatoes and 150 eggs. While Mr. Criddle enjoyed a tasty cider, Edwy unloaded the wagon, carrying the bags up a rickety set of stairs to a storage room. Hoping for an early start the next day, Mr. Criddle called on the Customs officer, Mr. Hemen, pleading for a nine o'clock opening. Edwy spent the night in the livery stable with the oxen resting up for the trip home.

Mr. Hemen did not open his office at 9, and by 10, Mr. Criddle was again knocking on his door. Finally, all was settled by noon. The larger box, weighing 896 pounds was difficult to load; the second crate, only 100 pounds, was easily added. Off they set for home. The ferry crossing was a little scary, and then Mr. Criddle cut the farmer's fence to avoid the mud hole Edwy had slogged through earlier.

The next morning, Mr. Criddle skipped his daily temperature readings. Instead, he excitedly pried open the smaller of the two boxes and removed the following:

6 gooseberry trees well alive – 54 strawberry plants in excellent condition . . . 6 currant trees – probably alright and a lot of Jer. Artichokes in pink of health.

He took time to instruct the boys on what to do with the plants and then excitedly delved into the second box. "I'll have my telescope again."

Packed around the instrument were many gifts, as well as possessions left at the time of their departure from Tulk's cottage five years earlier:

. . . coats (2 of 'em great), 8 pr breeks [2] – 8 waistcoats – 8 shirts, 2 of 'em flannel (one a white cricketing), 4 jerseys – 2 drawers – handkerchiefs, etc. Velvet dress for A. and other clothes – my Mother's work box [3] – some portfolios – drawings – numerous books, some my own – others of Tulkian origin (very useful) – old letters – concert programmes – Chinese picture books [4] – a mass of music – A's big desk – other boxes – cartridges, caps, wads – and

---

2　Breeks/Breeches: male covering for lower body usually to just below the knees.

3　Mary Ann Alabaster Criddle, 1805-1880. A widow from 1858, partly supported herself and Percy by commissioned children's portraits. Percy and Alice lived with her after their marriage, September 8, 1874. She leased a home from 1860 to 1878 in Addlestone, then rented a small cottage on Tulk's estate, close by.

4　Chaloner Alabaster, Percy's cousin, working in China came home on leave and brought books to his auntie.

carefully interwoven – permeating and pervading all – the Telescope – and a very pretty little instrument it is.

In no time at all he had the telescope assembled and delighted in the clarity of distant prairie flowers. Given a clear night sky, he would locate Jupiter and Saturn. Elise from her post at the stove marveled at his behaviour. *For him, it's Christmas in May.*

―•◦๑๑◦•―

When his excitement subsided, Mr. Criddle revisited his plan to obtain Cooke's quarter. To avoid the usual slow trip by oxen, he engaged a team and buggy for the drive to Brandon.

Mr. Criddle told Elise that evening, "McElroy is going to Brandon tomorrow. Want you to go along to make an application for a homestead."

Her heart pounded. *Imagine! I'm going to get land. I haven't been anywhere for so long . . . I'm nervous. Can Isabel come too? . . . I think not, she's needed here, especially if I'm away.*

She prepared breakfast and then, with a hug from Isabel, settled herself as comfortably as possible in the little compartment behind the buggy's only seat. *Edwy tells me I can thank the law for this holiday . . . every homesteader has to appear in person at the Lands Office.*

It felt magical with the early morning air caressing her cheeks as they sped along. As daylight strengthened, she marveled at the shades of green overtaking the drab colours of early spring. Catching a glimpse of purple along the roadside she wanted to stop, but the wheels sped onward. *Three years ago this was open prairie. Now there are fences and houses. How different from that hot August day. . . .* Hopefulness swept her into a world where dreams come true.

―•◦๑๑◦•―

Elise felt intimidated at the Dominion Lands Office as she watched the agent's surprised expression as Mr. Criddle explained, "Widow Vane is here to make application for Cooke's cancelled homestead. She has three sons old enough to work the land, but not yet of age to apply for themselves. Here's ten dollars for the fee."

The man stowed the money in his drawer and spread the form on the counter.[5]

With a decisive flare he wrote in the blanks, *May 4, 1886*, and pen poised, demanded, "Your legal name?"

"Elise Vane." When he hesitated, she spelled it out, "E-l-i-s-e V-a-n-e."

He added, 'widow'.

---

5 Certificate in private family collection. Mr. Criddle's Diary: May 4, 1885. "to Brandon yesterday with Dutchman to homestead NW ¼ 28.8.16."

DOMINION LANDS.

INTERIM HOMESTEAD RECEIPT.

Nº 7246

Office of Dominion Lands,

Souris District.

3 May 1886

I Certify that I have received from

Elise Vane — widow —

the sum of Ten Dollars, being the office fee for Homestead Entry

for N. W. Quarter of Section 28

Township + Range 16 West of W Meridian,

and that the said Elise Vane is, in consequence of such

entry and payment, vested with the rights conferred in such cases by the provisions

of the "Dominion Lands Act, 1883," respecting Homestead rights.

(OVER.)

Local Agent.

With the speed of his pen, the deed was done. *I've taken the first step toward having my own land. I'll have something to decorate my wall.* They dropped her letter for Friedrich at the post office, but she didn't see Minnie, or get into a store to check out the selection of fabric, the colours of knitting wool, or see a pair of shoes. Homeward bound, the men swapped yarns. Soothed by the rhythmic beat of the horses' feet and the rattle of the wheels, Elise watched the sun sink slowly toward the horizon. *I came to give my children a good future. My boys can do the breaking and planting with Percy's oxen. . . . I know people are to live on their homestead . . . we'll move.* She was carried off in a fantasy of having her own home . . . until a sudden thought punctured the bubble. *Will I have to walk back to St. Albans to make their breakfast every morning?*

At exactly 8:10 that evening they pulled up at the door. Mr. Criddle must have read her mind, "Don't worry. There's a two-mile limit – no need to live there – lots of time to build a house – it's three years before you have to apply – need only three month's residence. The homestead inspector will come, but he's just a rubber stamp."

<hr>

Mr. Criddle was soon checking out Elise's land.[6] Her homestead became, 'South Farm' in contrast to Mr. Criddle's own new quarter, 'North Farm'. It was on South Farm that spring that the boys tried to break its tough dry prairie sod with both teams of oxen. They were 'dead pumped' several times a day and, while the beasts rested, the boys snared gophers. On the days their mother had nothing to send for dinner, they skinned and roasted their catch while a lookout watched for Mr. Criddle. They could expect to be roasted, if they were caught eating uncouth rodents.[7] Knowing, however, that his mother worried, Harry confided, "Don't fret about us going hungry. We take snares . . . there are plenty of gophers to roast . . . don't taste so good, but we're hungry."

His mother chuckled, "I'll see if I can find something to hold some salt to take in your pocket. It will improve the flavour."

<hr>

Mr. Criddle wanted potatoes on all the breaking on North Farm. It was a very large field, but no one grumbled, for without them they would have had almost nothing to eat during the previous winter. Elise went ahead diligently cutting pails of potato eyes, not knowing Mr. Criddle had changed his strategy. Furious to see that she'd already finished, he fumed, "The potatoes are already small – the ground dry – was going to plant 'em whole. The poor crop will be all your fault!"

Along with the spring work, the push began to build the addition on the house. The logs had been free, but money for joists, windows, shingles, nails, and floor planking had to be found. Mr. Tulk, an engineer had sent plans and $120. Still the landowner whined, "I have JA's and found –perhaps $15 or $30 – but this is going to be a scrape through."

Potatoes were sold in Brandon, but needing every penny, a night's lodging was out of the question. The trip on May 13th was wasted since government services and banks were all closed for Arbor Day. Understandably upset, he fumed, "Some Canadian seems to have found out that arbor means tree – hence the name – so the mighty can take a holiday and plant trees."

Lonsbury was employed at $1.50 a day and as the walls rose so did the expenses.

. . . neighbours have been very good helping and have worked like Trojans . .
Sheeting has run short – some 350 ft – swindling measure. Nearly eaten out

<hr>

6 May 16, 1886. "Had a partial survey of Dutchman's Homestead. . . . Some good ground on it especially northern part but also much cedar to be eradicated."
7 Vane, Harry. "I remember we used to take dinner when there was any." Harry is said to have complained later in life of stomach trouble from eating so many gophers.

of house and home – 5 men Tuesday and Wednesday, 5 Thursday – probably 4 today – much consumption of victuals. Expect an empty flour bin and five cents in the purse when we're through – but – per contra – there will be the house.

As he ran low on nails and shingles he talked about economizing, "No staircase, floor upstairs must be the rough boards from the old roof – we'll live on shorts at 50 cents per hundredweight."[8]

❧

Elise's days were long, hot, and hectic. *This is like having the threshers every day.* As the bread vanished and the big pot of potatoes emptied in the blink an eye, she found herself wishing for Aladdin's lamp. *I'd call on the genie every time I need carrots, turnips, and onions to add to the potatoes in the pot . . . and a roast of beef while he's at it. . . . The youngsters are all working hard . . . but there's little for them by the time the men leave the table.*

At the end of a hot day in the kitchen she wiped her forehead and took a long awaited letter outdoors. Perched on the woodpile in a cool evening breeze, she caught up with her family.

Mannheim, June 17, 1886

Dear Elise!

Your dear letter dated 22 of last month I have received today. Also your dear letter of last January came into my possession along with Isabel's little letter, which gave me great joy. Often I have wanted to answer you since then, and now I am really sorry that I have always postponed it and thereby caused you unnecessary worries. At home I don't get down to writing, since I am not home very much and the noise and confusion that our children create in our very confined living quarters (since my mother-in-law has moved in with us) bother me. So I usually write to you when I am in my office at work and there too I am often interrupted.

I was very happy to hear that you are all well and I fervently wish you could remain so and that your wishes concerning a good year and a bountiful harvest would be realized.

In spring, which was quite rough, Mariechen suffered with coughing and breathing problems. Now she is improving. Her mother also suffers from aches and pains of the back and legs. She is an old, overweight woman and walking is a chore for her. Mariechen's family has suffered a heavy loss this winter through the death of her uncle, leading physician Braun of Konstanz, where I, only last fall, spent 14 days. I also was very much affected by his death. He was a very brave and loving person.

8 Vane, Harry. "Our food consisted of sweepings from the flour mill floor at Brandon which was flavored with rosin that was used on the belt of the mill. It was not very nice but we were hungry. We had shorts, bran and potatoes, and rabbits that we used to snare. A bag of flour but that was only used when we had visitors. We did not get any of that."

On Ascension Day (June 3) I was in Karlsruhe and visited the grave of our dear, unforgettable mother with Carl and Amalie. We remembered you at that occasion.

I have mailed you a small package of papers today, maybe you will find something of interest or else entertaining in them if you can still read the Pfalz dialect. As you probably know, the King of Bavaria turned insane and drowned himself in the Starnberger Lake. People got worked up about it, all the newspapers are full of the news. You will read lots about it in the papers.

I am including with this letter two small neckerchiefs. Isabel may choose one of them, as a thank you for her letter. When you write again, please include the names and ages of all your children. Our dear mother knew them all but I do not and certainly would like to know them.

I will write again soon and I greet you, Percy and your children most heartily. Your loving brother, Friedrich.

She thought about that crazy King Ludwig! *A sad ending for a king.*

So Friedrich finds his house noisy. . . . It's good he's not in this house. I'm pleased they took time to decorate Mama's grave. . . . Her struggles are over. I strive on. . . .

But, I'm not the only one with trouble. . . . Poor Mrs. Bruner. Such a fright to see Horatio carried in covered in blood . . . that horrid bull. Imagine her joy to see her son come around! Hunger doesn't seem so bad. Thank goodness they've cut off the beast's horns and put a ring in his nose.

<hr />

The neighbouring families took a holiday on July 1, but Mr. Criddle kept his crews working through the long hot day. That evening, ominous black clouds  rumbled up the western sky. A powerful gust of wind hit the west wall with such a punch it sprang inward sending a cloud of mortar across the room. Lightning, thunder, rain, and hail followed. Mr. Criddle said later, "I don't wish ever to get closer to a general smash – not so close in fact."

At dawn next morning, young Bellhouse pounded on the door hollering, "Help! Our roof fell in last night! Papa's hurt!"

Mr. Criddle rushed off and found the poor man dazed and shaken; his wife wailing. "We'd no lamp. My poor Charles. Such a deluge . . . rain, hail! . . . Dreadful, just dreadful."

Ordering libations of rum, Mr. Criddle soothed her by predicting a full recovery. In true pioneering spirit 17 men, including Calverley, who also lost the roof of his new house, turned out two days later to rebuild the home.

Two weeks later, the crops were once more shriveling in the heat. Mr. Criddle's litany of woes wasn't confined to the fields.

Only five chicks this summer and no hens wanting to sit – young turkeys dying off daily – the little duck has disappeared. Of two fine sows – one is dead. Of fourteen piglets – one lives. Ourselves, we've nothing but shorts and potatoes with an occasional rabbit – all of us half famished – really 'tis almost too disheartening. As for the garden – we shall have a tiny dish of peas tomorrow – onions a failure – ditto everything else. Perhaps next year may improve matters – if it doesn't we shall starve.

A renewed demand for potatoes in Brandon brought in enough money for more shingles to complete the roof and because Elise was unwell, Mrs. Criddle was pressed into duty. She too, after four rows on the roof, was 'about knocked up'. Her husband admitted, "There ought to have been another round at top, but shingles and nails are about played out. Ninety-four thousand shingles are expense enough."

He offered the family some good news, "I'll soon be making money as a magistrate. Mr. Todd, J.P., was very polite – had me swear allegiance to Her Most Gracious Majesty and take the necessary oaths.[9] I'll get my hands on some legal books – should pay better than the school board. By Jimmini – what shall I take up next?"

His friend, Mr. Owen, interrupted his building one afternoon. "Our group has split. I can't manage alone. I'm giving up on farming. Sold our house to Upper for $200. I still have to dispose of the sheep, equipment, and household."

Mr. Criddle enquired after their sitting room stove, and on learning the price was $6 replied, "Don't have the cash. No barley – oats poor – wheat very thin and hardly a foot high. I ought to take my beastly old scythe down to the swamp and half kill myself mowing for a week."

Mr. Owens sympathized, but didn't lower the price on his stove.

The boys took the scythe to the meadow and hayed, while Mr. Criddle carried on with his house and kept his eyes out for rain. "Too late for the crop, but I still hope the potatoes will exceed the size of mustard seeds."

Without rain, the atmosphere was tense. Two turkeys had to be sacrificed for sale in Brandon to buy twine, and during his absence Cherie's calf got loose and sucked her mother dry. Without milk for the house, the boys felt his wrath, "Confounded carelessness! You know Mrs. Criddle is not well and needs her hot toddy."[10]

9　July 14, 1886.
10　Boiled milk, sweetened with sugar, and whisky, to taste.

When the wheat proved too short for Ake's binder, Mr. Criddle hired another at a dollar a day. While the older boys harvested, Stuart and Evelyn deepened a 10' by 20' area of the west pond for a future bathing hole. And each day the house plans progressed:

I fully expect to get the Tulkian chambers ready for occupation in time – the last window in at 8 pm tonight. Siding, gable and cementing are the most important items now to be seen to – hereafter I have to grout and board sides of old house and make 2 rooms upstairs for the kids – Must make a 2nd chamber before winter unless I want someone frozen to death – cash – consequently lumber – is however not at present available.

The floor was laid and windows installed by Mr. Tulk's arrival. He unpacked gifts of clothes, tennis balls, Mr. Criddle's desired barometer and, best of all, a fine 10-bore choke by Rigby with case and complete fittings. Following a successful hunt, everyone celebrated.

Next day, the men constructed a table and that evening the family enjoyed tea in the new sitting room. The rest of the space, 10' by12', would be a private room for Mr. Tulk. The following morning, both teams of oxen set off for Brandon to stock up on food, buy bedding, a stove, and other furnishings. It was after midnight when Elise, keeping the kettle hot, was surprised when Minnie appeared, "I've come home, have a fever, and need a good rest."[11]

Mr. Tulk got right down to work helping to board up his walls and stuff them with sawdust for insulation. A day or two later, Elise packed food for the family's annual holiday to the Spruce.[12] Thankful for the day to herself, she heated some water, took it upstairs, and enjoyed the luxury of a full wash. *Now I shall rest and see if this fever will pass.* That evening she was back at the stove preparing the evening tea. The youngsters all talked at once, "You should have come! Mr. Tulk made up a game of cone throwing . . . lots of fun in the sand . . . sliding down the bank . . . bathed in the spring . . . see . . . sand in my ears."

A single day had not been enough rest for Elise and she became too ill to get out of bed. Minnie's fever also worsened and then Edwy succumbed. Mrs. Criddle and Isabel were left to cook and tend the sick. Mr. Criddle wondered, "Could the well water be the cause? We've been deepening the well and possibly the lower stratum of water is alkaloid."[13]

Mr. Tulk offered his thoughts, "I am afraid you are wrong. We heard that Brandon has many cases of typhoid fever."

11 Vane, Harry. "Minnie got typhoid fever and had to come home then Edwy and Stuart got it very badly and it was a matter of life and death for days."
12 September 6, 1886. "The annual grand Picnic on Saturday to the Spruce – 13 of us."
13 September 15, 1886. "The Boy has been ill for last 8 days – low fever – can't get him better – now the Dutchman is bad – nice go – cause doubtful."

The two argued, but Mr. Criddle wouldn't even consider typhoid.

Mr. Tulk said abruptly, "I need a ride to Brandon in the morning," and packed his clothes.

∗❦∗

Left high and dry to enjoy his new gun and the planned hunting season, Mr. Criddle moped about, "I get more lonely and disgusted the more I think of his departure. On every side I see something we should have seen together – some covey[14] to be stalked – some walk to be taken – something requiring his company."

The younger boys filled in for the very ill Edwy. "Don't worry," Harry told him. We're doing fine. Got up 21 small loads of hay . . . made a fine stack."

They also went threshing at the neighbours. Crops were poor as expected, and when their own was reckoned, the tally was heartbreaking.

> 110 bush wheat – full measure; and 1¼ bush. Barley – but then, Bellhouse' oxen had eaten nearly all the latter. This is <u>rather</u> a bad yield for 34 acres ploughing – 43 bush. seed – $1.30 string – 15 days harvesting, $9 threshing and a feed for 10 men. . . . Damn the Country – but I can't get out of it, so must hope for better luck next year. How I am to feed my poultry and pigs, to say nothing of the family for a twelvemonth, is not easily to be seen. It has to be done somehow, however. . .

When Stuart, Evelyn, and Isabel all fell ill, Elise tried to resume her duties to save Mrs. Criddle. But she herself suffered a relapse and was worse than ever.[15] By the beginning of October, Edwy began to get on his feet and gradually recovered. At the end of the month Mr. Criddle sent him off to work for McVey Senior at $6 a month and Minnie went back to work at the hotel. Stuart and Isabel convalesced and Elise pretended to be well.[16] Seeing a letter from Karl on the table, she thought. *This is just the tonic I need.*

Karlsruhe, October 27, 1886

My dear Elise!

A few days ago I received your letter, addressed to Friedrich and learned to my consternation, that you again experienced much sorrow. God willing, the sickness will not have left some bad after effects. We heartily wish that all of you, young and old, (great or small) are in good health and of good cheer.

You would like to know why I haven't written for so long? I cannot give you a good reason. But you and yours may be thoroughly convinced that the reason is not indifference. Amalie and I talk about you often and lament the fact that we live so terribly far apart. How often I am reminded of a prophecy our dear mother, now resting in the arms of God, used to say, when we as children, would fight with

---

14 A small flock of partridges.

15 October 18, 1886. "Dutchman struck down yesterday so we're nicely in for it."

16 November 1, 1886. "Stuart is getting on nicely now – can walk a little alone – Dico [Isabel] too is I believe mending – and perhaps the Dutchman – but I'm a bit doubtful as to her. No one else attacked so far, thank goodness."

one another: "Later some time you will be glad, if you could only be together." Fate has certainly fulfilled this prophecy and has not allowed any of us to be together. Friedrich and I don't see each other that often either, since it is too expensive to go to one another often.

Well, next Monday is All Souls day! As you probably remember, that is the time when the graves are cleaned and decorated. We also, although it is a Catholic custom, will go to the grave of our dear mother and will decorate it with flowers and wreaths.

It is time to leave the office and go home, so I will close with the hearty wish, that this letter will find you in good health. Amalie and I send you, Percy, and the children many thousand well-wishes, with the plea, that you will send a letter soon, and I also promise to write more often.

May God protect you! Your brother Karl

❧

In November the boys completed that year's required breaking on their mother's homestead but, any feelings of well-being were shattered when she heard Mr. Criddle say, "Pack your bags, Dico.[17] McVey is going to Brandon tomorrow and will take you. Minnie can help you find a position. The Devil drives and I can't help myself. I really have tried very hard to court the good office of the worthy Dame Fortune – but she seems to shun me. May good luck come next year."

Elise couldn't believe her ears. *Dear God! I've been so terribly ill . . . I'm just getting back on my feet. It's selfish of me, but can I manage the work? Who will milk the cows? Will Beatrice and Maida look after the milk, churn the butter?. . .* Her initial panic subsided and her thoughts turned to her daughters. *First Minnie and now Isabel working like slaves for strangers. Isabel's been sick too. . . . But she is young and strong . . . has already gone up to gather her things.* My brother Karl prayed, Behuet Euch Gott! *May God protect you. I pray God will protect my girls also.*

❧

Still missing Isabel's cheerful chatter, Elise opened what, she thought, would be an encouraging letter from Friedrich.

Mannheim. 8. Dezember, 1886

Liebe Schwester!

Lamentably, I have sad news to convey to you today. Mariechen's mother died on the 4th of the month in the evening at 10:45 after a long and difficult illness. Yesterday we buried her. From our Dr. Fischer we knew that her illness, cancer of the stomach and liver, was terminal and she would be relieved from pain only through death. In spite of being prepared for her death in this manner, it seemed sudden. Even though we, especially Mariechen feel the loss keenly, it is a comfort

---

17 Mr. Criddle's nickname for Isabel. My father always called her 'Auntie Belle'.

to know that we could care for her until the end and that now she is released of all her pain and sorrow.

After she suffered a severe attack of stomach pain so that she no longer could remain in her bed and we had helped her out and after half an hour helped her back into bed again, she fell asleep exhausted. Her breathing became weaker and weaker and, after breathing out two more times, she stopped and was gone.

Mariechen has been through a difficult time, for the nature of the illness was such, that her mother needed much care, and had this been prolonged a few more weeks, Mariechen too would have collapsed and become ill. Let us allow her the rest and remember her in good faith!

Elise's eyes welled with tears. *I was so happy at Friedrich and Marie's wedding that warm September day in '65. Widow Bauer always enjoyed people, and that day she was in particularly high spirits . . . a most gracious pastor's wife . . . made Percy and me so welcome. So many changes; I'm so far away!*

My letter from the beginning of November with a few ribbons you will probably have received. I also sent you a calendar, Lahrer hinkenden Boten, *that you probably haven't seen in a long time. I think it should provide you many an hour of entertainment during the long winter.-*

She rubbed her chin thoughtfully. *What, I wonder, has become of my calendar?* [18] *The ribbons, I remember, went to little Beatrice, she pleaded so.*

I don't know if you have been informed that our cousin Friedrich Harrer, younger brother to Hermann, got married and has taken on the Hotel zum Markgrafler in Freiburg im Breisgau from his in-laws.[19]

Our youngest daughter Julchen has given us a lot of cause to worry. Suddenly at night she had brain cramps so that she was beside herself and screamed. This was repeated almost every night. The doctor prescribed some sedatives. . . . Last night the attacks were not as severe. God willing, there is recovery in sight.

Since it is doubtful that I will get to writing you once more before New Years, I wish you all very merry holidays and a happy New Year. May all your wishes be fulfilled and may you be free of sorrow and pain.

With a hearty greeting to Percy, your children and you,
I remain your faithful brother, Friedrich

Early one Saturday morning as she lit the fire in the living room, she noticed Mr. Tulk's letter on the table. *I'd like to know how he is. What can be the harm if I read it? . . .*

---

18 *Lahr Limping Messenger* almanac has carried the fame of Lahr, a beautiful city in the Black Forest, throughout the world for 150 years.

19 Elise's Postmaster Uncle Friedrich, 1808-1874, and his wife had 12 children. Hermann, the oldest, was the direct ancestor of the present day Dr. Hermann Harrer who introduced me to his family as his 'Canadian Cousin'.

Firfield – Addlestone – Weybridge
Surrey – England – Dec. 12th, 1886

My Dear Percy,

Yours of Nov 20th came on the 10th. The news contained therein is a blow, yes a blow, fancy miles of lovely ice and I not there to enjoy same, then again deer stalking and no John Augustus to miss the blooming thing. Enough to make one tear ones hair from sheer envy. Not to put too fine a point on it I must congratulate you on your sport and success and hope that the meat was a pleasant addition to the larder.

So you decline to guess why I took a sudden departure, well if you w'ont, you w'ont, but you lose the chance of winning the bet and I keep the dollars.

Your remarks as to the rifle are doubtless correct but I fear that it is a trifle too powerful . . . .

Elise skipped the rest of that paragraph. *I'm only interested in the food they supply.*

You have made a good job of the walls as regards tightness but it seems a pity to have spoiled the appearance outside with the cement. I don't think that hay or straw would have (if properly protected) increased risk of fire in the house, but as you have not got any you may be cool but there is no fear of being too hot, so its all satisfactory. . . . I often wish I could have remained to share the doings in the Arctic Regions.

I do not see how to agree with you as to the fever, if it was Red River, it was doubtless caused by alkaloid water, but if Typhoid, bad drainage and poisoned air must have been the cause, added most likely to water contaminated with animal matter of one kind or other. Am glad that all are recovering which is almost more than I thought might be the case. . . .

Elise gasped, *Gracious! Mr. Tulk* **knew** *we had* **typhoid.** . . .
He thought we might **die.** . . .
She only glanced at the closing . . .

Christmas Greetings to all and best wishes for the New Year and all other times.
John Aug. Tulk

❦

Chapter Nine

Good Day to You

December 1886 was as bitter as their first year. Roaring fires could hardly keep the house warm during the day, while at night all heads had to be under the covers. As the wind whistled through the cracks in the walls, Elise recalled Mr. Criddle's promise to fill the cracks of the addition. *If only illness had not frightened Mr. Tulk away. His help made a difference even in the short time he was with us.*

Out rabbit hunting, Harry trudged home with a beautiful white owl. Proud as a peacock, he turned it over to Mr. Criddle and watched him making notes, "White covered with brownish black or grey spots – eye a whopper yellow and black – very strong blackish beak and claws – round bullet head, thick white breeches and under wing – extreme breadth, wings – tip to tip –five feet, weight about five pounds."

But if Harry had any idea they might roast it, his hope was short-lived. "The beggar is tremendously fat – I daresay he'd have tasted A-1 if prejudice didn't deprive us of it. I've been decorating the living room and J A's room – heads, beaks, feet – your owl will be a godsend – a fine addition to the honourable gentleman's oleographs[1] and sketches."

Elise found life difficult without Isabel's cheery support and reminded herself, *I must keep up for the others.* Her boys fed the animals and chickens, gathered eggs, and milked. Nor could the bucksaw lie idle, for they needed a steady flow of firewood. Harry managed to shoot some prairie chickens for his mother to roast for Christmas dinner. Mrs. Criddle, in spite of a toothache, prepared and served her plum pudding.

The meal over, the table was pushed aside for games. They began with one Elise didn't know, Hunt the Slipper.[2] Evelyn volunteered to be the nobleman with a hole in his shoe. His papa gave it to a cobbler in the outside circle saying, "You think he's uppity. Tease him. Hide his shoe behind your back. To get it back, he has to guess who has it."

To Evelyn he said, "Cover your eyes. Now say, 'Cobbler, cobbler, mend my shoe. Get it done by half-past-two'."

---

1 Imitation oil paintings printed on canvass.
2 Originated in 17th century, arising from 'bad' feelings in the lower classes toward the upper class gentry.

When Evelyn opened his eyes, the shoe had disappeared. "You'll have to be sharp – they can pass it behind your back. The one you catch takes your place."

Evelyn finally tracked down the shoe and after a few more noblemen; they changed to Blind Man's Bluff. Beatrice, now a big girl of six, wanted to go first. Her papa tied a towel around her head, spun her around several times, and said, "Okay, Bobo, tag one of those big boys."

She groped toward the voice, "Catch me! I'm right behind you!" But the body moved and all she swatted was air. Before she got too discouraged, Cecil let her catch him. Being small and agile, it wasn't long before he feigned one direction, but swept his arm low in another, and tagged long legged Norman. The game got more and more boisterous until the Vane boys had to quit for chores. After tea Elise took Beatrice and little Maida upstairs, sang them their lullaby, and tucked them into bed. As she tiptoed back down to finish up in the kitchen, she thought, *I have managed, but I'm wondering about Isabel. How did she make out cooking Christmas dinner for strangers? Is she lonely tonight?*

⁕

The bitter cold continued to New Year's. Mr. Criddle penned his thoughts.

Today we commence a new campaign. I hope we may have a little luck for a change. Though the farm has returned us nothing there are many things achieved – to wit, new stable – addition to house – furniture for part of same – my new gun – Barometer – J.A.T. being the principal Factor – In fact '86 should be looked on as the J.A.T. year – my telescope too. Still I should like to earn something – 'twould be a novelty. May pigs and fowls multiply – the cattle prosper – may I get in 60 acres of wheat and reap a good crop – may 1887 be a trump year.

During January he visited here and there, while his wife stayed close to the fires and conducted the infants' lessons. When a box from her cousin Louisa arrived at the customs, he got a lift with Bellhouse on a load of grain to fetch it. Elise heard many cries of delight during the unpacking. In the end she was given the rejects to use in patching or to make into blankets. When Mr. Criddle was home, he fed the fire in their room and worked on a novel. Occasionally Elise heard wailing rise above the drone of the children's lessons, "Wretched business; I wasn't born to be an author!"

The frustrated writer took up another cause. Too many settlers from a distance were cutting timber in the Tamarack without a license; he set out to stop the practice. When the timber inspector turned up and handed out fines, he boasted; "Let them keep to their own neighbourhood and be damned! I'll want logs for the Dutchman's house presently."

Elise perked up her ears; *my house . . . at last.*

Since Elise's serious illness the previous autumn Mr. Criddle had been incubating the idea of a will, should the worst happen, to avoid awkward questions. Having a copy of his Uncle Chaloner Alabaster's with its provisions for his soon to be orphaned children as a model, it was an easy matter to compose one for his housekeeper. He'd keep the will handy for signing, should suitable witnesses come to St. Albans.[3]

And sure enough, just before the February election, unsuspecting candidates, Burnett and Dewart from Millford area, came to the door looking for his vote. Mr. Criddle listened attentively to their political pitch and then asked Elise to serve tea. As they prepared to leave, he made his move, "I have a little favour to ask. Mrs. Vane doesn't get out very often – would appreciate if you would witness her will. I'll fetch it – be back in a moment."

Elise was thunderstruck. *A will . . . for me? Without even talking to me! Everything I have is my children's . . . Minnie is very responsible and isn't Edwy? . . . What can I do? In front of these men? At least I'll read it first.*

But Mr. Criddle was too fast for her. He quickly dated it and then without missing a beat, he handed her the pen and pointed to the appropriate place to write her name. She signed. He took the pen from her hand, and passed it to the men. They too, without looking it over, signed.

Smooth politician that he was, Mr. Burnett smiled, "Well, Mrs. Vane, you now have a legal will and don't need to worry about your children's future. We don't like to think about such things, but if something should happen to you, Mr. Criddle will look after your affairs very ably, I am sure. Being in the legal field myself I have seen some unfortunate situations, when having a will, would have saved a great deal of confusion. I'm happy to have been of assistance."

Rising from the table he added, "Well, we must be on our way. Good day to you, Mrs. Vane."

While Mr. Criddle saw the men out, Elise had a chance to skim down the page.

This is the last will of me, Elise Vane of Aweme Manitoba. I leave all my property, real personal and otherwise to Percy Criddle in trust for the maintenance and benefit of my children 'till the youngest of them surviving shall attain the age of twenty-one years whereupon the said Percy Criddle shall divide my said property equally among them and the heirs of such as having attained the age of twenty one years may have meanwhile deceased and I appoint the said Percy Criddle my sole executor and guardian of my said children and I give him power to do in all things as may seem best according to his judgment for the advantage of my said children's

---

3 Alabaster, Chaloner, London, 1840, gave Percy's mother, and by default, father, guardianship of his three children and his business until they came of age. Private family collection.

This is the last will of me Elise Vane of Aweme Manitoba I leave all my property real personal and otherwise to Percy Criddle in trust for the maintenance and benefit of my children 'till the youngest of them surviving shall have attained the age of twenty one years whereupon the said Percy Criddle shall divide my said property equally among them and the heirs of such as having attained the age of twenty one years may have meanwhile deceased and I appoint the said Percy Criddle my sole executor and guardian of my said children and I give him power to do in all things as may seem best according to his judgment for the advantage of my said childrens interests and carrying out the purport hereof Dated this sixteenth day of February Eighteen hundred and eighty seven

Elise Vane

interest and carrying out the purport hereof.
Dated this sixteenth day of February, Eighteen hundred and eighty seven.
Elise Vane

Signed by the above named testatrix in the presence of us present at the same time who in her presence in the presence of each other and at her request have hereunto subscribed our names as witnesses.
Frank Burnett
E. I. H. Dewart [4]

Their leaving took just enough time for her to finish and as she returned to the stove, he picked it up. Her mind still in turmoil she thought, *I have nothing to worry me. . . . Little does he know!*

⋯⋯

Because of the deep snow and severe weather, the cattle had not been able to feed themselves on the open prairie. The oxen strained their ropes to reach the straw of their roof through the poles. When a rope gave way, an amazingly long tongue wrapped around the straw and pulled. Their barn grew colder as the stuffing from the walls also disappeared. Nellie's third calf perished. Mr. Criddle rationalized, "It's the cold and rheumatism – ten dollars gone up the spout."

While Mr. Criddle dined often with neighbours and complained of gaining weight, the family had only sweepings from the mill. The so-called shorts were free for the taking, but they came mixed with resin from the belts and dirt from the floor. He told his household, "With not even eighty cents in the house, we have to eat it."[5]

---

4 Archives of Manitoba, Ref ATG 0064-8/GR 385/J-7-6-7/File #897
5 February 11, 1887. "Sweepings – paper, dirt, resin . . . . We shall have no grub at all soon."

Concerned as Elise was with the food shortage, having to open the door to angry parents unsettled her even more. In angry self-defense, Mr. Criddle passed on the blame, "Old Bellhouse has managed to make a complete mess of everything he's touched so far – and – the Superintendent, Mr. Somerset is a beastly ass and ought to be kicked out of office. He's nothing but an upstart Irish pedagogue of first class conceit and third class intellect. Though an erstwhile teacher of grammar and spelling, he has evidently never studied either himself."

His blustering didn't impress the parents, "The man said the lumber was poor, get it replaced! We want our children in school."[6]

Bellhouse threw up his hands, resigned as the school board's secretary-treasurer and handed the minute book and monies to Mr. Criddle. Pressure on the builder finally got the walls redone but Miss Bellhouse declined to continue her teaching.[7]

The Criddle-Bellhouse relations hit another snag when Mr. Criddle braved the beastly half-mile through a blizzard with Harry and Norman for the mail. Unfortunately, Mr. Bellhouse had not yet made it back from Two Rivers with the mailbag and they returned empty-handed. The storm raged on, and by Saturday morning their well was plugged with snow and the oxen's abode was draftier because Lion had lunched again. Out of that raging whiteness, McVey appeared at the door, "I need one of your boys. I'm out of hay and need help to fetch some from across the river."

Edwy went. Now it was Harry's job to fetch the mail. He returned to say, "The carrier didn't get through yesterday. Bellhouse hardly got home last night. He's not going again today."

"Weather be damned, the Queen's mail must get through! Take a note back to him." He scribbled, "If you don't change your mind, I shall write to the postmaster general."

Monday morning he wrote the searing note and then settled down to add to the fifty pages of his novel *Mira Kennedy*. It wasn't long before Elise heard more wailing, "I'm in a real mess – the chapters hang like damp clothes on a line."

She shrugged; *will he ever finish that novel?*

Edwy returned from McVey's with a chilling story for his mother. "It wasn't our first trip across the river, but I guess that load was heavier. We went through the ice. Wasn't too deep, but the horses sure didn't like it. Had a deuce of a merry time of it getting out. Anyway, Mama, all's well that ends well."

---

6 Wellwood, Rev. J. M., Inspector's Report: 1887. "That Aweme is about finished but very poor lumber has been used in the construction and it is in very unsatisfactory condition." Department of Education Library, Winnipeg.
7 The school had operated two months the previous fall. Miss Anderson started May 10 with a salary of $35 a month. Aweme Rate Payers Minute Book of the Aweme Union District School Division, Archives of Manitoba.

Elise's worried face relaxed. "My son, I could write a book about your adventures."

⁃⦿⧽⦿⧼⦿⁃

By April 2nd, most of the snow had melted and wheels replaced runners. Geese winged northward, ducks landed on the ponds, frogs serenaded. The boys reported bluebottle flies and caught a grasshopper. Mr. and Mrs. Criddle saw a flock of blackbirds on their way to Uppers.

Three weeks later, spring reigned in the land. But when Mr. Criddle went along to Two Rivers with the postmaster to pick up Aweme's mailbag, they found the river still more or less solid. Both Mr. Bellhouse and his complaint-prone client came to a full stop at its edge; neither appeared desirous of risking the crossing over rotting ice.

Mr. Criddle, nevertheless, returned home in triumph, "Upper took matters in stride – had a plank – laid it between the ice hummocks – stepped from one to another – got across the river – retrieved our mailbag. Letter from J. A. – he'll send lightning rods for the house – we must dig a well to ground them."

That spring the boys did all the land work, broadcasting and harrowing in the crops as directed. By April 28, Edwy and Harry had 23 acres of wheat on Elise's homestead and 19 acres on North Farm.[8] Gardening had also gone well and, with a good rain, the year looked very promising. Then the weather turned ugly. Horrid winds tore the soil away from the roots of the tender plants. Fierce, sudden gusts blew in a window, carried off what remained of the straw roofing on the outbuildings, and swept a great sandy hole two feet deep at the southwest corner of the house. Mr. Criddle summoned the boys, "We need dirt – the foundations of the blooming ship are being undermined – fill the hole and cover it with sods."

As the boys struggled with flying sand, their overseer wrote in his diary:

Work impossible – beastly, beastly, beastly. Whether the crops are injured I can't say – rather think not – but Clay and others think they <u>are</u>. Thick clouds of dust were tearing along all day from the fields and I had quite a task walking to Uppers [sic] where I found all in confusion – House supported by temporary struts to prevent it blowing over – Piano at SE corner for ballast – and sundry other precautions – Certainly the place shook and heaved as if it wanted to blow to pieces.

Both Bruner families had been invited for Sunday dinner, and in spite of the gale, the women

---

8 Wheat: '5 ½ pecks' [1peck = 2 gallons] per acre. He had bought "expensive seed from Mooney". [Nellie Moonie, later McClung, lived on her family's farm south of Treesbank.]

prepared a meal of roast goose, asparagus, and rhubarb pie. When the guests failed to arrive, the host marched back and forth muttering, "This is the third occasion the Bruners have accepted an invitation and have not kept their engagement – shall not ask them again. They are so barbarous that they don't know the rudeness they are committing. What the deuce is one to do among this settlement of bears – impossible to do entirely without 'em and yet one is everlastingly tempted to try."

The parents felt insulted, but the youngsters rejoiced feasting at the guests' table. Elise, more discreet, also enjoyed the fresh vegetables, to say nothing of the goose. The Bruners, she later learned, afraid of fire, dared not leave their children home alone in such a gale.

The flying sand didn't keep them from planting potatoes. Pail after pail of eyes were cut each night, and day after dirty day, they continued the backbreaking work. Done at last, Edwy and Harry moved on to breaking more land. A marvelous crop of mosquitoes had everyone but little Maida swatting. Not yet having learned the art, her poor head and face were covered with bites and scabs. Her papa stayed indoors, reusing his dismantled Shanty walls as partitions upstairs to complete his five-year plan for four rooms, each having a small window. For the first time Elise had a room of her own. *I am used to sleeping with the little girls, but they like to have a room of their own. I'm sure my boys appreciate their own space. But, our rooms are cut off from the warm stove pipes. What about winter? How are we to keep warm?*

In need of cash, Mr. Criddle struck a deal, $8 for six months of herding Upper's cattle. Cecil, small for heavy work but fleet of foot, became the herdsman. Then, to buy feed for the pigs and chickens, Harry and Edwy cut a load of wood to sell in Brandon. At the end of the day and desperate, they accepted an offer of only $2 for their load. They were sent again with small new potatoes. With no sales at any price, and afraid to take them home, they left the lot with a storekeeper who promised to try to find a buyer. The lads received another 'hot' reception.

Elise was upset with the punishment. *I'm sure they tried. He should have gone himself. . . .* She warmed up the leftover potatoes from the evening meal and smiled as she placed the bowl on the table, "New potatoes are very tasty. Brandon housewives don't know what they missed."

Nonetheless, she worried about her sons. *Their best never seems to be enough.*

Mannheim, June 25, 1887

Dear Elise!

Your dear letter from April 13, I received. It was a pleasure to read that you are again well. I hope, the warmer weather will help to make you stronger and you will completely regain your health. That your daughters support you with their earnings must certainly be a great help to you and I hope fervently that your expectations for a good crop may be realized.

Mariechen's coughing is somewhat better, but still is bad enough. Our doctor hopes she will improve with a change of air, and may go to Heidelberg or to Carl's place for a few weeks.

Too bad she cannot go just yet. Our servant girl was impertinent and we had to give her the walking ticket. We have a new one but she has to be trained first before Mariechen can leave. Our Anna is also sick and has been in bed the last couple of days. One always has many worries when children are unwell.

Elise imagined the sick girl. *Wouldn't I love to help! Good servants are hard to find; duties are not always at the top of their list.*

Our cousin Hermann, who had a position of chief secretary in Constanz for some years, has been appointed as Postdirector in Hochingen.

Karl has been promoted to the position of financial advisor by the Greatduke. You can imagine that this promotion has made all of us and also Karl and his wife happy. He would be glad to receive a few lines of congratulations from you.

She looked pleased. *He was always clever with numbers; I must congratulate him.*

For your sons I am enclosing some postage stamps hoping that there are some that they do not yet have. If they would like, I could send them some more but always of the same kind would perhaps be pointless, unless they can trade with someone else.

I thank Percy for his few lines and give him my greetings. . . . Let us hear from you soon!
With the heartiest greetings I am your brother who loves you,
Friedrich.[9]

—⋅⊱⋅⊰⋅—

Mrs. Criddle, in another delicate nine months, refused to work like a slave as she had the previous summer. Isabel was sent for at the end of June. Her mother focused on the positive. *I'm going to enjoy time with my daughter.*

Awakened by Turk's barking early one morning, Elise went out to investigate. Sure enough the fence was broken and the cattle gone. Cecil and the dog set off on the run to track them down. Later Norman returned from his usual morning ramble with a young owl he had already dubbed Mr. Charlie. His father took a great interest in the scrappy little fellow.

---

9 Friedrich's letters included problems in renting and selling his mother-in-law's house.

I've rigged it a perch – parrot style and clipped its right wing – 'tis located in sitting room and watches every movement – spreading its wings and hissing when approached – makes a chattering noise by clapping its beak.

. . . is taming down – takes bits of cooked rabbit – also bluebottles. We gave him a mouse this morning and after a lot of tearing about, clawing and biting bits off he managed to pouch the animal whole – since when he has closed his eyes and is taking a nap. He gets from his perch and up again unassisted – his temper violent.

. . . is getting on all right . . . think we overfeed him. He flies and jumps all over the shop every night – makes a deuce of a mess.

In spite of the wind, the crop still looked promising until one day Edwy and Harry came in looking very despondent, "There's a lot of smut in the wheat."[10] Mr. Criddle went, checked it over, and refused to believe the disease was anything to worry about. "I've hired a binder – we'll need twine – must get money somehow or starve."

The boys tried again selling a load of new potatoes. Getting only 80¢ a bushel they needed Minnie's contribution to help with the twine bill and dropped by the hotel. With her $1.50 they were able to head home with the twine.

Hunger and worry were taking their toll, so by the end of July no notice was taken of Edwy's 16th birthday. At least Nellie gave them something to celebrate. Good news indeed, for giving birth to a heifer, Nellie enabled the raising of a future milk producer.

When Isabel took Mrs. Criddle her breakfast on August 14, she returned to her mother with an alert. "She'll need you soon."

Without complications, another girl was added to the Criddle family. It was later in the day when the newborn Julia made her presence known to her papa and prompted him to write, "The babby [sic] has a fine voice and is above ordinary size – I think her a trifle uglier than usual."

Mr. Tulk's train arrived in Brandon late on August 21st and he set out in haste for St. Albans only to lose his way. After a night on the prairie, he turned up with his many gifts, the highlight being a well-stocked medicine chest in memory of the previous year's fever.

The gentlemen spent that day planning and on the next went to Brandon for food supplies and a load of lumber to wind-proof the house. Beginning with the

---

10   Fungal infection of wheat showing as a dirty black powder filling the kernels. Had a powerful taste and odour; infected grains unfit for human consumption. Farmers could soak their seed wheat in a solution of copper sulphate, or bluestone, to kill smut spores without damaging the seed.

sitting room, they lined the wall with boards, and then outside, stuffed the cracks with grouting mixed with moss from the swamp. The undertaking stretched on into the fall and required more journeys. On one of these Minnie caught a ride and stayed long enough for Mr. Criddle to capture her height—four feet ten inches, and weight—141 pounds. Elise, watching from the sidelines thought *I'm happy Minnie's place of work allows her to eat well.*

For threshing that fall, Mr. Criddle joined the Clark-Upper outfit. Edwy and Harry with their ox team were accepted in place of a man and horses. While at his role measuring the grain, Mr. Criddle marveled at the machine's output—150 bushels of grain per hour at each of Upper, Clay, and Calverley's. Expecting the same results from two stacks on his North and South Farms, he was bitterly disappointed with only 555 bushels. He explained the low yield, "The ground was ploughed last fall by the little boys during fever time."

His only load of oats yielded 15 bushels and again, he faulted the boys, "They seeded insufficiently – then badly blown out by wind."

When Edwy and Harry hauled wheat to Chater and got only 46¢ a bushel, Mr. Criddle still couldn't accept that disease was the reason for the low price.

Mr. Tulk returned from a month in Vancouver and got right to work. Before winter set in his happy friend crowed, "We now have a flagpole, and 'the shop' ought to be wind-tight and warm. After the boys bank up the house – we'll be all snug this winter."

Mrs. Criddle was recuperating and able to take time from the new baby to preside over the adults' formal English meals. The gentry enjoyed a return to intelligent conversation—politics, literature, and natural science. For her part, Elise didn't mind the extra work of having the gentleman in their midst. Her health improved with better food, and Isabel was a wonderful companion and comfort. Furthermore, she hadn't been asked to dig potatoes and even found time for a letter to Karl to congratulate him. It was passed on to Friedrich, who replied.

Mannheim, 15 Oktober, 1887

Liebe Elise!

For quite a while now I have wanted to write you but was always prevented from it by one thing or another. But I will no longer postpone giving a sign of life from myself. We are, praise God, all well and hope the same for you.

Winter seems to make an early entry this year. Quite cool all October, it snowed last night. That happens very rarely in our region. It likely is cold at your place already. I hope to God that you and we will live through a good winter.

I have no news to write, here everything is as of yore. Only in politics it is very restless and it is believed that sooner or later war between France and Germany will become inevitable.

Your letter got to me from Karl and I was happy to hear that your boys appreciated the postage stamps. I am again enclosing some, but probably there will not be any new ones.

Soon I will write you again and I would be glad to hear good news from you.

With heartfelt greetings . . . .
Dein Bruder, Friedrich

Dear Sister. I am enclosing a small photograph that is to portray me. Eugen Mais, son of my principal, does photography as a hobby . . . I was looking against the sun and also wearing my glasses, which makes it appear as though I have no eyes. But at least you will note that I no longer am young. . .

Friedrich Harrer

Elise accepted her brother's aging, but she was caught off guard by another unexpected change. She overheard Mr. Criddle tell Harry, "You are to do chores and take care of Mrs. McFadden when her husband is away. I'm sorry to lose you, but a little change will do you good."

Harry walked the five miles home at the end of the month and handed over his five dollars. When he had a chance, he told his mother, "Expected chores would be milking the cow, getting in wood and water. But on top of that, I'm to cut a load of wood one day and bucksaw it up the next. That's still not too bad. What I don't like is the cold house. Never take my clothes off and I'm to get up at three o'clock in the morning to keep the big box stove going." [11]

In sympathy his mother said, "I'm finding it colder myself this winter. It must be really cold for **you** to complain."

Mr. Tulk decided to stay all winter to find out if his work on the house made a difference. The first test came with an all-night, northeasterly gale and temperature down to - 28° F degrees. Having completed his morning tour with the thermometer, Mr. Criddle reported to his friend, "Our room was one degree above freezing, the sitting room two under, your room four under. The southeast room upstairs is still chilly – twelve degrees of frost. On the whole much improved."

Elise shivered. *I wish he'd take his thermometer to our rooms upstairs and take a reading of the temperature.*

---

11 Vane, Harry.

Elise received a welcome letter from Friedrich, just in time for Christmas.

Mannheim, November 28, 1887

Dear Elise!

My letter of last month with postage stamps you likely have received already.

Saturday Karl was here for a visit. I had the chance to make a small specu-lation, where I made a few Marks and I told Karl that as a result I would send 20 Mark to you as a Christmas gift. He gave me an additional 30 Mark as his Christmas gift. So today I sent $11.75 money order, and I think you should re-ceive the money before Christmas. May it serve to increase Christmas joy for you and yours!

Elise pondered his words and the wishes. *That's so kind of my brothers. Unfortu-nately, I didn't see it.*

I hope, dear Elise, that you, Percy and your dear children are well and healthy.

. . .

Mariechen, who had a bad cough again during the cold weather, has practi-cally lost it now. Our children are, praise God, healthy and enjoy a terribly good appetite.

The two older ones, Anna and Elsa, are in the higher classes in the higher girl's school and they have to work hard. Much is required of students nowadays so that there is little spare time.

I have wanted to ask you if the land where you live is being populated more and more, meaning whether the immigration is increasing, for it would increase the value of your land.

Population, well, I don't know, some settlers have gone . . . others have come. As to the value of the land? . . .

I am enclosing postage stamps for your boys; maybe they will find some new ones. Do they have the opportunity to exchange stamps that they don't need for others? I would gladly continue to send them stamps if they can make use of them.

We all wish you a very merry Christmas and more so a prosperous New Year.

With a hearty greeting . . . . I remain your loving brother Friedrich

Christmas was a very busy day for Elise. Mrs. Criddle served her pudding, in spite of a toothache, only to watch it disappear in a twinkling. Mr. Tulk's nuts, almonds, and figs went too quickly also. The games, though, went well; Mr. Criddle introduced a new one, Old Soldier. He chose Beatrice, gave her a walking stick and a ragged smock, "You are old and lame, and beg for something to wear. They can't answer you with yes, no, nay, or black, white, or grey. If you can make anyone say one of the forbidden words they have to pay you a forfeit. Here's what you say; 'Here comes an old soldier from Botany Bay. Have you got anything to give him today'?"

Catching the mood, Beatrice donned the smock and limped around the circle like a very old man. Stopping in front of Edwy, she croaked, "I'm an old soldier from Botany Bay. Have you a shirt to give me today? I'd like that one."

Edwy was so charmed by her acting that he fell into her trap and said, "Sorry, but I can't give it to you. It's the only white shirt I have."

She screamed with delight and ordered a piggyback ride.

Everyone was cheering them on when Edwy tripped. Both horse and rider plummeted headfirst under the table. The little girl's howls of laughter switched to a genuine howl. The festivities came to an abrupt end and Edwy took his injured head and damaged dignity out to do the chores with Cecil. Harry, having walked the five miles home, lay groaning with a terrible toothache. Their guest, young Swaisland, had a miserable cold and wasn't in any mood to play cards. To the host's disgust, he and Mr. Tulk spent the evening discussing London hotels. By the time Elise had finished in the kitchen she went up with the little girls and very soon, she, too, turned in.

⸻ ❧ ⸻

In the last mail of the old year Elise's heart skipped happily seeing Karl's writing on a letter.

Karlsruhe, December 21, 1887

Dear Elise!

> *Already for some time I wanted to answer your letter that we received while visiting in Heidelberg. Sorry to say, until now they were only good intentions. When I returned from Heidelberg I found such a stack of work in my office which has kept me from answering.*

> *I thank you heartily for your congratulations for my new position. Sorry to say, no pecuniary advantages are linked to this promotion.*

> *From your dear letter I gleaned very little optimistic reports. Amalie and I often talk with deep regret of your difficult fate and pray to God, He will finally turn it for the better. It is so difficult when you have to bear the ill fate far from home, alone, without friends.*

Karl understands my loneliness. . . . He can't make things better, but I feel his love. I miss my family. . . . I had friends, many good friends. How I long to have someone to talk to like our pastor. Without my faith . . . how could I keep up? But I must. . . .

> *We live in the blessed hope, that your wishes for a good harvest will have been fulfilled.*

> *By the time you receive this letter, Friedrich will have informed you that a few weeks ago I spent a day with them. We talked a lot about you on long walks we made on the shores of the Rhine.*

Her eyes filled with tears . . . . *I so miss our family walks. . . .*

Composed again, she read on.

> *May heaven shield and shelter you so that wellbeing, health and contentment could enter in your home. These are our wishes at the now fast ending year. So good luck for the New Year! O that we could experience the great joy to read in your next letter that our wishes were realized!*
>
> *From your faithful brother Karl*

Karl's words went with Elise as she climbed the stairs. *May my brother's wishes come true! Five years of cold, poor crops, and hunger. . . . Time for a change. My brother's prayers are my prayers.*

Chapter Ten

Mr. Tulk's Winter

Mr. Tulk, gentleman adventurer and lodger, certainly hit a memorable year to overwinter in Manitoba. The snowfall already exceeded past years when the old year ended with a raging blizzard. On New Year's morning Mr. Criddle carried his Fahrenheit thermometer from room to room and reported to his friend, "You'd never guess it's minus 26 degrees outdoors. Our room is 31, sitting room 25, and yours is 30.5. Our hard labour has paid off in comfort."

With the first mild day, Mr. Tulk got the youngsters outdoors building a splendid toboggan slide all the way from the top of the hill along the yard behind the barns to the west trail. For a few days winter seemed friendlier. But the temperatures plummeted again and everyone, upstairs and down, slept again with their heads under the covers, despite all the boasting about a warmer house. Every time the door opened, a blast of cold air swept across the floor in a great white cloud and someone hollered, "Shut the door!"

The boys asked Mr. Tulk "Is it cold enough for you, Sir?"

Both gentlemen studied the exciting phenomena to be seen in the sky.

Wonderful white circle on blue sky above moon tonight (first seen at 7 PM-about gone at 7.40) Say reaching from moon up to about 20 min. S of Polaris. Sun dogs (rather fine) in afternoon.

While they gazed upward, the boys were dealing with shortages on the ground. The chickens had eaten the last of their feed and they were now gobbling up the wheat meant for sale in the spring. The firewood supply was even more serious. Harry gathered courage and interrupted the men, "I'm sorry to say, Sir, but we're sawing up the last of our wood."

"Taken all in all," Mr. Criddle explained to his friend, "This is the severest and longest spell of bad weather we've ever had, and what with the abnormally deep snow – the gales and cold –the severest winter – since coming to the country." Being Mr. Tulk's first winter, he didn't disagree and nodded as his friend added, "Can't wait for the weather to moderate – fetch up wood we must."

Since Edwy had been sent to Lonsbury's for two months, 14-year-old Harry took charge.[1] He hitched up the oxen, and with the twelve-year olds, Cecil and

---

1 Edwy, now 16, could earn eight dollars a month, two dollars more than Harry.

Norman, went for wood.[2] It was bitterly cold, but they managed. The next problem was a greater challenge; the cattle, already on a starvation diet, had come to the absolute end of their food supply. Minus 39 was too cold for humans and beasts to be working outdoors for any length of time, yet the boys set out for Clay's straw stack two miles south. For the weakened oxen, it was heavy going breaking a trail. At the stack, the boys had to dig their way through drifts to get to the straw. After forking on a load they huddled a few minutes out of the wind in the hole they made taking out the straw. But, they couldn't stay and headed home. With every jolt, a little straw slipped off the sledge; and then midway, the 'bally' [3] thing overturned and the whole load was in the snow. They dared not give up. The sledge got righted, and the load gathered. On they went, more carefully than before.

Meanwhile, Elise was anxiously waiting for their return. *If only there had been more hay. It's such a bad winter. . . . The snow is so deep the beasts can't feed themselves. I hope this is the last time the boys have to risk their lives. Sending the lads so far in this weather is too dangerous . . .* She paused in her kneading of the bread. *The gentlemen are playing a game of cards in the sitting room. They don't seem to be worried. Please God bring our boys safely home.*

Sometime later Evelyn came in with an armful of wood and told her, "I see them coming."

After what seemed hours to Elise, Norman burst in the door. "Whew, it's jolly cold out there. Think I've got frostbite. Anyway, we've got the straw. They'll be in soon as they have the oxen looked after."

He hung his greatcoat on the peg and went into the sitting room. His papa confirmed the frost-bite, patted him on the back and said, "You're a fine example of British Pluck."

When her sons came in, Elise spotted an ash white nose. "Harry, your nose and cheeks! My gracious! I'm afraid you'll be in pain as soon as it thaws . . . and have lots of blistering."

Cecil tried to lighten her mood, "It pays to be a shrimp. I kept my nose out of trouble, but my hands and big toe are mighty cold! I guess we're all in for some pain. Anyway, the cattle won't starve for a few days."

⚬⚬⚬

As Mr. Criddle couldn't send a boy to the school board meeting, he left in the morning saying, "We have serious business today — somewhat tricky paying a teacher without money in the coffers." A strong east wind at his back blew him along the two plus miles to Lonsbury's. It was well after dark when he faced the

---

2 Harry, height 4.7, weight 78 lbs, Norman height 4.9, weight 75 lbs: Cecil height 3.10, weight 57 lbs.
3 Used as a mild expletive in the way we would say "darn".

wind that evening. He staggered in, "Help! I'm about done up." Elise rushed to take his coat. "Floundered through deep snow – had to stop every few paces to rest and turn my back to wind. Oh, my calves – hurt like the deuce!"

He hobbled to the table and as Elise set his food before him, added, "Never had such a blessed tramp before – don't desire another."

At the following board meeting he left again on foot and that afternoon Elise heard him hollering for Harry. Then stomping in, he announced, "I'm about frozen. Swapped our Nellie for Lonsbury's Jess – harness and sleigh. No shafts – not needed in this flat country. Bad trip for an old mare – took too long."

Later that night Harry told his mother, "Poor Jess was steaming! I led her about a bit and rubbed her down. She's been here with Lonsbury, so she knew where to go, but I hardly knew what to give her to eat. McFadden doesn't feed straw to his horses, says they need oats and good hay. Mr. C should have brought some along; he might have been warmer with hay in the sleigh."

In spite of the heavy trails their mail got through.

Mannheim, 6 January, 1888

Liebe Elise!

> *Your dear letter from Dec. 9 I received on the second day of this year, and I thank you heartily for the good wishes for the New Year. I hope you received my letters of the Nov. 28 and Dec.11.*
>
> *Your letter, which I today sent to Carl, gave us much joy, because you finally could report on a good crop this year, at least it had been better than in preceding years. Hopefully that contributed to celebrating a happy Christmas.*
>
> *I feel sorry for your Harry that he at such a tender age has to work among strangers. But hopefully he is treated well and is among friendly people. That Isabella can be at home this year must be a great help to you.*

She swallowed hard. *He understands the heartache I suffer having my children away working. Harry says he doesn't mind too much. His hours are long, but he learned quite a bit, and Mrs. McDougal feeds him well. I'm thankful to have Isabel this winter. Her cheerfulness makes the work so much easier. . . . Mrs. Criddle has enough to do with her baby and such dreadful toothaches. Mr. Tulk won't be staying forever, but I'd like to keep Isabel.* She read on:

> *From Christmas until two days ago it was a very cold 16 below zero Reamur [-20 C].[4] The Neckar River was completely frozen over here, to the joy of our girls who love to skate.*

Closing her eyes she tried to visualize the scene. *It's not possible for me to imagine enough ice on the river for skating. I don't remember such an occurrence.*

---

4   Réaumur: scale established in 1730 by the French naturalist, Réaumur. Zero, freezing point of water; 80 boiling.

Today Anna and Elsa have accompanied their Aunt Rivola to Heidelberg and will stay there two days. Monday their classes begin and they have to be home again.[5]

Rereading the sentence Elise thought back to her school days and her happy first days back from holidays. *My nieces are as carefree as I was at their age, while my youngsters work like slaves.*

This letter will probably arrive at the beginning of March and then we can again look forward to a warmer season. I enclose some postage stamps and close with the hope of hearing good news from all of you . . . your brother, Friedrich

Could you send me some Canadian postage stamps? I have friends who have stamp collections and they would be happy to receive some from Canada.

With warmer days, especially now that they had a horse and sleigh, visiting was in order for the Criddles and their guest. Leaving Mama Dutcheen in charge, Mrs. Criddle was free to go as long as she got back in time to nurse the baby. The trio dined at Calverley's, spent another day at Upper's, and then the following week drove to Lonsbury's. The next outing to Bruner's for Sunday dinner should have been postponed because the barometer was at its lowest ever recorded. But the sky was beautifully bright and they told Elise, "We'll be home long before the weather breaks."

Meanwhile at home, the wind strengthened and by afternoon they had a full-fledged blizzard. Darkness came early and her sons went out to do the chores. The howling wind accompanied Mama Ducheen's songs as she paced the floor trying to pacify the baby. Isabel was keeping Beatrice and little Maida occupied. Worried their parents had lost the trail, the Criddle boys kept going to the door and peering out into the stormy darkness. The baby lost patience with Mama Ducheen's little finger, and as a last resort she dipped a corner of a towel in sweetened water for her to suck. *This is not going to pacify her very long. . . . I pray they get here soon.* Little Julia was working into unmistakable hungry howls when they heard Mr. Criddle's voice over the wind, "Halloo, Harry! Yoo-hoo! Harry!" She breathed a sigh of relief. *Thank God. In the nick of time.*

The three snowmen staggered into the house. Their youngsters crowded around rejoicing as their parents peeled off their snow encrusted coverings. Mrs. Criddle took the crying baby from Elise and retreated with her girls to her quarters, while the gentlemen took their rum to the sitting room. Calm settled around the extremely relieved housekeeper. She added some sticks to the fire and sank to a chair with her head in her hands. *I mustn't complain, but I wish they could*

---

5 Anna and Harry born 1872, Elsa and Cecil born 1875, Julie born 1877.

have been a little faster. A few moments later she was composed enough to return to duty. *I'd better start tea.*

The following morning, serving breakfast, she learned a little more. Mrs. Criddle, still overwhelmed, sighed, "A dreadful journey. I despaired of ever reaching home."

Her husband added, "A pretty treat we had of it – thick clouds of snow and ice, tearing along – temp 20° – no end of mishaps – every stick of straw blown clear away so we had nothing but bare boards to squat on – daren't stand up. But we've to thank our stars the mare was quiet, or she'd have kicked us to smithereens through our running bang onto her heels every half minute."

In spite of that stressful afternoon, Elise would remember Mr. Tulk's winter as one of her most pleasant. She had Isabel's companionship and enough to eat. Her peace was interrupted only a few times when she opened the door to angry fathers. From bits of conversations, she gathered there was a problem with the finances because settlers hadn't paid their taxes. Then Bellhouse, backed up by Lonsbury and Johnson, accused Mr. Criddle of misappropriating school funds. It saddened her to hear him fuming, "I hope what I heard is true, that Bellhouse plans to sell out for five hundred dollars. The others could go too – our community will be more peaceful."

Harry and Cecil had another problem. The straw, almost gone again, had been carefully rationed. The day came when Lion was too weak to get up and they called Mr. Criddle. He looked at the bag of bones and railed at the boys, "It's starvation! I've been warning you for weeks past! I'll treat him – he may recover."

But Lion was too far gone and two days later, still not able to get up, Mr. Criddle resorted to the gun. And thus, their dependable ox departed this life. But the boys had no time to grieve, for besides the shortage of feed, the wood supply had run out again.

When Edwy returned home the end of March, he and Harry took a load of wheat to the mill in Brandon for flour and grits, plus other supplies for the kitchen. The next day, they told their mother "We had a good sleep in the livery barn loft. Lots of buffalo robes to keep us warm . . . thought of bringing you one. You'd have a warm blanket for the cold weather. But I guess it wouldn't be welcome here."

All winter Mr. Tulk had been drumming up a great spring goose hunt with some of the neighours. "We need a boat," he told the youngsters. "Let's build a real English punt with a flat bottom and square end. Has to be large enough for eight men."

He made out a list of materials and sent Edwy to Brandon. The project, its planning, sawing, hammering and painting, took them to the fifth of April. "Jolly good!" Mr. Criddle remarked, "You've made a handsome, strong, and definitely heavy ship."

On April 28 an elite group of hunters gathered in the early morning and loaded two wagons with the punt, tents, guns, and other supplies. Elise had prepared plenty of food for their outing. After the send-off she hoped for a chance to get caught up around the house and even have a few minutes to herself. Late that very same night, Mr. Criddle stomped in, "Our great adventure fizzled – a dreadfully cold trip to reach the lake and it was still frozen solid. The gang voted to bolt for home."

She looked over the pile of stuff on the kitchen floor. *This can wait. Edwy brought me a letter, I'll read it before anything else happens.*

Mannheim, March 31, 1888
Liebe Elise!

Early today I received your lines from the 14th of this month. Also your letter from the beginning of January has arrived. The latter I have mailed to Carl. I am very happy that you all are well.

We read about the blizzards in the Northwest of America and always thought of you, if by any chance you too had to suffer from the storms and the bitter cold.

Here the winter was difficult; there was more snow than since many years. Such a winter is very hard on the poor people; there is unemployment because construction is halted, expenses for fuel are higher.

Right now there are floods in northern Germany, more than 60 little towns and villages are under water and the suffering is great, since people have lost their cattle to drowning and many houses have collapsed, many rich people have become paupers. Collections are now made everywhere to help those affected by the flood.

Poor people! I remember the big flood in Heidelberg. Fortunately our home was on the high side of Hauptstrasse.

Our emperor Wilhelm is mourned deeply by the German people. But not only in Germany, the whole world, has shown their sympathy for this death, as has never before happened at the death of any duke or king.

Our present emperor Friedrich is well liked by the whole country and his health is improving. That he is including the crown prince Wilhelm in the business of the Government so that he has the opportunity to learn how to govern in the style of his father is certainly liked by the people. There will be no changes. Conditions have become more peaceful and everything is well organized! [6]

6   In the aftermath of the Franco-Prussian War, Wilhelm, King of Prussia, was proclaimed German emperor on January 18, 1871 in Versailles Palace. He was head of state and president (*primus inter pares* - first among

> *It has been decided in a large meeting of citizens that a statue for Emperor Wilhelm, the founder of the German empire, will be erected and already for this cause in the last two days 100,000 Marks have been designated.*

Elise could hardly believe what she read. *So many changes . . . he's so enthusiastic. Imagine all that money for a monument.*

> *I am happy to hear that Harry is such a wide-awake boy! Since he is able to fend for himself so well, he will find his way through life.*

What did I tell him about Harry? . . . I don't remember. He's always working on something. Friedrich ended his letter by saying everyone was well with the exception of Marie, who was still coughing. He prayed to God to grant good health to Elise and added:

> *Today I received a letter from an uncle of Mariechen from San Francisco. For many years things did not go so well for him but now he is happier with the business.*

She looked about her. *I hope good times will visit us soon.*

⤖

Aweme School's financial problems didn't prevent the new teacher's arrival and Mr. Criddle went to Lonsbury's to meet her. Curious, Elise listened in on his evaluation at tea. "Rather big, coarse, jolly, young female – bright – sensible and superior to Miss Armstrong generally – in fact only inferior to her as regards blue blood and small feet."

I wonder, Elise thought to herself, *will I recognize her from his description. I'm not strong on blue blood, but big feet? They must be like mine.*

Finally relieved from the constant round of stoking fires, Elise was unhappily conscripted to her former root-pulling-burning job. *I thought these days were over. We do need more hay, I'll try to keep poor starving Lion in mind to help me through.* Twice they had a fierce fight to keep their fire controlled. Several days and many blisters later, she longed for something easy like planting potatoes. . . . *There's not so many this year since so many were frozen in the root cellar last fall. The frost came before the boys got the straw replaced on the roof.*

As May 19, the date for Mr. Tulk's departure, drew closer, Elise hoped to have asparagus to serve as her parting gift. Almost ready, frost cut it instead. Thankfully, she found just enough to prepare a taste for his last tea. Mr. Criddle had been busy writing a fictional diary, imagining his friend's view of his winter with them and stood up to make his presentation, "I've taken the liberty to write your journal." He held up his manuscript, *Diary of a Noble Lord in Manitoba.* "Within

equals) of the federated monarchs (kings of Bavaria, Württemberg, Saxony, the grand dukes of Baden, Hesse, Mecklenburg, as well as other principalities, duchies and the free cities of Hamburg, Lübeck, and Bremen).

these humble pages you'll find the cast of St. Albans right down to our owl, Charlie – something to entertain you on the voyage."[7]

Next morning, everyone was out to wave farewell. Elise was especially sorry to see him go. *He took such an interest in the youngsters . . . this winter has been more pleasant than usual.*

⸻ ❦ ⸻

When Elise heard Smith sold out to a Scottish family coming from the Edmonton area due to their good crops being ruined by early frosts, she said to herself, *I don't think they have to worry so much about that here. We've had other catastrophes, but this year looks very promising. The boys tell me they've seeded more acres.* In fact, Mr. Criddle calculated 60 acres in wheat, 5½ oats, 3 barley, 3 potatoes, and 5/8 turnips. He sold Jess to a new neighbour for $20, rounded up his tools from Tulk's construction projects, and made an aquarium. "Something for the children," he said. Then, checking on the owl, found Charlie dead on the floor of his home, the granary. Seeing a dead mouse nearby, he knew the cause. "Strychnine poison! Why the deuce did they feed him that? Should have known it was poisoned."

Then, suffering from the vacuum left from his friend's departure, Mr. Criddle invited others: Uppers, McVeys, the new teacher, Miss Nesbitt, Bruner, and Clay, for a Saturday afternoon of tennis and cricket. As Elise and Isabel were washing dishes that night, they heard the dreaded message, "Very loath to let you go, but needs must when the Devil drives."

Elise was still working out how she would manage without Isabel's help when Mr. Criddle announced, "I've agreed with Upper to co-host a Two Rivers-Aweme community picnic."

He laid out his plans next morning, "Want three flagpoles in a row on the hill – the tallest in the middle for my rag, the others for the banners of Two Rivers and Aweme. Want the shelter decorated for the picnic dinner – lots of green boughs. Edwy and Harry mark out the tennis court – make sure the whitewash is thick and your lines straight. Cecil, look after the cricket field and equipment – have everything at hand. For the kids – two swings, put poles close by the picnickers. We'll have lots of races – mark the starting line and measure suitable finish lines for the races – children to the men. We've no time to waste."

For her part, Mrs. Criddle had been anything but pleased. She told Elise, "I've been ill since Christmas with horrid toothaches. How will I manage?" But by the next day she too had plans, "Here is a list for you. I'll be ever so busy with the guests.

---

7   Draft in family collection.

The day's weather was perfect, the homestead groomed and ready. The Vane boys were primed and on deck should anything be needed. Mr. and Mrs. Criddle welcomed their guests and at noon presided over the flag raising above a splendid gathering of 99 people, counting the children. Upper had been delayed at his store until three o'clock, so he arrived apologetically bearing what he considered a must for Canadian celebrations, the Union Jack. Straightaway he proceeded to make up for his lateness by lowering Mr. Criddle's flag to raise the official symbol of Canada and the Empire.

Elise was inside when she heard shouting. Going out she was surprised to see Mr. Criddle furiously re-attaching his own flag to the rope and hoisting it up the pole. A number of men had untied their horses; their wives were packing baskets and gathering their children. Norman answered her puzzled expression by explaining, "The Two Rivers 'tub-thumpers' have been given a lesson. On our premises our flag trumps Queen Victoria's."

The Aweme School crowd stayed on and the Criddles counted the day a resounding success.

<hr/>

Summer sped by. Haying went speedily that summer; the scythe replaced by neighbour Clay and his new mower, paid for by the boys' help later on. Signs pointed to the best harvest yet, so Mr. Criddle purchased a binder. He couldn't foresee the killing frost on the nights of August 8 and 9 and refused to accept its damage to his dream crop. Not until his more practical wife planted fifty kernels to test their germination. Only 35 sprouted. "In any case," he told her, "I'm very pleased with the binder – three oxen can pull it – works beautifully."

While his boys stooked and stacked the crop, Mr. Criddle located a small used seven stop organ for sale. He paid the $20 and, planning to recoup the money, set off across the river to promote a singing class every Saturday afternoon as well as private lessons—keyboard or voice. One student signed up, but his music business had to wait until he'd finished threshing. And what a disaster! Only 500 bushels of wheat and 42 of oats. He rationalized, yet again, "Not my fault – just my luck."

Because everyone in the country had suffered the same killing frost, grain buyers were accepting frozen grain at a reduced price. Their first load of wheat, 50 bushels at 76¢, netted him $38. Back with a second load the price had dropped six cents a bushel. Still enough, he claimed, for winter stores, boots, clothes, and to pay the dentist. Mrs. Criddle finally got her trip to Brandon to have those five troublesome teeth pulled.[8]

Meanwhile all his workers were busy, ploughing, hauling oat straw home from Swaisland's, clearing more swamp for next year's hay, cutting and drawing home 33 loads of firewood. Beatrice, now eight, preferred tending the baby or feeding the chickens and gathering eggs to housework. Besides, she also took lessons from her mother. So ever faithful Elise, day after day, with never a break – cooked, served, and washed up for the big Criddle family and the hard working young men—a daunting challenge.

As soon as they could be spared, Elise's sons were sent out to work—Edwy to Lonsbury's for a dollar a day, and Harry to Upper's for 85 cents a day. When Clay came looking for help to get some land cleared, Mr. Criddle thought he'd also make some extra cash. Norman wasn't well, so he took Stewart and Cecil. After a couple of days he decided it was too much work for the money and cashed in—two days for himself, four days for the boys. He unhappily pocketed Clay's $2.50 and vowed to avoid any future opportunities.

Elise's summer had been so busy she had not written her family. Her brothers must also have been busy, for she waited and watched many weeks before a letter made its way to her.

Mannheim, 15 Oktober, 1888

Liebe Elise!

Your dear letter from the 12th of September I have received I am very sorry that you, because of my long silence, have had worries, but it so happens that when you don't have time you think of writing and then again when you do have time you either don't remember, or you are not in the right mood for it.

A great cause for concern was also your news of another crop failure. When I read in the papers that in Canada crops were usually good I was happy for you and thought that this time your hard work would be rewarded by a good crop and good prices. For that reason your news touched me quite painfully, and more so, because I am not in a situation to help you substantially. Have you ever in your country had a good crop? Lamentably, I have never heard of it and it seems that each year your crops are endangered.

What could she say? *I'm afraid he's right. We hope for a bumper crop, then along comes a drought, wind, grubs, hail, smut, and this year, frost. Can there be any other catastrophe?*

We also, had a bad crop. The grapes did not ripen or else were destroyed by the cold weather. In the Black Forest they gathered them in snow. Here the ripe fruit could not be transported home and I saw the crops lying on the fields as so many piles of dung.

---

8 October 31, 1888.

Elise shuddered. *How perfectly awful . . . the poor vintagers.*

> *I pray that you might not lose courage. Hope for better times, which the loving God will surely send you soon!*

Thank you dear brother! Sometimes I despair, but my faith in God helps rekindle that hope, if not for me, for my children.

> *Dear Elise, Carl and I have decided to send you a Christmas gift again and today I sent through the mail in the usual manner fifty Mark = $11.80 to you and I just have to lament that it could not be more.*[9]

 She let the letter fall to her lap. *You, my brothers are so kindhearted . . . if only I had a little of your money to give Edwy to buy me a pair of shoes when he next goes to Brandon. That would be the very best of Christmas gifts.* Instead, to her sorrow, Harry was sent back to McFadden's as a chore boy for $5.50 a month.

Aweme School term ended December 1, with a little program for the parents. Miss Nesbitt's scholars, many of whom had never before attended school, were anxious to show that in so short a time, they had learned to read and write. As chairman of the school board, Mr. Criddle expounded back at home on their limited progress. His own experience with education had been anything but a happy one, and yet, in his memory, his achievements were far superior to the progress made in Miss Nesbitt's class. He blamed both her and the dreadful Manitoba textbooks for making schools a miserable sham and much too costly. It was the cost that weighed most heavily on his mind and he had already told Miss Nesbitt she would have to wait for her salary until the settlers paid their taxes. He continued to lambaste a system of education that raided the public coffers to pay to educate the unworthy and 'stupid' urchins of the ignorant poor. "The idea of a governess getting $40 a month with no more knowledge than a little reading and writing – elementary geography – the skin of history and moderate arithmetic – no accomplishments and not even able to speak her own language anything like correctly – is preposterous.... In England for say one hundred per annum – a girl has to be good looking – speak French, German, Italian – know something of Latin – must be a lady – a fair musician – besides all the grammar, arithmetic, history. . . ."[10]

He had such a governess under his own roof, but gave her little opportunity to share her talents and no pay. It was that talented musician, disguised as Widow Vane, who welcomed Miss Mair for her first 50¢ music lesson from Mr. Criddle.

---

9 Amount recorded as income in same month as Isabel, Minnie and the boys' wages. Archives of Manitoba. Percy Criddle Account Book, P336A. Apart from his diary all amounts are from this source and will not be footnoted.

10 December 1, 1888.

She also served his English guests from the other side of the river, while they enjoyed cards, chess, and music. Kept at home and apart, his neighbours probably guessed she was a poor widow with many children whom Criddle had rescued from a poorhouse in London and was lucky to have a roof over her family's head.

Just before Christmas she was delighted to receive another letter.

Mannheim, 5 Dez. 1888

Liebe Elise!

I hope you have received my letter and the money order mailed on the 15 of last month.

With this I send you another small Christmas present and I wish you very merry Christmas holidays and coming from the heart, wishes for much success and good health in the New Year.

I have no news to report on from our family, we are, thank God, pretty healthy and hope that all of you also enjoy good health . . . .

Her throat tightened. *How dear he is, and Marie, I miss them more every year. I long to walk with them along the cobblestone streets to church on Christmas Eve, to see the candles on the high altar, to sing with the great pipe organ. My heart aches for all I have loved and lost. . . .*

I made my choice and it's up to me to do my best with my path.

And so her routine continued: breakfast, dinner, tea – breakfast, dinner, tea – fitted between all the other tasks necessary to keep the household clean and happy. On and on she toiled to another Christmas Day, and to the end of the year when Mr. Criddle mused:

Can't exactly say it has been a bad or unhappy one – we have certainly got a firmer clutch on our new possessions and despite the wheat failure am I believe richer. Should we have luck next year – (and several chances thereof seem probable) we shall find ourselves fairly comfortable.

When her duties were finished for the day, Elise curled up in her cold little bed with her memories and a prayer for the future. *Next year, with God's help, I hope to have my own land!*

Chapter Eleven

It's Only a Formality

Elise wakened on New Year's morning and thought of the coming year. *If God is willing, 1889 will be the year I become a landowner! I've read the words on the sitting room wall: "To have and to hold said Parcel or Tract of Land unto the said Percy Criddle, his heirs and assigns forever." I'm longing to read 'my land for my heirs, forever'.*

As she stirred the porridge, she went over what Mr. Criddle said, "The regulation breaking and cropping are done on your homestead. We'll build a shanty; you can sign your name."

Then her dreams took a back seat to an eclipse of the moon on the second of January. Mr. Criddle had invited so many to view it through his telescope that he barely got a good view himself. Following the spectacle, they stomped the snow off their boots, came in, and settled around the coal oil lamp. Each man pulled out his pipe, nestled it comfortably between his teeth, opened his tobacco pouch, and fastidiously packed the bowl to satisfaction. Matches burst into flame and were laid to the tobacco as each owner expertly drew and puffed. Only as the clouds swirled upward did they sit back in their chairs and begin to talk. Elise reached the sugar bowl from the top shelf where it was saved for guests, set out the cups and spoons, poured the tea, and served them hot biscuits. She caught bits and pieces of their conversation; then mopping up afterwards, sighed, *all in a night's work, now to get my poor sore feet into bed.*

January was unusually mild. Several mornings on the way to empty the chamber pot in the 'parliament building', she paused to marvel at the beauty of her little world. Hoarfrost transformed the ordinary into exquisite art: the straw on the roof of the fowl house, the wagon wheels above the snow, the shrubs and grasses. The beauty lifted her spirits even as she returned to the dim light in the house.

When Mr. Criddle and his wife took advantage of the good weather to go visiting, Elise, already cook and scullery maid, became the children's governess. By nature creative, she hoped for a little variety by suggesting a program. *I'll ask Norman, he likes poetry; maybe he'll read one or two. Edwy has learned a piece on the organ. Harry is away, but Cecil could retell his story about his fish that got away. It's always funny. Stewart likes skits; could ask Norman and Evelyn. Beatrice is a little dramatist; she and her little sisters could act out 'The Grasshopper and the Ants'. We can end the concert by singing their favourite songs. Ideas can percolate during the afternoon and we'll have the concert after tea.*

And so they enjoyed themselves; the little ones were tucked into bed and sleeping by the time their parents returned.

Later in January the boys were to start logging for Elise's shanty. Before they went to bed Mr. Criddle said, "Get an early start. You don't travel fast with Bill and Lamb and it's a long way to the Tamarack."

Elise rose early to prepare their breakfast and knew from the chill of the house and frost on the windows that it was bitter outside. While they ate, she asked, "Why not put the trip off for a warmer day?"

"We got our orders. . . . We'll be fine, Mama."

She watched them put on their coats and go out into the frigid darkness. *What if they have trouble? Nobody else will be out there in this cold.* Her nerves were frayed even before darkness closed in. They came at last: first Norman, then Edwy, and Cecil, frosted eyebrows, caps, and collars. "Thank God you're safe!"

Norman called his brothers, "Can you look after the oxen? We're about frozen."

Elise spotted Norman's white cheeks and then Edwy's chin and neck. "Frostbite! You're in for some pain." To help them warm up she poured them cups of weak, but hot, tea. "I hope you won't go again on such a day. We need logs, but you are far more precious than the logs for my house."

February 1st, a Friday morning, the door burst open and in came Harry in a cloud of frosty air. His mother looked up, "Gracious! This isn't Sunday!"

"I'm home," he said, "Done! McFadden can't afford to keep me. And he charged me board for the Sundays that I didn't walk home."

He steeled himself for trouble as he handed his pay to Mr. Criddle who counted, "Seven dollars and thirty cents earned from December 17. Ninety-five cents too little – Liars, egg and bird! Thieves! – Solis sunt Canadienses." He stomped off to his room leaving Harry unpunished. Elise watched him pick up his bag and disappear upstairs. *I guess he picked the right moment to arrive.*

⁃◦⟋⦿⟍◦⁃

Aweme School's continuing financial shortfall kept secretary treasurer Criddle fussing, "Those no-goods haven't paid their taxes – if they don't – we'll sell their land!"

Elise wondered. *Have my taxes been paid? Friedrich's gift should have been enough.[1] But then again, my taxes go to Two Rivers School and wouldn't help balance Aweme's books.*

The tax problem paled in the midst of a violent winter storm. The wind shrieked and their house groaned so violently under its onslaught that it seemed the roof was being torn clean away. Mr. Criddle routed everyone upstairs out of their beds to comparative safety on the ground level. While the young Criddles took refuge with their mother, he kept all three Vane boys playing cards. For Elise, it was a long night of knitting.

After the blizzard, it was back to logging. Evelyn and Stuart used their time to make a better toboggan slide, a twisty one, 60 yards long. When the thrill of sliding wore off, the youngsters stood erect and slid on their boots. Then they built a seven-foot ramp for an even faster send-off. Elise heard the shouts from the kitchen and couldn't resist going out to watch. "No, I'll not try it. I'll just enjoy your antics." *How wonderful to be young! They work hard and play hard.*

⸙

Now that Edwy was approaching 18, Mr. Criddle gave up walking to parties. He collared his 'Boy' after a full day's work, "Fetch the team. I've been invited to a party." And Edwy would drive him. When the festivities wound down, Mr. Criddle waited for his driver to reappear out of the darkness. Edwy half joked with his mother, "I'm a coachman now. It's alright, I suppose. There's plenty of good food. I see some pretty girls."

But, when they didn't get home until sunrise, the gentleman's 'Boy' had trouble dragging himself through the next day's work.

St. Albans also entertained: one Sunday they had more guests than cups. Mrs. Criddle turned her embarrassment on her servant. "We've been waiting for our tea. You are slow today. We must have a lesson on serving more promptly."

Elise felt humiliated. *To be chastised in front of all these people . . . saving face at my expense. All I can do is wash these as quickly as possible and get them out again. I have to keep calm and remember a nest with stones is better than no nest at all.*

⸙

Spring came early that year, and with long lines of geese flying overhead, work began on Elise's house. The big moment for her three month residency on her homestead was approaching. They had already assembled a good number of logs for the house and to make the job go more quickly, neighbours Bruner, Swaisland, Lonsbury, and Clay were called on to help.[2]

---

1 Tax records of South Cypress Municipality.
2 March 17, 1889. "Engaged just now building Dutchman's house on S. Farm. . . ."

March 19th was set for the bee to raise the 16' by 18' shanty. The gang had to be fed, so Elise prepared the food at home and the boys carried it to the site a mile south. Everything went smoothly and in three days she overheard, "Dutchman's house is ready for occupation bar door and window which go in tomorrow – very snug – 1st rate shop."[3]

They finished it on Saturday. Sunday being a guest day, her services were needed at St. Albans. Monday, however, the washing done and tea served, she was free to leave. Light was already fading when she set out with Cecil, as a body guard, to walk the mile south. Although weary from an already long day, once outdoors in the nippy March air, she revived. *I feel rather nervous leaving the house full of people. Thank goodness I have Cecil with me.*

Sketch by Don McMaster

And so with old Wellingtons on her feet, she plodded along the trail heading south. For awhile, thanks to the Homestead Act, she would be free from leaping up at every call of her name. Cecil looked up and said, "Don't worry about anything Mama. I'll take care of you."

She smiled down at him, her youngest, only 14, four feet tall and only 60 pounds. "That's a brave promise. I do feel a bit nervous. . . . We must look like a pair of tramps trudging along with our blankets on our backs? I'll try not to worry. "

She had followed the boys' reports of how many logs high they made the walls, how they cut hinges for the door from an old leather boot. Sometimes, they told her, they had a good laugh when a leg slipped between the logs as they were laying clumps of sods on the roof. At last she was actually on her way to sleep in her very own house.

I've surely lived in a variety of places. Her memory slipped back through the years to former homes. *Mama told me I was born in an elegant old house off Münster Square in Freiburg before Papa was transferred north again. My favourite was our big old home facing the cobblestone square in Donaueschingen.[4] Mama would send me to meet my big handsome papa. He'd sweep me up with a hug and we'd sing our way*

---

3 March 22, 1889.
4 Black Forest town renowned as the source of the Danube. Postmasters were transferred regularly.

home. His death changed everything. We returned to Heidelberg; but into a house that had never known Papa's laughter. It was a good home, tucked halfway down Ketteng-asse [Chain Lane]. With Oma and Opa's help we overcame our sorrow and gradually filled it with music, and, in time, laughter. I loved the old street with the castle ruins on the mountain looking down, and the Neckar River flowing below.

When Percy took me across the English Channel to the great city of London, the two of us were happy in our secret little apartment on Palace Road. But poor little Mabel suffered so and after her death I couldn't stay. After Minnie's birth, Percy found grand rooms overlooking Nelson Square, but that didn't last. When Isabel was born he rented a more practical flat in the newly built row houses on St. George's Road. I liked it there, had friends, schools nearby and church bells that reminded me of home. The boys were all born there. When things went wrong dear friends helped me through.

We were stuck in steerage on the ship . . . certainly not a home. The tent? Pleasant enough at first, but then! Dear God, the cold. . . . My five and three little Criddles. . . . We only just survived. And now, I'm in the Criddle house. To have a home of my own, that is my most sincere wish. Why not pretend, while we're walking, that my dream has come true.

She imagined a tiny log cabin with smoke curling upward like a ribbon into the clear blue sky. There must be a kettle simmering on the stove and a brown tea pot on the shelf above. The little window with white lace curtains framing red geraniums calls out, "Come in." She paused to admire the fine wooden door with intricately carved ivy leaves. Then she lifted the polished brass latch and the door swung open. The room, cosily warm, has a table, set and waiting for her and her son. She glanced at him. *What is he thinking? I am proud of this young builder. Indeed, I am proud of all three fine sons, so capable, so quick to please. I must remember to tell them.*

Cecil broke into her reverie, "Here's your new house!" In the gathering darkness it looked very small, half hidden under the sod and straw roof. There was one little window beckoning, "Come sit down; rest your tired feet."

Cecil lifted the wooden latch, gave the door a shove, and stepped back for her to enter. It was dim inside. But, she could see—no table set for two, no bench on which to rest, no stove to warm them, no bed on which to sleep—only bits of snow and trampled grass from the builders' feet. *This is stark reality, cold, dark, empty. . . . My dream will have to wait.*

"We are almost back to tenting," Cecil said. "I left the axe here yesterday and I'll bring some boughs to make you a nice soft bed." Elise untied the ropes holding her blankets and they slid to the ground. She sank wearily upon them sighing, "How can I be discouraged with a fine son like this?" And before she had time to worry, he was back with enough branches to make her a bed.

"Now we need a fire to warm our bones," he said cheerfully. "I left a good stash of dry kindling. There are plenty of bits and pieces of wood round about."

Elise gathered some while Cecil cleared away the grass and dug a hollow near the door for a fire. He laid the wood expertly and soon they were cheered by the fire's light. Spaces between the roof sods allowed the smoke to escape, so they closed the door to the chilly night, and sat together watching the flames and soaking up their warmth.

It has been seven long years since Cecil gave up his role as my youngest care. I love him dearly. He's made so many sacrifices in his short life. . . .

Cecil still needed to find some branches for his own bed and left his mother sitting there alone in the firelight. Silent for a few moments she began humming a beautiful Schubert tune. *I often hummed the melody, but didn't feel free to sing the words, yet I, like the wanderer long for a peaceful end to my struggles.* Beginning softly, she was soon lost in the song:

Der du von dem Himmel bist	*Thou that from the heavens art,*
Alles Leid und Schmerzen stillest	*Every pain and sorrow stillest*
Den, der doppelt elend ist	*And the doubly wretched heart*
Doppelt mit erquickung füllest,	*Doubly with refreshment fillest,*
Ach! ich bin des Treibens müde!	*I am weary with contending!*
Was soll all der Schmerz und Lust?	*Why this rapture and unrest?*
Süßer Friede, Süßer Friede,	*Peace descending, Peace descending*
Komm, ach komm in meine Brust!	*Come, ah come into my breast!*
In meine Brust?	*Into my breast!*

When Cecil returned, he quietly laid down his branches and listened, enchanted by his mother's lovely voice. Without understanding her words, he caught something of her feelings. As she finished, he sat down beside her.

"I feel like a weary wanderer," she told him. "I am discouraged sometimes. It seems the struggle never ends. But these words promise that God will give those who keep on trying a double blessing of peace. I feel peace tonight in my heart. Someday we'll have our very own land."

Reaching her arm around Cecil's shoulder, she said assuredly, "Everything will be all right."

After a few quiet moments, they wrapped themselves in their blankets and settled down on their sweet-smelling cedar beds. *I feel more content than I have for a long, long time.*

At sunrise they returned to St. Albans, Elise to the stove to cook the shorts for the family breakfast, Cecil to the barn to care for the animals.

⸎

---

5 *Wanderers Nachtlied I* (Wanderer's Night Song), by Johann Wolfgang von Goethe (1749-1832) set to music by Franz Schubert (1797-1828).

Mother and son treasured their night in the little house, but it was their only night. Able to attest to the fact that she slept on her homestead, her intention to apply for her patent was carried forward in a letter.

Aweme, Manitoba

March 28, 1889

Sir,

I hereby notify you that it is my intention to apply for a Patent of NW ¼ of 28 8 16 W this summer. I having duly completed the necessary 40 acres of ploughing and 25 acres of cropping and being now in the act of putting in my three months residence.

> *I am Sir*
> *Your obedient Servant*
> *Elise Vane* [6]

Addressed to the Commissioner, Dominion Lands, Mr. Criddle passed it through Aweme's little postal wicket to Mr. Bellhouse. There was a satisfying thump of the postal stamp and the letter dropped into the mailbag for its journey to set the wheels in motion toward her official application that coming summer.[7]

Elise knew homesteaders were expected to live on their land. She felt uneasy and puzzled. *The boys need breakfast by six, so I'm up an hour earlier to get the fire going to cook their big pot of cereal. They work in the fields until at least seven in the evening and often it's the darkness that forces them to quit for the day. When the boys go to Brandon the day begins even earlier and with luck they'll be home again by nine-thirty that night. If I walked that long mile to my house after their tea I'd have only a few hours to sleep. And merciful heavens, what if I overslept. . . .*

She saw no adjustments in her housekeeping duties and the days were already too long for her poor sore feet. *I'm afraid it's impossible, I have nothing . . . how can I make it my home?* Yet, she worried about the consequences of not living on her homestead. Mr. Criddle assured her, "Nobody will be checking to see if you actually sleep there," and so she gave up the idea and stayed on serving the busy family at St. Albans.

A highlight that spring came on a clear frosty night when the ponds, formed by melting snow, froze into an endless lake—smooth and glassy. Everyone, by sharing skates, took advantage of the rare chance to skim effortlessly over the land. The heavier boys felt even more daring as the ice dipped and cracked under them as they skated.

---

6 Homestead documents are from originals in the Archives of Manitoba during the 1970s. They are now available to view on Microfilm GR # 2186. Material from other sources will be noted.

7 March 29, 1889. "Dutchman written this day to appraise [sic] Dominion Lands Commission that she will apply for Patent this summer."

Following that glorious morning, Harry was sent harrowing for $2.25 a week. Edwy and Norman ran another germination test: 22 out of 50 kernels sprouted, so in spite of Mr. Criddle's grumbling, they increased the ratio of seed per acre. By April 19th, the crop was in on both new homesteads and the seeds harrowed in. Beautifully smooth, the fields awaited the spring rains. Instead they got wind, day after day of high winds. The powdered soil mixed with smoke of prairie fires blotted out the sun. In the midst of those dark days most of the family came down with severe colds, leaving the few to plant potatoes—two and a half acres of them. By then Harry was back and he and Edwy cut wood to sell in Brandon.[8] On their second load, Mr. Criddle went along to do some business at the Lands Office. Elise, expecting them at any moment, kept their meal hot.

No reason was given for their lateness until Mr. Criddle withdrew. Then Harry opened up. "We had a bit of an accident after unloading our wood at the back of the Little Central Hotel. It was a tight space and we didn't turn sharp enough. The wagon tongue caught on the wall and spooked Bill and Lamb. First thing we knew we were standing with a wagon, its tongue splintered, pieces of harness, and no oxen."

Elise held her breath; Harry carried on. "We cut a tree at the river to splice the tongue with the wire we carry along. We never know when we'll need it or binder twine. Anyway we had the stuff to get the harness back together. Your boys were busy alright."

Seeing their mother's face relax, both fellows started to see the humour and spun out their tale including their 'lord's' reaction. Soon all three were smothering their laughter. "Besides," Harry added, "The cost of new harness can't come out of our wages. We don't have any!"

That seemed hilarious in the wee hours of the morning. They shouldn't have been surprised that it brought Mr. Criddle away from his diary. He growled at Edwy, "I planned for you to homestead my pre-emption as soon as you are eighteen – the Government has given it away for University purposes." He turned to go back to his room saying, "Damn the Government! Damn careless boys!"

The Homestead Inspector arrived May 16 to check Elise's homestead. She caught a glimpse of him at the door, but Mr. Criddle shook his hand and they went out. *Gracious, it's my homestead and I didn't even have a chance to meet him! Will he be back to speak with me?*

But Mr. Arsonault didn't even come in for a cup of tea. He didn't need her to fill in the form.

---

8 "Wood 2 trips, $4.00; eggs, $.80; 5 bundles of asparagus, $.70."

Name ***Essie [sic] Vane***, Land NW *28.8.16* entered May 1886 to the Commissioner, according to the Dominion Lands Act, 1884.
Post Office nearer to the land ***Aweme***.

In residence or not:	***Sleeping on homestead now. Since March 25, 1889 she has slept on homestead and working on 34.8.16. within two miles.⁹ She has resided on said farm 34.8.16 from May 1886–March 1889. Works with a friend's family.***
Size of House:	***16 x 18 feet, Round log shanty, Value $35.***
Particulars	***Sod and straw roof.***
Other buildings:	***Stable: pole and straw and fetter*** Value ***Nil***
Fencing:	***Nil***
Wells	***Nil***
Breaking:	***36 acres in crop, Value $144.*** ***6 acres broken in 1889, Value $12.00***
Nature of soil:	***Light sandy.*** Subsoil—***sandy***
Area fit for cultivation	***95 acres***
Timber:	***60 acres scrubby***
Hay land:	***5 acres.***
General remarks:	***$2.50 acre.***

Dated: *May 25ᵗʰ, 1889* Signed: ***John J. Arsonault.***

The back page of the form had space for a sketch of the buildings and land use of the homesteader, but he drew nothing, didn't even mark the location of her house.

⊸⊱∘⊰⊷

Elise assumed all was well and heard nothing to the contrary. A few days later she was delighted when Isabel and a young friend, Mr. Knight, arrived for the weekend. To celebrate the occasion, everyone but herself, Mrs. Criddle, and the babies, went fishing in the Assiniboine. Besides having a jolly time, they caught 18 small minnows for the aquarium. Two weeks later Mr. Criddle sent Isabel back to Brandon, with the parting words, "Hate letting you go – but what else can I do?"[10]

Isabel didn't seem to mind. Her mother waved and wondered, *her young man, will he be coming again?* A letter from Germany took her attention another direction.

Mannheim, May 2, 1889
Dear Sister!
Your dear letter from March 21, 1889 I have received and although I had the best intentions to answer immediately I have not gotten around to it. We continually have so much work in the business and evenings I come home tired and exhausted.

---

9   For whatever reason the inspector recorded the wrong section number. Criddle homesteaded 32.8.16.
10 Account Book, P. Criddle; May 17 to Aug 1, income: boys, wood and produce, $30.30. Minnie and Isabel's wages: $34.75.

She thought back . . . *I wrote that just before we went to sleep in my house. I was so uneasy about our future, but that night . . . singing of another weary wanderer, I found peace. . . . It was so special, just Cecil and me in the firelight. But of course I can't share that.*

> *We were all happy to learn from your letter that you are all well. We are, thank God, also well. Mariechen was plagued with much coughing throughout the winter, so that she could go out only twice or thrice times and we feared pneumonia might set in but it luckily did not, and since the weather has become warmer her state of health has improved. I hope the summer will bring her permanent relief from her cough.*
>
> *That Percy was able to acquire a harmonium [reed organ] has given me pleasure for you. It will be a real treat for you and should give you many a pleasurable hour.*

Elise nodded. *Music is good for the soul. At first I thought it would be pleasant to have the organ near, but most of the time the sitting room is close enough.*

> *Anna and Elsa are progressing quite well in their piano playing and I too, often sit down at the piano and warm up the melodies out of the old 'Goldenen N------heft' which I played thirty years ago. I too have made some progress, but there is no drive and the longtime unpracticed fingers have become too stiff for piano and no longer want to obey.*

She paused remembering . . . *such happy times. I was the little sister . . . sometimes I played with my brothers, but usually they played for me to sing. I loved performing for the family. . . . Mama fixed my hair, coiled my braids just so . . . I dressed in my best. Uncle said, "You should go far with your beautiful voice.". . . I did enjoy their praise.* She glanced down at her hands once slim and beautiful, now so rough, so knobby. *If Friedrich's fingers are a problem, just look at these poor things. But my music isn't lost. I don't know how I would survive without my songs.*

> *The weather has been very agreeable and at times warm gentle rains have fallen. We hope you too have fruitful weather and that your diligence and work could be rewarded with a good crop.*

A warm gentle rain, that's what we need. Ours too often come in a storm: wind, lightning, thunder, and sometimes hail. I pray that this will be the promised year of plenty.

> *Greet Percy and all your children heartily from all of us . . . .*

She wiped a tear from her cheek, *Friedrich always ends the same. . . I need his best wishes, they feel like a warm cloak wrapped around my shoulders. But wait; there is more in the envelope.* She pulled out two notes and a photo—Anna. *What a lovely young lady she is! Time goes so fast. Seems no time since they lost their first little Anna and now they have this lovely young woman.*

Dear Aunt!

Recently I had a photograph made of myself and I will give you a small pleasure by sending you a small copy with this letter. I hope these few lines find all of you in good health.
I remain, with many hearty greetings to all of you
Deine Dich liebende Nichte (Your loving niece),
Anna

And the other was from Elsa:

Liebe Tante!

With your dear letter we received your congratulations for my confirmation, for which I want to express my heartfelt gratitude with this.
It gave me great joy that you remembered me and I remain, with a hearty greeting and kiss for you and your loved ones.
Deine Dich liebende Nichte (Your loving Niece),
Elsa Harrer

Tears welled up. *How dear they are.* She closed her eyes. *I'm imagining how it feels to have a genuine Heidelberg greeting, an Elsa kiss on each cheek. As for passing them on to my children; that I can't. They're so thoroughly British, they'd think her kisses much too forward.*

⚬⚬⚬

Just when the garden looked promising, a hard frost killed everything above the ground. *I wonder,* thought Elise, *do our Canadian neighbours suffer the same fate? Harry tells me they wait to plant their garden until after the full moon in June. It seems late, but every year we are replanting after a frost.*

And then, instead of the rain they still so desperately needed, they were invaded by grubs. The vegetables that had survived the frost: onions, carrots, and beets were infested. The landowner wailed, "I wish some dammed ass would come along and offer me six thousand for this blessed place. I should leave the Country. Go south – New Zealand – or California."[11]

He stayed out of the hot sun, papering the upstairs walls. It was his boys who walked in the heat of the day, pulling weeds from the wheat. And then one hot afternoon, Minnie appeared, "Surprise Mama! I persuaded Mr. Camp to bring me out for a few days. I've brought you some hand-me-downs. I think you'll like them."

By that time Minnie was swamped in the children's hugs. Back in the kitchen they opened Minnie's parcel. Elise was delighted to find among other things some underclothes and stockings, "Dear Minnie, what would I do without you! I am ever so grateful."

---

11 May 30, 1889.

When her daughter left on a load of produce a few days later, Elise called after her, "Thanks for coming. Don't forget to thank your lady."

Although the crops were wilting in the heat, Sunday dinners, tennis and cricket matches continued and Elise did her best to prepare their meals from the limited larder. Finally, even Mr. Criddle admitted in his diary, "We are nearly out of grub."

The drought also brought an invasion of rodents. Gophers were everywhere, and so destructive the government offered a bounty for every tail turned in. She suggested to Cecil, "You're out on the prairie watching the cattle all day. Take some snares with you. Get rid of the gophers and make some money."[12]

But the practice was labeled 'Impolitics'. Neither Cecil nor any of the others capitalized on the opportunity to make two cents a tail. It looked as if they would have no crop at all, so hearing a rumour that the selling price of wheat was an unheard of dollar a bushel was just too much. No one believed it, yet it set off an explosion in Elise's ears.

> Let's hope 'tis true – and not merely Canadian yarn – By Jove – I think worse and worse of the blessed Canadians every time I see a fresh one – Liars egg and bird – thieves – unmannered – ignorant – conceited – pig headed – bigoted – priest-ridden – quack doctor ridden – devoid of law – utterly dishonest in all things – preferring to cheat even when playing at games – damned ugly – so far as the female part at any rate are concerned – utterly lacking in all taste whatever – finally – the very scum of creation without any redeeming features.

The young people tiptoed up the stairs, hoping the dust would settle by morning.

At the end of Elise's three months of 'permanent' residence, things were busy at St. Albans. The haying was partly to blame, but equally at fault was the summer entertainment schedule. With so many visitors, how could Mrs. Criddle excuse Elise from her duties, even for a day?

"There is no need to rush," Mr. Criddle assured her, "It's only a formality."

And so farmer Vane's homestead remained in limbo while she toiled in the Criddle kitchen.

---

12 Many prairie boys told of their tobacco tins of decomposing tails.

Chapter Twelve

Complications

Elise and her witnesses finally got away from St. Albans on July 24 to make her application for the homestead patent. She and Mr. Swaisland had been coached to give the proper answers and some of them were problematic for her. *I speak English well, but I definitely have a German accent. How am I to explain that I was born in England? I'm to say I'm a farmer, a widow with five children, and the head of the family. I'm not to give my occupation.*

The men up front in the driver's seat were not worried; Elise heard fragments of their jokes and conversations. *Even though I've been told it's only a formality . . . there's nothing to worry me, I can't help myself.* She hardly noticed the lovely road-side flowers and farms along the way.

Entering the office, Mr. Criddle, known to the agent, introduced her and Mr. Swaisland. Choosing the three necessary forms from the slots on a shelf Mr. Hiam stood at his counter, pen in hand. "The first witness?"

The young redhead stepped forward. The agent read the questions and entered Swaisland's answers. He was a farmer living on Section 14, Township 9, Range 17 West of the 1st Meridian. He had known the applicant four years residing on NE 32.8.16. W. Yes, she was entitled to an entry for this quarter section and had built her house the end of February '89. "Where had she resided when absent from her homestead and what was her occupation there?"

That's the two-part question; he's to answer only the first.

But Swaisland let both slip out, "Serving on North East 32.8.16.W, within two miles."

"Do you have any interest, direct or indirect, in this application?"

"No."

"Do you believe the claimant was acting in good faith in obtaining her application for patent?"[1]

"I do."

He swore that his statements were true, and signed, Ivan Swaisland.

---

1 Every effort has been made to reproduce the original text of the homestead material and may differ from current punctuation, spellings and expression.

Mr. Hiam laid the form aside and addressed Elise, "You are submitting the application? Your name is Elise Vane?"

She nodded and he entered her name and homestead: **NW Section 28, Township 8, Range 16 West of 1ˢᵗ Meridian.** And then, pen dipped and poised, he leaned forward.

She felt the heavy presence of a man on each side. *I hope my knees don't give way. If I want this land for my boys, I have to get through this.*

Down the page they went, question by question:

2. Are you a British subject by birth or naturalization? **Birth**
3. What is your trade, profession or calling? **Farming**
4. When did you obtain entry for this homestead? **3 May '86**
5. When did you build your house thereon? **End of February '89.**
6. When did you perfect your entry by taking in your own person possession of the land and beginning continuous residence thereon? State each month and cultivation thereof within two miles?
   3ʳᵈ of May '86 residing on NE ¼ 32.8.16 W.
7. What portion of each year since that date have you resided thereon?
   From 3ʳᵈ May '86 till 25 March '89 on NE ¼ 32.8.16.
   From 25ᵗʰ March '89 until 1ˢᵗ July '89 upon Homestead. [In the 'eyes' of the Homestead Act living there permanently on her own land]
8. When absent from your homestead where have you resided and what has been your occupation? **Residing on NE 32.8.16 W.**

She felt a little easier, *He didn't press for my occupation.*

9. Of whom does your family consist; when did they commence residence on this homestead and for what portion of each year have they resided upon it? **5 children, 1 resided with me on the place and within 2 miles.**
10. How much breaking have you upon your homestead in each year since you obtained entry? And how many acres have you cultivated each year?
    '86 – broke 23 acres.
    '87 – broke 15 cropped 23.
    '88 – broke 20 cropped 38.
    '89 – cropped 38 acres.
11. How many horned cattle, horses, sheep and pigs have you had on your homestead each year since date of perfecting your entry? Give numbers in each year. **1 Team Oxen working the place –**
12. What is the size of your house? And what is its appraised value?
    16 ft. 6 in. X 19 ft. 6 in. – $50.
13. What is the extent of fencing you have and what is the present value thereof? **None.**
14. What other buildings have you erected? What other improvements have you made and what is the cash value of the same?
    1 granary - no value -

15. Are there any indication of minerals? . . . **No minerals, land suitable for mixed farming**
16. Have you had any other homestead entry? **No.**
17. Have you assigned or transferred or agreed to assign or transfer any portion of your homestead or pre-emption right or any part thereof? If so when and to whom? **No.**

On the reverse side of the form she marked the location of her house and crop. Then, with the questions completed, Mr. Hiam filled in her name and asked her to read the oath.

I, *Elise Vane* do solemnly swear that the answers to the forgoing questions are true and correct in every particular. That I claim a Patent for this Homestead under the provisions of the Dominion Lands Act.

That I obtained an entry, and claim a Patent for the same for my own benefit, and not in the interest or for the benefit of any other person or persons whomsoever.[2]

Her throat tightened and she swallowed nervously. *I'm to sign that every answer I gave is true in every particular! Sign under oath and in front of these men? Dear God in Heaven!*

Her witnesses waited, Mr. Hiam pointed to the space for her name and said, "Sign here."

Blood rushed to her face. *I'm cornered. . . .* She dipped the pen in the ink and formed the letters *E-l-i-s-e V - a - n - e.*

She dared not raise her eyes as she stepped back. Hiam proceeded as if no crime had been committed, and taking up the third and last form he wrote **Percy Criddle, NE 32.8.16 W.** He began, questioned and filled in the answer.

1. What is your occupation? **Farmer**
2. How long have you known Elise Vane? **30 years**
3. Was she entitled to an entry for this quarter section? **Yes**

The troublesome question; "When absent from her homestead where has she resided and what has been her occupation?" **Living on NE 32.8.16 W**

Relieved for a moment, she wondered: *Doesn't the occupation need to appear on the form?*

The men had already moved on. "Have you any interest, direct or indirect in this application? **No.**

"Do you believe the claimant has acted in good faith in obtaining her entry and in application for her Patent?" **I do.**

Without hesitation he went on to swear to the truth of his statements: "I, **Percy Criddle** of Aweme, make oath and say that the answers to the foregoing questions are true and correct in every particular." He signed his name and gave the form to the agent to complete.

2 See the appendix for this homestead application.

"Sworn before me at **Brandon** on this **26ᵗʰ day of July 1889, W. H. Hiam**, Local Agent of Dominion Lands for **Souris** District."

Picking up the forms, Mr. Hiam said, "Well, that's all there is to it, Mrs. Vane. I'll get these forms on the way and you'll have your homestead. It's been a pleasure to serve you."

Elise nodded. *It's over . . . none of my worries raised a ripple.*

There was a long drive home to come to terms with what she had done. *Surely a loving God won't hold this sin against me. My sons need land . . . . But I didn't expect to have to lie to get it. What would have happened if I had said no? No, I have not told the truth in every particular. My name? My letters from home come in care of Percy Criddle. He calls me the Dutchman, she calls me Huddock, the little ones—Mama Dutcheen, Norman and his brothers—Huckey. I'm their servant; 'Make a cup of tea', 'Put another stick of wood on the fire', 'My dress needs a pressing before I leave for din-ner'. . . . Swaisland has visited often; still it's possible he hasn't even heard 'Mrs. Vane'. I expected and steeled myself to write it. But to swear to its truth? Dear God! I dare not think of what would have happened had I said, I was born in Germany or, I'm not Mrs. Vane. . . . But I signed, and I was not the only liar. Swaisland didn't come until the next year, if I remember rightly, and 30 years since Percy and I met.*

*I can't do anything about them. But, it's **my soul** that I worry about.*

Accompanied by the rise and fall of the men's voices; the wheels rattled and grated through the hours. Elise pondered her guilt and her family's future until at last she prayed. *Our Father, which art in heaven, Hallowed be thy name. Thy kingdom come, Thy will be done on earth as it is in Heaven . . . And forgive us our trespasses as we forgive them that trespass against us. And lead us not into temptation: but deliver us from evil. . . .*

As the day cooled, the shadows lengthened, and the great dome of the sky darkened into sunset, she regained her composure and with it her will to survive.

Lord, thou hast been our refuge: from one generation to another,
before the mountains were brought forth, or ever the earth and the world were
made; thou art God from everlasting, and world without end.

On reaching St. Albans, she served the gentlemen their tea, tidied up, and crawled under her covers. *It would have been wonderful while I was in Brandon to have called on my daughters, to see where they worked, to thank Minnie's lady for her gifts.*

Sleep came as a blessing.

For Mr. Criddle it was all in a day's work and the next morning he wrote briefly, "Took the Dutchman yesterday with Mr. Swaisland to apply for her patent – an uneventful journey."³

---

3 July 27, 1889.

Elise carried on through the hot dry summer, as more guests than ever came for cricket, tennis, music, and cards. Sometimes the company ate them out of house and home, unaware of the difficulty she was having in scraping the bottom of the barrel. Funds from rhubarb, potatoes, wood, the girls' wages, and the boys' labour, carried Mr. and Mrs. Criddle of St. Albans and their guests blissfully along.[4]

In the intervening time, Mr. Hiam had paid no heed to the Homestead Inspector's report and prepared the Certificate of Recommendation for the Homestead Patent for the Commissioner's signature to be forwarded on to Ottawa.

Certificate of Recommendation for Homestead Patent 159596

I Certify that Elise Vane who is the holder of a Homestead Entry for NW ¼ of 28.8.16. W of the 1ˢᵗ Meridian has complied with the provision of the law required to be conformed to, in order to entitle him to receive a patent for such Homestead, and that I have recommended the issue of such a patent.

W. H. Hiam Local Agent

He wrote a covering letter to accompany the file to his superior, Commissioner Smith of Dominion Lands in Winnipeg.

Sir,

I beg to enclose herewith for your approval the application for patent, duly recommended, of Elise Vane of Aweme who holds entry for the NW ¼ of Section 28 Township 8 Range 16 W M.

I have the honour to be Sir, Your obedient servant

W. H. Hiam

But the file was not forwarded to Ottawa as he expected. It landed back on his desk.

Sir,

Referring to your letter of the 29ᵗʰ ultimo[5] I am directed by the Commissioner to return herewith the file . . . . covering the application for patent of Mrs. Elise Vane . . . , and to say that although Mrs. Vane appears to have complied with the requirements of the subclause under which she claims her patent, it is necessary that she show that she is a head of a family and therefore entitled to patent.

I have the honour to be, Sir, your obedient, servant,

(Unsigned) Secretary

---

4 Criddle, Percy. *Farm Accounts March 27, 1888–May 10, 1891*. May: Rhubarb - $.95; Potatoes for the following: June - $.95; July 22 - $9.00, August - $6.25, September - $6.25: Wood: September - $7.00. From this point, the financial records are taken from this source. Archives of Manitoba: P 318 – P 319.
5 Latin; occurring in the month preceding.

On the farm, meanwhile, summer was rapidly slipping away, and the haying had hardly begun. Looking around for another team of oxen and finding none, Mr. Criddle employed Swaisland and his team to help the boys. He engaged Lonsbury to drive him to Brandon. Returning with two beautiful mares he shouted, "Halloo! Come see what I've bought!"[6]

They all trooped out and stood in shocked silence. "Harvest won't wait – got a new Jess, and that's Dolly. Horses are faster." He handed Lonsbury $5 for the trip and put the steeds in the care of the boys who were both awestruck and proud.

Elise, on the other hand, had a host of thoughts. *My Papa had an eye for a good horse! He needed a fleet of horses for the coaches. But for us? We've no money for food, a stamp, or writing paper. Isn't this extravagant? How much did such a fine team cost? He's in a jolly mood now, but I have a sinking feeling there is trouble ahead. I remember, the price of a horse is only the beginning. I can't help thinking of poor skin and bones Jess when he sold her last summer. Horses need plenty of hay plus a generous scoop of grain. The boys will have to cut more hay and take care that it's properly dried. Papa had a nose for musty hay, said it ruined a good horse in no time.[7]*

Cecil was grooming the horses 10 days later when Jess let him have it with her hind leg. Elise flew to the door when he cried for help to see blood trickling through his fingers covering his lower face. She helped him to a chair, got a cloth, and called Mr. Criddle. He took a good look at the lad's injury and said, "A bad gash – right through your upper lip – but no teeth broken. Your mother can patch you up."

With that, he went back to his room muttering, "Damn all horses say I. They want everlasting attention – eat no end of grub – do no more work than oxen – cost more – are more delicate - and finally get kicking or biting someone. Damn all horses."

❧❦❧

Next morning he announced, "You need both horses and oxen for harvesting – I'll walk to Brandon. Tulk is coming any day now."

But, he really needed to visit the Lands Office where his housekeeper's homestead was on hold, pending clarification of her qualifications as a bona fide settler. He went over the letter, "What the devil does he mean? 'Mrs. Vane **appears** to have complied.' Isn't she a **widow**?"

Mr. Hiam explained, "They are asking if your friend is really heading up a family."

---

6   Aug. 21, 1889. "Purchased two mares, 4 and 8 years old for $390.00"
7   Heaves: Chronic Obstructive Pulmonary Disease in horses known for centuries: caused by musty, poorly cured hay.

Returning home the next day without Mr. Tulk, Elise sensed something was amiss. Before long he came out with a letter and notepaper, "Want you to copy this."

She lowered herself to the chair and flinched to see 'widow since 1874'. *That's the autumn he left us. . . .* She took the pen, dipped it in the ink and began:

August 17, 1889.

Sir,

In reply to your letter dated the 10th inst. I beg to tell you that I have been a widow since Sept. 1874 and that I am a head of a family having five living sons and daughters.

I thought I had already given this information.

I am sir
Your obedient Servant,

Elise Vane

With nary a word, he made off with the letter to his room. *I can't get used to signing V-a-n-e . . . it hurts so. Vane . . . our ever so special secret love name. For business reasons Percy needed me to be Mrs. Criddle and that's how I stayed for 11 years. It was a shock when he dug Vane up in Liverpool.*

❦

Mr. Tulk arrived a few days later and found his own way to St. Albans. For the boys, he brought a new Rugby 16-bore muzzle loader which they put to use right away. Elise appreciated the game they shot, but the gentleman helped her in two more ways—his calming influence, and Isabel's presence. *It's such a pleasure to have her company. With Mr. Tulk occupying his private room at St. Albans, her money isn't needed.*[8]

❦

Mr. Hiam received Mrs. Vane's letter and sent her file back to Winnipeg.

Sir:

In answer to your letter of the 5th instant No. 144752 Ref. 19388. I beg to return per current parcel post the application for patent of Mrs. Elsie [sic]Vane NW21-8-16 W to which is attached a letter setting forth that she is the head of a family.

I am Sir
Your obedient Servant
W.H. Hiam

---

8   Income 1889: Mr. Tulk, "August 20, $10. November 16, $25. "

Various notes on the side of Hiam's letter followed the Commissioner's steps. "The date given for Mrs. Vane's residence clearly shows she did not live permanently on her land and furthermore did not intend to do so. . . . This must stand until we obtain a decision from the M. O. [Minister's Office] as to the manner in which cases such as this are to be dealt with." And at a later date, having checked with his superior, he wrote on the same form, "Must then be in residence upon application."

Whereupon, Commissioner A. M. Smith Esq. wrote directly to Mr. [sic] Elise Vane, Aweme, Manitoba, with a copy to Mr. Hiam. The postal stamps recorded its journey: Winnipeg Sept 6, Brandon Sept 6, Two Rivers Sept 9, and Aweme Sept 14, 1889.

By a strange coincidence, a letter from Germany arrived in the same mail. Mr. Criddle opened Friedrich's letter, but only glanced it over and handed it to Elise. He opened the letter addressed to the head of the homestead family, Elise Vane Esq.[9] Sensing trouble, Mr. Tulk withdrew to his private quarters, and Elise retreated with her brother's letter to a chair by the stove. She examined a photograph and then plunged into a longer than usual letter.

Isabel

Mannheim, August 11, 1889

Dear Elise!

I received some time ago your dear lines as well as a photograph of Minnie and Isabel. You have given us much joy by sending this, for silently we had long wished you would send us photographs of your family. What joy our dear mother would have had, had she seen them! On the occasion of a visit in Karlsruhe I showed them to Carl. We both were pleasantly surprised at how tall and pretty your girls are. Give them my heartiest thanks and tell them that they gave me great joy. If it should ever be possible, maybe they could send Carl some as well. . . .

She paused. *I thought they would be pleased. I'll ask for two more for Carl and Amalie.*

With this I send you a photograph of Elsa, who was confirmed this Easter. I once sent you a photo of her when she was a little girl of 6-7 years. Elsa will turn 15 in September, but is already taller than Anna and just as strong. Don't you find that she looks like Isabel a lot? I also think she resembles you when you were her age.

Minnie

Elsa

Elise nodded. *Isabel is great deal like me, and not only in looks.*

> *Anna has finished her schooling and we are worried what to do with her. She is not suited for a teaching career; there is also only a small chance of getting employment, for there are hundreds of teachers looking for employment. We will enroll her in a housekeeping school where she will learn to become a seamstress and all the other things connected with this.*
>
> *Elsa finishes school next year so we still have time to think of her future. She is very talented, but is very willful and always ready for mischief. They both have a good education, now they shall learn how to apply it in housekeeping, so that they will be able to stand on their own feet, should that ever become a necessity.*

Her nieces, as she had done, were getting a good education. Finishing his letter she realized all was quiet and, standing up, saw the official letter open on the table.

> *Mr. [Sic] Elise Vane*
> *Aweme, Manitoba[10]*
> *Sept 5, 1889*
> *Sir,*
>
> *I am directed to inform you that your application for patent for the N. W ¼ of sec. 28,8,16 1st M, under the "two miles radius" clause of the Dominion Lands Act cannot be approved as it appears that you were absent from your homestead 20 days next prior to the date of application and that therefore failed to comply with that part of the clause in question which requires a settler to be in residence on his land three months prior to such date. You should make a fresh application when you can show that you have fulfilled this requirement. . . .*

She felt weak. *I'd like to escape to my little house. . . . But it's not possible to survive there.* Instead, she busied herself with tea preparations. *What will he do now? He's not one to be pushed around by bureaucratic colonials.*

Her intuition was correct. He came from his room with a draft for her to copy. *It looks like a long one.* She pushed the big pot to the back of the stove and sat down.

"Be careful – no ink blots. Paper's expensive."

Nervously she began.

> *Aweme, September 14, 1889.*
> *Sir,*
>
> *I am greatly astonished at a letter this day received from Assistant secretary of your department dated 5th inst.*

He looked over her shoulder. "Copy it exactly. Underline – 'absent, and my homestead'." He pointed, "See to it that you put in the brackets and the question mark."

---

10 The address of recipient was at the end of the letter but in the interest of clarity it is placed at the beginning.

He followed her pen as she wrote.

Wherein I am informed that I was <u>absent</u> from <u>my homestead</u> 26 days ere making my application for Patent, I failed to comply with the clause which requires a settler to be in residence 3 months next prior to the date of application. Allow me to tell you, that I have been within a mile of my homestead all the time and my sons have been at work on it almost daily throughout the summer, though I have not slept on it since I completed my three months residence 26 (?) before making my application—

That it would be necessary for me to make my application immediately on completion of residence – I had not the smallest idea, otherwise I would have done so, though being a woman and owning no horses of my own I am dependent on neighbors to take me into Brandon (20 miles distant) –

As I have undoubtedly put in my full three months residence, considerably exceeded the amount of ploughing and cropping required by law and have merely committed an unintentional error of dates in not applying for my Patent absolutely at once, I trust that I may not be forced to go through a further 3 months residence now that winter is approaching (at considerable hardship and loss) but that under the circumstances you will reconsider the matter and duly grant me my recommend.[11]

Your obedient servant,

Elise Vane

She thought, *certainly fitting, so obedient, I lie. . . .* The pages were whisked up; he looked them over and fitted them into an addressed envelope. Then moving toward the coats, he called his friend. "Want a little fresh air J. A.? A walk to the post office before tea?"

Elise added a stick to the fire to get the pot boiling again. *This is not the end of the matter. I'm quite sure it doesn't answer the Commissioner's concerns.*

⋅❧⋅⋅⋈⋅⋅❧⋅

Following the disaster of Mr. Tulk's spring hunt, he looked forward to a fall safari. The hunters, Messrs. Tulk, Criddle, Sutcliffe and Köhler once again departed in two heavily loaded wagons. The drive north was uncomfortably cold, and once on location at the lake, they were mired in mud and muskeg. Adding to the difficulties, Mr. Tulk's precious punt proved much too cumbersome. But what tipped the expedition into evacuation mode was the complete lack of game birds; there wasn't a duck, goose, or swan to be seen. The hunters sent a message to the Boy, "Get Swaisland and come in haste."

Elise heated the water to wash the soggy mud-coated pants and socks. *Such is the life of the gentry. I would have liked to talk to the German, Mr. Köhler, but I couldn't bear another lesson about talking to guests, or should I say, **not** talking to guests.*

---

11 The draft is in private family collection.

A few days later Elise was asked to prepare a lunch, "J.A. and I are going to survey and stake out your homestead and properly fix its boundaries."

She almost blurted out, *I'd like to go along, to explore my land and see the little house in the daylight. It's such a beautiful autumn day.* But, she didn't. *It would be humiliating in front of Mr. Tulk to be told, 'Haven't you got enough to do? Why would you want to waste time wandering about the countryside?'*

⁂

The Commissioner's response came September 24. Mr. Criddle read it and left it on the table.

Madam,

In reply to your letter of the 14th instant I am to say that the Commissioner regrets that in view of the provisions of the Dominion Lands Act, the decision with respect to your application for Patent for the NW ¼ 28.8.16 W 1st M. which has already been communicated to you must be adhered to, as the Act contemplates that a settler taking advantage of the 'two miles radius' clause shall become a 'bona fide' permanent resident on the homestead quarter Section before applying for patent. . . .

Elise was still digesting the news when her agent reappeared, "I've a letter to Commissioner Smith – give him something to think about – sit down – need to make the outgoing mail."

Wiping her hands, she pulled up a chair and copied.[12]

Sir,

I have the honour to acknowledge the reply of your Secretary dated 24th instant to my letter of the 14th instant addressed to you.

As you decline (doubtless for official reasons) to grant me that which I consider my clear and undoubted right, I presume the proper course is for me to submit my case to the Minister of the Interior in Ottawa enclosing for his perusal copies of my correspondence with you.

I have the honour to be Sir, your obedient servant,
Elise Vane

By the following week that letter was followed by a long letter to the Minister of the Interior in Ottawa. Elise was called to sit down again. *What am I getting into this time?* But, he stood over her and she copied:

Aweme, Oct 2, 1889

Sir,

I have the honour to submit to your consideration a case of great hardship to myself, I homesteaded the NW ¼ 28.8.16 W in Manitoba in 1886 under the 2 mile radius clause and faithfully and honestly completed all my settler duties on Time last making my application to the Land Office at Brandon for my Patent- twenty six days afterwards.

---

12 This letter in homestead records. The draft in private collection.

After waiting nearly 2 months, I received a communication from the Commissioner at Winnipeg informing me that I had <u>failed to comply with that part of the clause which requires a settler to be in residence on his land three months next prior to date of application and that I should make a fresh application when I can show that I had fulfilled this requirement.</u>

I enclose you copies of my correspondence with the Commissioner [13] on the subject whereby you will perceive that if I have committed any error at all it had been but of a trivial nature. Being a Widow with but scanty means I soon after the completion of my three months residence returned to the house of the lady for whom I have for some years been acting as house keeper (within one mile of my Homestead) and a few days later having obtained my witnesses made my application. You will readily see that it is not easy for a settler in a wild country to obtain his or her witnesses for an exact day and get them to drive 20 miles out and back, while in my case I have no horses of my own - in addition to which I had no knowledge that there was any rule requiring <u>immediate</u> application (as interpreted by the Commissioner. . .

I think that I have now stated all that is required for your just consideration of my case and have therefore only to add my prayer that you will exercise your authority to save me from great hardship (my crop this year has proved a complete failure) and I believe in justice, by granting me my Patent forthwith instead of forcing me to reside yet another 3 months on my homestead just as winter is approaching and losing my employment as well.

I have the honour to be Sir
Your obedient Servant,
Elise Vane[14]

He reached for her pages, added them to the sheaf he already copied, and went to mail them.

Elise held her head in her hands. *I applied as an independent homesteader. Now I'm a victim, a poor widow appealing for pity. As for fulfilling all my settler duties? Not so. That shanty is not good enough for a home. I have no animals, chickens; no well, no garden, not even a parliament building for my bodily functions. Land and a home of my own seems only a dream. And the 26 day delay was not caused by the lack of a witness. Lonsbury was often over for tennis and drops his own work any time he's needed. I'm a pawn, forbidden to speak of God, but now praying to the commissioner to save me from hardship and injustice.* Her anger, always held in check, burst its bonds. *Justice! I can use a little justice all right! To apply for a homestead where my children and I cannot live. . . . And the last straw for this camel, I'd lose my employment! This position pays 'nichts' and takes all . . . . . It's vassalage, serfdom, bondage, enslavement! I've been sucked in by the promise of land and a good future for my sons.*

---

13 The enclosures explain why Elise's Homestead file includes letters written by her and copies in Mr. Criddle's handwriting.
14 The original draft is in a private collection.

The door opened. Mr. Criddle was back. He opened a letter and dropped the envelope on the table.[15] Elise noticed the German stamp and Friedrich's writing when she brought his tea. *I'm longing for news from home. . . . I'll just have to wait 'til he's finished.*

Mannheim, September 22, 1889

Liebe Elise!

> *I have received your dear lines from August 31 and was glad to read that you all were well. I wrote to you about eight weeks ago and included a photograph of Elsa and at the same time expressed our delight over the pretty photograph of Minnie and Isabel. I would be sorry if the letter with Elsa's Photo would not have come into your possession, but since I don't recall the exact day when I mailed your letter I still hope you received it after you mailed your letter.*

She frowned. *I've been upset . . . but I should have written. I've been cruel . . . again.*

> *Also very sorry, I am that again this year you cannot be completely satisfied with your crop. Yet you can be happy that you were not among the most unfortunate ones.*

When she wrote Friedrich she hadn't known how poor the crops were. *I dare not tell him we got only 212 bushels from all 70 acres. I'm afraid we **are** among the most unfortunate.*

> *It has been very cool for eight days already, even had night frost, which harmed especially the tobacco. During the last days we already heated the house. It is extraordinary, for usually we have a warm October. Maybe we will still have a nice 'Old Ladies Summer'.*
>
> *Elsa will attend school one more year. Anna is taking a home economics course and shows great aptitudes. Her teachers and board members have praise for her work. Julie is a small, happy-go-lucky little thing, that always has to be pushed to do her work. Hopefully she will become more diligent as her understanding increases.*
>
> *Carl and Amalie are well, I hope to see them shortly. Mariechen too is well. Hopefully the winter will be kind so that she will not suffer from her cough as she did last winter.*
>
> *I hope you too will have a mild winter and good health . . . . Your loving brother, Friedrich.*

After tea, Elise asked Mrs. Criddle for paper. *I will make up for my negligence this very night.* Once the dishes were washed and back on the shelf, she sat at the table within the soft glow of the coal oil lamp and wrote:

Lieber Friedrich!

The pencil hovered; *but what can I say? So many things have happened since I wrote . . . yet they can't be told. If only I could spill the load that weighs down my heart;*

---

15 Addressed to Mr. Percy Criddle Esq. Aweme, Manitoba, Canada, North America. Private family.

173

confess my unhappy secrets kept first for mother's sake and now for my dear brothers.
I've waited too long. . . . It would be cruel. . . . And would it help? . . . Furthermore,
I couldn't get such a letter past my censor. I'll let Friedrich know I received his letter,
thank him for dear Elsa's picture, and write about the weather and the poor crop.

I deeply regret that I haven't written.

. . . .

From the sister who loves you,
Elise

She folded her letter, stood it on the shelf between the cups, picked up the
lamp and wearily climbed the stairs. 'Widow Vane' once again turned to her faith,
believing that God was still in his heaven and good would yet come to her and her
children.

Chapter Thirteen

Your Obedient Servant

When the Commissioner's response to 'Widow Vane's' letter arrived she watched Mr. Criddle grow more and more agitated as he read, until he flung the pages to the floor. As soon as his door banged shut and she was sure he was there to stay, she picked them up.

Department of the Interior,
Ottawa, 11th October, 1889

Madam,

I have the honour by direction to acknowledge the receipt of your letter of the 2nd instant . . . in which you appeal against the Commissioner's decision to the effect that as you did not make application for your patent until 26 days after the completion of your three months residence, your application could not be recommended.

In reply I am to say that while the Minister regrets that you should have been unaware of what the law required, he is unable to order the Commissioner to recommend your application for patent, as the law clearly lays down the conditions on which patent may be acquired, and if you have not strictly complied with these conditions, the Minister has no power to relax them. I may point out to you that the object of the provision in the Act permitting the homesteader to reside for a certain period within two miles of the homestead, was to enable those who, for want of means, were debarred from undertaking, in the first year or so of their homesteading, the additional expense attendant on a separate house and establishment, and it was premised that by inserting in the clause the provision that the homesteader should, after 2 years and 9 months residence within two miles of the homestead and extra cultivating thereof, live in a habitable house upon the homestead for the three months next prior to the application for patent, some guarantee would thereby be obtained that the homesteader intended, after the completion of that 3 month's residence on the homestead, to continue in permanent residence thereon, making it his or her home.

She nervously stroked her chin. *If I understand correctly, I not only should have lived there three months, I should have moved there and made my home there. I broke the law. . . . I'm still breaking the law.*

In your own case, as is admitted by the statement in your letter, the intention of the Act has not been fulfilled, as it is to be inferred that after a perfunctory 3 months residence on the land, you had to all intents and purposes abandoned the homestead as a home, and taken up another vocation.

I have the honour to be, Madam,
Your obedient servant,
LYNDWODE PEREIRA, [Stamped]
Assistant Secretary

She groaned silently. *The delay in my application gave my situation away, but the Commissioner is sadly mistaken if he thinks I have given up on my dream. And I have not taken up a new vocation! . . . No, this homesteader is stuck serving here. . . .*

Gradually she calmed down and saw things more clearly. *Right now, this is the only roof we have over our heads. I have no money, nor do my sons. We work, but not for ourselves. But my boys are strong and healthy, surely we will get away.*

Within a short time she received the commissioner's reply.

The master came from his room with another copy-job and she yielded to his bidding.

November 5, 1889
Sir,

I have the honour to inform you that being unable to obtain redress from the Minister of the Interior I am about to commence a further 3 month residence on my homestead at the completion of which I shall again apply for Patent.

It seems very hard that I am forced to do this, being a true homesteader and having faithfully executed and more than executed all my duties appertaining thereto.

I have the honour to be your obedient servant . . .

The obedient servant signed her name and shivered. *It was spring when we slept in the little house, yet we were none too warm. How are we to keep from freezing to death during the coldest months? Of one thing I'm certain; there'll be no delay this time when the three months are over.* And then another thought popped into her head. *What official will travel twenty miles in winter's cold to find out if I'm living there? I don't think I'll be sleeping there at all.*

Within a short time she received the Commissioner's acknowledgement of her letter. Note the name 'Elisa'. Indicates German pronunciation. Private collection

Madame,
I have the honor [1] to acknowledge the receipt of your letters of the 5th instant, stating that you intend to put in three months further residence upon your homestead the NW ¼ Sec.28.8.16.1stM.

---

1 The use of the American spelling 'honor' in this letter and a few other instances is curious.

> *I have the honor to be Madam*
> *Your obedient servant,*
> *R. A. Ruttan, Secretary*

The Criddles and their guest continued to enjoy their cultural pursuits until Mr. Tulk departed. Isabel also left to find a Brandon family in need of a domestic. Another winter encircled the family at St. Albans, even the housekeeper who had written to say she was residing on her homestead.

⊸❧⊷

Elise unfolded a letter. *Friedrich . . . my life-saver.*

> *Dear Sister!*
> *I have received your dear lines of last month. I was happy to learn that all of you are well, also that you received the letter containing Elsa's photo.*
> *My letter from the 18th of September should have reached you. I feared already that the letter with the photo had been lost, it seems to have travelled longer than is usually the case. Also my greatest wish, Elise, would be to see you face to face - that always reminds me of what our dear mother used to say, when we got into childhood squabbles: "Some time later you will be very happy if only you could be together." And it has come to that, now we are happy if only we know of each other, that we are healthy.*

The words triggered a long forgotten memory. *I remember stepping down from the coach in Heidelberg on our return after papa's death and mama's family came to meet our coach. Now I understand all those tears and hugs.*

> *Maybe the possibility will come that we can see each other, but for that to happen a lucky coincidence would have to take place.*

Dear Friedrich, to see each other again! Unless you come here? The second of joy, turned to horror. Lieber Herr Gott! Oh, dear God! Calm down dear heart. Friedrich is not able to travel abroad like Mr. Tulk.

> *If only the dear Lord will grant us health, everything else is bearable. Also that which we cannot change we have to accept.*

She reread, 'have to accept'. *Should I accept my lot? Not yet . . . I've not yet given up.*

> *Today I sent a Christmas gift of 50 marks. $11.80 in the same way I always do, which, hopefully will soon be in your possession.*

In a moment of optimism she thought—*money for stockings . . . shoes! . . . No, but I'll have the sweet smell of tobacco and maybe a sip of Christmas rum.*

> *Lately we met Saunchen Krackel, who inquired after you happily. I hardly recognized her, she has become quite corpulent and old; she is said to have lost a lot of money to the husband of her sister Anna, who has become a victim of alcohol and looks very old and neglected.*

Corpulent! Lovely Saunchen? If she came here she'd soon be skin and bones as I am.

We are faring not worse than others. We could always use more money, for our children use a lot, also prices of staples have really gone up, like meat, bread, coal and the income has not kept pace. But the main thing still is good health! . . .

With Friedrich's Christmas greetings to warm her heart Elise went up to bed. Having long since given up kneeling in the cold, she wrapped her blankets closely about her and prayed: *I thank you, Father in heaven, through your dear Son Jesus Christ, that you have graciously protected me through this day. . . .*

On a clear November morning Elise noticed smoke from a train drifting upward to the southwest.[2] *Edwy says he could haul our wheat there if only we could get a bridge. The trouble is—every settler wants it near his own farm.* Just as she turned to go into the house she met Cecil on his way out. "I'm going with Harry for a few days."

A lump formed in her throat. *Am I losing my youngest too?*

But Cecil wasn't away long; the chore boy's many functions weren't so willingly picked up by Beatrice or her brothers. Harry and Edwy logged, or cut and hauled wood to Brandon. Refusing to give up his quest for meat, Norman took Cecil to help him scare up a deer, and with luck help carry home the meat. Elise gave them bread and cautioned, "Please do take care."

Pausing at the door, she watched them trudge eastward. *Almost the same age, but Norman looks a foot taller. I hope the long-legged one will break trail in the deep snow.*

The short winter day passed and when darkness fell, a lantern was hung on the flagpole and time dragged on. Mr. Criddle couldn't send Edwy and Harry out to search, for they were away in Brandon. At last he decided to walk to Bellhouses' for help, and was just pulling on his heavy pants when the door burst open, and the two boys stumbled in. Norman caught his breath and explained. "Close to the time we should have started back, we came across fresh deer tracks. I was sure I could bag it and set off after it. At dusk, I realized the folly of the chase and turned back. We tramped several miles and then Cecil, hip deep in snow, sank down in its softness. 'I need a bit of a rest,' he said. I pleaded, 'Get up. We've got to get home.' Said he didn't care, told me to go ahead. He'd come in awhile. I made him get up and steadied him. We walked a little further, but he went down again. I yanked on his coat, 'Get up, or you'll freeze to death!' I hauled him up on his feet again. Picked up the gun and got a little further. . . . Anyway, here we are."

Norman was praised as a hero; Cecil was given a dose of hot grog and taken off to bed by Mrs. Criddle. Washing up their dishes, his mother's heart raced. *What would I do without Cecil, my youngest, my confidant? This land will be my Waterloo!*

---

2 Northern Pacific Railway came northwest from Morris in 1890 to Brandon.

Harry and Edwy made more wood-selling trips to Brandon. Needing to juggle a number of outstanding bills, Mr. Criddle often went along, although his expenses, from 60¢ to $2.60 cut into their profit. Bower's bill for groceries and dry goods climbed ever upward, and by February was $122.83. That credit was their lifeline: boots for all those working feet, oatmeal, flour, currants, canned meat, coal oil, tea, sugar, matches and tobacco, soap, pitchforks, shot, and nails.[3] Larger debts loomed: binder, new seeder, a second plough, and a fanning mill. While the horses made travel faster, their oats were expensive, and come spring their first payment was due. The wolf was kept from the door with Minnie and Isabel's November and December wages of $25; Friedrich's Christmas gift, $11.80; plus the boys' contribution of $22 from the sale of seven loads of wood.

Christmas of '89 was celebrated with a good dinner and a whole bottle of rum extended with hot water and sugar. The old year ended with cold so extreme their aquarium had a quarter inch of ice by morning, and the calf, Fly, was found frozen stiff as a board in the barn. "A bad end to a bad year," Mr. Criddle lamented, "Let's hope the coming days are to be prosperous all round."

Elise echoed a silent *amen*.

On New Year's Day Harry fell ill. By next morning Mrs. Criddle couldn't get up; by early afternoon Elise crept up to bed, and that evening Maida and Stuart were stricken. The grippe had arrived. On the 3rd it was Edwy, by the 4th Beatrice and Evelyn, and on the 6th Norman and Cecil fell ill. By the 11th the older Vane boys had recovered, and it being a fine day, they set out to investigate new markets for their wood in the town of Wawanesa. Back that night, they told their mother, "It's in a lovely valley, growing fast—homes, stores, a grain elevator, a hotel. And, you'll never guess, we met our old neighbour Peter Smith, all jolly. He has a blacksmith shop and is building a house. His wife's away in Ontario. But we won't be going there to sell wood. The roads down into the valley are poor and too steep for our heavy loads."

Elise recovered enough to fulfill her duties, but the long hours and skimpy diet prolonged her recovery. One evening she slipped away right after tea. *I'll take up a lamp and read my letter while I warm up my bed.*

Mannheim, December 31, 1889

Dear Elise!

I hope you have received my letter of Nov. 21 and the money order.

Her hand flew to her mouth. *My goodness! I haven't thanked him.*

I was sick for a week with fever and a sore throat, a sickness quite prominent here. We used to call it Grippe but now it is known as Influenza.

---

3 Vane, Harry. "Bower helped a lot."

She wondered: *Is it the same as our grippe? I don't think we'll switch to the new name in this home.*

> *I have completely recovered, have much catching up to do in the office and have to work extra since eight of our office employees are now sick. That is the reason I did not get around to writing sooner, but I couldn't let the old year pass by without sending you and your loved ones the heartiest greetings and best wishes for the New Year.*
>
> *May the good Lord give you health, wellbeing and contentment and may he keep all unpleasantness far from you.*

Elise took a big breath. *I'll take your first wish—health.*

> *Our children send you a greeting card, with many hearty kisses! We hope all of you are well! The children, Anna and Elsa had practiced a piano piece, four hands, for Christmas, the Overture, "Poet and Peasant," a very lovely melody! They played it well and gave us much joy.*

Imagining the happy scene, Elise received another of Friedrich's letters.

> *It will be 9 PM right away and I am writing this in my office where we will be working until 10 PM because of the end of year inventory. Already banging is happening on the streets coming from shots fired to celebrate the New Year and I desire to be at home with my family and drink the customary New Year's punch with my loved ones. We will also drink a glass to you, maybe your ears will ring, as the saying goes, when someone far away thinks of you.*

She thought back to New Year's Eve. *Did my ears ring? All I remember is shivering that cold night and thinking they'd discover my frozen body, like poor Fly's, in the morning.*

Friedrich ended his visit with the words: *"Best greetings to Percy!"* Still weak from her illness, tears came easily. *Oh dear Brother, you always include him. . . . My sorrow doesn't lessen—betrayed every day. . . . I'm such a sight . . . not even proper shoes for my sore feet. My children are sent away to earn money. . . .* It was not often that she allowed herself to cry, but that night she could not dry her tears and there was no one to comfort her.

As Elise had expected, she spent no cold nights in her little shanty, although her sons found refuge there during a blizzard. She fretted as the weather worsened wishing they had not gone for wood, but Mr. Criddle didn't worry, "They'll be fine – have plenty of wood to keep themselves warm – they must have a little food left over for breakfast."[4]

---

4   February 7, 1890. "Two of the crew at Dutchman's shanty – Will have to stay there for the present."

He wasn't concerned about the boys, but something else was brewing that would, as soon as he learned about it, worry him. A letter with uncommonly fine penmanship, postmarked Aweme, January 31, 1890, arrived in Winnipeg. Its elegant confident style, combined with the allegation it contained, raised the Commissioner's eyebrows.

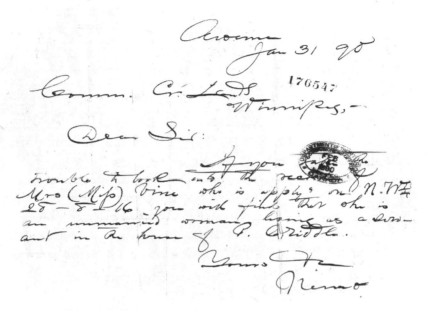

Aweme, Manitoba, Jan 31, 1890

Comm Cr. Lands
Winnipeg
Dear Sir,
    If you take the time to look into the record of Mrs. (Miss) Vine [sic] who is applying on NW ¼ of 28-8-16 you will find that she is an unmarried woman living as a Servant in the house of P. Criddle.
       Yours etc, Nemo [5]

He handed it to his secretary, "Send this letter to the Homestead Inspector in Brandon to ascertain the validity of the allegation."

    The Commissioner directs me to send you the annonymous [sic] letter relating to the homestead of Mrs. or Miss Vine, Vane the NW 28-8-16 W and to request you to enquire into the matter when you are next in that neighourhood.
    I have the honor to be, Sir . . .

---

5 Nemo: Latin, no one; in English, anonymous. Original letter, Private family collection.

But Mr. Cook was not about to take a nasty 20-mile drive to check, especially when he learned that Mr. Criddle would soon be back with the lady in question to file her application.

When the boys sold another load of wood, their three dollars were not enough to cover expenses: boots for Maida $1.25, dried apples .45, coal oil .45, tea $1.00, sugar $1.00, nails .20, axe handle .25, bran $1.25, and iron $1.25. Spending only 35 cents for his personal needs, Mr. Criddle extended all his debts, "I'll be back in town on the twenty-fourth."

It was crispy cold and dark when they set out. It would be slow going for the roads were drifted and heavy; Edwy drove, the two men sat beside him. His mother was bundled up in the back, facing the eastern sky. She watched the light strengthen, the stars fade. When the winter sun finally eased over the horizon, it cast long dark shadows on the white snow. Had this been a pleasure trip she might have composed a poem to capture the beauty. But her creativity was overwhelmed by this, her second application. *I am to give Germany as my birthplace. But, to explain that I'm a British citizen, I'm to declare a marriage in an undetermined territory. Will he ask which territory? And then will he ask about my three-month residence? I'm not an easy liar.*

Edwy delivered the trio to the Lands Office. First witness, **John Lonsbury,** farmer of **6.9.16 W.** gave the following information. He'd known Mrs. Vane since **August 1882** on **NW 32.8.16 W.** Mr. Hiam crossed out each 'he' in the questions and wrote 'she'. For the troublesome item seven—"When absent from her homestead, where has she resided and what has been her occupation?" he supplied, **NE 32.8.16 with Mr. Criddle.** Elise thought it a rather ambiguous occupation, but Mr. Hiam didn't even pause. Of whom does her family consist? **Her statement is correct.** How much breaking has she done? **Her statement is correct.** *How curious, I haven't yet made any statements.*

They continued down the page: house, **16' by 18'** value $50.[6] He had **no interest in her application** and **yes,** he believed she acted in good faith in obtaining her entry. He signed under oath that all was true and correct in every particular.

It was her turn. Elise watched as her particulars were entered. **Elise Vane** in support of <u>his</u> application for a patent on **28.26.16.1 W.** *Hiam doesn't cross out 'his' as he did on Lonsbury's form. Does he think I can't read?* She gave her age as **49,** and post office, **Aweme.**

---

6 Homestead inspector reported value of house, $35.

2. Are you a British subject by birth or Naturalization? **German by birth—Resided in British Territory since 1864, was married to a British Subject.**

3. What is your trade or occupation? **Farmer**

4. When did you get entry for this homestead? **3 May '86**

5. When did you build your house thereon? **In March 1889**

6. When did you perfect your entry to your homestead by taking in your own person possession of the land and beginning continuous residence thereof? **Since 1882 on NW 32.8.16 W, have lived there continuously on NW 32.8.16 within Two miles.**

7. What part of each year since that date have you resided thereon? State each month. **Since 1882 on NW 32.8.16 W From the 15th of March '89 to about the 25th of June '89 and from the 17th of Nov. '89 to date—**

8. When absent from your homestead where have you resided and what has been your occupation? **Living on NE 32.8.16 W acting as a housekeeper for Mr. Criddle.**

9. Of whom does your family consist? . . .**3 sons and 2 daughters.** What portion of each year since that date have they resided upon it **The three sons have been doing the same residence as myself.**

They continued to the question, "Have you assigned or transferred or agreed to assign or transfer your homestead or any part thereof? If so which and to whom?"

She answered truthfully, **"No."** *I would never let my homestead slip through my fingers.*

Mr. Hiam read her the oath.

I, *Elise Vane*, do solemnly swear the answers to the forgoing questions are true and correct in every particular. . . .
That I obtained an entry, and claim a Patent for the same for my own benefit, and not in the interest or for the benefit of any other person or person whomsoever.
Sworn by me at Brandon this 24th day of February 1890 having been read over and explained to the said applicant.

She signed and moved back to make room for Mr. Criddle.

Mr. Hiam filled in **Percy Criddle** of **32.8.16.West**, in reference to the application of **Elise Vane** for Letter Patent.

1. What is your occupation? **Farmer**

2. How long have you known Elise Vane, the applicant in this case? **Since 1873.**

Elise flinched. *Why 1873? What happened to our four year engagement and the years we lived together in London?*

Mr. Hiam crossed out 'him' and added 'she'.

3. Was ~~he~~ she entitled to an entry for this quarter section? **Yes**

6. What portion of each year since that date has ~~he~~ she resided thereon? State each month. **Her statement is correct**

7. When absent from her homestead, where has ~~he~~ she resided, and what has been ~~his~~ her occupation? **On NW 32.8.16 with her as housekeeper.**

8. Of whom does ~~his~~ her family consist? **Her statement is correct.**

9. How much breaking . . .? **Her statement is correct.**

10. How many horned cattle . . .? **Has used mine.**

11. What size and value of house? **16 by 18 Value $50.**

16. Have you any interest, direct or indirect in this application? **No.**

17. Do you believe the claimant has acted in good faith? . . . **Yes.**

Mr. Criddle signed that his answers were true in every particular. Then, just as they were preparing to leave, the Homestead Inspector popped out of his office, "Mrs. Vane, I need to ask you a few questions. Please come in."

They followed him into his office. "The Commissioner asked me to get some information from you. What country were you born in, Mrs. Vane? Are you a British subject? There seems to be a problem. A letter claims you are an unmarried woman living with Mr. Criddle."

Clearly rattled, Elise tried to recall what had been said.

"I was born in Germany of German parents. I married an Englishman in 1864. My husband died in '74, before my youngest was born. I came to Canada in 1882 with five children."

Hiam's eyes shifted to Mr. Criddle, "Do you have something to add?"

"She had both a marriage and her husband's death certificate. Lost them in a trunk in Winnipeg – I went down the street – when I returned, it was nowhere to be found."

Elise felt her stomach tighten as he went on, "I have known her family for the past thirty years. I believe she was married. That's what she said on her application, swore to it under oath. Mrs. Vane has been housekeeper for us since '74 or '75 and has always borne a good character. Furthermore if you care to question Mr. Lonsbury, here with us – or Mr. McManes, or any other neighbour – they will all tell you Mrs. Vane is a respectable woman and a bona fide settler."

Obviously angry he continued, "Let me have a good look at that letter and I'll find the lying Canadian who slanders her."

Elise pulled her mantle around her face. Somehow she made her way to the street where Edwy helped her into the wagon and tucked the blankets around her. They made a brief stop at Bower's where the $122.83 bill was extended another month with $1.10 interest.

The temperature had dropped to a bitter 29 below by the time they headed out of town for the long drive home. Edwy alternated his hands on the reins, while the two men settled down under wraps. They talked until Lonsbury dozed off leaving Mr. Criddle to concentrate on the allegation written so elegantly. He was so engrossed he didn't even notice his nose was freezing.

Elise, humiliated and shaken, kept hers under the blankets, thankful for privacy. The old feelings of betrayal overwhelmed her. *To be caught like this is my worst nightmare. Am I to be hung out for all to scorn? What will become of me? I need the good Shepherd to guide me through this dark valley.* . . . As the horses trotted ever onward, a phrase emerged from the chaos of her thoughts: *"Ich bin immer bei euch, jeden Tag, bis zum Ende der Welt. Lo, I am with you always, even unto the end of the world.* Miles later, feeling more settled, she prayed, *Lord Jesus help me forgive.* . . . Folding back the blankets, she watched the sun slide down the steely, cloudless sky. Edwy's form grew darker and she heard his occasional, "Kch, kch," as he encouraged Jess and Dolly to keep up their steady pace. With only a sliver of a moon, the stars shimmered so brightly she might have caught them in her hands, had she been willing to take them from under the blankets. In time the intense cold crept through her blankets first to her feet, and then her hands. They pained so intensely she could think of nothing else until her ordeal ended with Edwy's "Whoa!" Climbing down from the wagon, she hobbled stiffly inside and hurriedly fried up some potatoes for the hungry men. She dreamed that night of pouring tea for an 'unknown' neighbour.

◦◦◦

Even as their sleigh had pulled away, Mr. Cook began his letter to the Commissioner.

> . . . *I beg to inform you that I have today seen Mrs. Vane at Brandon and obtained the following information from her viz.; she was born in Germany of German parentage and married an Englishman in 1864, and resided there up to the time she came to this country in 1882.*
>
> *Her husband died in 1874, leaving five children behind. Her marriage certificate and certificate of her husband's death were lost in Winnipeg in 1882.*
>
> *Mr. Criddle of Sect. 32 who is a <u>thoroughly reliable man</u> states that Mrs. Vane has been housekeeper for him since 1874 or 1875 and that he has known her family for the past thirty years, and that he believes her to have been married, and that she has always borne a good character, and that her statement contained in her application for patent dated today is correct.*
>
> *You will observe that in the said application she swears she was married. Messrs Lounsbury [sic], McManus and other settlers in the vicinity say that Mrs. Vane is a respectable woman and that she is a bona fide settler.*
>
> *The anonymous letter is herewith attached.*
>
> *I have the honour to be Sir, your obedient servant. R.S. Cook*

Hiam was also preparing Elise's papers and recommending her application.

Two days later and still seething, Mr. Criddle worked on a draft for the same gentleman. He spoiled not a few sheets of paper, adding and subtracting words.

> *I went to the L [and] off [ice] at Bdn on Monday as a witness for my house-keeper Mrs. Vane who was applying for her homestead Patent.*
>
> *I there saw a letter signed 'Nemo' addressed to you and containing a certain scurrilous statement concerning the said Mrs. Vane. – I shall esteem it a favour if you will allow me to have this letter as though I can well guess its author I should like to show it to those who can identify the hand writing.*
>
> *– When this has been done I will send you 'Nemo's real name* ~~that you will be able to ascertain~~ *when you will be quickly able to ascertain the value of his com. If you cause enquiries to be made among* **any** *of his neighbours. Mrs. Vane has acted as housekeeper for my late mother, myself and my wife for many years* ~~to our complete satisfaction~~ *and I trust she will have better luck with her application this time than she had before when through want of knowledge she failed to satisfy the requirements of the law.* ~~She has put in a hard time at her place this winter and doubtless the circumstances of her case will influence you in granting her recommend with as little delay as possible.~~[7]

He read it over, made some adjustments, wrote out his final copy, and dropped it off at the post office.

Private Collection

Mr. Smith stamped the letter March 3, 1890 and filed it as 19388. When the rest of the file arrived from Brandon, he mumbled, quietly at first, but ever more loudly, as he went down the page, "Well, **now** the lady is not English, but

---

7 Draft letter in Private collection. Letter # 19388 with the Homestead records.

German—lived in a British territory and married a British subject. . . . I wonder what territory—India? Jamaica? Sugar? Maybe she's a disgraced daughter of one of those big sugar manufacturers in London. And this time we get honesty. She's a farmer that does housekeeping on the side for Mr. Criddle—convenient for him. Her sons have been in residence with her for these last cold months . . . interesting! How did the Criddles manage without their housekeeper at this time of year, with fires to tend and all? She has no livestock of any kind—rather slim going I'd say."

What have her witnesses to say? He skimmed down Lonsbury's page, "Nothing here."

He picked up Criddle's page. "He's known her since 1874. Didn't he say 30 years somewhere? She resides in his home—his housekeeper. He allows her sons to use his animals to work her place. I'm thinking that they might work his place as well. Not much of a house at $50. I see he has no interest in this application, direct or indirect. Well, well. Mmm."

He picked up Elise's form again, turned it over and read, "I recommend the forgoing application for Patent, believing that the homestead requirements of the Dominion Lands Act have, in this case, been complied with."

Indignant, the Commissioner glowered and shifted his gaze to secretary and said, "Hiam signed this application just as he did last summer. I didn't accept it then and I don't now." He took the referral form and wrote while he talked 'Not entitled, 2nd entry'.

On March 1, Mr. Criddle made another trip to Brandon on a load of wood. Worried about losing his 'trophy', he found a string to pull that would cause a change of heart in the Winnipeg Lands office. He collected: $2 from Isabel, $10 from Minnie, and a paltry $2 from the boys' whole load of wood. Purchases were held to a minimum.

Boots for Alice	$3.00
Matches	$0.25
Oil	$0.35
Currants	$0.50
Apples	$0.50
C. Beef	$1.00
Soda	$0.10
Tea	$1.00
Postage	$0.08
Sugar	$1.00

Mr. Criddle's strategy worked. Three days later the Commissioner passed the quarter section of sandy land, within the two-mile limit, over to his second in command muttering, "It's not worth my time to fight, but I am not going to put my name on this deal."

The word 'Acting' was inserted before Commissioner and the form approving Elise Vane's homestead was on its way to the Department of the Interior, Ottawa.

Back in town 11 days later, they collected a box from England for Mrs. Criddle along with a list of items she required. Isabel contributed $3—Minnie none.

Cash had to be found somewhere or Mr. Criddle and his country estate would come to a humiliating end. He went over the possibilities. *Wood? Bottom has fallen out of the market. Eggs? Hens just beginning to lay again after the dark days of winter; need eggs to put under a sitting hen to hatch. The boys sent out to work? No, need them to build a shanty to fulfill my own new homestead requirement.* Percy was still scheming, when he received the 'Nemo' letter he'd requested in order to identify the author. But the letter also included the statement: "I may add that Mrs. Vane's application has received the Commissioner's approval and that a certificate of recommendation was forwarded to her address on the 5ᵗʰ instant.

Mr. Criddle no longer needed Nemo's identity; it was cash he had to find.

For her part, Elise was elated. A final search on the land for prior claims came up empty so her homestead was assured. But a sad discovery cut off her joy. Faithful Turk, her companion as she went about the morning chores, found some poisoned coyote bait. Never again would he wag his tail in greeting. She and the tearful children buried their friend down by the gardens.

On March 26 Mr. Criddle took another walk to Brandon. He wanted an absolute guarantee that nothing would delay Elise's homestead. Mr. Sifton obliged, "Get Mrs. Vane and a witness to sign this and we'll send it off to Ottawa to have her Patent sent directly to us. No more worry."

At Bower's he picked up tobacco, sugar, matches, beef, and soap, and added the cost to the bill with a promise to pay next month. He also extended Adam's harness bill to April 26. That night he confided in his diary: "No money to be got anywhere — pretty well stuck up."

As soon as the boys completed his shanty on NE 4.8.16, he took out Sifton's form and told Elise, "It's in your best interest to have a lawyer look after your Patent. Just sign this affidavit."

To the Minister of the Interior, and all Others
Know by all Men by these Presents that
I ***Elise Vane*** *of the County of Norfolk in the province of Manitoba widow,*
For good and valuable reasons have nominated, constituted, and appointed, and by these presents do nominate and appoint CLIFFORD SIFTON, of the city of Brandon in the county of Brandon, my true and legal Attorney, irrevocable for me and in my name to ask, demand and receive from the government of Canada, the said minister of the interior . . . . , letters of Patent from the Crown, and all deeds, . . . relating to the Title of the ***North West quarter*** of Section ***Twenty eight*** . . . to give good and sufficient receipt, discharge and acquaintance therefore, and to appoint a substitute to act in his [sic] place in receiving the said Letters Patent. . .

As witness my hand and seal this Eleventh day of April AD 1890.
Signed sealed and delivered in the presence of

Edwy Vane   Elise Vane

⁎⁂⁎

Mr. Criddle set the boys seeding, and then left on foot for Brandon to deliver the document. Next day on his return the river had changed; melt water stretched along both sides of the centre ice. He was obliged to step from land to water to the ice, then from the ice through water to reach the bank. His boots squished the rest of that long walk and everyone heard his howls as Mrs. Criddle pulled his boots and socks free from the blisters.

Meanwhile Sifton mailed Elise's affidavit to the Honourable Minister of the Interior in Ottawa.

Re: NW ¼ 28.8.16 W/m

Elise Vane
Dear Sir,

> *We beg to enclose a power of attorney to receive the patent for the above land and to request that the same will be forwarded as therein directed when issued.*
> *We are sir, your obedient . . .*

A reply affirmed the matter. "The patent in question is now in the course of preparation and will be forwarded to Mr. Sifton's address, provided Elise Vane does not countermand the above-mentioned order."

Elise expected her patent every mail. She was serving tea when Mr. Criddle told her, "Mrs. Criddle tells me our food supplies are running low. Mr. Bower won't give us any – but we don't need to starve – I've arranged for you to see Mr. Kirchhoffer – he'll give you a three hundred dollar mortgage on your homestead – that should tide us over until harvest."[8]

Elise turned white, *Ach du liebe Zeit! Dear God in Heaven!* Retreating to the stove, she clutched the edge of the warming oven and hung there limply, her nose just above the pots and steaming kettle. *A mortgage on my precious land and I don't even have it yet! What about my dreams? $300! How can I ever pay back such a debt? Lieber Gott! What about my sons?*

Ten expectant faces around the table turned to her as if it were up to her to keep food on their plates. *I'm trapped! If I say "No, we'll have an eruption equal to Vesuvius."*

---

8   Kirchhoffer moved to Manitoba 1883. He founded the Plum Creek settlement and the town of Souris, Manitoba. He practiced law in Brandon and was member from West Brandon in the Legislature of Manitoba before 1890.

Before she could respond, Mrs. Criddle, who loved peace, said sharply, "Ungrateful woman! Look at all we have done for you. You wouldn't have that land without my husband's help."

The words stung like a whip. *Am I ungrateful? Perhaps I am.* Her sons kept their heads down having learned never to cross Mr. Criddle. *I have no one to support me. If I refuse, what then?*

⊶⦿⊷

Thus, Elise was borne off to Brandon, April 24, for her date with Kirchhoffer. The ice having gone out of the Assiniboine, they went via Bruner's Crossing. She forgot her troubles for a few minutes and clung anxiously to the side of the wagon as the swift-flowing water rose over the wheel hubs. But they made it, and the straining team pulled them up the bank to level ground once more. And on they went.

She could have enjoyed the lovely spring air, the songs of meadowlarks, the greening of the poplars. But the beauty went unnoticed. *Who is this Kirchhoffer? Why go to him when Sifton is looking after my homestead patent? Does Kirchhoffer know that I don't even have the land yet?* She gasped, *but Sifton does . . . . He might not approve a mortgage.*

Her thoughts ran wild . . . *Could I escape in Brandon? Mama told me my old Grossmutter got away . . . but she had a refuge. Where could I go? I have no friends to turn to . . . Without a cent, who would take me in.* Her thoughts turned round and round like the wheels on the wagon.

She steeled herself for the ordeal, climbed down, and straightened her skirts. As Mr. Criddle reached for the latch on the office door he saw the note: **GONE DUCK HUNTING**.

Finding his voice he said, "Kirchhoffer said 1 o'clock – he forgot – twenty miles for this!" Desperation spawned a new plan. He whipped out a paper and wrote a note giving the lawyer authority to conduct Elise's business. She signed it right there on the street with people passing. "Kirchhoffer won't refuse your note since the fault is his."

Then assured of the cash, he shopped: Adams, brass for the harness $35; then to Bower's

Beef	$1.00	Nails	$0.20
Sugar	$1.00	Window Glass	$0.75
Tea	$1.00	3 Boards	$0.70
Matches	$0.15	Flour	$2.35
Currants	$0.50	2 bgs 2nds	$2.50
Broom	$0.60	Tobacco	$0.30
Oil	$0.25	Coal Oil	$0.45
Shot	$0.30	Bran	$0.20
Powder	$0.10	2 Combs	$0.30
Onion Seed	$0.25	5 Cups and Saucers	$0.50

Boots for the workers: Mr. Criddle (size 7), Edwy (7), Harry (6), Norman (6), Evelyn (4), Stewart (5), Cecil (3) - 7 pairs of boots - Total $17.00

The stores were loaded into the wagon and they proceeded to pick up Aweme's new teacher. Edwy helped Miss Hooper up beside him on the front seat and they waved to Mr. Criddle. Elise, her heart full of grief, sat among the supplies. *Hope may be hiding somewhere in the universe, but I have no strength to consider where that might be.* Mindlessly, she allowed the miles to soothe her worn body and shattered spirit.

⸻ ❧ ⸻

As soon as Mr. Criddle saw them off he called on Minnie for his money. When she passed him $10 he said, "You still owe me four dollars from last month."

Next morning at Kirchhoffer's he hit another snag. "It's a good sum of money for a lawyer like me to put together in an hour. You'll have to come in again next week to finalize the deal and pick up the cash."

Thoroughly disgusted; Mr. Criddle's mood didn't improve over the 18 mile walk home. The delay of a week mattered little to Elise for her money flowed the following Thursday.[9]

Proceeds of Mortgage South Farm $300.00
less $24.00 cost and $6.00 Trust and Loan Finances $270.00
His own "Expenses" 1.20
Billy Greer on account horses 1st installment 60.00
Smith and Sherriff on account Plough and Binder 50.00
A. M. Patton balance of interest on Loan 17.40
Renewed Bower's note due May 10th for 3 months 3.15
10 Bushels of seed oats 10.80
Postage .15, Tabac 1.00, pipes .10, Pins .50, cloats[10] .15, Boot Laces .50
Stopped at McVey's: for seed wheat. $52.50

Home again, the jubilant Mr. Criddle crowed, "Got the creditors off my back. Sunday is coming – Tennis anyone?"

⸻ ❧ ⸻

Elise's life cycled on: breakfast, dinner, tea, washing, mopping, mending – never ending. Mrs. Criddle's delicate state told Elise another baby was on the way. Children had always been her joy but the everlasting drudgery, taxed not only her health, but her loving spirit.

Fortunately, her brother's letter reminded her yet again that she was loved.

Mannheim, April 9, 1890
Dear Elise!
    It is now more than a fourth of a year since I have written you (and we have received no letters from you anymore, nor any news) I hope it is not illness that

---

9 Diary and account book records in Criddle file at the Archives of Manitoba.
10 Victorian medication for a sore throat.

causes this for I read in the papers that also in Canada the Influenza was on the rampage and have often worried that you too were suffering from it. May that not have been the case! For it is an evil sickness, that causes suffering even later on.

Elise nodded. *I know about influenza alright. I'm still weak. . . . Any good news?*

In Heidelberg they have built a cableway from Kremeneck to the castle and the Molkenkur, which was opened a few days ago.

She visualized the ramparts of the castle above the town. *Imagine having a ride all the way up to the Molkenkur. Percy and I had such fun climbing. . . .*
Curiosity led her eyes back to the letter.

Max Sauer, whom you will remember, has been installed as pastor half a year ago in Neckarau, which lies at half an hour distance from here. He's changed, I would not have recognized him. He has visited us a couple of times together with his wife and has asked me to give you his greetings.

She smiled. *Remember Max? . . . Of course: clever, witty, and loved to sing. Was in my confirmation class . . . . So, he's Pastor Sauer. Memories are my treasures.*

<hr>

Mr. Criddle's shanty had been completed, and with the warm spring weather he began his three-month-residence necessary to fulfill the last homestead requirement. The long evenings were ideal for reading—*Bleak House* followed by *David Copperfield*. He hardly knew which book he liked better. One morning he arrived home so early Elise had not yet cooked the porridge. "A blessed bird woke me soon after daylight – got inside somehow and was endeavouring to fly out through the windowpane. It couldn't – so got up to liberate it. Couldn't sleep, so I dressed and came home."

Elise added another stick to the fire and compared their so-called three month's residences. *I rose early the only morning I spent in my little house, to walk back to make the porridge; he comes early and waits for me to fill his bowl.*

As soon as the boys finished seeding, they were sent to cut wood to finance feed grain for their horses and chickens. Mr. Criddle speculated, "Crops really growing at last and with luck we may yet pull through all right – but times are preciously anxious."

The boys had just left for Brandon with their 14th load of wood when Mr. Criddle approached Elise, "I need some salt. Want to do a little experiment, might improve our chances of good crops."

He mumbled something about hating Greek and Latin as he went out. Elise shook her head. *As I recall, the Romans slaughtered the inhabitants of Carthage and burned the city. And then to make sure nothing would ever grow there again, scattered salt on the land. If it doesn't do as Percy expects, I'll not hear about it again.* That evening the gentleman wrote in his diary:

Sprinkled about 3 pints salt on Seven Sisters Field this morning (just after dew had dried off) over a patch of wheat (about 2 in. high) 16 yards by 8 yards – near NW corner – 20 yards from corner – The wheat on either side being about same thickness – must watch results.

⁓

Minnie took a new position at the Northern Pacific Hotel in Wawanesa, close enough to get home with a friend for a Saturday overnight. Having her cheery daughter gave Elise energy to prepare for the expected folks from Sutcliffe's corner[11] coming for Sunday's tennis and cricket. In spite of aching feet Elise served the guests, and still managed to notice Norman watching Cannon Cooper sketch.[12] Mr. Köhler, always the photographer, took a picture of the boys.

Sketch: Cannon J. Cooper

Back Row: Edwy, Stuart, Harry, Evelyn, Front: Cecil, Norman

11 Coopers, Köhlers, Husbands, Sutcliffes.
12 Rev'd Cannon Cooper, visiting his son from England in 1890, made a sketch of St. Albans.

Meanwhile, on May 1, 1890, John Joseph McGee in Ottawa signed Mrs. Vane's patent for her land. Sifton sent it to Aweme and Elise read as she expected; ". . . unto the said Elise Vane and her heirs forever . . ."[13] Instead of elation, however, she felt despair. *Will my mortgaged homestead bind me, and my heirs, to be obedient servants forever?*

444

SHORT FORM.

JOHN J. McGEE
DEPUTY GOVERNOR.

CANADA.

Victoria, by the Grace of God, of the United Kingdom of Great Britain and Ireland, QUEEN, Defender of the Faith, &c., &c., &c.

To all to whom these Presents shall come—GREETING:

Whereas the Lands, hereinafter described, are part of the lands known as "Dominion Lands" and mentioned in an Act of the Parliament of Canada, passed in the forty-sixth year of Our Reign, and known as the "Dominion Lands Act."

And Whereas Elise Vane, of Township Eight Range Sixteen West of the Principal Meridian in the Province of Manitoba in Our Dominion of Canada, Farmer ...

... applied for a grant of the said lands and her claim to such grant having been duly investigated by Us, she has been found duly entitled thereto.

Now Know Ye, that by these Presents We do grant, convey and assure, unto the said Elise Vane, her heirs and assigns forever, all th... Parcel or Tract of land, situate, lying and being in the Eighth Township in the Sixteenth Range West of the Principal Meridian in the Province of Manitoba, in Our Dominion of Canada, and being composed of The North West quarter of Section Twenty ... of the said Township, containing by admeasurement one hundred and sixty acres, more or less.

To have and to hold the said Parcel or Tract of Land, unto the said Elise Vane, her heirs and assigns for ever; ...

GIVEN under the Great Seal of Canada—Witness, John Joseph McGee, Esquire, Deputy of Our Right Trusty and Well Beloved, the Right Honourable Sir Frederick Arthur Stanley, Baron Stanley of Preston, in the County of Lancaster, in the Peerage of Great Britain and Ireland, Knight Grand Cross of Our Most Honourable Order of the Bath, Governor General of Canada.

At OTTAWA, this First day of May in the year of Our Lord, one thousand eight hundred and ninety and in the fifty-third year of Our Reign.

BY COMMAND,

... Secretary of State.

A. M. BURGESS,
Deputy of the Minister of the Interior.

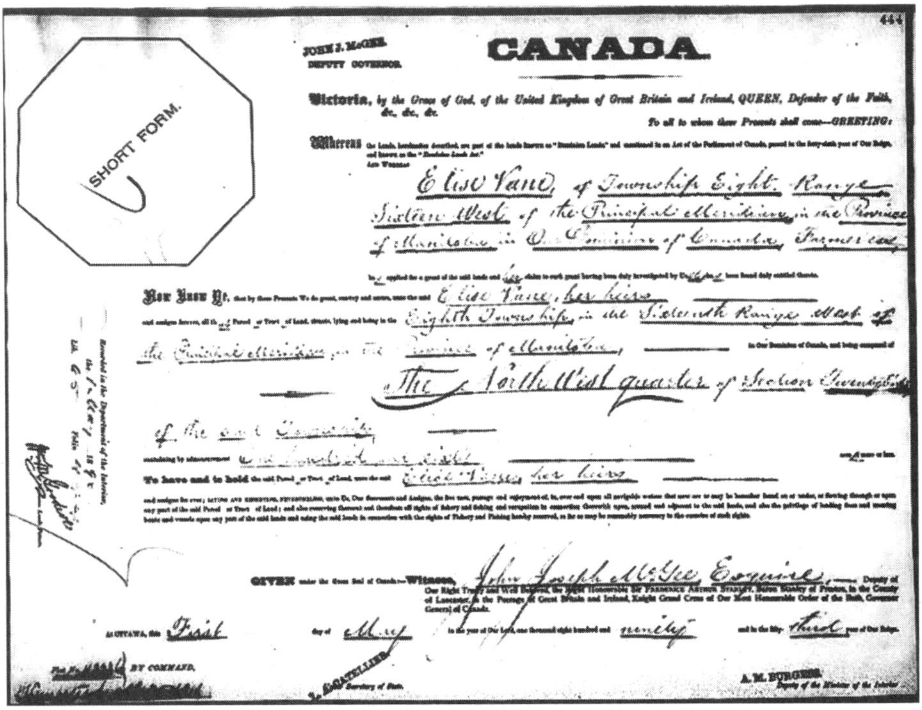

National Archives Ottawa

13 Patent: Elise Vane. Volume 65, Folio 444, Microfilm reel number: C-5989, Library and Archives Canada.

Chapter Fourteen

The Debtor

Elise's homestead document was tacked to the wall above the bed in her tiny room above the stairs. Achieving her dream of land for her sons had changed nothing. Sometimes she fancied it whispering, "You owe, you owe, a debt you owe."

I cannot see how this will end. But if God is willing, good will yet come to us. In any case, nothing comes from brooding. I must keep up—everyone depends on me.

Mrs. Criddle, being in the family way took her breakfast in bed, combining family time with her children's lessons.[1] Elise did her best to have meals ready— early and late—for the young men seeding another hoped-for bumper crop. The long days had her wishing for Isabel's help. *I'll have a busy summer tending Mrs. Criddle . . . but it seems my daughter's wages are more important than my need for her help. If only I had boots or shoes like the girls to relieve my aching feet.*

The pain reminded Elise of the sisters in an old tale. *They had sore feet, but it was their own doing. If I remember correctly, the wife of a rich man fell ill and called her only daughter to her sickbed; "Dear child, if you are good and say your prayers faithfully, our dear Lord will always help you, and I shall look down from heaven and always be with you." Then the mother closed her eyes and passed away. Her father soon remarried. The stepmother and stepsisters were unkind to the girl making her do all manner of dirty work—called her Aschputtel.[2] When she asked to go with them to a ball at the palace, they threw peas into the fireplace and told her to pick them out—every single pea.* Elise paused; *I've not told this story to the children . . . much too gruesome. It was my sore feet that got me remembering. The sisters cut off their toes so they could fit into the tiny slipper the prince found after his beautiful princess ran away. He carried it from home to home, vowing to marry the girl who could wear it. My feet may be big but I'm not willing to chop off my toes to get into Mrs. Criddle's hand-me-downs. Truly though, if I had something for my feet . . . I can't help envying Mrs. Criddle every time she gets a new pair of boots.[3] I wish she would order a pair*

---

1 Criddle, Maida.

2 Brothers Grimm, *Household Tales.* J. M. Dent co., 1906. p. 80 'Aschputtel' (lowly kitchen maid) translated Cinderella. Inscription in the book: *"Violet from Mama with love, Christmas, 1908."*

3 Account book. 1890: March 11, Boots A [Alice] $3.00; September 4, Boots A. $3.00. Dec. 19, Boots A. $3.00.

for me. Seems I can wish all I want . . . but as the old saying goes, "If wishes were horses, then beggars would ride." Forcing her weary body, step-by-step up to bed, she gathered her day into a prayer. *Dear God in heaven, in your mercy, give me the forbearance to keep going.*

On July 17 her boys sold 11 bags of new potatoes for $16, and a load of wood for $3. With $.40 for asparagus, $1.50 for rhubarb, and $13 from their sisters, they paid for the household supplies, but not the $17 twine bill. When not on the road, they hayed. Elise hardly had time to wish Edwy well on his 19th birthday.

One hot sultry day, while the boys sweated in the hayfield, Mr. Criddle went with Swaisland to Sutcliffe's for tennis. They cooled off with a swim in the river and then dropped in on Lonsbury. Mrs. Lonsbury, toddler underfoot, was busy with the afternoon chores and thinking of the evening meal for her boarder, Aweme's teacher. That evening Elise overheard him tell his wife, "Looked as if Mrs. Lonsbury had swallowed a thunderbolt – had on the exact same shambly – worn-out half blucher[4] bred shoes, two sizes too big, she had on when I first saw her eighteen months ago – one couldn't help seeing 'em everlastingly – dreadful – truly dreadful."

Remembering the new bride, Elise thought, *her dreams of being a happy farmer's wife have come to this. Now with a little one, she cooks for her husband plus a 'city girl' and does it all, chores and garden, with no extra help.* Mr. Criddle went on to criticize her little boy. "Young Lonsbury looks like an enormous ill-shaped lump of dough which wants rolling out to cover some gigantic pie with. His ma – clearly thinks the world would cease to wag were anything to happen to him."

Elise imagined Mrs. Lonsbury tending her child, then serving Mr. Criddle. *He's not used to waiting . . . expects me to jump right up to serve him.*[5]

A severe frost early in August blackened the leaves of the beans and citrons and still ripening wheat. "Next time," Mr. Criddle told the boys, "we'll make bonfires to keep the frost away."

The frost hastened the harvest. Edwy sharpened the knives on the binder, oiled all its moving parts, assembled the canvasses, and spent a frustrating day trying to adjust the knotter. The wheat was borne up and gathered; the needle appeared to connect with the twine, but the bundle fell loose to the ground. He told Mr. Criddle "Can't afford to waste another day. I'll take it to Smith Sherriff tomorrow. Maybe the pinion wheel on the bill hook is worn. Might need a new part."

---

4 Laced shoes with eyelets sewn from a single leather vamp, named after a 19th century Prussian general wanting better footwear for his troops and adopted throughout Europe.
5 Oral tradition claimed the neighbours were amazed at the way Mrs. Vane jumped to serve Mr. Criddle.

The dealership, for a price, sent their expert to the farm and harvesting got underway. Elise was preparing their evening meal when Mr. Criddle dropped a letter on the table as he passed through to his room. She hurried over and picked it up. *I've been so anxious for news. . . .*

Mannheim, August 2, 1890

Dear Elise!

> *Your dear letter of June 18th I have received. We were happy to learn from it that all of you are well. May heaven grant that your expectations for a good crop may also be realized. We are just reading so much about all the tornadoes in America that do a lot of harm. Hopefully you have not had to suffer as a result of them.*

She felt relieved. *Everything seems fine there and we didn't have a tornado.*

> *Our two oldest girls are, during the vacation, at Aunt Rivola's in Heidelberg and will come home on Monday. Julchen accompanied Aunt Amalie, who was in Heidelberg, to Karlsruhe and will stay with Carl for 14 days. So we are alone, but Mariechen has a lot of work since the landlord has agreed to have two of our rooms papered, which was very necessary, for we have lived here for 15 years without having anything done to the rooms.*

Elise hadn't met Amalie but appreciated the way she supported Friedrich's daughters.[6] *Too bad my brothers live away from their home town and in different cities.*

> *Dear Elise, on the 7th of September of this year it will be 25 years since Mariechen and I got married and, naturally, we are going to have a small celebration. I wish that you could be present. Of course we will remember you on that day as well and will drink to your health. I am enclosing 2 dollars so that you too can, on that day, celebrate with us. Drink a glass of wine or whatever is customary in that country, even if it would be only an extra good coffee as a Sunday to drink to our health.*

She closed her eyes. *I can't remember the last time I even smelled coffee brewing. Good Baden wine will never reach me, but I have an imagination, and on the seventh of September I'll transform my chipped cup into a wine goblet. . . . I'll drink to your health with sparkling clean 'Adam's ale' from the well.*

> *Most likely Mariechen's Uncle Georg from Riga will come here for that day, for he was present at our wedding 25 years ago. Is it possible that we have been married 25 years already? Time has raced by and it seems the older you become the faster time goes. I would have liked to send you more (money) but my budget does not allow it, so use the little as I suggested.*

> *Maria and I have decided to have a photograph made of ourselves on our (silver) wedding day and so we shall send you one.*

Elise smiled. *Imagine! A photo after almost 30 years! Does Marie still do her hair the same? My brother's prized beard? Friedrich never writes about such things. I don't*

---

6 May 19, 1881. Marriage; Amalie Burgweger to Carl Harrer, senior financial advisor for the Dukedom. Traubuch, St. Peter and Providence, Heidelberg. Band 36, p. 142.

give him details of my life either. Even if I had a photo of myself, I'd not send it. They'd see how old I have become. 'Eine alte Frau' is what I am. . . . Yet it seems only yesterday we were there for their wedding. I was so happy in the company of my English fiancé. Percy and I had been engaged for two years already and we were planning our own big day. But as soon as the festivities were over he had important business in London. He waved and called as the train pulled away; "I'll write soon." [7]

Percy and Elise, engagement photo.

A voice broke into her reverie –

"Mrs. Criddle will not be out for tea – her Aunt Louisa passed away."[8]

The little girls soon gathered around Mama Dutcheen, "Papa said that Louisa is dead. Mama's crying. Will we still get our boxes?"

Elise soothed their fears and asked them to help her by setting the table for tea.

Two days later, the morning of August 19, she had her hands full as both midwife and housekeeper assisting her third little Criddle—Talbot, make his debut into the world. Caring for both mother and newborn kept her so busy, Harry's 18th birthday on the 25th almost slipped by without his mother's good wishes.

⸰⟞⟑⟊⟍⸰

The summer of 1890 was exceptional—rainy cool days between good hot, growing weather. Hopes were high, even considering a late spring frost, and the early one August. When the sun shone, Edwy traded off the horses with the oxen to keep the binder running, cutting as many as ten acres in a single day. Mr. Criddle estimated his 91 acres of wheat, 12¼ of oats, and 3¼ of barley would feed the livestock and end the money shortage. But, until that cash rolled in, Edwy and Harry marketed—potatoes $2, rhubarb $.25, and citrons $2.95. Isabel added a dollar to their five as she joined them for her return to the farm to prepare for Mr. Tulk's arrival.

---

7 Percy returned to London spring of 1863 after their engagement and from then on visited periodically. Friedrich married Marie Bauer, Sept. 7, 1865, in St. Peter and Providence. Stadtarchiv, Heidelberg.
8 Louisa Nicol died July 11, 1890. Alice was 11 when her mother Marion Nicol died; 18 when her father, Fredrick Nicol died. She lived with her aunt and uncle and cousins, George, and twins, Henry and Louisa until her marriage.

The very next day a letter from the gentleman upset those plans, "We are making changes at Firfield and I must be here to consult with the architect. It is doubtful if I will get away this fall."

From an unhappy chorus of disappointment, Elise heard, "Minnie only sent $8 of the $13 owing – Dico must go back now and find a new place in Brandon."

Fortunately for Elise, with the threshers still to feed, the threat wasn't carried out.

Firfiield, Addlestone, Surrey

The drizzly weather culminated September 6th, in a harvester's nightmare. Stalking from window, to door, to window in frenzied despair, Mr. Criddle moaned, "A terror – rain, rain, all day – hail. Our whole crop is going to glory."

When Sunday morning dawned, they found every stook scattered about on the wet ground. The boys spent the day picking up the soaking, battered sheaves and Elise heard no mention of Friedrich and Marie's anniversary. Unbeknown to them, she went on the wings of her imagination across the ocean to join the festivities. She sampled the festive Black Forest cake, sipped the sparkling red wine, toasted the happy couple, and sang with her family to her heart's content.

❦

Isabel stayed on helping her mother with the cooking, but was not particular about washing Talbot's 'nappies'. The cold rainy weather finally broke into Indian summer and gave the boys the opportunity to cut and stack a second crop of hay. Criddle's name had been added to Elder's list to be threshed and when the outfit arrived in the community, Mr. Criddle noted Bruner's wheat went 19 bushels per acre, Lonsbury's 21. He hoped for better. But the rains returned, and the harvesters sat around talking and playing cards. On one such dreary day, to everyone's astonishment, Mr. Tulk's hired rig pulled up. Yet, even that esteemed gentleman couldn't change the weather or curb Mr. Criddle's bad mood. Elise kept her courage up by waiting for Friedrich and Marie's anniversary photo.

It came at last, and she held it up to the light. . . . *How beautiful they are!* . . . Then to keep from weeping, she laid it aside to read about their big day.

Mannheim, September 28, 1890

Dear Elise!

I wrote you August 2. As I told you in the letter we celebrated our 25th anniversary on Sept. 7, thanks be to God, in good health. We were very happy that

Friedrich's and Maria's
25th anniversary

day, many of our relatives from far away showed up, even Mariechen's Uncle Georg from Riga, Russia with his wife had come, which gave us great joy, we had not seen them in the last five years.

We were made happy by many gifts and flowers. From my colleagues we received a lovely porcelain dinner set of 70 pieces and from my principals we received a leather case containing 12 of each: silver spoons, forks and knives, very heavy and expensive, with a dedication written in gold letters, everything bearing monograms. This proof of recognition has given us great joy.

Elise could hardly imagine such fine gifts. *Such generous friends . . . Once, long ago, I too had six lovely silver spoons. . . . And Anna embroidered her parents a lovely runner for the piano . . . Elsa, another for the sofa. They can be proud of their daughters.*

We regretted very much that you and Percy could not be present. We thought of you a lot and remembered how gay we had all been at our wedding 25 years ago. We drank to your health again.

She looked away. *Oh Friedrich. You didn't mean to hurt . . . I remember you made a wonderful toast to our upcoming wedding. . . .* She wiped away tears, finished his letter and then took up the photo. *Older, yes, but still my dear brother. Please say my name; it's been such a long time since anyone called me Elise. Say it your way, gentle and comforting, "E-l-ee-z-ə."* [9]

Suddenly she realized the time and jumped up. *Better hurry with tea. . . .* She folded the letter and stood it with the photo on the shelf. *Maybe tomorrow the clouds will roll up and move out, leaving the sun to dry things out so I can send a good report on our harvest.*

Good weather did return and the men went back to work. Edwy hitched his team to the separator to move it to the next farm. At exactly the same time young Horatio Bruner was preparing the steam engine and lifted the safety vent—PSHSH, right beside Edwy's team. Startled, they fled. Edwy held fast to the lines, but lost his balance. Mr. Criddle rushed to the body lying in the wake of the wagon, fearing the worst. Everyone held their breath until he announced,

---

9 Pronunciation in German: Three syllables. The first E is short as in met, final e sounds as the a in abut.

"He's breathing." Following considerable prodding he got up, "He fell at an angle apparently. One hand went under the steel lugs. No broken bones, he'll be alright eventually."[10]

Young Jimmy Fortune helped Edwy onto a wagon for home. Mr. Criddle turned on the perceived cause of the accident—young Brunner, ". . . * * * . . ."

Meanwhile, the horses had hauled their heavy load only a short distance across the field; Harry took his brother's place and threshing carried on.

Elise met the casualty at the door. *Oh mein Gott!*

She ever so carefully washed away the dirt, bandaged the hand, and got him up to bed. *Thank God for a miracle. He just needs time to mend.*

The outfit eventually reached the Criddles.

N. Farm Wheat (Criddle's new homestead, 40 acres)	650 bushels
Home Farm Wheat (13 acres)	212 bushels
S. Farm wheat (Elise's homestead, 37 acres)	552 bushels
	Total 1414 bushels

They would have oats to keep the horses trotting; their wheat was as follows:

Although only 15 ½ bushels per acre, it appeared to Elise to be a lot of wheat. Within a few days Edwy was hauling grain to market in spite of his injured hand. Harry, now considered a man, went to Lonsbury's to earn 15 dollars a month. The rest of the workforce settled down to digging all those potatoes and turnips and racing against the coming frost to get them safely inside the refurbished root cellar.[11] That done, Mr. Criddle reassigned them to the bush, "I've made a deal — wood for cash — against the harness loan."

After the first snowfall, when prairie fires were less of a threat, they cleared and burned more swamp for hay. The gentlemen bagged eight chickens one day,

---

10 Oct. 21, 1890.
11 Two hundred sixty bushels, for the table and animals.

five ducks on another. Roasted to perfection, the mallards made a fitting feast for Mr. Tulk's natal day.[12] Disappointed yet again in not getting a deer, he departed for the green fields of England.

Edwy's first load of wheat rated "No. 1", and sold for 75¢ a bushel. That $32 along with Mr. Tulk's board of $25 would change hands quickly. Axle grease, grain bags, and boots had been added to Mrs. Criddle's list:

Frazer's ($40.33 owing) for:

2 blankets $9.00	30 yards of cotton and 30 yards flannel $10.50
3 pairs of mitts - boys $3.25	20 yards of shirting $3.00 -- $16.50
Buttons: $0.80	Axle grease $0.15
Pins $0.10 --- $4.15	2 doz. bags $5.50 --$5.65
6 pounds of yarn (knitting) $3.00	
23 ¾ yards tweed $11.88 -- $15.38	Bobby, Maida, lined boots and Julia plain -- $4.35
½ tea $0.24, Coal oil $0.60 -- $0.84	Solomon, felt boots, Stewart, Evelyn -- $6.35

The next five loads of wheat also brought a good price, but after November 15th, it dropped to 60¢ and then to 50. So many bills waited in line, that every drop in the price infuriated Mr. Criddle.

Edwy left for Douglas, 20 level miles across country, with a capacity load of 53 bushels. Mr. Criddle saw him off, "Tis beautiful wheat – will bring a good price."

His mother worried. *Edwy's under such pressure to get the best price.*

Many miles later, the buyer looked at the sample, shook his head, "Frozen. Forty cents. My best offer. Take it or leave it."

Stunned, Edwy looked at Jimmy Fortune who had also brought a load. "Will you stop in at our place and tell them I've gone to Brandon. Hope to get a better price. I'll be late."

Edwy had to lighten his load twice to cross the Assiniboine. It was after dark when he finally arrived at the Brandon elevator. The agent held a handful up to the lantern's light, poured it from one hand to the other and said, "Your wheat's frozen . . . forty cents!"

Edwy's heart sank. He knew Mr. Criddle would be in a terrible funk, but he'd been on the road all day. He was tired; it was late; and he was still 20 miles from home. He let it go.

Mr. Criddle had reason to be upset. With 500 bushels selling at that price he wouldn't 'get out of the fire'. A day later he faced the facts, "If it comes to the worst – why – we must still pinch and scrape for another season."

---

12 John Augustus Tulk: b. Nov. 5, 1839. Five years Percy's senior and not living or attending school in London, indicates they were not boyhood friends. Mrs. Criddle moved to Addlestone in 1860 so they may have met after Percy's return from Germany in 1863, or travelling on the same train into London after his marriage to Alice in 1874. According to Myrna Vane Paquette, Minnie remembered Mr. Tulk coming to visit in his own coach.

Mr. Criddle took his wife to dinner at Fortunes for her birthday. Isabel took advantage of their absence and said to Beatrice and Maida, "I'm leaving for Brandon first thing in the morning. Will you help me celebrate my Mama's birthday today?"[13]

The girls were delighted with the idea and helped bake a cake. They took Mama Dutcheen by the hands and made her sit at the table like a lady. They outdid themselves pretending to be her servants. The next morning Isabel hugged her mother goodbye and set off on Edwy's load of wheat to find another position.

Elise expected another gift; Minnie had written that she was coming with the mail carrier to Two Rivers. But the fellow lost his way so badly they didn't reach Two Rivers until after dark. Nelson Clark kindly piloted her safely across the river and home. Her brothers teased, "You sure have poor luck with guides! It's bad when you have to trust your life to a Methodist."[14]

Minnie handed Mr. Criddle her $5, and broke the news, "I won't have any more for awhile. I'm home for a rest."

Edwy meanwhile, hauled wheat day after day, often accompanied by his financial manager.

Billy Greer second payment on the horses	$40.00	Billy Greer, 3rd payment on horses	$40.00
Bower's note		Taxes self and Vane	$18.25
[grocery bill]	$122.83	Alf Pattern on account	
Watson's Manf. Co.	$59.85	of loan	$30.00
Smith Sheriff	$30.00	land (PO Ac.) E [lise]	
Fanning machine	$26.00	interest on loan	$16.00

And purchases of many odds and ends:

Tribune Newspaper	$1.00	6 Cups and Saucers	$0.60
Horseshoeing	$1.60	6 Knives	$0.65
Music Paper	$0.25	Medicine (Mine)	$1.50
5' Thick Rope	$0.85	Corned Beef	$1.00
Pail	$0.50	Soda	$0.10
Soap	$0.25	4 Lamp Glasses	$0.45
5 Yards of Rope for	$0.85	Postage	$0.20
Well		Stew Pan	$0.40
50' Lumber	$3.00	3 Bags Sweepings	$4.50
Nails	$0.25	Flour	$2.25
Boots - Bobby	$1.75	Grindstone Handle	$0.25
Car Grease	$0.15	Adams' Brass for Pair	$7.00
Tea	$1.00	of Breeching and Whip	
6 Plates	$0.60	Boots - Alice	$3.00

13 Elise's birth record states November 24, 1840, Freiburg, Germany. Mr. Criddle's diary: "Nov. 25, Dutchman."
14 Nelson, youngest son of Alexander Clark, the Two Rivers' Postmaster, the same age as Edwy.

For Christmas and holiday dinners.

Apples	$0.25	Almonds	$0.20
Currants	$0.50	Raisins	$0.50
Nutmeg	$0.10	Ginger	$0.10
Rum	$1.00	Flour	$3.00
Mixed Peel	$0.20		

From the end of October when the wool and fabric arrived, both women sewed: new nappies, tweed pants for the boys, undergarments for everyone. Sewing gave Elise a legitimate reason to sit and save her feet. After dark she knit by candlelight, stopping only to add wood to the fire. She hoped for a letter before Christmas and wasn't disappointed.

Mannheim, November 22.

Liebe Elise!

Your dear letter of October I have received, probably at the same time you received mine from Sept. 28 with the enclosure of our photograph. We all were happy to learn that you are healthy and hope that this letter finds you still in good health. As usual, I sent your letter to Carl and I hope he overcomes his usual letter writing laziness and sends you a few lines. His wife wrote us that Carl was suffering from a severe cough and now he has to, after other remedies failed, drink a tea made of Haberstroh [some kind of straw] with honey, which may help but certainly does not taste especially well. I too, at present, have a more severe cough than usual and drink in the morning a tea made with Wiesbaden Kochsalz [cooking salts] dissolved in hot water.

Her hand went to her mouth. *My dear brothers! You are young and strong to me. But you say you are ill. I pray the new medicines restore your health.*

Carl has sent some money to which I am adding my amount, a total of $11.80 to Poste restante Brandon. Accept it as a Christmas gift from us with our wish, that you would celebrate Christmas happily and in good health.

She wondered. *My Christmas money . . . I owe Sifton for obtaining my patent. Still, it would be wonderful to get a pair of shoes. . . . Or should I remind myself? "If wishes were horses . . ."*

Last Saturday we attended Anna's first Ball, where we were quite happy and entertained. But we cannot afford too much of that thing, for it costs a considerable amount of money that we can use for something more important and useful. But something we have to do in this regard for the girls in memory of our own youth, where we were happy at a dance, which probably cost our dear mother more at the time than it does me now!

Our parties! Remember! Indeed I do. We took so much for granted and Mama always encouraged us, "Do your best, success and prosperity are waiting for you." No one foresaw the economic downturn. Reliable old companies bankrupt; millions of hungry people gone to America. My brothers weathered the storms, but they aren't rich. As for me . . . the pot of gold at the end of the rainbow isn't any closer.

> *Anna has learned to be a seamstress and has sewn quite pretty dresses for herself, Elsa and Julchen. She enjoys it a lot and for us it is a help also in the pecuniary aspect when she sews for the family, for seamstresses charge a lot of money. Usually the sewing costs as much as the materials, therefore it is quite a saving that Anna sews the dresses.*

Elise felt shamed. *My niece's sewing helped Friedrich save money to send me a Christmas present. Dear Anna should spend the money on herself, to attend a concert. I agree dressmaking is a wonderful skill. My talent with needle and thread helped in England.* She read Friedrich's usual best wishes and then picked up their photo.

⁂

Edwy, in Brandon with his 16ᵗʰ load of wheat, cashed Elise's gift but didn't buy her a fashionable pair of boots, or even shoes. Mr. Criddle was in town right after Christmas and paid the lawyer.[15]

Their Christmas, more bountiful than usual, passed without fanfare. New Year's Eve, the Criddles hosted a party that kept Elise on her feet, serving guests until 4 a.m. He summed up his year:

> *. . . It has been fairly successful with us – far ahead of what we have been used to of late – and we have a lot of progress to report and increased prospects for the coming year. More stock; more hay land; bigger acreage of crop land; finally ever growing power with better skill – finally continued good health – Sans Deo Semper.*

'Always without God' was Mr. Criddle's way. If he thanked anyone, it tended to be himself. But Elise, like Job of old, cried to God for relief. And like Job, God's response seemed to be more hardships grinding away at her loving spirit. When the temperature in her little room dipped to thirty degrees of frost, and she just couldn't get warm in her little bed, she wondered about many things. *How does Edwy keep from freezing on his long cold drives? Are they making headway with the debts? What is happening to the mortgage on my homestead? Will I even survive this night?*

⁂

Minnie, still home, was not content to sit around. At every opportunity she cajoled her brothers into accepting invitations. Mr. Criddle went too, but because of her baby, Mrs. Criddle didn't wish to risk it. No one considered taking Mama Dutcheen. She watched the party-goers climb aboard the sleigh and wrap them-

---

15   December 27, 1890. "Dutchman—Sifton, $4."

selves against the cold. The horses responded to Edwy's slap of the lines; and the merry voices faded into the night. Indoors, Elise added wood to the stoves, tended to the children, and saw them into bed.

Then as her knitting needles clicked she imagined the young folks dancing. In a flight of youthful fancy her imagination took over. *I'll be like Aschputtel—become the English Cinderella . . . transform my dowdy self and go to the party.* She imagined her prince approach; she curtsied, he guided her to the centre of the room. *My prince—Nemo of the fancy handwriting— already knows I'm living a disguise. . . . We'll dance. My magic won't end at midnight; we'll waltze till the sun comes up.*

Mrs. Criddle, in bed with the baby, never knew what foolish capers Elise dreamed up, alone by the stove on a long winter's night.

When Minnie went back to work, Elise missed her dreadfully and not just for her helping hands. Life was truly dull. No more teasing and banter; the boys talked only of work. *That girl has a way with her. I can't put my finger on it, but as Harry says, "Mr. C is easier on all of us when Minnie's around."*

And seeing how easily Minnie waved goodbye, Elise fancied doing the same. *I still have my green dress in the trunk* [16] *. . . It's plain but attractive, a little out of fashion, and I'm much thinner. . . . Never mind, I'll freshen it up on the line, give it a pressing, and I'll be all set. I have all the qualifications of a governess: French, German, English, literature, music, art, deportment* [17] *. . . everything necessary for a position in France, England or Germany. Is there a family in Brandon looking for a first class nanny? If not, I could try dressmaking. Ladies are always in need of a fine seamstress and I have my ice-blue silk concert dress as an example of my skills. Or, failing that, I could take a job as a cook. . . . And, if I get away, my boys can too.*

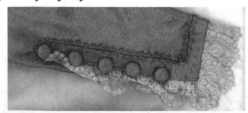

Elise's green everyday dress and her silk dress can be seen at the Burrough of the Gleann Museum, Glenboro, Manitoba

16 Dated by Dr. Carl Ludwig Fuchs, Kurpfälzisches Museum, Heidelberg, Germany. May, 2004.
17 School Report: Elise Harrer, 1854. *Erhardt'schen Lehr– u. Erziehungs-Anstalt für Mädchen*, Institut Erhardt, Heidelberg, Baden.

Her dreams were sideswiped by dear little Talbot who took to howling at the top of his lungs. Elise tried to find the cause. *I'm sure Mrs. Criddle followed the proper diet for nursing mothers . . . his nappies are fine. But there was a set-too in the masters' room this afternoon. Did it add something to her baby's milk?*

In any case, the poor little fellow screamed nonstop through the night. Elise heard his papa's angry shouts, and threat, "I'll send for the doctor."

Right after breakfast the disgruntled man stomped off to Lonsbury's, out of range of the commotion, and baby Talbot recovered without the help of the doctor or father. The following morning the boys were eating breakfast as he passed through the kitchen on his way to bed, "I fell into an all night poker game with Aweme's new teacher."

Elise asked herself. *What would Mrs. Criddle have done if I had not been here to rock the little fellow? She certainly needs help . . . But after nine years, is it still **my** duty?*

Scenarios ran through her mind. She imagined herself, eyes cast down, voice uncertain, saying to Mrs. Criddle. *"I have been thinking of going to Brandon to find work."*

No, that won't do. I must be firmer. . . . "I've decided to take a position in Brandon,"

That doesn't sound right either. Just imagining the scene made her nervous and as often happened in times of stress, a line from an old story popped into her mind, *"I'm going to seek my fortune." . . . The famous four, most unlikely candidates. First, a faithful old donkey, no longer able to carry heavy corn sacks to the market, learned his demise was imminent. He slyly took his leave. Having a good strong voice, he would set up as a street musician in the city.*

The ass soon came upon a dog panting beside the road, "Why so desperate old fellow?"

"My teeth are gone; I'm no longer useful. They plan to knock me on the head this very night." The ass invited the dog to join him as a musician and the pair trotted on till they met a cat, . . . The poor creature was in shock from an attempt by his mistress to have him drowned. The three went on and soon came upon a cock perched on a gate and screaming out with all his might and main. "Bravo Chanticleer! That's a famous noise. Pray what is this all this about?'

"I'm facing the axe, headed for the cooking pot. They're going to make me into broth for the guests on Sunday."

"Better come with us," said the ass. "If we can sing in tune we might get up a concert." And the four went jollily on together.

But they couldn't reach Bremen that day . . . .

Elise chuckled. *Such a strange old tale! But,* **they** *were no longer wanted. My problem is exactly the opposite; there's always someone calling for Mama Dutcheen. Seems I belong here . . . necessary as the kitchen stove. If I left, there would be lamentations on every front. I'd be blamed for the commotion. And the children . . . dear me, what of the children!*

Besides, there is a mortgage hanging around my neck.

Chapter Fifteen

Cecil's Miracle

Mr. Criddle paced back and forth waving a paper. "Billy Greer is lowering the boom – wants to be paid in full for the horses!"

Back from Brandon, he announced, "I saved the day."[1]

He didn't explain; moved on to "By next year wheat will be shipping out by rail from Treesbank – Edwy will be able to make two trips a day."

But by the next evening he held up a page and said, "I've got something here for my book on the settlement of the great northwest," and read:

> The Bdnites are now learning to put on style – fancy'emselves immensely. I preferred 'em when they were simply and openly a mere band of clumsy thieves and robbers. Now – they are the thieves and robbers as before – only – they're stuck all over with odd patches and shreds from the worn garments of civilization gone astray at the clearance sale of some long deceased old char man. Of course the Loan Office sharks, lawyers, Parsons and other blood suckers form one set while the tailors, cobblers, etc, belong to a 2nd circle. Below these come the hairdressers – washerwomen and petty tradesmen – and – all look down with contempt on the poor Farmer – and perhaps they're right for the Farmers are the dullest, most pig-headed besotted dishonest ignorant lot in the country.

Elise, in the background, struggling to make sense of it, thought, *I hope he doesn't ask me to say anything. Anyway, if I'm a washerwoman, that's above the farmers. Did Mr. Greer forget he is a gentleman and call him a farmer? A dull lot—besotted, ignorant, and dishonest. And pig-headed? Pigs, I've discovered, are clever enough to be stubborn and wise enough to value their freedom.* She chuckled, recalling the chaos of chasing them back into their pen.

Elise waited for news about her brothers' health as winter dragged. When a letter came, she checked the date, December 28. *Gracious, so long in the mail.* He'd sent a photo . . . *Julie? . . . A lovely girl! Now I have all three nieces.*

---

1 Income: "Per Kirkhoffer as agent for W. Sidney: P. Anson Cartwright of Souris on two notes to become due on February 21, 1891 and January I, 1892 respectively. The 1st for 120.50, and the 2nd for 217.00 payable at the Imperial Bank Brandon. Billy Greer balance on horses – 299.59"

Dear Sister!

Yesterday I received your dear lines from Dec. 8. You in turn will have received in the meantime my money order from Nov. 21 and letters from Nov. 22 and Dec. 15.[2]

From your dear little letter we were happy to learn that you are well and that the result of your crops this time was more satisfactory. We wish you for the New Year success, health and good results for the much and difficult labor you have spent.

The lovely Christmas festivities are now over. Hopefully you could enjoy them in good health and be happy.

My festivities! You touched a sore spot; I spent the day in the kitchen. I miss our good times terribly . . . especially Christmas Eve at the church. Our pastor climbing the steps to the high pulpit, opening that big Bible and reading the story of the Christ Child's

Heiliggeistkirche - Holy Spirit Church

birth—the shepherds, twinkling stars, and angels singing: "Ehre sei Gott in der Höhe, und Friede auf Erden, und des Menschen ein Wohlgefallen." (Glory to God in the Highest, and on earth peace, good will toward all.) . . . . I'd heard too much about wars . . . didn't want any more fighting. I pretended to tag along with the shepherds looking for the baby Jesus. I loved babies, especially my little brother. The wise men . . . I didn't like their presents. I asked Mama, "What will the baby do with them?" My memories are lost to my children. And yet, they like music. If only I could take them to the Christmas Oratorio in the Church of the Holy Spirit. Wunderbar! She lifted the letter and read on—

Our gifts to each other were practical, things we needed and postponed getting them until Christmas. Mariechen received a dress which Anna had sewn; from the children she received varied embroidered articles. The girls received new umbrellas which were badly needed, music, like an album of Schubert's Lieder etc. I received ½ dozen new shirts, towels etc.

She imagined the happy scene. *Gifts for each other in spite of hard times. . . . We could make things here for each other . . . would be fun—a poem, a picture? But. . . .*

We had Julchen photographed for the first time and I allow myself the pleasure of sending you the photograph. Now you have all of our family together and you can, since we can't get together personally, at least pay us a photographic family visit.

---

2 Friedrich's December 15th letter is not in our collection.

She held up the photo. . . . *I keep you all safe . . . just have to lift the lid of my trunk.*

> *I can't really make myself a concept of your dwelling and environment since you always refer only very briefly to it in your letters. Does immigration increase in your area, so that the countryside becomes more densely populated? I wish someone in your family would send me a sketch of your house and surroundings. That would give me a lot of pleasure.*

Oops, she looked about, *our home? Friedrich, you are too close. You'd ask why so large a house. If I drew a small one, it wouldn't please my censor. You'll just have to keep wondering.*

> *Our girls go skating as often as time allows in the city park. We are happy they do this for the healthful exercise this provides and since they don't get out too much otherwise.*
> *Well, fare well, dear Elise, greet Percy and your dear children.*
> *Your brother, Friedrich*

She folded the letter. *He didn't even mention his cough—are they both better?* It was still in her hand when a messenger came to the door; "Mrs. Lonsbury's baby is dead." [3]

Mr. Criddle left immediately and returned later that evening: "Fine baby boy born just three days ago – no complications – died this afternoon – overfed – and on wrong food – result continued vomiting – and I suppose – rupture of gall bladder."[4]

Overfed, wrong food, a newborn? . . . In any case she has lost her baby. . . . Can any pain equal that of losing one's child? It's close to the date my little Mabel died. Elise's heart ached for herself as she sympathized with Mrs. Lonsbury. Neighbours dug his little grave in the frozen ground; Mr. Criddle read the Service. Elise said prayers as she worked.

❧⸻❧

Mr. Criddle applied for another loan. Mrs. Criddle added her needs to his list—pail, kettle, chairs, calico, and boots for herself, Stewart and Evelyn. When the cheque arrived he ordered an early breakfast and in spite of bitter weather set off to tend to his bills.

Kirkhoffer on note dated Jan. 21	76.50
Watson and Co. on Binder	50.00
A.C. Frazer and Co. (dry goods and fabric)	47.83
Mill on account of flour	15.00
Smith Sherrif [sic] balance on account of threshing	16.00

3 Lonsbury, Douglas. March 12, 1891. Manitoba Vtal Satistics.
4 Veldhuis, Dr. Keimpe. MD FRCPC. "Probable Diagnosis: Intestinal atresia: within the first two days after birth, signs of intestinal obstruction develop; abdominal distension, bilious vomiting, jaundiced skin colour, and failure to pass meconium."

Safely home again Edwy told his mother, "Slept in the hotel. Rather a big step-up from my usual bed in the loft of the livery barn." Then he said with a grin, "You'll never guess what else I did." He paused, "Registered a homestead, that's what; the Southwest quarter of 4.9.16. I'll be a landowner too. Land adjoins this and we'll make a pasture for the cattle."

Elise was pleased, until he next returned from Brandon and called her out to see his new plough and seeder. Her voice trembled, "My son, have you gone into debt?"[5]

"Don't worry Mama. It will only take five loads of wheat to get clear again."

⁃⊶⊷⁃

New neighbours settled nearby: Little and his large family northeast on the former Ruttan farm; the Ellis[6] and Dixon families south and west. Mr. Criddle crowed, "If all their children come to our school we shall be quite set up." When he learned they were all Canadians and Methodists, his tone changed: "All Tub-thumpers – beastly nuisance. Why Methodists should always be sneaks and hypocrites – besides being hideously bigoted and ignorant – but so it is."

Elise gave up hope of meeting them, even before the family plunged into another spell of illness. Julia and baby Talbot were the first—violent croupy coughs and high fevers.[7] Maida, Norman and Evelyn followed, and next day Stuart and Beatrice added to the wretched chorus. Their papa puzzled. "What it is I can't make out – unless one may call it a kind of perpetual influenza with variations." He tried all his cures: Chlorodyne, Ipecac, Steedman's Powders, Rhubarb, and Quinine.[8] When he could do no more, he sat at his little organ composing a sonata. And since only the baby slept downstairs with his parents, Elise, upstairs, carried her lamp from child to child, nights on end.[9]

Fortunately the Vane boys stayed on the job and spring work forged ahead. When their two very pregnant mares found the new seeder heavy pulling, Edwy spelled them off by taking the oxen from the plough. When not busy in the fields, or herding cattle, there were other projects: posts and rails for the new paddock, a new crib in the well, a new stable for the horses, more rows of rhubarb and onions, acres of potatoes and turnips. It was also their duty to report the sightings of unusual creatures and, if possible, obtain specimens—bird, butterfly, or insect.

5 Notes in Edwy Vane's name: Smith Sheriff for plough, $22.00, payable January 2, 1892: Patterson and Bros. Co. for seeder, $80.00 plus 8% interest, payable January 2, 1892 at Winnipeg. Criddle Account Book.
6 Little and Ellis, Essex County, Ontario. Both wives were sisters of Alexander Clark's wife.
7 March 18, 1891.
8 April 8, 1891. "Children very ill." Mr. Criddle's remedies: Chlorodyne: a cure for just about everything. Ingredients included opium and chloroform, so it was little wonder that a patient slept well. Ipecac: was used in cough mixtures as an expectorant from the 18th until the early 20th century. Steedman's Powders: contained opium used to quiet children. Rhubarb extract and syrup used for a variety of ills, including "bowel-complaints" and indigestion. Quinine: to reduce fever.
9 March 18, 1891. ". . . bad colds and coughs of a somewhat 'grippy' type. . . . very fashionable just now – generally terminating in departure to a better world under the auspices of Brandon leeches."

Gradually the coughing sessions wound down to only occasional night calls. Elise watched the soft brown prairie come to life and dreamed of fresh asparagus. One night, her boys tended all-night bonfires to keep away the frost but neither the garden, nor the sprouting wheat survived. Feeling down about the set-back, Elise nevertheless perked up when Edwy called from the door, "Here's a letter from Uncle Friedrich . . . will cheer you up."

Eagerly, she laid down her stir stick.

Mannheim, April 5, 1891

Dear Elise!

Your dear letter I received weeks ago and as usual, sent it to Carl. On Dec. 28 I wrote you a letter and included a photo of our Julie. Lamentably I forgot to put the letter into the mail and left it in my coat, which I didn't wear for several weeks. I was very unpleasantly surprised when about the middle of February I found the letter that I deemed to be in your possession long ago. I sent it to you immediately and I hope you have received it.

She nodded. *That explains why his Christmas letter took so long to get here.*

We had a patient in Elsa all of January, she was very sick and caused us much worry. She had some kind of a brain infection with tremendous headaches and had to apply ice to her head for about 14 days. Now she is feeling, thanks be to God, quite well.

We're far apart but both of us had sleepless nights. Did it affect Marie's health?

Mariechen has suffered from her cough the last several months and we are anxiously waiting for warmer weather to set in, which we hope will alleviate her malady."

She shook her head: *will Marie ever be free of that cough?*

We have had a very cold winter with very little snow covering. Today and yesterday was a warmer rain for the first time at 7 degrees Reamur. Usually we have green pastures at this time of the year, now everything is yellow and rusty and there are no early green vegetables. . . .

Elise frowned. *Cold weather . . . I'd wish he'd tell me about the Easter services.* She closed her eyes and sat pretending. *I hear the church bell—bong – bong – bong – bong, calling us to worship. I'm walking with mama and my brothers along the cobblestone streets. We go through the open doors . . . the air vibrates with music. Oh, the organ and the singing! Our halleluiahs! And above the altar, I see the risen Jesus in all his glorious, stained glass splendor, ascending to our Father in heaven.*[10] She clasped her head in her hands. *Oh, I am so dreadfully homesick.* Recovering she wondered: *are things the same? Do the little girls wear their hair as I did? Their mothers . . . are their skirts gathered or fall straight in front with a bustle at the back? The sleeves—*

10   St. Peter and Providence Church in Heidelberg.

tight or loose, puffed or plain? Would Friedrich think me foolish to ask?

His letter ended with a wish for good health and added that he'd sent some Austrian and Bavarian stamps for the boys. *I don't see them. . . . But I do need health. I've been feeling so terribly tired. The English don't worry about servants; so long as the work is done. I mustn't complain; my boys work hard too. They tell me they have four hundred posts already pounded into the ground on Edwy's homestead. He says the paddock will be forty acres.*

One horridly hot windy afternoon Harry shouted in the door; "Fire! Everybody! Help!" Elise grabbed the broom and rushed out. They fought for dear-life all afternoon and finally overcame the flames. By the time Elise dragged herself into the house, she was desperately weary and she crawled into bed as soon as she could that evening. She felt little better in the morning. In the following days her breathing became even more difficult. *We saved our place from the fire, but I've not felt well ever since I was out in that smoke and dust. I wish I had stayed home with Mrs. Criddle and the little ones.*

The morning of May 27th, Elise didn't make it down to cook the porridge. She tried to dress, but the pain in her chest was so intense she simply crumpled back onto her bed. *The pain, I can hardly get a breath. I've been sick before, but this is different. . . . It's strange not to be in the kitchen making breakfast. . . .*[11]

Her boys gathered in the kitchen like hungry orphans with no one to feed them. Finding some bread, Harry and Edwy ate, but feeling compelled to carry out Mr. Criddle's orders, left Cecil to check on their mother. Perhaps she had just slept in and would be feeling ashamed. Thus, after his morning chores, Cecil sat on the edge of her bed and asked hopefully, "Are you alright, Mama?" She tried to put on a brave front, but he could see that, indeed, his mother was ill. He brought a cup of water; "Please have a drink, Mama, try . . . I'll help you sit up."

But she was not interested, "You need to go, my dear boy. The cattle are waiting. I'll be alright. Perhaps by tea I'll feel better."

And so Elise began a new chapter in her life at St. Albans. The tables had turned and instead of caring for others, she herself was helpless. When her sons checked on her that evening, they were shocked. Their upbeat, always cheerful mother was so changed. She had no smile, no questions about their day, and no

---

11 Veldhuis, Dr. Keimpe. MD FRCPC: "Probable provisional diagnosis: Nocardia bacteria are found in soil around the world. Contaminated dust containing nocardia bacteria is inhaled or gets into an open wound. The bacterial infection usually starts in the lungs spreads most often to the brain and skin. Main risk factor for getting nocardiosis is a weakened immune system."

words of encouragement. She was not interested in the food they brought up to her. They slipped out saying, "We hope you are better in the morning, Mama," but they were afraid and went downstairs to talk to Mr. Criddle. He made a note in his diary: "Dutchman ill."

Elise had days and nights of pain-filled hours to come to grips with her condition. *I remember Evelyn's horrid abscess. It grew so big he couldn't hold his head straight . . . and so painful, he howled when I applied hot cloths. It kept swelling until it looked like a huge red transparent egg, purplish in the centre. I suggested sending for Dr. Husband; he'd been here for tennis. But my idea was shot down: "No, I've no faith in the doctor. Besides if it's cancer, nothing can be done. And it would cost ten dollars and where was the money to come from?"[12] Mrs. Criddle had a swelling too. . . . They recovered . . . if mine's the same, I should soon come to the end of my suffering.* But as the days passed she worried. *I'm not getting better. Time isn't helping me.*

Mrs. Criddle most certainly could not be expected to care for a servant. Furthermore, she was already overburdened making up for her housekeeper's absence in the kitchen. And so Cecil was relieved of his duties herding cattle to attend to his mother. He picked and took her flowers. He brought her a drink before going out to milk in the early morning, and after, took up warm water to bathe her face and arms. He placed a chair beside her bed and whenever his chores allowed, he sat there. To distract her from her pain he passed on as much news as he could. But Cecil often ran out of ideas to talk about since his world was confined to milking, splitting wood, feeding pigs, and sitting on the prairie with the cattle, gophers, and the sky.

In desperation he recalled his former life in England: "I was just seven when we left our home on St. George's Road, but I remember lots of things." He watched his mother's face and thought she was remembering too. He pressed on, "We had happy times, walking to the Thames and guessing where the boats came from. As the ships worked their way past us up the river you helped us guess—China, India, or the Indies? Sometimes it was the cargo in their holds—tea, silk, sugar cane? I learned a lot. You knew so much about the world, Mama. And one time we saw the *S. S. Glengyle* sail downriver.[13] You explained she was headed to Siam loaded with supplies Uncle Henry ordered for the king. Papa had packed four boxes with instruments and books to teach his people modern ways. I remember binocu-

King Chulalonkorn, R.S

---

12 February 17, 1886.

13 Alabaster, Henry. Information from his letters obtained from Angela Alabaster in England.

lars; you told us how his majesty might use them. Uncle Henry had his own big box. Aunt Palacia was homesick for English food. She wanted a tin of Oxford sausages. What were they, Mama?". . . But his mother didn't respond. "And survey instruments Uncle Henry needed to lay out a road system. . . ." Cecil's voice trailed off; his mother had fallen into a restless sleep.

❧◦❧

Not able to examine his housekeeper, Mr. Criddle depended on the boys' descriptions for her diagnosis and wrote in his diary: "The Dutchman is internally all wrong and tumour painful." The household learned two weeks was a long time to be entirely without a housekeeper. Elise tried to get up, lighten the load for Mrs. Criddle, but she hardly made it down the stairs. True to his manly limitations, Mr. Criddle could only mention his wife's distress. "Alice is about knocked up with overwork and suffering from toothache."

Elise sank beyond caring. Cecil tended her needs and tried to get her to drink. His older brothers dropped in on their way to bed, "Jess and Dolly have beautiful foals. You'll love them, Mama. I hope you'll soon get out to see them." A few nights later they told her, "We had a terrible scare; Jess is going to be alright, but she almost killed herself in the barbed-wire fence." Days later, they said, "Tonight we'll be out all night. It's going to freeze and we're burning straw to save the wheat." And after a violent thunderstorm Harry said, "The biggest downpour ever. There's water everywhere. Good we live on sandy land or we'd be up to our knees in mud."

Her boys continued to report their mother's condition to the downstairs, and it was not encouraging. Mr. Criddle wrote: "The Dutchman gets no better – indeed – I think she's worse – is weak – helpless more or less and . . . down most of the time."

Days passed; Cecil was desperate. He laid cold cloths on her head and bathed her face and arms. Still trying to take her mind off the pain he said, "Edwy brought out a new teacher, a young man straight from England. He'll be the fourth teacher this year. Sure hope he stays." On June 13, he asked her, "Do you remember, Sir John A. MacDonald?" When she didn't answer, he added a little lamely, "He died. Mr. C says Canada has lost a great leader."

His voice broke as he said it for Cecil was afraid he was losing his own mother. The only thing he hadn't tried was prayer. He remembered the people in Steerage gathering around when his mother prayed. He wanted to ask God to save his mother, but how? He couldn't read his mother's church book, and no use asking Mr. Criddle.[14] But, he had to try. Taking his sleeping mother's pale hand in his own sturdy calloused

---

14 Elise's service book was requested by Isabel after her mother's death.

ones, he closed his eyes, and imagined God looking down on them. "Please, God, do not take my mother. I need her. We all need her. I will do everything I can to help her, if only you will save her life. Maybe I'm asking for a miracle . . . but I hope you can do it." Then remembering prayers couldn't just end without the special word, he added, "Amen."

When Lonsburys and Sutcliffes came for a Sunday of tennis and cricket; Elise roused when she heard laughter and cheers and murmured, *they'll be expecting tea later on* . . . The guests, however, did not come in. Cecil told her later, "Lonsbury had to check out some horses in the Pound. The others wanted to get over that wretched ferry at Upper's before dark." Before his mother drifted off, he heard Mrs. Criddle's unusually shrill voice, "It's time to call Isabel home; I'm being worked to death."[15]

The invalid heard it too and thought *double duty as hostess, and servant is demanding*.

In the week following, Mr. Criddle's composing went well; measure by measure his Sonata was taking shape. The sound wafted up the stairs to Elise where her pain-filled mind transformed the notes into melodies from her past. For a few moments she was a little girl rocking her baby brother to sleep, *Schlafe, schlafe, holder, süßer Knabe*. A short time later she was a romantic teenager searching the hillside for a little wild rose, singing Schubert's lovely *Sah ein Knab ein Röslein stehen*.

As the days stretched into weeks, Elise's condition worsened; neither time nor Cecil's prayers were bringing healing to the sufferer. On June 18, Cecil told his mother, "Edwy's gone for Dr. Husband. It's not far. He'll be here soon, unless he's away seeing to someone else.[16]

Dr. Husband . . . I've poured his tea . . . he's a kind man.

At the sound of his steps on the stairs she rallied. Mr. Criddle followed the doctor in and hovered at his side.

Dr. Husband leaned over her, "How are you today, Mrs. Vane?"

Before she answered, he went on as doctors have a habit of doing, "When did all this begin?"

"A month ago," Mr. Criddle answered, "pain in her chest."

Dr. Husband

15 June 16, 1891.

16 H. Aubrey Husband, before moving to Manitoba in 1885, won distinction as a writer of medical text-books, remarkable for lucidity and conciseness: *The Students' Handbook of the Practice of Medicine* went into several editions; *Sanitary Law; Nurse and Baby; The Student's Pocket Prescriber, Medical Jurisprudence*. Particularly in the latter subject he was an authority, not only by virtue of his books, but through lectureship in the Extra-Academical School of Edinburgh on Medical Jurisprudence and Public Health. Born on the family estate in Jamaica, he studied medicine in Edinburgh, B.Sc., M.B., M.C., F.R.C.S.E.

The doctor bent forward, pulled back her blanket and unbuttoned her nightgown. With a sharp intake of air he said, "Yes, you **do** have a problem. No wonder, Mrs. Vane, you are suffering. It looks as if you are about ready to burst. Bear with me."

He took a tool from his black bag. "I'm going to make a little cut here. Try to give you some relief."

Only a disappointing drop or two of blood oozed from the cut and he said, "Looks like it is not going to do anything for us today."

He dressed the wound, pulled up the covers, and smiled down at her pain-filled face. "I'll come back in a few days to check on you again."

His presence moved Mr. Criddle to his medicine chest and he told Cecil to give her 15 drops of laudanum with sal volatile.[17] After the doctor left, he wrote up his report:

. . . thinks the tumour is a cold abscess – stuck a knife in but no results bar a little blood. I believe the thing is come to a head – and – I trust the doctor may be right though that is bad enough. He is to come again on Sunday.

On the doctor's return he told the patient, "I'm going to reopen that abscess and insert a tube to drain the fluid into this pail on the floor. The end of the tube must remain under water. We don't want any air getting into it and cause trouble. We need all that puss out of there. You'll have to be patient; it's going to take awhile."[18]

Watery fluid began draining and as the day wore on her pain lessened. Cecil noticed her face relax and she smiled at her sons as they gathered at her bedside before going to roost.

"You really had us worried, Mama. Now you'll be up and about in no time."

For his part, Mr. Criddle made another entry:

The Doctor opened the Dutchman's abscess this morning – and about a pint of gruelly pus was discharged in an hour through a tube into water. It is still running (8.15 PM) more or less - and I hope danger is over – the pain and swelling are practically gone.

Elise did not, however, jump out of bed the next morning to prepare break-fast as the family hoped. Because of the severity of the pain in her chest and the re-sultant difficulty breathing, she'd paid no attention to a number of painful lumps developing on her legs. Now she confided to her son, "I'm afraid I have something on my legs. Am I getting boils?"

17 Laudanum: Victorian treatment for pain, opium dissolved in alcohol. Sal Volatile: ammonium carbonate – smelling salts used to revive a person who had fainted.
18 Veldhuis, Dr. Keimpe. MD FRCPC: "The description of the continuous underwater drain (tube) strongly suggests an empyema - an infection producing pus in the pleural cavity. The drain is underwater to act as a valve, preventing air from entering the pleural cavity and causing the lung to collapse."

He pulled back the covers, and when he nodded, she asked, "Can you poultice them?"

No one at St. Albans recognized the abscesses signaled a dangerous progression of the disease, and it was a cheerful gathering when Minnie came home the following Sunday. Cecil propped his mama up in bed and she bravely announced; "The worst is over; I'll soon be up and about."

But their hope for a rapid recovery was too optimistic. Dr. Husband should have attended again. Elise's soft tissues were infected; she was indeed, dangerously ill.[19]

The wound kept draining through June 26 and Cecil continued to care for his mother. Isabel was fetched to save Mrs. Criddle from death by housework. Although Isabel was busy downstairs, it was comforting for Elise to have her daughter near by.

Spring cycled into summer. When black clouds loomed in the western sky, Cecil came up to tell her, "I think we're in for a storm. Don't worry. You are safe here in your bed."

He joined the others outside and watched, fascinated, and fearful, as the clouds mushroomed larger and larger covering the sun. Then even the cloud's rim of gold was swallowed by the boiling black mass punctuated with ever brighter zigzag daggers of lightning. At the last minute they scurried indoors and pushed the door shut. United by fear in the semi-darkness they stood in the kitchen as their protective log walls groaned under the sudden onslaught of wind and rain. Then a blinding flash-sizzle-explosion shook the house and rattled the stoves.

Gripping her blankets, Elise thought, *We've been hit by lightning! I'm still here —alive! Was it Mr. Tulk's lightning rods that saved us? I've been frightened of lightning ever since our first night in Brandon.* Hearing nothing but the storm, she worried about the children.

They were huddled in the centre of the kitchen just as she had taught them; "Keep far away from the windows and stove pipes. Count slowly after a lightening flash. Each number is a second, a second is a mile." They counted; after each sizzling flash, "One, two, three."

Family collection

BOOM! "Three miles away." Another, "One, two." Ear splitting cymbals! "Two miles away." Another flash, "One, two, three, four, five." Rolling thunder! "Five miles." They counted until the flashes grew weaker, the thunder less violent. The

---

19 Empyema: Patients who develop abscesses caused by this infection may need surgery to completely drain the abscesses. There is a significant death rate if more than one site is involved (disseminated nocardiosis). Were the brain to become involved the outcome would be fatal. The immune system plays a large role in how well they do.

storm passed; the boys ventured out to check the barns and animals. Maida and Julia climbed the stairs to bed, and slipped into Mama Dutcheen's little room. "There was an awful smell. We were scared, but we counted like you taught us."

Elise patted their heads and sent them off with a "Good-night, little ones."

⁃⋯⊱⧉⊰⋯⁃

Elise was still confined to bed on June 30ᵗʰ during another crisis, this time frost, not immediately life threatening, but destructive nevertheless. She hadn't yet seen the foals, and already their mothers had to go back to work. Edwy harnessed the anxious mares for a test run to the post office, and told her that night, "I wish you could have seen the young rascals dancing beside their mothers."

With Jess and Doll back in harness, Mr. Criddle asked Edwy to drive him to Wawanesa, "I'd like to consult further with Dr. Husband about your mother's condition."

On the way, they picked up the Mair ladies to picnic in the valley beside the river. Edwy heard nothing about his mother's illness except, "Big jabber at the doctor's."[20]

The swellings on Elise's legs developed into full-fledged abscesses. Cecil, still on duty, kept up the hot compresses; tearing more strips of old cotton sheets to absorb the draining pus. First one, then two, then three, released their unsightly liquid, giving Cecil hope that his mother was on the mend. He removed the smelly encrusted bandages and replaced them with fresh ones. Isabel washed and boiled them ready for the next round. Reports on his mother's health continued to flow to the gentleman and lady downstairs.

July 6: Dutchman not getting on over well – abscess 11 burst of itself last week and is still running. No. 1 closed but I expect not permanently.

Beatrice stopped by to tell her, "My baby chickens have hatched. I have 146 now! Imagine! You should see the mother hens, bustling around with their chicks, scratching in the ground, making such fuss, "Cluck, cluck, cluck – come, see the tasty bugs I've dug for you." The enthusiastic little girl pleaded, "I wish you could come out to see them."

"You've done well. I'll see them one day."

Courtesy, Billy Dudeck, Frazerwood, Manitoba

20   Dr. Husband moved his office to Wawanesa when Millford was vacated. He kept his farm near Sutcliffe's and Köhler's. A daughter married Mr. Köhler.

One hot evening Harry forgot the rule of keeping bad news away from their mother; "We were ploughing this afternoon. Bill lay down right there in the field and wouldn't get up. We've been working the oxen extra because of the foaling. I guess he needs grain like the horses."

On the other hand, the boys had some good news for their mother. "Mr. Lonsbury gave us a pair of piglets in exchange for our help; we're going to keep them as a start for raising our own pigs. You'd like them Mama, they are cute little fellows."

Threats about other people's animals reached Elise's ears. "I'll pound Clay's pigs for running on my South Farm potatoes . . . Little's cattle on my North Farm wheat." The boys chased the beasts out of their crops, but she wondered, *do they ever round them up and take them to Lonsbury's pound? It's a lot of work . . . and the owner has to be able and willing to pay for the damage and expenses.* Another evening Elise heard a great thundering of hoofs and commotion of neighing, bawling, and shouts. Cecil told her 25 horses were running free and the boys had their chance to be real cowboys. *What next,* she thought; *I hope they haven't been on our crops.*

All the while Cecil soldiered on as his mother's nursemaid. Wanting to believe she was improving, his optimism showed in Mr. Criddle's reports.

July 13: Dutchman getting better daily.
July 23: Dutchman slowly recovering.
July 29: Dutchman gaining strength — one of the holes however still discharges freely.[21]

By mid August Elise was able to get downstairs and prepare her own dressings for the still weeping craters. Cecil picked up his outside work and her sons toiled on. Their theme, with variations, was work; hoeing, weeding, ploughing, haying, harvesting. Farming was enough to drive a person crazy. Mr. Swaisland was taken ill to Brandon and a neighbour heard it was softening of the brain. No one would vouch for the truth of the rumour.

Another violent storm swept through the countryside. Strong winds drove the rain into the chimneys and waterfalls poured out every seam in the stove pipes. Isabel had no end of scrubbing away black pools on the floor, and washing every piece of contaminated clothing.

Although Elise's abscesses kept weeping she was getting stronger. Mr. Criddle noted her progress in contrast to Swaisland's decline.

August 17: Dutchman getting steadily better.
       Swaisland has gone clean off his head — mad in fact - and is to be shut up in an asylum.

---

21 There is no reliable alternative to surgical incision and drainage of an abscess. Heat alone may cause small superficial abscesses to resolve.

Now that wheat could be shipped from Treesbank, Mr. Criddle's attention moved on to getting a bridge across the Assiniboine. Council still had his petition, but the rate payers on the south side of the river were pushing for a ferry. He left for the 'Pow-Wow', expecting a fight. That night he wrote:

> Rather a row – some fine Methodist rascality unearthed. Matters left much as they were though Dewart tried hard to bamboozle us into sanctioning a ferry at Clark's. Threatened him with legal proceedings if he exceeded powers given him by council. More bother ahead but the Municipality is in touch with me. I hope we may get our bridge with a little patience and determination.

Harry bragged on his birthday, "All the grain is cut and stooked." Unfortunately, a killing frost that night put an end to the watermelons, his favourite treat.

Elise was peeling potatoes when she heard. "Swaisland is dead."[22] She hadn't even known he was ill. *Gracious! In the asylum? . . . He was such a fine young fellow. But for Cecil's care I might have ended up there myself. Pain does strange things to a mind.*

In October, Elise and Isabel baked for the arrival of their 'noble' guest, Mr. Tulk. The happy welcome turned sour; "They've lost my most crucial box; a new gun and all my gifts."

Once they were found, he settled in to enjoy his holiday.

Edwy drove the gentry, including Mrs. Criddle—now that she could leave Talbot—to various social engagements. At Dr. Husband's they had fine conversation and music, topped off with a most excellent meal. Edwy told his mother, "The doctor enquired after you. Too bad you couldn't enjoy the likes of our dinner. The roast beef was splendid."

Norman, hungry for meat, picked up the gun and took Cecil deer hunting. Once again he failed, "Saw tracks, had some shots, but got nothing."

Elise had longed for a letter through that long, painful summer, and when she received one, tears of joy trickled down her cheeks.

---

22 August 28, 1891. Was his condition also from the soil which in his case spread to his brain?

Mannheim, August 5, 1891

Dear Elise!

Today I received your dear letter of July 15, from which I learn with deep concern that you were sick for a long time. I can see by your writing that you still are quite weak not well yet, but hope that these lines will find you in a better frame of health. I wrote you on June 28 and already at that time I was worried that you could be sick, since you had not written for so long and now I am sorry to see that my concerns were well grounded.

I had no time to write last winter, and then I took ill myself. I wrote as soon as I could hold the pencil. I don't remember getting Friedrich's letter. I wonder what became of it.[23] Going back to the page, she read; *"I send you two dollars and I would be glad if in that way I could aid you in your convalescing."* . . . . *What could I buy? First, paper, stamps and a pencil so that I could write my family when I wished. And then a pair of shoes.* . . . *But will the money stretch? Mrs. Criddle said her boots were $3. I'd have to get cheaper ones, give up the paper and stamps. Then she bit her lip. I won't have the choice.* . . . *Never mind, what else does he say?*

Elsa is well again but it was a long slow process and finally we changed to another doctor who applied different more effective medication. We also needed to see an eye specialist with her, all of which has been quite expensive.

She thought of Dr. Husband coming to her; *how wonderful for Elsa.*

Since Carl has been in Baden Baden, I have not received any news from him.[24] *I shall send him your letter.*

She gazed into the distance imagining the spa. *Bathing in mineral waters sounds pleasant. I wonder if the waters could cure my poor legs.* . . .

Then finding her place in the letter she read on:

You, dear sister, I wish you improvement and complete recuperation from your illness, and I would be happy to receive news of that nature soon. Now farewell and recover completely.

Dear Brother, will I ever be well? I'm still weak, my legs large as stove pipes. These horrid abscesses won't stop seeping. **If** *only your* **wishes** *could make me well* . . . *Gracious, I've used that little word if, again.*

Young Swaisland didn't make it, but I'm still here. I can stand . . . *even climb the steps again without help. I'm thankful for my boys* . . . *the children's love, my family.*

---

23 Friedrich's letter of June 28, 1891 is not among our collection of Elise's German letters.
24 Baden-Baden: the town of Baden in the province of Baden. Baden translates as "to bath/bathe". Known to the Romans, rediscovered in the 19th century.

The words of an old hymn welled up within and forgetting the rule—English only under the Criddle roof, she began to sing:

Ich ruf zu dir, Herr Jesu Christ,	*I call to you, Lord Jesus Christ,*
Ich bitt, erhör mein Klagen,	*I pray, hear my lamentation*
Verleih mir Gnad zu dieser Frist,	*Bestow your grace on me at this time,*
Laß mich doch nicht verzagen;	*Do not let me despair;*
Den rechten Glauben, Herr, ich mein,	*I think that I have the right faith, Lord,*
Den wollest du mir geben,	*Which you wanted to give me,*
Dir zu leben,	*To live for you,*
Mein Nächsten nütz zu sein,	*To be useful to my neighbour,*
Dein Wort zu halten eben.[25]	*To rightly keep your word.*

Her sons had just come up to bed. They sat mesmerized, side by side on the edge of their bed. The words or the language didn't matter, their mother was singing. In the silence following, Cecil confessed, "Last summer I was afraid Mama was going to die . . . that I would never hear her sing again. I prayed to God to let her stay with us. I think **it is** a miracle."

---

25 *Ich ruf zu dir, Herr Jesu Christ,* hymn (1529), by Johann Agricola.

Chapter Sixteen

A Contented Heart

By October Elise was back to work, peeling potatoes and baking raisin pies for the threshing gang. She had a stack of bread, huge pots of turnips, and potatoes, and a big kettle of boiling water for the tea. Harry's pig had been sacrificed since the promised ducks hadn't appeared. The men dug into the meal as if it were their last. Even after downing huge platefuls of the first course, she heard, "Who can eat the most pieces of pie?" Meals were part of a thresher's deal, and the men rated the farmers accordingly.

Mair's threshing outfit

As Elise cleared the table and refilled the kettles for washing all those empty plates, she thought about the harvest. *These meals are the climax of our whole summer; and my boys deserve some good meals. All their ploughing, seeding, harrowing, cutting, and stooking come together at that machine. I see Edwy's eyes are sore tonight from working in the dust cutting the twine as each sheaf sinks into the machine's mouth.* Mr. Criddle's only concern was the 1,413 bushels of wheat that trickled down the spout.

Next day Edwy started hauling grain, Harry and Cecil ploughed, and others cleared more acres for next summer's haying. Elise, out for a few minutes on a dew-sparkling morning recalled a few lines from a song about a jolly ploughboy. But, as she served breakfast, she noticed gloomy faces and wondered; *are they keeping something from me?* That evening Cecil admitted, "Old Bill usually gets up after a few minutes of rest, but this afternoon, even with the whip he didn't budge. I'm afraid the old boy has ploughed his last furrow."

Cecil was right. Next day Mr. Tulk fired the single shot and they buried Bill's boney old carcass down by the trail. Because Bill's long time partner couldn't pull the plough alone, he was to be fattened on turnips and hay to provide for the family in another way. Elise thought sadly, *a cruel reality of our life.* Her next hardship was having her Harry traded to Mair's for cheap frozen wheat for next spring's seed.

Minnie's weekend visit helped lift her mother's spirits, but the following week Elise thought more about her situation. *It's been ten long years since we lived in that tent, yet the Promised Land and a home of our own seems no closer. My girls are grown women; my little boys are hard-working men, and so busy, I hardly see them. I see more of Norman with his notes and insect drawings spread out on the table. He seems discontented; I feel that way sometimes. I think he pines for the life he lost in England. I can never forget his teary eyes peering out from that blanket . . . and those frightful trips to the bush for firewood! I hope he can get away someday; he's more suited to studies, drawing, and painting. I noticed him watching Cannon Cooper sketching. All his grandmother's brushes and painting supplies are here. To be able to use my training in art to coach him would help me. . . . It's hard to be hiding my talents, when I see so many things I could be teaching the children.*

⁕

Tired of being hungry, Norman took Cecil hunting.[1] With no luck, they were eating Mama Dutcheen's turnips and potatoes that night. He said, "At least Papa will be pleased: we didn't waste any ammunition. I know now where **not** to look. I'll get a deer next time."

Elise felt like saying, *Edwy should be hunting, he's our best shot. But he's always on the road hauling grain.*

Anxious to get his wheat sold before the price fell, Mr. Criddle engaged young Jim Fortune to accompany Edwy with a second load. That evening when horses appeared in the distance, Cecil raised an alarm, "I see only one driver. Has something happened?"

He couldn't wait, and set off on the run to meet them. Elise stood with the others, puzzling as the team came closer: *Jimmy's driving Edwy's team . . . there's another behind . . . can't see two drivers!* Growing dread clutched Elise's heart. Much closer, Jim pointed into the wagon box and hollered, "Edwy's here! He's hurt!"

When the team pulled up at the house, Cecil went to the back. Elise's heart was in her mouth as Edwy slowly sat up and painfully maneuvered to the back of the wagon box. The boys helped him down, into the kitchen, and onto a chair.

Jim told them, "I don't think there's anything broken. After the accident he got back up."

---

1 Criddle, Norman: "My memory of the period was one of extreme depression, crops had been poor and prices low. Hunger generally accompanied us in our daily work." *The Canadian Field Naturalist,* Vol XLVII, Ottawa. p. 177.

They unlaced Edwy's boots and ever so carefully pulled them off. Jim explained, "He was driving my colts down a cut and the wagon ran up on them. They spooked, the wheel hit a ridge."

"I guess I'm lucky to be alive, tried to jump. Didn't make it. Front wheel got both legs. My boot saved that one a little," motioning to his left foot. "This one sure caught it! We weren't many miles from Chater . . . decided to keep on. Jimmy did all the unloading. The pain wasn't so bad at first. It's the very deuce now. You'd better go home Jim; they'll be waiting for you. Tell your dad to get some breeching for your harness. Thanks for your help."

Edwy gritted his teeth while his mother cleaned and bandaged the wounds. Finally she looked up, "There. You'll need to take it easy. Do you want something to eat?"

"I'm not hungry. . . . Maybe a drink of water."

At that point, Mr. Criddle arrived on the scene and heard the story. "You were a fool to drive those colts – not properly trained – should be more careful." After prodding Edwy's leg, and deciding his Boy was in no serious danger, he went back to his book. Cecil helped his big brother up to bed.

Time, their usual healer, was on Edwy's side. The pain and swelling subsided, although not soon enough to drive Mr. Tulk to Brandon. Lonsbury had that honour. Mr. Criddle saw his friend off on the east-bound train minutes ahead of a blizzard. The unfortunate Awemites had a devil of a time making it back through the storm.

A few days later Isabel walked with Beatrice to the deceased Swaisland's auction, and then got a ride to Brandon. Edwy recovered enough to drive Mr. and Mrs. Criddle to Fortune's for dinner, and two days later was back on the job hauling grain. Norman moved downstairs to the gentleman's room, and spent his time examining and drawing all the specimens he could lay his hands on.[2]

As soon as the ice on the Assiniboine could bear the weight of a load of grain Edwy took his first load to Treesbank. The price was excellent—seventy cents! The five and a half miles both ways took a mere five hours and ten minutes. The time shrank by an hour, and then with very slick roads, Edwy managed two trips in one day. His mother was delighted. *He can make both trips in less time than it takes just to reach Brandon.*

Treesbank elevator

---

2 Criddle, Norman: "I was . . . fortunate in having as associates my brothers Evelyn and Stuart as well as Messrs. Edwy, Harry and Cecil Vane, all keen observers for whose assistance in preparing this paper I am much indebted." *The Canadian Field-Naturalist* Vol. XLIII, Ottawa. p. 176.

Elise looked forward to the Glee Club in December. *It will be wonderful for the youngsters to meet others. Harry's away, Cecil too or choring, and Edwy's hauling, but I hope they can take part.* Word of the event spread and as a result, Mr. Criddle received an invitation to sing at Blythe's community concert. He set off west in a jolly mood. But in no time at all he was back hopping mad. "They wanted me to pay a quarter to get in the door – left them high and dry – insulting Methodist plot."

December 19, as planned, his Glee Club gathered with ten singers, including Mr. Criddle's favourite, Jenny Mair. As they sang, Elise remembered singing with her brothers. *I hope I hear from them before Christmas . . . that they are all well.*

Fortunately, she got her wish.

Dear Elise!

Your dear letter of September 1, I have received. It has given all of us great joy and peace that you report positively concerning your health. God willing, it has steadily improved in the meantime and you are now restored to perfect health.

Dear Friedrich, I'm not sure I'll ever be free of these abscesses. I'm still weak and tire easily . . . must be getting old. . . . Let's see 1840 to 1891. My goodness, fifty one!

I was also happy to read that you believe to have received a good crop. The price for wheat and corn is very high here, namely because of Russia's export laws and so you will likely receive a good price for your grain.

Today I sent you $11.80 the usual way, as a Christmas gift for you from Karl and me and I hope the money will soon be in your possession.

She nodded. *The money arrived; possession is another matter.*

Karl has also gone through some trying times. For several weeks his wife lay sick with typhus and we all were quite worried. She had to have a special nurse for some weeks because Karl had to work at the office and their servant girl is not reliable. The last few weeks she has been improving but she has to be very careful since she had a setback once.

Typhus! How dreadful! Thank God, she's recovering. My dear brother, not well himself and Amalie ill. Elise read to the end of the letter and tucked it into her apron pocket. *I'll read it again before I blow out my lamp tonight.*

Harry came home for Christmas with a credit of $52 for 34 days of work—almost enough for next spring's seed. Next morning he went with Edwy to deliver their last load of wheat to Treesbank and pick up the first load of seed. Mr.

Criddle got a lift with them to the neighbours and walked back. Stomping snow from his boots, he said, "Nasty day – a storm brewing. Thermometer dropping at a rapid rate – going to be a cold night."

Elise had tried to ignore the wind whistling through the cracks. Scraping a tiny spot clear on the window pane, she peered out. *Nothing but white! My boys are out there!* As early darkness closed in on the wild night, she worried all the more. *Maybe they'll stay at Mair's. Yet, tomorrow is Christmas. I'm afraid they'll try to get home.*

Cecil kept watch and hours later called, "They're back!"

Sinking to a chair, Elise breathed a sigh of relief, *Gott sei Dank!*

Cecil took the broom to the snowmen. Edwy shed his greatcoat saying, "What a day! Good thing Harry was with me. We had trouble on the river hill. Part way up, we heard CRACK! The wagon dropped like a stone. The horses, pulling hard, stumbled forward taking the front runners of the sleigh with them. The lines pulled hard and I hollered, Whoa!"

"The peg had snapped and we had to unload all the grain bags to lift the sleigh box out of the way. I had wire, but our fingers were beastly cold getting the front and back together again. Got the box back on, loaded up the bags, and were on our way hoping the elevator was still open. He'd warned us: "Be closing early for Christmas." Lucky for us, he was still there. By the time we left the elevator it was snowing heavily and wind was picking up. Fairly blew us out of town. We raced north to Mair's for the seed. "Better stay here," they said, but we wanted to get home. We worked as fast as we could and set out. I could hardly see the end of my nose. We nearly changed our minds about staying, but we thought you'd be worrying all night. I shouted to Jess and Doll: "Christmas tomorrow. You girls know the way. Take us home! And they got us here." Then, half joking, half serious, he added, "Left to us, we'd be frozen somewhere along the trail and someone would come across us in a day or two."[3]

Their mother sighed, "Thank the horses! And thank God! I couldn't have a better present."

Christmas dinner was Elise's next challenge: *Poor old Lamb, his work is done. I can't be sentimental.*[4] *He'll be tough, though, and need lots of cooking.*

The meal went well, Mr. Criddle praised the beef along with other good things: "Apples – Brazil nuts – almonds – rum – taters – carrots – turnip sprouts, and the pudding – best we've had in this country."

---

3 All-time record cold for Brandon, - 39.9 Celsius, December 26, 1891. *Manitoba Co-operator*, December 15, 2011.

4 Second ox of the team. He was fattened, and being so large, their neighbour, Little assisted with the slaughtering.

Preparing for bed on New Year's Eve, Elise counted her blessings: *last summer I hardly expected to live. . . . Now I can get about; my children are well, and I've heard from my brothers. I remember Mama telling us, "You will sleep peacefully when you end your day with prayer." These many years and I still end my day with our family prayer.* She pulled the covers tightly around her neck, tucked them under her chin and began:

> *I give you thanks, heavenly Father, through your dear Son Jesus Christ, that you have graciously protected me through this day. I beseech you to forgive all my sin and wrong which I have done. Graciously protect me during the coming night. Into your hands I commend my body and soul and all that is mine. Let your holy angels have charge of me, that the wicked one may have no power over me. Amen.*

She paused and added: *Love and protect my sons . . . Minnie and Isabel, and my dear ones far away, Friedrich, Marie, Karl and Amalie, Anna, Elsa and Julie . . . and all those cousins I hardly know.[5] Send your angels to watch over them. . .*

Amen again. . . I am content.

⋅⋅⋅❦⋅⋅⋅

January, 1892 was so cold Elise couldn't keep the house comfortable. She hurried downstairs each morning, got the fire burning, put on the porridge, and hovered over it to soak up some warmth. *Porridge is a blessing. I'm thawing out while I stir the pot.* But they ran out of food before there was a break in the weather and Edwy had to brave the brutal cold. Back from Brandon with a frozen nose, he had bad news. "Grocer Bower had a fire Friday. Don't know if he will reopen."[6]

Meanwhile, Mr. Criddle was in his glory preparing for his Glee Club. He wrote a waltze [sic] for Jenny Mair and a chorale for the group. He would begin the season with his *Canadian Carol.*

> *The steers are in the pasture, the birds are all asleep;*
> *The sun has set this hour since, The stars begin to peep.*
> *The moon will soon be rising, The air breathes soft and cool;*
> *And here comes Biddy with her pail and her three-legg'd milking stool.*

> *Chorus:*

> > *Then out ye lads and lasses gay! Let's have a dance amid the hay.*
> > *We'll make our shepherd Geordie play His pipes till grey of morning.*
> > *Come Jane and Biddy and Pete and Bill, Sally and Jack and Kate and Phil,*
> > *Let's light a smudge beside the hill and dance till grey of morning.*

> *The sheep have all come home now; the lambs are in the yard,*
> *The dog is tethered by the gate, There's nothing more to guard.*

---

5 Her father's younger brother, Friedrich, had a large family whom Elise would have known as a child but as her family stayed in Heidelberg and the others settled in the southern part of Baden, the two families gradually lost touch. Descendents of her oldest cousin Hermann welcomed the author to Germany.
6   Vane, Harry. "Bower helped us a lot."

The hens are on their perches, The geese are in the shed,
And baby's in her little cot, And mother's gone to bed.[7]

Elise had biscuits ready to serve and enjoyed the singing. Yet, she also suffered. *I fell under the spell of Percy's charms. Now he's enjoying these young ladies, especially Jenny. Does Mrs. Criddle notice?* Ellis and Martin, young neighbours living just south of St. Albans, arrived without an invitation. They weren't welcome and wouldn't come again. The grippe, however, another intruder, came and stayed. Glee Club sessions were put on hold while the lady with the lamp tended the victims. Sitting beside a fevered child, Elise thought of Karl and Amalie. *Are they well? Have my prayers been answered?*

When a letter arrived she opened it eagerly.

Mannheim, December 29, 1891

Liebe Elise!

I wrote you on November 28 and I think my letter and the money order you should have received already.

She paused. **My** *Christmas gift! Thank goodness he doesn't ask how I spent it. I hope some of it went to Dr. Husband for saving my life.*

I send our very best and heartiest well wishes, may the New Year make a good entrance and bring you success, health and contentment!

Pretending to hear her brother's voice she reread his good wishes, ". . . *das neue Jahr sich recht gut anlassen und Euch Glueck, Gesundheit und Zufriedenheit bringen!" Sounds so beautiful. . . . Success and health are out of my control, but contentment, I can do something about. God has brought me through my illness. I pray for the grace to find contentment.*

I will be happy to receive good news from you and I beg that, as soon as you find time, to write once again. With hearty greetings from Mariechen . . . . I remain, your loving brother
Friedrich

PS. Karl was here lately. His wife is doing fine, but he is plagued with a bad cough.

Elise stowed the letter in her pocket. *Thank God, Amalie's better.*

When the flu victims recovered, Glee Club invitations were sent out but only a few singers arrived. Mr. Criddle's ego suffered another blow when Lonsbury

---

7 Criddle, Percy, *Old Canadian Carol*, January 1892. Private collection.

didn't include him in Edwy and Harry's invitation to his party. It didn't help to hear Harry's report next morning, "A hundred people, lots of dancing and jolly good food."

He planned another session of his Glee Club.

Elise had kept her contented frame of mind through the sickness, but her resolve faltered when she wanted to bake and the bottom of the flour barrel appeared. Then, just as she popped the biscuits into the oven, she heard him sing. "I'm invited to sing in Millford. Going to impress the cultured elite – sing the aria from *Martha*." And he started right in:

Oh so sweet! Oh so true!
This is how my eyes saw you,
Oh so kind and so pure!
Of this my heart was very sure.

Elise's blue silk concert dress.

Elise was shocked, *Has he no pity? Does he not remember singing that to win my heart?* On he went, reaching for the high notes, building the crescendos in a most dramatic fashion. "Before you came was only sorrow. Worried gloom was my tomorrow. Then with you life blossomed new, Only joy with you I knew. . ."

Elise asked Beatrice to take the biscuits from the oven when they were done, pushed the big pot to the back of the stove, took her cloak from the peg, and went out into the cold. Emotions long hidden had overtaken her contented heart. She had returned, not to the time he first sang the song to her, but to their home on St. George's Road. *I encouraged him in his music, spent days and nights alone with the babies. He said he needed to practice with a piano and we didn't have one. That year I was expecting again, but not until late summer. I managed to purchase a length of beautiful ice-blue silk to sew a special concert dress[8] for his recital on March 21st. I stitched it with love and finished it just in time. It fit perfectly; I was so very excited. My friend had agreed to stay with our little girls. . . . But that morning he came home and said, "I've changed my*

---

8   Dated by Dr. Carl Ludwig Fuchs, Kurpfälzisches Museum, Heidelberg, Germany. May, 2004.

plans. I'm staying across the Thames. I need to practice – haven't time to come back for you. You have plenty to do here."

Off he went singing with nary a kiss for me, or hugs for his little daughters. As his voice faded away, I stood there frozen, the children at my feet. My dreams! My love! I don't remember how long . . . and then I crumbled to the floor sobbing! . . .

I felt dear little Minnie's chubby arms around my neck and when I couldn't stop the tears, she looked at me so knowingly and said, "I lov' 'ou Mama."

I hadn't wanted to believe Percy had found a new love . . . . But those tears washed away my blindness. He knew I was sewing a dress for his special concert. He'd promised this celebration ever since he brought me to London. I lived for the day when he'd be finished and become a great musician. . . . We were to be married! All his promises had come to this! He was taking another woman to his concert!

Elise found herself at the barn door and went in. The cows turned their heads and stared; their steamy breath showing her that their home was none too warm. Knowing Beauty best, she went up beside her. After giving her a few pats, Elise leaned against the warm body and put her arm over the cow's back. With her face against the cow's warm shoulder, the tears flowed. . . .

"I never thought I'd be looking for comfort from you, Beauty. I hope you don't mind."

The cow's steady breathing calmed her. She looked about in the dim light and noticed the others steadily chewing their cud. *It's peaceful here. The smell is . . . pungent, but not unpleasant . . . doesn't come close to the stench in steerage. Strange, I should think of that. Seems we carry all our memories, good and bad with us as we go through life.*

She lingered, shivering even with the cow's warmth. *I must go back. . . . Take courage dear heart. You've lived with his betrayal for 20 years already.*

There was another low turnout of singers that night, and Mrs. Criddle, usually so gracious, was unusually sharp. Elise wondered. *Does she also have memories mixed up with that song?*

Unaware of its effect on the women, Mr. Criddle continued to practice their song, until he took out his yellowed Italian translation. "Anyone can sing English."

Mrs. Criddle seemed more at ease, but the change of language did little for Elise. She searched her heart for a way to regain her composure. . . . Finally she concluded, yet again, *I can't change him. It's not easy, but I must try to keep a contented heart. It's a beautiful song, I'll sing along under my breath . . . but into the stew on the stove.*

The night of the concert Mr. Criddle stayed with the Sutcliffes and arrived home late the next day in fine fettle, "I planned to visit with Dr. Husband, but two of his patients had the infernal audacity to be ill – called him away. Mrs. Husband has a new piano – lifeless affair–handsome case – three pedals – what for I don't know – heaven knows how many octaves – fairly even touch – but as I say – no life in the beastly thing. Came from the States and cost five or six hundred dollars. Did pretty well at the concert – considering that I'm not so young as I was. Some of the Canucks gave really capital recitations. Tambly wrote a farce – much applause. Rather close sailing – a farce in a church – next door to the cemetery."[9]

Elise's thoughts were on the piano. *Oh, for the touch of the keys. . . . I'd be happy with any number of octaves and three pedals! . . . But I'll never have a chance to play it. . . . If ever there is to be a piano here, we'll need a few years of 40 bushels to the acre.*

⚬⚬⚬

All winter the boys cut and hauled logs for a 24' by 18' structure to be built just to the east of St. Albans. "It's to be my 'E' House. A store house – granary – ball room and general utility shop. It will have a real gable roof, shingles, and we'll line the walls before next winter."

Is he dreaming of concerts? People coming from far and wide to St. George's Hall on the Prairie? Right away Elise's mind went to food. *No choral event can end without a lunch . . . from what will we make it? Will he charge? . . . I resolved not to fret. Take no thought for the morrow for the morrow will take thought for the things of itself.*

Spring came; Minnie visited; Aweme School reopened; their last meal from the old ox was consumed; and the new oxen, Bruce and Spider, began their training. The boys made their trip to Brandon with potatoes and brought home supplies and upsetting news. "They had a fire at Isabel's place and she lost most of her clothes. She's really down about her precious locket and chain."

But Edwy had worse news; "Lonsbury, Fortune, and Bruner all have sick horses. Glanders, they say, and have to be destroyed—government orders. It came up from Dakota in eighty-six with a shipment of horses and mules. Very contagious, can pass to humans. Young Jim Fortune has just come down with something."

The Vane boys stayed healthy and in spite of the winds and dust, continued breaking new land. One afternoon Mr. Criddle returned from Brandon sporting a piece of paper. "I've purchased the NE quarter of 5.9.16 at three dollars an acre

---

9 According to a sketch by Canon Cooper, the Methodist Church was situated above the village to the east, and thus not far from Millford Cemetery.

and have ten years to pay – had to act or another settler might buy it.[10] Land is going fast right now. It's due west of my North Farm – we'll call it 'Five' – it's a pretty quarter, perhaps too light – and nearly all clear of scrub cedar."

Elise shook her head. *Is he being hopeful or foolish? Finances are so preciously tight. . . Edwy earned that $17.50 breaking ten acres for a new settler, and we're in need of food stuffs. He's asked Edwy to drive him and Mrs. Criddle to dinner at McVey's tomorrow. What shall I feed the family?*

As she had in the past, Elise tried to think of a story. *I know tales about giants and trolls, beggars and bears, kings and princesses . . . but I don't remember any about dust storms.* She said to the youngsters, "We know a lot about dust. Could we make up a story?" She noticed disappointed eyes—red, rimmed round with dirt. "Would a poem be easier? Can you make one?"

They looked doubtful. "Start with something like—I have dust on my face, dust up my nose." They smiled; she tried another, "Where is the sun today?"

They worked away. Norman, more practiced at writing soon had one to offer.

"My title is *Dust*," and he read his poem.

Dust, dust, dust,
Drifting sand moving over the land.
Weeds roving like a cattle band.
Wind so strong that it's hard to stand,
And dust, dust, dust.
Dust, dust, dust.
Some of it rising high in the sky,
Much of it getting into one's eye.
Low dirty clouds roving quickly by
With dust dirty dust,
Dust, dust, dust.
Every cranny and every nook,
Over the dinner and into the book,
There will be dust wherever you look,
Dust, dust, dust.[11]

They clapped, "You're a poet Norman."

❧

Alexander Clark's oldest son, Adam, had been hunting with his dog across the Souris River. Returning in the evening, his gun went off as he was getting out of his boat—hit him in the chest. Bleeding badly, he managed to make it up the hill to his yard and called out to his wife.[12]

---

10   June 23, 1892. ". . . on 10 year system of installments and 6% interest."
11   Criddle, Norman: Provincial Archives of Manitoba.
12   Clark, Adam: born 1843, Essex County, Ontario. Travelled with his wife Susan Collins in one of the six covered wagons to the west in 1879. Wintered in Pincher Creek, Alberta, where his father Alexander, operated the experimental farm for two years and looked after rations for Sitting Bull and his people. Adam was scout

Elise could hardly believe the news. *If a man like Adam, one of the few settlers who crossed the prairie and hunted buffalo, could die by his own gun, it could happen to anyone.* **My** *sons are always trekking around the country with guns.* That evening she heard the whip-poor-will's sad call. *The song seems fitting for tonight. I've never met poor Mrs. Clark, but I know they're a large family. I'm sure she'll be comforted.* The sadness swept Elise back to the tragedy of her own father's death: his cold still face, her poor mother bending over him weeping, her big brothers trying to be men, and her own bewildered ten-year-old self holding on to her little brother.[13] *The whip-poor-will sings for me too.*

※

As the weeks passed Elise was surrounded by illness; Mrs. Criddle had a bilious attack, Mrs. Fortune had pleurisy and her son Jim was failing. Neither a Scottish doctor from Brandon nor Dr. Husband could help the boy. Mr. Criddle said, "I see nothing in Jimmy's case to prevent a cure in three days – unless the boy has glanders."

The lad's illness was heavy on Elise's heart. *He was so good with Edwy the night of the accident. It's not long since he was helping with Percy's new building. I like his Scottish accent.*

From early June to July 16, Jim went steadily down hill. Near the end, Mr. Criddle told a subdued group around the tea table, "I have no hope for the boy. Rheumatism has been flying about him for some time past – must have gone to his heart – probably on Saturday last and on Monday night – terrible heart beating and most alarming symptoms."

Jim passed away in his nineteenth year.[14] His poor mother could not be consoled: "We crossed the ocean to get land for our Jimmy. Next month we are to sign our homestead papers and our Jimmy is gone. Jane is a fine lassie, but a daughter can't farm."

※

Anxious eyes scanned the western horizon for clouds; they watched promising formations climb the sky, only to pass on by. Mr. Criddle kept up a constant commentary: "Could we but get a fair crop this year we should be comparatively rich – but a failure will be quite the other way about. Damn the weather. The hens aren't laying. We're short on food stuffs. The purse is empty." Yet, when Sut-

---

and hunter for the group. Settled with his father at Two Rivers in 1881. Died June 9, 1892, buried on the hill in Millford Cemetery. Children: Emma and George. Clark family records.

13 Harrer, Carl: Grand Ducal Postmaster, age 44, died January15, 1849. Catholic Church St. Johann, Donaueschingen, Baden.

14 Jim Fortune died July 16, 1892. Connected to the Presbyterian Church in Douglas, Jim was buried in Madford Cemetery, just north of Douglas.

cliffe, Köhler, and two Coopers came for cricket on Sunday, Elise had to scrounge enough for their tea. The guests came in early because of a rain shower, but when Mr. Criddle checked the rain gage, he found only 13/100 of an inch had fallen.

Anxiety took over Mr. Criddle; he heralded every hopeful wisp of cloud on the western horizon. Unlike his neighbours, he had the leisure to record what he saw:

> Exquisitely grand and lovely thunder clouds tonight overhead – pink-gray – light blue – on copper colored ground. The sky all around is fine – blue black predominating – but the rain hangs fire so far – for variety there is blue sky in odd places intermingled with a golden sunset.
> 10 min later – Most of the sky's beauty has now gone – in place of it there are savage black masses – interspersed with copper background and crossed with fleecy inky patches here and there. The outlines are rounded and rolling – over lapping. . .

Elise also worried; *are we ever to get a good crop? I'd like to pray for rain. . . . But I've heard Percy say often enough, "I take no stock in such rubbish."*

⤜⤜☙ ⤚⤚

There was thunder about the stifling hot night of July 9. Next morning the barometer continued to fall. That afternoon Elise heard, "Come out! Look at that sky!" Arms pointed to the north where a revolving cloud dipped down like a water spout and dust rose to meet the blue-black mass. *It's so eerie . . . terrible things are happening not far away, yet behind me is clear blue sky.* Next day they learned what havoc that funnel had wrought:

> . . . about 100 yards broad and extended for 10 miles ere it blew itself out. On either side of its course there seems to have been a great fall of hail which destroyed the crop completely. . . two people killed, a lot badly injured - 9 horses killed – 3 houses torn to bits, many other buildings completely destroyed – a threshing engine whirled away and smashed – and all the neighbourhood wrecked. They say there are great holes blasted in the ground – in fact it must have been a terrible business . . .

By the time rain finally bucketed down, their wheat was beyond salvation. Mr. Criddle wailed, "A fortnight earlier a fine crop, now perhaps, something."

Some of the vegetables revived. The boys brought Elise a pail of little new potatoes from the patch on the hill and nothing could have tasted better. While they ate, Elise overheard, "I'm planning a bachelors' festival in honour of the Boy's twenty-first birthday."

Her thoughts leaped from happiness to the practical. *He'll enjoy the tennis and cricket. But where will we get the makings for the feast?* Fortunately, Cecil knew about a patch of wild raspberries and with the help of Stuart, Evelyn, and the girls,

Edwy Vane

they picked all they could find. His mother needed only a little flour and sugar, an egg and butter to make a delicious fruit pudding.

While the pudding baked, Stuart was hitching up the young oxen. He leaned down to fasten a trace, and Spider landed a kick squarely in his lower stomach. His father retaliated, and when he could no longer swing his stick, he had Edwy, and then Cecil follow up: "Tis not the first time Spider has adopted Canadian fashions, but we mean to civilize him or kill him by degrees."

The birthday dawned bright and sunny. Edwy's mother cooked the oatmeal to perfection and greeted him with, "Many happy returns of the day, my oldest son."

While she set out the food she wondered: *do these people ever talk about 'Mr. Criddle' and his extraordinary circumstances? I'm sure none of them have two women—one to be the gracious hostess and one to serve. Men would think it an advantage. My lads work so hard. I sometimes think he treats us so differently because he is afraid neighbours will guess the truth.[15] English servants do wear black so that explains my never changing dresses. But he and Mrs. Criddle insist their boys wear clothes from England, rather than home sewn ones.*

Edwy's birthday festival went well; the boys enjoyed the sports, and everyone the food. Only Elise's swollen legs and tired feet complained.

Köhler's Photo

15 Tradition of neighbours: "We never guessed! The boys were treated so differently it never crossed our minds that the Vane boys were his own children." Percy himself didn't consider them his children. Percy's Diary in England on the birth of Stuart; Dec 6, 1877. "Third son born to me at 10:25 pm on Tuesday, Dec 4."

While the boys hayed and harvested, Mr. Criddle read a book on cattle breeding. "Shorthorns are the farmer's cow," he told them. "Just what we need – all round source of milk – cream – calf every year – grows well on rough grass."

Cooper's prized Shorthorn heifer

Isabel and a friend came out from Brandon one weekend during harvest. They laughed when Mr. Criddle changed Dolly Knight to Dolly Varden.[16] Elise thought: *he gives names easily, Isabel has been Dido so long, one would think it her real name—Dido this and Dido that. She's such a good-natured girl; comes every year to help. Mr. Tulk leaves and she starts over at a new place. Strange how Minnie isn't called home to help; Minnie visits. My girls are as different as night and day. I love them both dearly.*

No one offered the girls a ride back to Brandon Monday morning. "Don't worry Mama. We don't mind walking. I'd like to see Wawanesa. Might catch a ride with someone once we get across the river."

On August 25th, Elise wished Harry a happy birthday. *I worry about him. Harry's wages put food on our table, but he's not a favourite. Perhaps it's fortunate he works away so much. . . . He's always coming up with ideas that get shot down. Strange though, Edwy is the Boy, Cecil is Solomon, but Harry is always Harry.*[17]

Their harvest began with binder trouble and more followed. An early frost finished everything that had survived the drought. The waltz Mr. Criddle was composing for Jenny Mair gave him no end of difficulty; Mr. Tulk's trunk went missing again; Mrs. Criddle was not well; her baby had a bad session of diarrhoea, and Julia developed a high fever. Still, there was food on the table thanks to Mr. Tulk's dollar-a-day board, Harry's earnings at Mair's and Cecil's fall ploughing at Bruner's.

The threshers arrived, the machine was set up and ready to go. Then the machine broke down and while they waited for repairs, the men kept eating. The cost grew while the bushels stayed the same. To pay for threshing those 571 bushels of wheat, and 241 of oats, Edwy left immediately with a loaded wagon. He returned in despair; "Fifty-three cents a bushel. We're just giving it away."

Next day Mr. Criddle told Elise, "Alice will not be out – is knocked up – and feverish."

Elise didn't blame her. *I'm sure the poor price doesn't help. Our hunters better have good luck or we'll be eating nothing but potatoes and turnips . . . and there are not so many of them this year.* Fortunately, Norman shot a deer, and Mr. Tulk, just before he departed, got a goose.

---

16   In Charles Dickens', *Barnaby Rudge*, flirtatious Dolly Varden wore flashy attire and colorful dresses.
17   Harry: also the name of both Percy's father and grandfather Criddle.

Elise dreaded butchering days! That morning the victim's squeals pierced her to the core. Soon after they died away, Mr. Criddle stormed in, marched through the kitchen, and into his room. Sometime later Harry brought in the sow's heart to roast. "I guess you figured something was wrong." His mother nodded. With an eye on Mr. Criddle's door he explained, "Mr. C hit the pig on the head with the axe but didn't knock it down. It wouldn't stand still. Couldn't hit it properly and he got excited. He kept swinging; killed it eventually. He stood there giving orders while we did the scalding. Stuart said, 'This pig has got some bad bruises. Some are in the middle of its back.' Mr. C **did not like** that remark! Left us to it."[18]

Christmas Day was the coldest on record. Elise's job was almost to be envied as she prepared the meal—roast pork, carrots, potatoes, and of course Mrs. Criddle's pudding steamed on the back of the stove. Those who had to went out for chores and milking, fetching water and filling the wood boxes. The card players stayed close to the sitting room stove. After the evening meal, Elise finished the dishes, tidied the kitchen, and made her weary way upstairs. *I've had no news from my brothers for such a long time. . . . My resolve to live each day with a contented heart is so very difficult.*

She paused at the end of her usual prayer, and added: *loving God, I need your angels more than ever.*

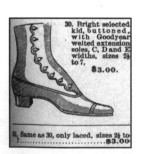

30. Bright selected kid, buttoned, with Goodyear welted extension soles, C, D and E widths, sizes 2½ to 7, $3.00.

31. Same as 30, only laced, sizes 2½ to 7 ....$3.00

---

18 Vane, Harry.

Chapter Seventeen

The Fattened Ox

Elise had some trying weeks in January. Little Talbot, with his many scurvy-like sores, came howling every time he bumped against something. She picked him up and held him tightly to her bosom and rocked him back and forth purring, "Owee, owee, owee, owee," just as she had been comforted as a child. Usually her owee, owee, evolved into his favourite nursery rhyme:

Ride a cock horse to Banbury Cross
To see a fine lady upon a white horse,
Rings on her fingers and bells on her toes,
She shall have music wherever she goes. . . .

And it wasn't long before the little fellow was off and running. And all the while Elise worried about her brothers and waited anxiously for news. *Has a letter gone astray? Are they protecting me from something?*

Norman spent most of his winter days drawing at the table, oblivious of the little ones. He looked up at Elise sweeping the floor nearby: "When I was a kid in England I liked to watch my Grandmamma paint. She'd let me stay as long as I was quiet." He drew a leaf and added, "I'm drawing these dried plants we collected last summer. Mr. Tulk couldn't find a book to tell me their names so I'm hoping somebody can identify them from my pictures." Then leaning back, he added, "I think this looks like the real thing, except this bent leaf."

"It's difficult working from pressed flowers and to get its curve and colouring right. You have done well."

Mrs. Criddle, feeling out-of-sorts, had kept to her room. Elise reasoned there would be another little one by harvest. . . . *Thinking of summer, I could use some of its heat right now; cold floors and chilblains go together. I'll write Karl tonight and warm my feet on the oven door:*

Mein Bruder!

A letter from you has not reached us for a long time. I think of you and pray that you and Amalie are well, as we are. God be thanked!

I cannot begin to find words to describe the cold this January. Can you believe me when I tell you the thermometer went down to -34 degrees Fahrenheit? The wind blew snow through the cracks into our sitting room and made snowdrifts on the floor. Imagine! Our geraniums are down in the cellar to keep them from the frost. And yet even there they may not be safe from this extreme cold.

When the boys work outdoors they have to take care of their noses to keep them from freezing. Neighbours have Buffalo fur coats with high collars that are wonderfully warm, but our boys do not. They are too expensive.

Three nights later she finished her letter.

The blizzard is over at last. It's calm and the full moon makes the night as bright as day. Percy called us out to see a most unusual sight, a paraselenes, his fancy name for the bright spot on the lunar halo. Sundogs we see more often in the morning, but moondogs are rare. I thought of you and wished I could, like the moon, look down upon you.

We are all well, the boys send their greetings. I hope soon to receive good news from you.

Receive my heartiest wishes, also to Amalie. I remain your loving sister, Elise. Please remember me to Friedrich, Marie, and their beautiful children.

Weeks passed and still anxious, Elise was delighted to be handed an envelope, "Thank you. It's Karl's writing!" *Is it bad news about Amalie?* She drew out the contents; *no black border. Gott sei Dank!*

Meine liebe Schwester!

I, together with Amalie, was very happy to receive a sign of life from you. At our place here in Karlsruhe we are all fine! Amalie and I are healthy, in spite of a tough winter. We have a lot of snow and at times up to 20 degrees cold. For me it isn't pleasant to go back and forth to work four times a day, half an hour each time. I always have a lot of work, a reason why I don't get around to writing letters very often.

For the lovely photographs of Minnie [left] and Isabel [below] we thank you heartily. They must be lovely girls. Isabel seems to be taking after you. Photographs of your sons would give me great joy.

Minnie

Isabel

She paused: *The girls have their own money. Next year we'll have better crops.*

Out of your letter I would have liked to have learned how things are going with all of you, how you live. Because we in Germany have really no concept of how you arrange your way of life there. I can well imagine that you have to fight many obstacles until you advance to the point where you can say that things are going well. May the good Lord shield you from sickness and other ill fate!

With our brother Friedrich and his family things have not gone well this past year. Especially with Friedrich it was quite crucial, which caused all of us many worries. Now he is somewhat better. God be thanked! He is of good cheer again, before he was so disinterested that it was quite scary. May he live long! His family still needs him badly.

She ended off Carl's letter, but kept thinking. *Friedrich mentioned needing more money but I didn't expect he was having so much trouble. He was always the one helping. I remember, as if it were yesterday, sitting by the window reading his comforting letter when Wilhelm died. It's my turn to write him something cheerful . . . no blizzards. Let's see . . . Would Percy's cure for Mrs. Fortune bring a chuckle? The doctors hadn't helped her so <u>he</u> offered a cure: cocktails twice a day and lots of whiskey.*[1] *No, why did I even think of it? She's been unwell, more so since her Jimmy died. Maybe he and Mr. Fortune had a shot of whiskey this afternoon, but surely, Mrs. Fortune would not. I doubt he said that to her . . . was only poking fun at the Methodists who deny themselves such comfort. Nor can I mention Talbot's earaches, Stuart's early morning nosebleed, or Mrs. Criddle's condition. Percy says it's peritonitis, I guess I was wrong to think another little one was on the way. . . . He might be amused by Percy saying he has given up smoking because of a wretched cough, except, for the odd whiff? I'll wait for happier news.*

❧

Several men arranged to board with the Criddles while they logged in the Tamarack. Edwy drove to Brandon for supplies; Harry and crew butchered a young pig. Elise cooked, thankful to have the makings for bread and puddings. *I'm happy to have flour, but it's not the cheerful news I need for a brother half a world away.*

Once the boarders left, Elise found her good news. Mr. Criddle announced, "I've decided not to sing at the Millford concert. In my stead – I'll train the Boy."

From then on Elise overheard the lessons:

Anthea, I am going hence with some small stock of innocence . . . .
Bid me despair and I'll despair, Under that cypress-tree;
Or bid me die, and I will dare E'en death to die for thee.
Thou art my life, my love, my heart, The very eyes of me;
And hast command of every part, To live and die for thee.[2]

Elise tried to put her memories of the song aside as Edwy practiced. *He has a fine voice. Is it possible there will be a young lady in the audience to impress?*

The morning after the concert he told her, "Everyone agreed it was the best concert ever. I made it through my song and people clapped, so I guess it was okay. Mrs. Husband's friend from England has a beautiful voice, like yours, Mama. Lonsbury presented a farce. . . . I laughed till my sides hurt. I'll tell you more later, have work to do."

He was out the door, but she had the good news she needed for Friedrich's letter.

---

1 February 18, 1893.
2 Herrick, Robert. A 17th century English poet.

Aweme, Manitoba April 2, 1893

Lieber Bruder!

I have been very happy to receive a sign of life from Karl and learn that he and Amalie are well. To hear that my prayers have been answered is very good news.

Karl has perhaps been to visit you and Marie. How I would like to be with you on such an occasion. I cannot tell you how important your letters are to help me live more cheerfully. I am perfectly well now.

"Perfectly well." I exaggerate. . . It might be true if only these boils would stop erupting.

You may remember that Edwy has a fine voice. He tells me our horses, Jess and Doll, like it when he serenades them. Percy asked him to sing at a concert and chose "Anthea."

The distance was too great for me to travel, so I was content to wait for their return. The first performer was a professional singer from a London Music Hall singing, "Ta-ra-ra Boom-de-ay," which pleased everyone. It's the very latest.

Percy said Edwy sounded nervous at the beginning, but his finish had all the pathos needed for a love song. You may be sure I am proud. Oh that we, dear brother, could sing together again.

She paused. *I shouldn't have added that . . . but it's written . . . can't be changed.*

Edwy now has a house on his own land. The boys had enough logs and invited neighbours to a bee and raised the walls in a day. I told you already how we do things here? The boys will finish the door and windows and put on the roof. I am proud of my sons.

I pray you will soon send good news that you are all completely well. With heartfelt greetings from all here, I remain your loving sister,
Elise

⁓◦◠◦⁓

The spring sun slowly pushed the snow back to the edges of the bluffs. The nights were cold enough to freeze the ponds left by the melting snow so the boys skated until they had to start work.

One morning Beatrice offered to untie the cows so they could enjoy themselves a little longer. She didn't expect the cows to mind and walked up beside Laura. Startled, the cow pulled back just as Beatrice tugged on the knot and it tightened around her thumb. She hollered, "Come back here, you ornery beast!" The frightened cow jerked so hard the rope broke. Laura was free. So was Beatrice, but she had left her thumb nail in the knot. The injured girl lit out for the house screaming at the top of her lungs. Elise heard her coming, opened the door, and stood aside as she rushed by to her parents' room.

The boys heard the commotion, pulled off their skates, and came running. Hearing about the accident, they looked for the missing part, as if it could be reattached.

Sure enough, the nail was still in the rope and they raced it up to Beatrice who unleashed a whole new flood of tears. The boys soon had wounds of their own and, to top off their punishment, Mr. Criddle said, "You're to blame if Bobby is disfigured for life."

———

When Mr. Tulk sent notice of Harry Smith's death in St. Bartholomew's Hospital, Elise felt the loss of a friend.[3] *Dear Harry— I first thought he was scoundrel. Percy complained that he mishandled his mother's money and didn't allow him enough. But once I got to England and met him I changed my opinion. In '73 Percy gave up the idea of teaching music and joined Harry's business; 'Smith and Criddle' in the elegant Hop Exchange. But it didn't go well and they gave up the expensive office and moved into our front room.*

Hop Exchange

131 St. George's Road

Until they split I saw Harry more than Percy. Even after their partnership ended in '78, Harry came on occasion. He liked to talk about his wife and little ones. She heard music and listened. Gracious, is he singing a hymn?

*O Lord, Thy love's unbounded, . . .
But oh! the hope of being/ For ever with the Lord, . . .
It fills our heart with comfort, It fills our lips with praise,
So that amidst our sorrow/ A joyful song we raise.*

Harry's death must affect him more than he admits. I know the words . . . but what a strange tune! I wish he would sing it again to a familiar tune.

———

The end of April, with the roads their muddiest, Edwy drove Mr. Criddle to Brandon to be sworn in as Justice of the Peace for another term. When he called

---

3 Harry Smith, the father, looked after Harry Criddle's business affairs and continued after his death in 1857 with Mrs. Criddle. Harry Smith, the son, and Percy became partners in 1874; Percy took over his mother's finances. Percy had three economic advantages at the time of his marriage: his wife's small inheritance; his mother's paintings; acting as a middleman for his cousin in Siam until 1878. Sources: Southwark Local History Library, Kelly's London Directory, The Hop Exchange, census, and private letters.

on Minnie for her contributions, she announced, "I'm engaged, going to marry Mr. John Bligh."

Isabel's lady was away on a holiday so she climbed aboard to return with them to St. Albans. All three were shocked by Minnie's news. "What does he do? Where will they live?"

It was late when Edwy pulled up at the door, but Elise was still up, the kettle hot.

"Sit down Mama. I have something to tell you."

Her mother sensed Isabel's excitement; *it must surely be good.*

"Minnie is going to marry Mr. Bligh!"

"Gracious! Minnie never hinted at the possibility." A moment later she'd recovered enough to say; "Minnie's twenty-five, old enough to know her own mind."

She got up to brew the tea. *Just imagine . . . my Minnie a married woman.*

❦

Mr. Bligh brought Minnie out to meet the family a few days later and everything seemed settled except for the date of the event. After the waving arm faded in the distance, Elise thought of her dear friend in London.[4] *She was always fond of Minnie and is lonely now that her husband is gone. Our 'Olger' was a tower of strength after Percy left us. Mr. and Mrs. Foulger made sure the five little Criddles enjoyed Christmas and made up for the papa who'd forgotten them. I told her often, 'A friend in need is a friend indeed.' I'll write and give her Minnie's good news.*

Aweme, Manitoba, May 16, 1893

My dear Mrs. Foulger,

I am sorry to hear that you have been ill and have some happy news. I hope it helps you in your loneliness. Minnie is engaged to Mr. John Bligh. They surprised us last weekend by driving out from Brandon for a visit. She is very happy and we of course all agree with her that he is a splendid young man. They did not yet inform us as to their wedding plans.

Our prospects this year are promising. The boys work hard always and each year they have cultivated more land. Isabel has been home, which gives me great pleasure. Unfortunately she goes to Brandon in the morning. Her lady was away and wants her back now she is home again.

Emma Foulger

---

4   1881 census lists Robert and Emma Foulger living at the same address as 'Elise Criddle' and children, 131 St. George's Rd. Robert was a foreman Bricklayer, age 41, Emma was 43.

The boys take great pleasure playing football and are in high demand from neighbouring teams. They boast that their team wins. I suppose they can't be blamed for crowing a little now and then. It gives me pleasure when they enjoy themselves.

We are all well and everyone wishes to be remembered to you, dear Olger,
Your affectionate friend, Elise

❧

Isabel went back to Brandon; the whip-poor-will returned and a lovely rain raised the Criddle prospects. A $3 purchase of a red and white spotted bull calf would, in a year or so, save a great many trips with their cows to the neighbors. Edwy and Harry played for Blythe at the First of July celebrations. Then the weather turned hot, much too hot for the obligatory road work. After sweltering through the day building a road straight south to the new ferry crossing, Mr. Criddle sweetened the bitter pill with a cooling swim in the river.

Elise, on the other hand, had no such relief. Hoping for a breeze, she carried a chair to the open window and placed her little wooden secretary on her knees. Its slanted lid gave her a good surface on which to write. *I won't mention Minnie's engagement . . . wait for more definite plans.*

My dear Bruder!

Your good news has been well received. May you and Amalie live long and happily. With us, we are well, as perhaps you know already from Friedrich. At that time we expected a fine crop, but once again we are to be disappointed. Never before has the temperature been so hot – our wheat shrivels more every day.

We have been picking berries to make into jam and already have 13 jars of strawberry, 8 gooseberry, 5 raspberry, and 3 currant. We will enjoy them next winter on our bread in the morning.

Elise paused. *I wish it were true. . . . Like the tea, the jam will be for others.*

Harry is 21 years old this year and always busy and happy. He likes music and is playing the violin at every opportunity. Of Edwy I have written in my letter to Friedrich. Cecil is always helping me, when he is at home he keeps the wood box full. We expect our Isabel to come home in the fall when Mr. Tulk comes from England. Minnie is well and happy.

. . .

From your sister who loves you, Elise

She folded the letter. *I'll ask for an envelope and stamp tomorrow.*

Upstairs, the air was stifling. As usual she looked in on the little ones. *They manage to sleep in spite of the heat.* Ignoring her aches and pains, she prayed for her loved ones. Then lying coverless on her bed she told herself: *I'll imagine I'm walking along a cool shaded path in the forest.*

❧

The weather got hotter: 102° Fahrenheit with strong dry winds that sucked moisture from every living thing. As Mrs. Criddle awaited the birth of her eighth child, she stayed away from the hot kitchen. *It's a blessing to shut the door to their quarters to keep as cool as possible.* August 6, soon after Elise had cleared away the dinner dishes, she was summoned. Soon after, the wee girl slipped into the world as smoothly as a bar of soap. Cooing to yet another miracle, Elise passed her tenderly to her mother. Papa Criddle wrote in his diary that night, "Apparently mother and daughter are doing fine." Mrs. Criddle named her baby Alma. In another ten days she could be up and about.

A breeze, which at first brought relief, soon became an enemy. It swept up the topsoil and darkened the days. The chairs, the table, their beds, every flat surface had a covering of grit. On Julia's birthday, her papa warned, "There's a beastly fire out east. If the wind changes – our whole settlement will be wiped out."

Haying was tough in the wind, but the boys managed to get some stacked. Then Edwy borrowed a horse from Bellhouse to hitch with the oxen to pull their old binder. For the new one, he obtained another horse from Lonsbury to put with Jess and Doll. The crop went down quickly and then, while others stooked and stacked, Edwy paid for the borrowed horses by cutting their owners' crops. The wind finally died, but it left an enormous windswept cavity around their house. While the boys shoveled load after load of dirt into the hole, Mr. Criddle composed a new tune for Shakespeare's *Blow, Blow Thou Winter Wind.*

That crop was their poorest: only six bushels to the acre. From the meagre proceeds must come the money to pay the threshing bills. It was all too much for Mrs. Criddle; she took to her bed again. Elise thought; *I'm glad I wrote my brother before I knew the facts.*

When Mr. Tulk arrived, so did Isabel. *He brings a double blessing, my daughter's help and enough to eat.* When the gentlemen went calling, Beatrice, now a young lady of 13, took her mother's place when they went visiting. From her, Elise learned Sutcliffes had built a fine new frame house.

All three Vane boys were working away, so when a neighbour asked for help threshing, Mr. Criddle had to pick up the fork. Home that night, grimy and exhausted, he growled; "Beastly day! I was on the straw stack feeding the machine – horrid wind. My eyes are full of chaff. Need a tub with warm water in my room."

Four of Mr. Criddle's gentlemen friends from Brandon brought their guns for 'fun among the chickens'. As Elise served them that evening she noticed Mr. Tulk fidgeting. *I don't think he enjoys the coarse talk.* Nor did he join the group later as tobacco and whiskey mixed with cards. *Is he thinking, as I do, that Percy is losing a little too much money?* By the time Elise had the dishes put away, Mr. Tulk had withdrawn to his room and closed the door. *Is he offended? What will we do if Mr. Tulk goes home and doesn't come again?*

⌘

Mr. Tambly arrived at the door looking for landowners to support his stand against a 'mill bonus.' [5] The enquiry led to Elise, and the two men decided that she, as a landowner, could cast another vote against. She couldn't believe her ears; *I might be in favour if I knew why the money is needed.* But, in a matter of minutes she found herself seated on the second seat of a democrat,[6] behind a fine team of drivers, speeding south to Treesbank. Sitting upright, facing forward, she had full view of the countryside. *This is travelling in style . . . a most unexpected holiday.* The men were engrossed in conversation so she had to guess whose farms she was passing. The Assiniboine was low and easily forded; *the banks are not as steep as I imagined.* It wasn't far to the village. *Gracious! I had no idea it would be such a busy place. Harness shop, blacksmith, stores. Everything one might need is here. Why does Edwy drive all the way to Brandon for supplies?* They pulled up at a hitching rail; Mr. Tambly jumped down and snapped a lead on his horses. She tried to take in everything before she had to take his hand to step down. "Thank you. I'm no longer nimble."

Treesbank Store and Post Office

She followed the men into the post office where Mr. Sutcliffe was looking after the voting. Surprised to see her, he nevertheless nodded as he greeted the men. She marked her 'X' in the proper box and in what seemed like a moment she was homeward bound. *I may never come this way again. It would be lovely to tell my brothers about the sights. But, how can I explain that I have lived here already 12 years and have never seen the countryside only two miles south?*

⌘

Edwy brought a parcel from Minnie to his mother. Mrs. Criddle and the girls crowded around to watch her open it. The quickly scribbled note said:

> *Dear Mama,*
> *I know you like hand-me-downs and my lady gave me these for you. There are raisins for some good puddings and my ten dollars. Don't be too disappointed, but our wedding is postponed. Will tell you more later.*
> *Love, Minnie.*

---

5   Mill rate used to calculate taxes.
6   Buggy with two seats facing forward.

She set the raisins aside, the ten one-dollar bills went into Mrs. Criddle's pocket. Then holding up a beautiful blue blouse, Elise exclaimed; "Minnie knows blue's my favourite colour."

Mrs. Criddle reached out, "Could I see it?"

She held it up by the shoulders and said, "Come here Beatrice." Applying the garment to her daughter's chest she nodded happily. And before Elise had time to blink, Mrs. Criddle said, "It is indeed, a lovely shade. It will do fine for Bobo." [7]

Elise's heart sank. She hid her disappointment by taking up the next garment, a bright cotton dress and thought, *how beautifully cool this would be to wear in the hot kitchen.* But Mrs. Criddle spoke again, "We can make that down for Maida. It's her colour. There's another? Yes, that will do fine for Julia."

Elise was left with the brown paper, a note, and the raisins. *Minnie thought she had the perfect gift for me. She often says, "Why don't you wear something different? How can you put up with wearing those old black things? The maids in Brandon don't wear black all the time." But Minnie doesn't see what happens. Even if Mrs. Criddle didn't want me to wear the bright colours, I could have kept the blue 'body'[8] in my trunk for Minnie's wedding . . . or Isabel's. It would be lovely with my black jacket and taffeta skirt. . . . Anyway it belongs to Beatrice now. I'll have to come up with something to tell Minnie before Edwy goes to Brandon.*

She had the letter thought out by the end of the week:

Aweme, Manitoba October 14, 1893

My dear Minnie!

I want to thank you, dear Minnie, for your gifts. The Body [sic] you sent for me is just what would please me most. Mrs. Criddle, however, thought it bright and unsuitable, perhaps too small for me, and has appropriated it for Bobby. She says, "It does splendidly for her." I have to agree. The little frocks will please Julia and Maida.

You tell us that your marriage to Mr. Bligh has been postponed. You know, my dear Minnie, I wish only for you to be happy. You will know best how to arrange matters. No doubt everything will work out alright.

You have written by now, I expect to Olger. She is always so fond of you and will be very happy to hear from you. I told her already about your engagement to Mr. Bligh.

Goodbye dear Minnie, believe me ever
Your affectionate Mama[9]
[PS] Mrs. Criddle is writing to you and will tell you all the news.

Meanwhile, in her room Mrs. Criddle had penned her letter.

---

7 Beatrice was nicknamed Bobby or Bobo.
8 Blouse
9 Elise and Mrs. Criddle's letters are in family collection.

St. Albans, Aweme, October 15ᵗʰ, 1893

My dear Minnie,

We were very glad to get your letter and the contents. We will have two or three splendid cakes and enjoy them very much. I did not tell Papa anything about the money, as he was asking whether you had sent him a ten dollar bill. When I said "No," he remarked "OK, I was afraid not." He has been having a queer sort of rheumatism, which gave him a great deal of pain, however he seems much better now and walked out from Brandon yesterday morning – going out shooting in the afternoon, so he can't be very bad.

That Body [sic] you sent was much too small for Mama Dutcheen, so I calmly appropriated it for Bobo and it does splendidly for her. The little frocks I shall be able to do something with soon, but what little wee necks they have! Mr. Tulk is very fidgety this time and I don't think he will come again for some years, which is perhaps a good thing – of course, if he only comes to see Dido we are just as well without him.

I am rather glad your marriage is put off – it is a bad year and you might have a bad beginning; it is much better to have a little more money than is absolutely necessary than to have too little.

Glad you are keeping well, Goodbye. Bobby won't wait any longer.

Yours affectionately

Alice Criddle

Isabel went with Edwy next and delivered the letters to Minnie before calling at the Knights' home. Edwy had a terrible disappointment. The grain buyer offered only forty-six cents a bushel! It felt like robbery, but they needed groceries and let it go.

⁕⁂⁕

Mr. Criddle's friends returned for big game hunting. As Elise suspected, they got nothing, but enjoyed their host and pressed him to carry on the card games with them the following weekend in town. Edwy drove him and Mr. Tulk to Brandon to keep the engagement. Mr. Criddle stepped down and waited for Mr. Tulk. But to Edwy's great surprise the gentleman said, "I've decided to drive home with Edwy. Have a good time."

Edwy had a thousand questions and made good use of his opportunity. "You visited your brother in Egypt. He's an engineer, is he not? What were they building at the upper end of the Nile? Did you enjoy riding camels? Did you see the pyramids? . . . . "

After fording the Assiniboine, Edwy switched to India, Mr. Tulk's treks, and the elephants. For once the drive was too short.

⁕⁂⁕

Hunting fever coursed through the veins of every man who could free himself from chores. Evelyn was the first to hit anything, although they didn't rate his enormous jack rabbit very high. Elise took it from him and made a big pot of rabbit stew. As the hungry hunters gobbled it down, she tried valiantly to follow the conversation. *I just can't keep up with who got how many shots at what.* It was Norman who actually brought down the first deer, a young one, only 39 pounds. On a day unsuitable for hunting, they held a shooting match in which Edwy, as usual, won the honours. The hunters had no more success before Mr. Tulk departed.

Isabel stayed on for a time. With an extra pair of hands, Elise had time to write her brother. *I'll try to say a little more about our life.*

November 18, 1893

Dear Friedrich,

It is time to send my best wishes for a blessed Christmas to my dear brother and his family.

Our horses, Jess and Doll, had foals the year I was ill. Now the boys are going to try driving them for the first time. Of course they are very used to the boys and are not at all nervous. But they are young and lively so Edwy is going to travel faster than usual. If all goes well Edwy will use them in the fields planting grain next spring. God willing our crop will be better.

This year our boys have been going in for white tail deer hunting with great success. Harry shot three young deer in one day. A few days later got a doe and later a buck and a doe. You can imagine how they talk at mealtime. We have plenty of venison and I tease them that they will get fat. You can understand that our life here is very different.

My paper is almost filled. Please remember me to Karl and Amalie. I pray that God will keep you and your family well this Christmas season. Percy sends greetings. The children also send best wishes to their cousins.

Goodbye, dear brother, I remain your sister who loves you,
Elise

Mother and daughter chatted a few minutes before going to bed. *I can tell Isabel wants to go soon. Is it town life . . . or a matter of the heart?*

On mail day Mr. Criddle dropped a letter on the table, "From J.A. You can read it if you like."

Isabel picked it up and read it to the assembled.

The Windsor, Montreal, Friday, November 17th, 1893

My Dear Percy,

Reached here this morn, all well after a very pleasant run. We go on board the Vancouver this evening and sail at daylight tomorrow. I have telegraphed home to let them know of my safe arrival here.

You ought to receive this next Friday by which time I hope to be well on the way to England.

Please give my kindest regards to all at home, not forgetting Dido and the boys. . . . Shall let you know when I reach home
Yours, John Aug. Tulk

Isabel blushed at being singled out while the boys were flattered. Their mother praised them all, "You did your best to make his stay pleasant."

⊷◦⊶

On her birthday Isabel hugged her mother and climbed up on the wagon beside Edwy to the same old refrain: "Very sorry to let you go but the horrid hard times drive me to it – no money." But that day he added, "I've exchanged two loads of hay for Bellhouse's old ox. We'll fatten him – get a good price in Brandon – just before Christmas."

⊷◦⊶

Elise always felt lonely after Isabel's departure. She welcomed a letter.

Karlsruhe, October 20, 1893.

Meine liebe Schwester! My dear Sister!

As we gathered from the letter you had written to Friedrich, you and yours are well and cheerful, which is most important. For one can, when one is healthy, face the misfortunes of life much better.

We are very sorry that your expectations of a good crop have been ruined by the excessive heat. Our crops in Germany were in general good. Grapes are better than they have been in the last 20 years.

Friedrich and his family are all healthy; we will visit them in Mannheim one of these Sundays. Oh, how nice it would be if you and your family could also be there. Amalie and I often wish we wouldn't be so far apart!

I have, in order to recover from the great heat that overwhelmed us in Karlsruhe, spent fourteen days at the end of August in Donaueschingen. It made me very happy to see our old homeland, where our father rests, again. Our house doesn't exist anymore.

Tears filled her eyes. *What would I give to return to that place where everything was good? The way a family should be. But Papa died. The very next day strange men came to record all our Papa's possessions for the inheritance. Wilhelm and I clung to Mama. They counted every item: cupboards, cups, towels, silver spoons, knives, wine goblets—everything. They counted my clothes; my bothers'; Mama's petticoats, skirts, shoes, pillow cases, everything. And Papa's navy blue jacket with the brass buttons; his helmet and sword. . . . A horrid, scary, time. I try to forget. Yet it pops up when I least expect it. . . .* She wiped her eyes. *What else did Karl discover in our old hometown?*

Acquaintances I met very few. The majority died or disappeared but I met Elise Kuhl. She inquired after you in a very lively manner and begged me to greet you from her. She remembers you in old love and friendship.

Somebody in the office is asking for me, so I shall close with the heartfelt wishes for your and your family's wellbeing. Amalie and I greet you and your children with a thousand kisses and greetings! Percy also is greeted heartily.

Dein Dich liebender Bruder (Your brother who loves you),

Karl.

For some moments Elise sat remembering, two Elises, *like twins, we were. . . .* Then as if startled, she sprang to her feet. *The potatoes aren't peeled.* The letter was up between the cups in a flash. *It takes a good many potatoes to fill those thirteen plates.*

When the family had their regular December weigh-in, everyone had gained and, to Elise's joy, Cecil was seven pounds heavier than in June. *If he keeps on he'll soon be 100 pounds. He's still four inches short of five feet.* Mr. Criddle put the scales away and pulled out a letter from his pocket; "J. A. got home – everyone was well. His brother was busy sewering[10] Addlestone. His niece thanks you for the birds' eggs. He sends greeting to everyone."

Elise looked forward to a respite after the busy autumn: the new baby, Mr. Tulk, and all the hunters. On hearing the whole Bellhouse family were ill, she prayed: *Dear God, even if it has to be a miracle. . . . Please, no illness here this winter.*

A few mornings before Christmas, the huge and more or less fattened ox was tethered to the back of Edwy's wagon. Spirits ran high in anticipation of all the good things he would be bringing. Late that night a downcast Edwy had to confess, "I went everywhere. No one wanted to buy our fattened ox. I'm sorry; I couldn't buy the things you wanted."

A shortage of fixings for Christmas dinner was the least of Mr. Criddle's problems; he had bills coming due, and unpaid taxes. He took his rage out on his Boy while Elise cringed: *Punishing Edwy doesn't pay the bills. What will become of us?*

Having been prepared weeks before, Mrs. Criddle's plum pudding was the highlight of their Christmas dinner.

On the eve of the New Year, Elise worried. *Things do look bleak. Will I ever be strong again? It's time to put my trust in a loving God: I give you thanks, heavenly Father, through your dear Son Jesus Christ, that you have graciously protected me. Let your holy angels have charge of me . . . and dear God, of my dear ones. Amen.*

---

10 The Tulks were civil engineers.

Chapter Eighteen

A Lady With a Lamp

Following the Christmas season, neighbours were found to assist with the slaughter of the huge ox. Heart, liver, and kidneys, the delicacies, were transported into the house. After the carcass was sawed into quarters and laid out on the kitchen table, saws and knives went into action. Meal-sized portions were carried outside to freeze in a wooden box. The helpers went home with their pails filled, pay for the day's work.

Elise now had plenty of beef, though tough, to add to their potatoes, turnips, and onions. On the other hand, the flour barrel was nearly empty. She thought of the poor widow in the Bible. *Elijah, the prophet, came hungry to her door and asked for food. She used her last bit of flour and oil to bake him a little cake. Our pastor told us to memorize the prophet's words. "The barrel of meal shall not waste neither shall the cruise of oil fail, until the day that the Lord sendeth rain upon the earth." You never know when your faith in God's caring love will be tested. I'm being tested.*

Their colts roamed free during the winter, pawing through the snow to reach the prairie grasses, but they hadn't been seen following a blizzard. Edwy thought they'd drifted with the storm to the sand hills so he and Harry donned moccasins and went scouting. Sure enough, eight miles east they spotted the pair. But try as they might, the young rascals wouldn't be caught. They went back next day and had Norman walk around them to come from behind. Edwy and Harry slowly and patiently advanced, holding out a handful of oats. The colts snorted and tossed their heads, but hunger gradually won over fear. They gingerly sampled the grain on the outstretched hand and that was enough to tempt a nose into the pail for more. As they munched, on went the halters and the capture was complete. Homeward they traipsed, mile after mile; Harry and Edwy each leading a colt and Norman bringing up the rear. The crests of the sand hills were almost bare of snow, but every hollow was drifted full. Even though Norman didn't break the trail, he wasn't used to such exertion and had just enough strength left to holler when he reached the warm kitchen, "We got the beggars!"

Taking one look at his son, his papa stormed, "I'd like to give the beasts a deuced good hammering."

◈──◈◐◈──◈

The following day, the three Vane boys and Evelyn played football on the frozen river, "Our side against the other." Home they came in triumph, "We won easily, three to nothing. You can be proud of your boys, Mama."

Elise's mind was busy with more than pride. *The boys have so little time to enjoy their youth. Percy dreams up the projects and makes sure they follow his directions. They build; he writes letters, reads, and rereads his favourite books, plays at music, and visits. Furthermore, he has me serving into the wee hours of the morning when his callers can be persuaded to stay for cards. Does keeping busy help him forget that our taxes are overdue? At least his choral society is on the sidelines this winter. Is it because of the empty flour barrel or that Jenny Mair is engaged to Mr. Wright?*

Elise's position in the centre of activity meant very little happened that she didn't know about. And being a thoughtful person, she put two and two together. *Mr. Tulk's gift of the medicine chest stocked with pain killers gives Percy a doorway to our ailing neighbours. Do they guess he knows nothing about illness except what he reads in Dr. Watson's book? I'm fortunate he sent for Dr. Husband and saved my life. Besides doctoring, he's Game Guardian, Justice of the Peace, and chair, secretary, and treasurer of Aweme School Board. He hires and pays the teachers; expects them to light the fire in the mornings, sweep the floor, and fill the water pail, whether they want to or not. He makes a fuss when people ask to use the school for church, Sunday school, or community dances. When the other two trustees disagree with him and allow it, he takes his anger out on us. . . . Thank goodness for Maida. That little girl knows how to get her papa to ease up on the beatings; he can't resist her tears.*[1]

Norman, Stuart, and Beatrice began coughing a 'queer dry sort of cough'. Their mother turned to Mrs. Beeton's section on childhood illnesses and read, "Coughing works on the principle of imitation." She warned them, "You must absolutely stop coughing. The little ones will copy you. It can develop into something dreadful like whooping cough."[2]

When their papa's doctoring failed, Elise's anxiety grew. *I dare not say anything, but it sounds like the first stage of whooping cough. I have fought this foe. Bad enough for the older ones but for the little ones . . . I can't bear to think of it.*

A few days later there was a knock on the door: "Calverley's baby is dead."

Mr. Criddle called Edwy, "Take me there. Then go on to Millford Cemetery to dig the grave.[3]

Home again he said, "Diarrhoea. They didn't send for me or Dr. Husband."

Elise sympathized. *The poor little mite. Diarrhoea? . . .*

---

1 Criddle, Alma. Notes made in preparation for writing *Criddle-De-Diddle-Ensis*. Family collection.
2 Beeton. "This is a truly spasmodic disease, and is only infectious through the faculty of imitation. . . ." p.1057.
3 February 7, 1894.

The flour barrel was empty; so on a morning when any sensible man would stay indoors, Edwy was sent to Brandon. Elise wanted to object. *Send him to Treesbank, it's only five miles. Edwy doesn't have a big buffalo coat with a high collar to pull up around his head like the other men.* She felt no sympathy that night for Mr. Criddle pacing the floor, muttering, "How I hate these journeys. I'm always low spirited till the Boy gets home again."

Edwy made it home and sat down to eat his mother's warmed up potatoes, "Beastly cold!"

As he ate, a gut-wrenching cough caught his attention.

"Sounds like an ogre has poor Norman by the neck."

"Are you thinking of the ogre in Jack and the Beanstalk," his mother asked. "Remember how you boys used to rhyme it off; Fee-fi-fo-fum, I smell the blood of an Englishman."

When Norman kept on coughing, Elise admitted, "I'm afraid he has something you had when you were little. You don't need to worry."

In any case, Edwy spent most of his time outdoors; hauling home seed-wheat, conveying Mr. Criddle to various destinations, hauling logs, and cutting wood. All the while St. Albans reverberated through another week of coughing.

One stormy morning, Dr. Husband's son, Aubrey, and two Coopers landed on the doorstep. "We planned to camp out while we logged. Didn't see this beastly blizzard coming; can't even see our horses' tails."

Elise added more potatoes to the pot for the three days they were stormbound. For the card players, a capital arrangement; for the housekeeper, another straw too many.

After two weeks of the dry coughing, Elise was awakened by Stuart in the throes of a violent nonstop cough until he gasped a breath. Immediately his whole body was again wracked by coughing and the cycle continued. Ending at last Elise crawled back into bed knowing her worst fear had come true. *Stuart has whooping cough!*

It was not long before she was roused again. Beatrice's attack followed the same pattern, violent coughing—a gasp for breath, and more coughing. The poor girl seemed to turn inside out and Mama Dutcheen could do nothing but hold her. When it was over, she tucked the covers closely around the young lady's chin and found her way back to bed. *I'd better sleep while I can; tough times are on the way.* Sometime later she heard coughing below. *Sounds like Norman. His parents are down there. This brings back all those sleepless nights as my little ones coughed through their 'hundred days'.* By the time it was quiet, the day was dawning. *I must dress, light the fire, and face the day.*

Mrs. Criddle still clung to Mrs. Beeton's advice; "Think of the baby! Distract each other before your coughing goes too far."

But the other three youngsters were already coughing. *Maida and Julia are older, careful nursing should get them through this. But Talbot! So many little ones are lost.* She knew that nourishment was crucial to survival and kept a pot of porridge warm on the back of the stove. *I'm glad now Edwy went that cold day and bought oatmeal. Even if it comes back up with the next attack, every little bit that stays down, even for a short time, helps.* She skimmed some of the jellylike liquid off the top and spooned a little into them after each bout.

Three weeks of coughing and Mr. Criddle wrote, "Youngsters have hooping-cough.[sic]"[4]

Elise thought grimly, *I vow Edwy's ogre will not claim any of these dear children.* Then she shuddered, remembering: *"Be he alive or be he dead, I'll grind his bones to make me bread!"*

❧

Mrs. Criddle stayed isolated with her baby in their quarters. Mama Dutcheen continued to stoke the fires and care for the rest of the children. The little girls whooped up their food, and when the bout ended she fed them again hoping the next attack held off to let them get some nourishment. Talbot was the greatest challenge. She held him tightly during his spasms. But with so much pressure on his little system he often soiled himself. *Poor little fellow . . . getting thinner in spite of the gruel I spoon into him. Is this the 'diarrhoea' that took little Calverley?*

Six weeks into the nightmare Evelyn joined the chorus and little Talbot was still coughing. His 'blood shotten' eyes bulged; his body turned blue. Elise kept a basin at hand and thought, *caring for a child with whooping cough is as close to hell as one can get.* When that bout ended she fed him and patted his little head. "There, now, keep that in your tummy where it will do some good." *Mama Dutcheen is not giving up.*

As the fourth week began, her boys played football against the formidable Rounthwaite team. The game ended in a tie but the Vane boys had earned both teams' respect. As they replayed the ups and downs of the game for their mother, she thought: *it's good they get away from all the coughing to enjoy themselves and make friends.*

One cold night on Elise's return from her usual trip out, she stopped to take in a spectacular display of luminous purples and shimmering reds sweeping across the sky. *Northern lights are often beautiful, but this surpasses anything I've ever seen. There's my star twinkling amid the colours. . . .* Awed by the sight she recited her favourite poem.

---

4 Spelled without the 'w' in Criddle's original diary as well as in Mrs. Beeton and Dr.Watson's medical book.

Schöner Stern, hast du mir auch entzogen,
Deinen milden, liebvollen Schein.
Der mich mächtig zu dir hingezogen,
Muss ich doch dir ewig dankbar sein,
Denn du lehrtest himmelwärts mich blicken
Selig glauben an ein bessres Sein;
Will dein Licht mich hier nicht mehr beglücken,
Stern, im Himmel werd' ich bei dir sein.

Beautiful star, even though you
have deprived me of your mild loving glow,
which so strongly attracted me to you,
I still must be eternally grateful to you,
for you taught me to look heavenward,
blessedly have faith in a better Being;
When your light no longer makes me happy,
Star, in heaven, I'll be with you.

I'm glad we studied that poem . . . after all these years it still touches my heart. What a group of girls we were. . . . Do the others ever think of Elise Harrer? We've changed but my star shines just as brightly. And it still draws me to God.

The cold stole through her cloak. *I've got to go in and carry on.*

❦

Elise was exhausted by the end of another week. Baby Alma, only six months old, was coughing. Mrs. Criddle was frantic; it was time to fetch Isabel. Mr. Criddle went along with Edwy, hoping Bower would extend his food bill another month. They found the door padlocked and a sign: CLOSED BANKRUPT. Edwy delivered the disgruntled gentleman to his buddies, "I'll be lucky tonight. Win some money at cards."

Unfortunately he was dealt very bad hands, so the next morning he had to find another grocer willing to extend credit. Diplomacy was his currency against his next harvest.

On the home front, the hundred-day affliction was entering week five. Baby Alma was turning blue. The possibility of losing their darling terrified both parents.

By the sixth week their papa thought the older children somewhat better. But Talbot's episodes were still so violent his nose bled from the pressure and he had taken on the look of a skeleton. Elise kept a verse running in her head: *"Aber die den Herrn harren . . . . They that wait upon the LORD shall renew their strength; they shall mount up with wings as eagles; they shall run, and not be weary; and they shall walk, and not faint."*

Her boys played Rounthwaite—triumphed three goals to one.

In the seventh week of the affliction, a buggy arrived from Brandon. Isabel's 'lady' wanted her domestic back. *Surely they will not let her go.* But they did.

Hectic days and sleepless nights had robbed Elise of rest. Her weakened body was losing the battle, yet, she stubbornly carried on. *It's still touch-and-go with the little ones, but the goal is within reach. If I can get through another week, the whooping cough almost certainly will have run its course.*

⸙

During March another sound was added to the coughing. Edwy and Harry had been drafted by Mr. Criddle to sing at a Two Rivers concert. He chose an Italian piece, challenging even for boys with a good ear for harmony. It took hours of drilling for all the 'ah ah ah ah ah ah ah das' of *Vadasi Via* to fall into place. At last their music director crowed, "This will be a sensation! Doesn't matter that the people don't know what it means."

Elise had no energy or time to wonder about the meaning; sick children, meals, and those latent abscesses were overwhelming her. When she learned Mr. Criddle planned a party for the singers following the concert, she almost despaired. *Struggling through this nightmare and I'm to prepare for guests. . . .*

The concert goers returned in high spirits. Harry told her, "We sang well. Mr. C was pleased. Says we'll sing it again tonight. You'll be able to hear us."

She tried to smile, but she was too exhausted to remain on duty. The party had only begun when she dragged herself slowly and painfully up the stairs. *If the little ones need care, someone else will have to take my place tonight. I may be winning the battle against whooping cough, but I am losing my own health. And it's only sixty days.*

In the middle of April, just as Mr. Criddle proclaimed the epidemic on the wane, it returned with a vengeance. Fearing their housekeeper might go down completely as she had in '91, the Criddles made adjustments. Elise still managed the meals, but no longer jumped up at night. Mrs. Criddle in spite of a cold and bad cough nursed both little ones. When Talbot relapsed, his parents were up in the night administering mustard plasters, a hot bath, and ipecac. When they thought the worst was over, new symptoms appeared. Mr. Criddle struggled to name the illness and wrote, "I'm now satisfied that this addition to the cough plague is a modified attack of grippe. Several patients have considerable fever, headache, white and spotted tongues." But later that night he added, "I must say that whooping-cough is the most annoying – beastly – obstinate – alarming disorder I've ever come across."

When the coughing finally faded away, there was no celebration. There should have been, for all eight Criddle children survived. But Elise's fearless determination and sacrifice had reawakened her semi-dormant abscesses. She got to her feet each morning through sheer determination. *They are content as long as my work gets done. I don't want to worry my sons; they also work from dawn to dark. Edwy has his shanty built and is going there to sleep. Will he give Harry and Cecil a chance to homestead too?*

Cecil and Harry were working on 'Five' one hot windy day. Beatrice and her papa were away visiting when the call went out; "Prairie fire! On Five!" The wind had swept the fire northward but the smoldering and blackened southern wake was still dangerous. It took all the Criddle boys, plus Bellhouse and several Littles to stamp it out. Mr. Criddle accused young Albert Little of starting the fire. "I was only here because Mama sent me to fetch you. My little brother is ill."

Then Mr. Bellhouse turned to Mr. Criddle, "Your boys were there. They started it.

"Did you set that fire?" Mr. Criddle asked.

"No! We were eating our lunch."

"Just as I thought, my boys had nothing to do with it. They are not insane enough to set things on fire purposely. If they had started it by accident, they would immediately own up to it."

The two looked at each other knowingly as if to say, "We got away with that one but we'd better be more careful from now on."[5]

Mr. Criddle grumbled as they walked home, "Bellhouse probably judges the moral status of my boys by that of his own brats."

A few days later more smoke billowed overhead from the opposite direction. Their red distress flag was hoisted and flew straight out under a blazing sun. In short order six men, seven horses, and three ploughs were frantically ploughing a fire guard. Late that night, exhausted and hungry, their faces streaked by dust-encrusted lines, the boys assured their mother, "You don't need to worry. We ploughed a wide strip."

But the fire leapt the guard and all forces were out again by dawn.

With the opening of the school year that April, a new face appeared at St. Albans. Miss Steer, the new Two Rivers teacher, came for tennis and cricket. Mr. Criddle enjoyed conversing with the educated young woman and invited her to stay over. Elise was used to arranging sleeping accommodations for male visitors on the floor in the sitting room or in Mr. Tulk's room with Norman. But she didn't need to worry; when the master of the house wished to have a guest, no one complained. The teacher slept with Beatrice.

---

5 Vane, Harry.

Miss Steer demonstrated her good breeding by paying no attention to the servants. But over time Elise heard snatches of conversation and patched together a good deal about her. She was a year out from England and oldest of a large family. Mr. Steer, a builder, decided free land in Canada West would be a great opportunity for his four sons. They had taken a homestead in a new area—Ochre River, just south of Lake Dauphin. Miss Steer had just completed teacher training. *I'm not surprised she misses her family and likes to be with a family so like her own.*

Mr. Criddle was soon quoting the School Act for all Miss Steer's problems. Knowing nothing of his history with Two Rivers School back in '84, she didn't realize her close ties with him would stir up old animosities. Unpleasantness at her boarding place gave her more reason to spend the weekends at St. Albans where she felt accepted and understood. Mr. Criddle praised her in return; "She's full of fun; free from the humbugging canting conceited style of the Manitoba third class teacher type."[6]

Emily Steer

Elise heard Miss Steer tell Norman, "St. Albans is my home away from home." She brought a photograph and Mr. Criddle hung it on the wall above his organ. They discussed astronomy, stamps, literature, and the merits of Dickens's books. Elise felt uneasy. *I can't help thinking of the attention he once paid to me.*

One Sunday evening with the family gathered around the organ, Mr. Criddle sang, "O Rest in the Lord, wait patiently for Him and He shall give thee thy heart's desires. . . ." Edwy's eyes strayed to the photograph and decided in an instant, there was the girl of his dreams, his heart's desire. But instead of joy, he despaired. How could a penniless farmhand win the love of such a woman? Was he foolish to think Miss Steer could ever care for him? He'd better take care not to show his feelings, or he might lose the chance to even see her.

To liven up the season, the Criddles organized a party for the young people. Isabel and her friends came from Brandon and joined in the fun. Elise felt a pang; *Isabel has always helped, but not tonight. I can see she enjoys her Will Knight and I want her to be happy. I must carry on in spite of my swollen legs. The others can't know how they throb under my skirt.*

Those abscesses made every day a struggle, with constant summer guests and Miss Steer a part of the family. Then Mr. Criddle also took Miss Parrott, Aweme's teacher, under his wing saying, "She has a fine singing voice that needs only a few lessons to make it A-One."

She came often for lessons and her monthly pay. She usually stayed for tea.

6   June 24, 1894.

The third week of July, Edwy and Harry took seven bushels of new potatoes to peddle around Brandon. Bower, their friendly grocer, used to take any unsold vegetables. Now they had to sell everything, and if they failed Mr. Criddle would cut off their excursion to the Blythe picnic. It took them eight hours, but by handing over $6.45 they got to the football match.

⁂

In early August a relative of McVey's from Toronto paid the Criddles a visit. When he offered to take a photograph everyone hurried to put on their best outfits. All that is, but Elise. *I am such a wreck. Besides, these shabby clothes won't do.*

The children clamoured for her, "Please Mama Dutcheen."

"I'm not up to having my picture taken. Go ahead without me."

"Please, we want you in the picture with us. I'll help you," Beatrice begged. "Today is special. Don't you have a nice dress in your trunk?"

Elise gave in. Beatrice helped her up the stairs to her trunk on the landing. She took the key from her pocket; turned the lock and lifted the lid. Moving her pictures aside she dug through her precious possessions. Bypassing the lovely blue silk, she pulled out a taffeta skirt given to her soon after she arrived in England.

"It's beautiful," Beatrice said, "I see a black jacket to wear with it. We must hurry or they'll take the picture without us."

They carried the clothes to Elise's little room. "Put them on over my dress. I'm always cold these days."

Beatrice lifted the skirt over Elise's head, eased it down over her bony frame, and fastened the waist. Her arms slipped into the jacket and they did up the buttons. Then, covering her head with her only hat, she pulled the ribbon tightly and tied a bow under her chin. "I'll be in the picture to please you. But I'll hide as much as possible. I'm so thin—all that is left of me is my nose."

Beatrice hurried her downstairs and outside where everyone was arranged and waiting. Cecil had her chair ready at the edge of the group and stood behind her. Beatrice kneeled on the ground. They were ready.

Mr. McVey scanned the group from behind his camera, smiled, and said, "Don't move. Watch for the birdie." Ducking under a large black cloth he counted; "One—two—three!" There was a click. He reappeared and asked the little ones, "Did you see the birdie? No, well, we'll try again. Look now, keep very still." He counted again and the shutter clicked.

Talbot pointed, "Is there a birdie in there?"

Mr. McVey said, "There, we're all done. Come over tomorrow, Mr. Criddle, you can pick up your pictures."[7]

Elise felt a strong feeling of foreboding. . . . *It's too late; the deed is done.*

---

7   August 7, 1894.

Seeing the photo next day she grimaced: *I look like death itself... should have stayed inside. But just look at the children! I worked myself to the bone for them and this photo is the proof of my success. The youngsters are beautiful, pictures of health.*

Standing: Cecil, Evelyn, Stuart, Harry. Middle row: Elise, Mr. Criddle, Julia, Mrs. Criddle holding Alma, Norman, Front: Beatrice, Maida, Talbot, Edwy. Photo by Köhler

Minnie came for a fortnight's rest. Mr. and Mrs. Criddle enjoyed her; she bantered with the boys. On her last evening she asked her mother, "Have you heard from your brothers?"

"Not since last January."

"Maybe they're waiting for you to write. I'll get you some paper. I'll post your letter in Wawanesa tomorrow."

"But there are dishes to be done."

"Never mind, Mama. The dishes will get done without you tonight." And she sat her mother down by the open window. "A short letter is better than none. Let them know you have been ill, but getting stronger now."

And so Elise began:

Aweme, Manitoba, August 19, 1894.

Mein Bruder!

A letter from you has not reached me for many months. I pray every day that you and Amalie are well. After your letter came last winter I was terribly busy and did not take enough rest. My old illness returned. They tell me I look better now.

This summer the boys are playing many games of football and are highly regarded. Harry and Cecil are often away working and the money they bring home

is a great help. Edwy is always busy here and is a great comfort to me. Rain did not come again this summer, so our harvest is poor. If ever we should have a good crop, I will thank God.

Minnie is home for a holiday. She is cheerful as always. I wish she could stay longer but she likes to have her own money.

Isabel is very happy. Her friend, Mr. Knight has been out to visit. I will not be surprised if they marry next summer.

Receive my heartiest wishes, also to Amalie.

I remain your loving sister,

Elise.

Please remember me to Friedrich, Marie, and their beautiful children.

Elise's health improved, but slowly, for it was impossible for her to take care, and get the rest she needed. Miss Steer moved from her unhappy boarding place to the Ellis home, which stirred up more resentment with her school board. Miss Parrott's singing lessons continued and she also began staying overnight. One evening, after a long session, Mr. Criddle introduced her to the night skies: double stars, the moon, Mars, and Jupiter. Another evening they went off to visit the Little family. Elise worried more and more. *I understand her interest in music, stars, and stamps, but she seems quite enchanted with him. I trusted Percy on a night long ago and it changed my life forever. Mrs. Criddle, I notice is bringing her sewing out to the sitting room.*

Indeed, she was stitching when her husband came in with the mail and read her Mr. Tulk's letter. Elise listened in. *He's an old acquaintance in England and has been so very kind.*

Addlestone – Surrey August 5th, 1894

Dear Percy,

Yours of July 19th came on the 1st August. I will send you a few lines now, most likely the last before starting for the West. As requested I have got a pair of tennis shoes for you, guess they are the right size, price 9/6 at Stores, two packs cards (new), 4 nail brushes.

Music — I don't think that there is any special modern composer, certainly not for the piano, educated people go in for the good composers ancient and modern, songs I don't know anything about. There are plenty which come out, have a short (very) life, are so pretty, and then forgotten. The great men hold the power now as always.

Have no lathe books to lend Dr. Husband, so can't oblige him. Yes I will go over and talk lathes while you entertain the ladies. Delighted to hear that the crops are looking so well, let us pray that there may be a decent harvest this time. Grand showers, hot sun, no frost and you will once more know what it is to feel the rustle of dollar (10) bills in your pocket. . . .

I had 10 days in Jersey as usual, very showery but hot and calm, had various grand bathes, water pleasant.

Most of my packing is done, so that is off one's mind and I can enjoy the last days at home without agonizing thoughts of omitting, say a toothpick, from the list of unnecessaries. Now I tell you for the third time that I shall not reach Brandon until Thursday, Sept 18ᵗʰ in the afternoon so please make necessary arrangements to meet me if convenient as I shall require help to tackle the baggage.

All well here, kindest regards to all at St. Albans.

Yours, John Aug. Tulk ⁸

Elise went back to the stove. *What good news. Isabel will come home. She is always such a blessing. . . . We enjoy each other. Perhaps my legs might be less swollen if I can stay off my feet a little. As for Mr. Tulk, he'll learn soon enough another harvest has failed.*

Beatrice had been to Fortunes with her papa and came to Elise with a heavy heart. "Jane is trying her best to care for her mother. She loves to have her friends come but Papa gave her a lecture today. 'Shut the door. Keep them out. It's bad for your mother. If you let a score of Methodist hags in here, I'm not going to waste my time coming!' Jane doesn't know what to do. She's afraid her mother is following Jimmy to the grave."

Elise sympathized, "It must be hard for Jane. I'm sure she appreciates a friend like you."

❧

Harvest was a crushing disappointment—only a few more bushels than the low of the previous year. The boys' wages and Mr. Tulk's board would have to carry them along. Nevertheless, Edwy's required breaking and cropping had been done on his homestead and the inspector's report gone in. Edwy had company for his trip to apply for his patent: Mr. Tulk was curious about the process, Mr. Criddle was the witness, and Isabel went to visit her lover.

Elise was doubly thankful to have Mr. Tulk that fall. She needed Isabel's help, but was also thankful to have another young woman around when Miss Parrott visited. *I'm sure she appreciates his support, but I wish he would have his wife or Beatrice along when he takes her visiting.* Elise worried even more when she heard him say, "I'm going to Glen Souris with Miss Parrott to meet her mother."

The following Saturday Miss Parrott came asking for Mr. Criddle.

"This is my letter of resignation. I am here to get my pay and say goodbye."

Of course Mr. Criddle tried to persuade her otherwise and said he couldn't give her all the pay she was owed. Yet she left with such determined steps, Elise felt a sense of envy. *Miss Parrott is a talented young woman. . . . She'll find another school.*

---

8 Tulk's letters are in the family collection.

When Elise heard Miss Steer ask for a ride to Brandon on school business she worried. *Is she looking for another school?* But next day she returned along with two tall brothers, Eddie and Harry. There was no end to the games, music, and cards that weekend. Isabel and her mother had no end of baking, cooking, and washing up.

Turkey shoots were common leading up to Christmas. Hearing of one in Douglas, Harry decided to try his luck and went with Edwy on a load of wheat. That night Harry presented his mother with three turkeys. "I entered six competitions and won three. How's that for your boy?"

Edwy stepped out from behind, "Here's another. By the time I had the grain unloaded there was only one contest left. Got only 42¢ a bushel for the wheat, but we came out alright."

In the midst of cooking up the turkey feast, Elise was handed a letter. *From Karl! I just have to know how he is.* She pulled the letter out of the envelope:

Karlsruhe, November 6, 1894
Liebe Elise!

I have received your dear letter and forwarded it to Friedrich in Mannheim, Lit. O.6 No.3/4.

Too bad that we learned very little that is uplifting from your dear lines. Hopefully you are fully recovered and you can fulfill your difficult vocation. If only once good fortune could make its entrance at your place! Faith in God, who has always helped, one must not lose! With Friedrich it is not going so well either. Lamentably, he has not found employment yet. He is presently occupied at the Gantmasse [large auction house]. But how long will that be possible! For a man the age of Friedrich it is very difficult to get employment. It is fortunate that his health is much improved. Let us hope to God, that with his help everything will turn out for the good.

Amalie and I are fine. I get these coughing spells from time to time which necessitates that I am housebound for a few days.

Amalie sends greetings. For today, farewell, and together with Percy and the children receive my greetings.

Dein Bruder Karl

She folded the pages. *I feel downhearted . . . melancholy, is that the right word? Bad news and I'm so weary.* She served the meal, but her mood didn't lift. On her way to bed, she sat the lamp down beside her trunk and took out her *Poesie* book. Then, sitting on the edge of her bed she turned the aging pages.

Each poem is a memory. Number thirty-one—Es lebt ein Gott! *"Let no one rob you of your faith that there is a God who cares." I have to believe God cares for me.*

A shout came from below, "Must you keep that lamp burning?"

She snuffed out the flame. *Prayers do not need light to find their way to a God who cares.*

December brought changes: Miss Parrott took a school at Stonewall, Mr. Tulk left on the west-bound train for Australia, and Jane's mother departed this world. Their Christmas table had two new faces: Isabel's Will Knight and Miss Steer. Parties followed nightly.

Their servant worked on painfully, telling herself, *those who survive whooping cough only suffer its ravages once. I will not be carrying my lamp from bed to bed through another hundred days of hell.*

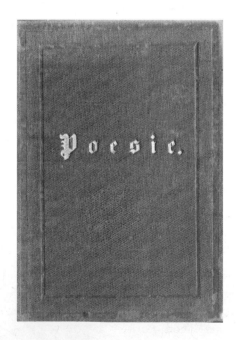

Chapter Nineteen

A Life Sentence for a Trusting Heart

Miss Steer learned that her plan to stay at Two Rivers School was opposed by two of the three trustees. Accusations flew back and forth between the parents who thought the extra time in school would benefit their children and those who wanted to close the school during January, February, and March. Miss Steer, hoping to keep the children at their books, took her troubles to Mr. Criddle. He urged her not to give in, saying, "Those dastardly Canadians with their underhanded dealings."

The conflict dominated conversations at St. Albans. Elise remembered her mother quoting Luther: *Jah, die bösen Gedanken. Wir können nicht hindern das die Vögel über uns hinfliegen aber wir können hindern dass sie auf unseren Köpfen Nester bauen. / We cannot prevent the angry thoughts flying over us like birds, but we can prevent them building nests on our heads.* Mulling over the situation she worried that if the parents and children were arguing it might be difficult for Miss Steer. *She might be wiser to follow Miss Parrott's example and find another school. It must be ten years since Percy tried to prevent the Two Rivers settlers from opening their school and getting his land removed from their district. McManes and Calverley will likely see this as meddling in their affairs again.*

Following disruptions at the school, Edwy drove Miss Steer and her supporter, Trustee Martin, to Brandon for advice from the education authorities. She decided to stay on; Martin's first step was to have the school finances audited. Finding the books in good order, he proceeded to lay charges against Calverley and McManes for disturbing classes under breach of the School Act. They were to be heard by the Justice of the Peace, P. Criddle Esq.

January 24th the concerned parties gathered at St. Albans, along with Mr. Sutcliffe representing the municipality. Elise's role was to prepare dinner for an extra 20 people. Only at the end of the day did she learn the outcome. McManes was given a 'mitigated penalty' of $5 plus costs. He was also deposed as the long-standing secretary-treasurer of the board. Mr. Martin dropped the charges against Calverley on condition that they work together. Peace was to reign; school to reopen.

But McManes wanted his trusteeship back. Mr. Criddle went calling on the rate payers. He persuaded Ellis, with whom Miss Steer boarded, to run against McManes but could only persuade Bousfield to vote for the new man.

Elise was pulled into the fray. "I'm taking you to Two Rivers School on Thursday."

"Gracious! Why me?" she asked in alarm.

"You're a ratepayer – your school taxes go to Two Rivers. Got to get rid of that brute McManes. Tired of his law-breaking maneuvers. Need a new trustee to keep the school open. Ellis needs votes. I'll take Harry too."

Elise's mind raced. *Harry is fond of Miss Steer . . . he'll vote for Ellis. Can there be more than one ratepayer for my homestead? Can a woman vote for a trustee?*[1] She was quite sure all the men agreed that women belonged in the home, by nature not fit to make political decisions. The very prospect of being thrust into this forbidden world was frightening. *I feel like a pawn on Mr. Criddle's chessboard. . . . I've played the game enough to know pawns are readily sacrificed.*

She asked Harry, "Do I have to go?"

"I'll stay with you," he promised.

In spite of a winter storm, Edwy was dispatched to fetch another voter, Mr. Clay, over-wintering in Glenboro, 25 miles away. Elise braced herself for the ordeal.

Thursday morning, she hurried through her breakfast duties, tucked her hair under her bonnet, borrowed boots, and wrapped herself in a cloak. Harry helped with the high step to the sleigh box and it seemed no time before the horses pulled up to the porch door of the little school. Mr. Criddle stepped down and quickly disappeared inside. Harry drove on and tied the horses to a post alongside the other teams. He helped his mother down from the sleigh and, taking her arm, they walked resolutely to the neat little clapboard school.

It was a bright morning and Elise could see almost nothing when she first stepped into the schoolroom. She did, however, notice a lull in the conversation. As soon as her eyes adjusted to the dimness, she cast about for an out-of-the-way seat. Seeing the children's benches pushed back, she moved quickly to the closest. Harry sat with her, although other men were standing.

Elise realized her worst fear; she **was** the **only** woman. She sensed eyes examining her from cap to boots and back up again. *Is this how a slave feels on mounting the auction block? Did I hear my name? Are they talking about me? They sound angry. What if they don't allow me to vote? . . . I must remain calm.*

To steady herself she concentrated on the little classroom: Queen Victoria

---

1 An Act Respecting Public Schools. Revised Statutes of Manitoba, Volume 11, 1891. "2. (e) Ratepayer means an assessed householder, owner or tenant, any person entered on the assessment role as a farmer's son."

gazing serenely from her frame, the water pail and dipper, the teacher's desk with a row of text books for all eight grades. The air was heavy with an aroma of wood smoke mixed with the smell of farmers' boots. Red hot spots from the roaring fire glowed on the stovetop. Her eyes moved upward along the black pipe, encircled by shimmering heat waves. She followed it up to the elbow and along the length of the ceiling. There the pipe turned and disappeared through the roof. *Would that I could escape like the smoke, up and out—vanish into the clear blue sky! . . .*

Feeling calmer, she recognized some of the men—*McManes, Martin, Calverley, and Ellis. And there is Clay. So, Edwy managed to get him safely here from Glenboro.*

At the appointed hour of ten, everyone sat down. The chairman, chosen for this special meeting, introduced the business; "The ratepayers of Two Rivers School District # 299 are here for the specific purpose of electing a trustee. [2] There are two candidates, Mr. McManes and Mr. Ellis. We will begin without delay. Starting with Mr. Calverley on my left we will proceed clockwise. Each person in turn will stand, raise his right hand and give the name of his choice. The Secretary will tally the votes." The voting proceeded: "My vote is for Mr. McManes," — "I choose Mr. Ellis," — "Mr. Ellis," — "Mr. McManes," — "Mr. McManes". At her side, Harry stood and voted, "Mr. Ellis."

Elise's heart pounded; she felt every eye. But strengthened by the only other woman in the room, Her Majesty Queen Victoria, she prepared the name carefully planted on her tongue. Then on her feet, she raised her right hand and said firmly, "Mr. Ellis." Seated again she thought, *I have voted like a man!* The next man rose and the voting continued. The race was close. Clay voted "Mr. Ellis," and the win looked certain since Bousfield had promised Mr. Criddle to vote for Ellis. He stood to vote, but he said, "Mr. McManes."

Sketch by Don McMaster

---

2   Two Rivers School # 299, organized 1884, located on 27.8.6. Secretary Treasurer, Mr. James McManes.

The secretary paused, tallied, and then announced, "We have a tie. In such a case the chairman will cast the deciding vote."

Rising, he said, "My vote goes to Mr. Ellis."

Dead silence followed, but only for a moment. Then the McManes camp erupted in disbelief. "We've been outmanoeuvred again by Criddle, this time using his woman!"[3]

Calverley struggled to control his language out of respect for the presence of a female. He stomped over to Mr. Criddle, and wagging his finger shouted, "You're the meanest man I've ever known!"

Frightened by the bubbling anger, Elise slipped hurriedly out the door, across the yard, and managed to climb into the sleigh. *How dreadful . . . so humiliating! The rage in that room—unbelievable! The anger will keep on festering; neighbours will be talking about this forever.*

Harry came out, untied the team and drove to the door to await the well-pleased Mr. Criddle. "It was a tight squeeze. Needed those extra voters I rounded up. That two-faced Bousfield – the abject sneaking look of the animal. Sniggering and grinning in a cretinous[4] manner. He never for an instant dared to lift his eyes and look someone in the face."

Once safely back in the kitchen, Elise gradually stopped shaking. She gave this, her sixth outing from St. Albans, a very low mark.

That night before her prayers, Elise revisited the schoolhouse. *The fury I felt against me for voting . . . against my will, but still, I voted. I need to remember what Luther said, that if you are forced to do things against your wishes, ponder how Jesus was bound and led thither and yon. My humiliation is nothing compared to his.*

⚬—◦◦◦—◦

The 21 students[5] resumed their lessons while Miss Steer kept a rather nervous ear to the door. A few days later Mr. Calverley notified both Martin and Ellis that they were disqualified from acting as trustees. Elise worried. *Are they challenging the election because of my vote?* She heard of other skirmishes, but one in particular stood out: McManes caught Harry Steer, the teacher's brother, taking a shortcut across his land and charged him with trespassing.[6]

Miss Steer continued to spend every weekend at St. Albans. On her birthday, April 9th, she told Mr. Criddle, "I thank you and your family for your kindness. I am so far from my family."

---

3 Criddle, Norman. January 31, 1895. "Mrs. Vane, Harry went with Papa to the Two Rivers School house to a rate payers meeting to elect Ellis as a trustee. . ." Archives of Manitoba.
4 A deformed or idiot manner.
5 Summative half-yearly returns for school districts 1884-1899. Two Rivers report of 1895 signed by E. L. Steer. GR 571 Microfilm #M692 Archives of Manitoba.
6 February 17, 1895.

Elise understood. *It's been months since I've had a letter from my brothers. Has Karl recovered? Did Friedrich find a position? Did Marie get over her cough? All I can do is pray and entrust them to God's loving care and wait for news.*

Maida, now 11, but still a child at heart, came to the kitchen on May 2nd, "Will you make me a birthday cake, Mama Dutcheen? I'm planning a tea party."

Familiar with the children's leafy retreat at the bottom of the garden, Elise baked a little cake and helped the children gather the items they would need. Tolly carried water, Julia was trusted with the cups, Beatrice carried plates and spoons. Maida had both her mother's embroidered tea cloth and the birthday cake. Baby Alma toddled along with her rag doll. The bright sunshine and breeze kept the mosquitoes from joining their happy parade.

Once the table was set, Maida shooed everyone out. She changed into her imaginary party dress, arranged her hair before an invisible mirror and stood ready for her guests.

The first arrived, "Knock! Knock!"

Pretending to open the door, Princess Maida smiled graciously and said, "My dear Lady Beatrice. I'm charmed to see you. And you have brought dear little Miss Alma. Please do come in. Take a seat. The others will be here soon."

The two settled themselves on the ground at the edge of the tea cloth. Julia and Tolly also knocked, were greeted, and invited to sit down. Elise, wearing a shawl and elegant white lace gloves, was the last to arrive. Princess Maida's eyes sparkled as she looked up at her grown-up guest.[7] Curtseying gracefully she said, "How do you do, Queen Huckey. I'm pleased you have accepted my invitation. Do come in," and seated her in the place of honour. The tea began. . .

Elise understood. *It's been months since I've had a letter from my brothers. Has*

As spring passed into summer Elise noticed Edwy was Johnny-on-the-spot whenever Miss Steer needed a ride back to her boarding place. Although he was outdoors most of the time, on rare occasions, she caught a smile across the room and worried for her boy. *Edwy is only a poor farm boy with little chance of improving his prospects. Would Miss Steer return his love?*

A week later Minnie wrote from Wawanesa asking for a ride home. Edwy, not usually one to answer on the spot, sat right down and wrote her back, without a word to Mr. Criddle.

---

7   Criddle, Alma. "And Maida remembered a day when "Huckey" [Elise]. . . dressed up to come down to the little playhouse the girls had made for themselves in the shrubbery. She delighted their hearts by joining them in a game of 'Lady come to see,' and her magic of make-believe matched their own." *Criddle-De-Diddle-Ensis.* p. 204.

Aweme, May 28, 1895

My dear Minnie,

. . . Now I want you to do a favour for me. Here it is. If you have written before you get this naming the 6th for me to come and fetch you, write again putting it off till the 8th (which is a Saturday) if you possibly can.

. . . I have a special reason for asking you to do this for me, which I will explain when I see you. I want to go to Wawanesa on a Saturday. I want P.C. to know nothing about my writing to you and trying to arrange for a Saturday so when you write a second time (always supposing you have written the first which I expect you have) putting it off till Saturday, don't let him know the reason for it (supposing you can manage to make it a Saturday when you come home) he doesn't know I am writing at all and I don't want him to know. There I hope that is plain enough for you to understand. . . .

We had a jolly day down by the river on the 24th. Suppose there was no holiday for you. We will all make it as jolly as we can for you when you get home to make up for it all. Everybody well here, hoping you are the same and that you will be home by the evening of 8th of June or the 15th.

Write at once—so that we shall get your letter in time.

Your affectionate brother,

Edwy Vane.[8]

Later that week Mr. Criddle received a letter from Minnie to the effect that she couldn't get away until Saturday and would Edwy fetch her that day. Saturday night his mother noticed his jovial mood, but she thought he was just happy to have his sister home. Neither he nor Minnie breathed a word of having an extra person along.

❦

Mr. Criddle was so totally opposed to Isabel marrying Will Knight, he walked to Wawanesa to see Minnie. "Persuade Isabel to put off her wedding. She's fond of Mr. Tulk. If she marries she'll not be able to come out this fall to see to his needs."

Elise worried too, for her boys agreed that Will didn't seem very ambitious. Edwy and Harry were given a day off to walk to Wawanesa. "We're worried," they said to Minnie, "will you talk to Isabel? Try to get her to change her mind, or at least delay things."

But Minnie worked in Wawanesa, and the lovers in Brandon followed their own hearts.

Preoccupied with events, but unable to prevent what he saw as a calamity, Mr. Criddle sat at his little organ playing Bach's immortal *Forty-eighth* until his poor wife complained, "It's worse than having the malligrubs[9] for seven years and perfectly beastly!"

---

8 Edwy Vane. This and later letters are all from private collections.
9 Term of Scottish origin—a griping of the intestines.

On a lovely Sunday in early June, Mr. and Mrs. Sutcliffe, Köhler, and Cooper left their own tennis courts and forded the river to spend the day at St. Albans. For Elise it was just a regular busy Sunday until she learned that Mr. Köhler would be taking a family photo. She cringed. *No, please, I would rather not. Last summer's comments about me still hurt; I simply cannot bear it, not again.* She said, "I'm sorry. Not today. I have too much work preparing tea for so many."

But the children begged; "You are part of our family."

Seeing her wag her head to refuse, they added, "We want you; you **must**."

She thought fast, *I can't wear my good skirt; that went to Beatrice for parties last winter. Black is the proper colour for servants. . . . I'm already wearing my best.*

To Maida she said, "All I need is my bonnet. Will you bring it for me, dear?" Once again she allowed herself to be ushered out to the waiting group. While everyone awaited the 'birdie', Elise prayed. *Dear God in heaven let me not be an eyesore as Percy points out so often.*

Will brought Isabel one Sunday to discuss their plans, "We want to be married as soon as we can. My sister Violet will be my witness."

Mr. Criddle spoke up, "I'll sign for Dido."

Will went on, "Isabel needs her parents' names for the minister's records."

Her mother beckoned, "Come, Isabel, I'll write it down for you."

On an old envelope in the kitchen, she wrote—Sabina Elise. "Sabina for my grandmother; Elise because my mother liked it. My last name, the same as your uncles—Harrer. As for your father's name, you heard that announcement on the dock at Liverpool."

Isabel's family did not share her happiness. Cecil in particular felt he was losing his sister and Minnie came to cheer them up. In the end their mother counselled, "We all want Isabel to be happy. Will Knight is her choice and we must support them."

For all her brave front, Elise had her own misgivings. *I hope Isabel isn't facing the problem I had. I wanted to be Percy's wife, but didn't anticipate such intimacy before marriage. He was a gentleman . . . I trusted him.*[10] *We obtained the forms,*[11] *I filled in mine . . .* She paused revisiting the dreadful scene as Percy fumed, *"Stupid German rules: they want my profession and who I work for . . . have to be twenty-five!*

---

10 Percy being unwell spent five weeks in Heidelberg and wrote. "Elise is rather seedy today – sends her love." Letter to his mother September 15, 1866. Private collection.
11 Groom's Application for the Formulation of a Marriage Certificate in Elise's personal papers. Private collection.

*. . . Need my parents' permission! Utter bosh . . . won't get that, my Governor's[12] dead."
Percy left me weeping . . . said he'd be back in three months for Christmas. I did a lot of
crying before I confided in my mother. My poor brothers . . . they had trusted Percy too!*

———— ❦ ————

The night before Isabel's wedding on the 10th of July, Mrs. Criddle told her
housekeeper, "It's wild raspberry season and every pair of hands is needed."

I can hardly believe they would be so cruel as to keep me from sharing my daughter's special day. Surely they will change their minds.

But there was no change of plans, and the servant stood forlornly in the
doorway, tears trickling down her cheeks as her oldest son helped the pretty Miss
Steer—taking in a Teachers' Convention—to step up to the seat beside him. Edwy
was used to leaving his mother behind and hardly appreciated how much she
longed to be with her daughter. Mr. Criddle went out muttering, "It's a deuced
nuisance!" and climbed up beside the young folks. Elise thought; *it would **not** be
a nuisance for **me**, but you don't want me there.*

Edwy said, "Get-up" and slapped the lines on his horses' backs and left the
bride's mother weeping alone in the doorway. *My precious Isabel, I pray to our
loving God that you will be happy.* She made the jam, but her thoughts were elsewhere. *The wedding's to be at Will's parents' home. Unusual, but I'm pleased they will
have a minister. The new dress Isabel hoped to get, is it blue, her favourite colour? The
colour doesn't matter . . . she will be a lovely bride.*

———— ❦ ————

Isabel and William stood before Rev. Mason pledging their love through sickness and health until parted by death. The Reverend declared them man and
wife and led them to the wedding register. He had already entered the necessary
information; all they needed was to add their signatures. Will read down the
page, William Thomas Knight, 29, resident of Brandon, born in Toronto, bachelor, delivery clerk, English Church, son of John Charles Knight and Mary Ann
Marshall. He wrote his name and passed the pen to Isabel. She glanced over her
record, Isabel Vane, 25, resident of Brandon, born in London, England, spinster,
Congregationalist. Parents: Harry Vane and Elise Sabina Harrer. She hesitated a
moment thinking Sabina should be first, and signed, 'Isabel Vane'. The witnesses
entered their names below, 'Violet Knight, Brandon'; 'Percy Criddle, Aweme'.
Elise's precious daughter was now Mrs. William Knight.[13]

The bride's mother waited up until almost midnight to hear about the wedding. Mr. Criddle came in complaining of missing out on his usual night of gam-
bling because Miss Steer had to come home for school.

---

12 British term for a boy's father.
13 July 10, 1895. Marriage registration. Vital Statistics, Manitoba.

Elise timidly asked, "Did they get married?"

"Yes, they tied the knot," and he stomped off to his room.

Edwy had been sent on an errand and hadn't attended the ceremony. *I'll have to wait for Isabel to answer my questions. . . . What excuse can I give my brothers for not attending? Can't be the cold—it's July. . . . Still, they will appreciate that Isabel's father was there.*

❦

Eddie and Reggie Steer called in one evening in July. "We're on our way to the Ellis place. We came to take our sister home for a holiday. That's if Emily is still game after we tell her about our troubles coming down. We've had a terrible seven days of it. Rain and more rain—road's a terror! We'll be leaving for Ochre River in the morning."

Soon after Miss Steer's departure, Mr. and Mrs. Knight came for an overnight. Isabel wore her blue dress and answered all her mother's questions about the big day. Will promised to bring her again when he came out to hunt chickens.

❦

A life-giving rain watered his parched fields and a relieved Mr. Criddle said, "While the soaker is reviving the crops – I'll take you boys to the river – give you a few wrinkles in swimming."

Cecil came in that evening obviously upset, and went to his mother. "You know Mr. C took us swimming. Wanted to teach us the breast stroke. Well, we got tired of that pretty fast and dog-paddled across to a little island. Coming back we spread out. Edwy, being taller, went downriver where the water was deeper. Halfway across I heard, 'Where's Edwy?' I stood up in the shallow water and looked downriver. He's probably trying to fool us, will come up in a minute. But the river just kept on flowing, little eddies swirling in the brown water, so peacefully. I remembered those three graves up on the hill. Men drowned years ago. A person comes up three times before they go down for good, they say. I prayed, hoped . . . after a few more scary moments, sure enough, I spied his head and arms flailing in the water quite a way downstream close to the bank. The current was fast. But he grabbed a low willow hanging over the water. It held. Harry got to him first."[14]

Elise's face was white, "Thank God. I worry every time you go to that river." She couldn't resist a little motherly warning. "I grew up beside the Neckar River. There were drownings every year. Rivers are dangerous—the currents change, there are undercurrents and the river bottom shifts. There can be a deep hole when shortly before the water was shallow. You can't trust a river. Oh, please do take care!"

---

14 Harry Vane

It was a blessing their mother couldn't see their next adventure. Laura had calved a month earlier. The calf was fine, but his mother wasn't doing well. So Harry and Edwy were told to take her to the Brandon auction. Elise gave them some biscuits to eat on the way and they set off in the moonlight shortly before two A.M. Later that afternoon she saw angry black clouds to the north and prayed for their safety.

Much later, they came through the door looking like a pair of drowned rats; "We had one deuce of a time! We're jolly glad to get home."

Their mother's first thoughts were, *thank God.* To her sons, she said, "Gracious! Take off those wet things. I'll fry up some potatoes."

As soon as the sharp edge of Harry's hunger was gone, he satisfied his mother's curiosity. "We had a hard time to get to Brandon by nine. Laura wasn't in a hurry to leave her calf. We changed off, one leading, half dragging, and the other be-hind—encouraging her with a switch on the rump. When Edwy's switch wore out, I heard him muttering in the dark, 'Should have saved that willow branch from the river last week. Strong enough to save me from drowning; could use it again.' The sun came up looking extra rosy. I said to Edwy, 'Is there any truth to the saying: Red sky in the morning a sailor's warning; red sky at night, a sailor's delight?'"

Edwy broke in, "I told him, Mr. C says it's old-fashioned bosh."

"Anyway," Harry said, "we got there. After the sale, we collected the money and left Laura to her fate. Lowering his voice, he went on, "We were tempted to check into the hotel, have a full course meal, take a nap, and then win some money off his card playing cronies. He'd never know we'd spent any. Anyway, we started back—no dinner and no rest. Partway, the sky got scary. We'd taken a shortcut across country, no homes anywhere about and we decided to run for it. The sun disappeared; got darker and darker. We raced to keep ahead of the siz-zling sky, booming at our backs. But the storm travelled faster than we did. All of a sudden we could hardly move against the wind. We had lightning and thunder front and back, and buckets of rain pounding down. We couldn't just stand and be struck like McVey's nice team of horses. So we kept on. You can see, Mama, we've survived. We needed a good rain. Thank you for the supper. I think I'll call it a day and hit the hay."

She sent a prayer heavenward, *thank you for watching over my precious sons.*

❧ ⁃❧⁃ ❧

Elise's legs and feet were swollen and painful, but she stirred the boiling jelly, and wondered how Miss Steer was making out on her hundred mile journey home. Fortunately, Mr. Criddle received a long letter from her and read it out to everyone.

Ocher River P.O. Manitoba July 23rd '95
Dear Mr. Criddle,

You will no doubt be pleased to know that I arrived here safely yesterday at noon. We really did have a terrible journey, wet, cold, sunless and muddy. The mud on the roads is worse than anything I have ever seen; the bridges which cross the creeks have been moved and washed away by the floods. The water was at least 18 inches lower than when my brother left here but it was deep enough and <u>muddy</u> enough to prevent the horses getting through with the wagon. More than once we had to unload and carry the goods across what was left of the bridge.

We travelled so slowly that I THOUGHT "Utopia" would never be reached; however we got home yesterday at noon, minus the wagons which we had to leave in a creek 4 miles away.

You made fun of my pony, but he was very useful to me coming up. Most of the way Reggie had to walk in front of the team to test the road and often cut a new way through. Eddie drove the team and I followed with my thorough-bred. He didn't stop or falter once but went straight through everything after the team. <u>Needless to say I am prouder of him than ever.</u>

We were on our way from Tuesday when I left Ellis' till yesterday. Three nights of which we camped out. The mosquitoes are rather lively companions- rather too lively for me and when there are so many they rather try one's temper.

This place is not so wooded as I expected. The trees are not so big, but the vegetation in the underbrush is very luxuriant. I found my parents and the children very well and all were glad to see me safe and sound. I am glad to be at home and looking forward to a good holiday.

Hoping all the members of your family are quite well and with kind regards to Mrs. Criddle and all.

Believe me to remain,

Yours truly, Emily L. Steer.

Back row: Mr. Steer [Henry], Dorothy [cousin], Mrs. Steer [Emily], Edie, Reg,
Front row: Fred [cousin], May, Unknown, Frank.

Elise could hear the pride in Edwy's voice when he explained, "Emily named her pony Shepherd F. Knapp after the famous Morgan stallion. Sounds like he lives up to his namesake."

The rest of their summer was hot and dry. As the crops shriveled, Mr. Criddle fretted himself sick. Facing another scanty harvest, all three Vane boys were hired out and the Criddle boys managed the chores.

One evening Miss Steer dropped in, "I'm back, safe and sound. Mother came along to see the country and thank the Ellises for giving me a good home. She's resting. They're leaving first thing, so the boys can get back to harvest."

It was after Mr. Tulk's arrival, that Mr. and Mrs. Sutcliffe came for the day and brought Mr. Köhler's photos. When they were passed around the table after dinner, there were comments about the children and how they had grown since the picture was taken in the spring. When the photo reached Mr. Criddle, he took his time evaluating, "They are very nice . . . but all the boys look too grave." Then he chuckled, adding a most odious remark, "Only one eyesore."[15]

Back Row: Cecil, Edwy, Mr Criddle, Stuart. Middle Row: Elise, Evelyn, Julia, Mrs. Criddle holding Alma, Maida, Beatrice. Front Row: Norman, Talbot, Harry. Köhler photo.

15   September 16, 1895.

Everyone knew the target. All eyes turned toward the kitchen.

Elise, her face crimson with humiliation, bolted for the door. *I've born insult, condemnation, shame, but this is too much!* She ran as best she could on her poor swollen legs. Glancing back she saw only the dog following. Then out behind the barns she hesitated. *I **have nowhere** to go . . . I've never gone anywhere alone.* She collapsed on a log. *I'm an eyesore! Cruel, how terribly cruel! After all I have done for him. That first winter, without warm clothes, freezing as I cooked outdoors and every day going with my children to find wood for him and his lady to burn in their little shanty. They were warm, while I took care of all the children in that freezing cold tent. We suffered so!*

And summers . . . hauling logs and all that grubbing in the fields. I thought my back would break, that I'd die of heatstroke.

And all the hungry times when I ate little so the children could have my skimpy share. My poor stunted Cecil shows how close he came to starving. . . .

Four times I tended Mrs. Criddle through her delicate months and brought her babies safely into the world. . . .

Fighting prairie fires! . . . The dust and smoke . . .

All those weeks, the sleepless nights—I tended their whooping children! . . .

Is it any wonder my health is broken? I've lost my youthful beauty . . . old before my time.

*Work, work, work, right through Isabel's wedding. All for the sake of a promise that I'd help his wife. There's never a word of praise, never a thank you. It's for **me** to be grateful. I should be happy to have a roof over my head, thankful that **I** have a family to serve until **I die.***

A life sentence for a trusting heart!

Her body began to tremble and years of suffering shook her thin frame. She bent down, wrapped her arms around Caesar's furry neck and sobbed.

When I agreed to come as Mrs. Criddle's servant, I couldn't foresee the loneliness, the criticisms, and the horrid nickname. No money of my own, not even for shoes or stockings for my poor swollen legs. . . . Nor a comb for my hair.

Tears streamed down her careworn face. . . .

How long, she knew not. Still the tears flowed.

She was conscious of voices as the guests departed.

Later yet, she heard Talbot and Alma calling high and clear in the distance, "Mama Dutcheen! Mama Dutcheen!" Their little voices touched a chord in her heart and she sat up and rubbed her eyes. But she didn't answer, neither she nor the dog moved. The voices came closer, "Mama Dutcheen, where are you?" The children peeked around the corner of the barn and shouted happily, "Here you are, Mama Dutcheen! We've been looking everywhere for you. We want a bedtime story and a song."

How could she turn them down?

"If you help me up from this log."

They each took hold and tugged. Mama Dutcheen slowly and painfully got to her feet. She stood stiffly for a few moments and then enclosed a little hand in each of her large bony ones. The trio, followed by the dog, his tail wagging happily, walked slowly back around the barns and up to the house.

⁓❧⁓

While the Vane boys earned money by threshing for others, the gentlemen hunted. One morning before breakfast, Miss Steer, with her pony and rig, took Mr. Criddle chicken shooting. At sunset, out again with Beatrice, he boasted, "Got ten chickens in eight shots."

During the three days of threshing the men consumed what seemed to Elise a mountain of food. Their 190 acres of wheat produced 2,690 bushels. Not so bad if 700 of them had not been smutty, caused apparently by the diseased seed Edwy had bought.

To sell the first load, Mr. Tulk asked to go along with Edwy to congratulate the new Mrs. Knight. And once there he issued an invitation, "Come out for few days, visit with your mother."

Her husband let her go.

Isabel burst through the door, "Surprise, surprise! Mama, I've come to tease you."

The children came running for hugs; Mr. Tulk looked on, well pleased with himself. It was only for a few days, but she was good medicine; for Maida, still lethargic; for Mr. Tulk who got his morning tea in bed; and for Elise who learned she was going to be a Grossmutter. They enjoyed the few days together as Isabel shared her hopes and fears looking ahead to motherhood. *My Isabel is very happy and I am also, knowing she has a home of her own.*

All too soon Elise was alone again facing a disturbing piece of news. "A young man died of diphtheria just west of us. Lots of people went to the funeral before they knew the cause. I suppose we'll all suffer."

Please God, Elise thought, *protect us. I cannot survive another epidemic.*

The boys gathered wood for their annual fifth of November bonfire; the biggest and best ever. Miss Steer added to the fun, and Mr. Tulk made a glorious fireworks display. Next day, his holiday over, Edwy delivered him to Brandon.

⁓❧⁓

There were big changes that fall. Upper let his land go for taxes and moved south of the river; McVey sold his farm to B. Marshall. John Ellis said, "I came so we could live close to relatives, but I can't feed my family on this sandy land. I'm moving back to the rich farmlands of Essex County, Ontario." Miss Steer had to find another boarding place and Two Rivers School attendance fell to just over ten.

On the other hand, the Denny[16] brothers arranged to buy Mr. Criddle's north homestead and over-winter in Elise's little house. *I hope they fill the cracks . . . Cecil and I found it drafty.* Then she learned Mr. Tulk had left money to purchase the NE ¼ of 1.9.17 for Harry and Norman. Harry was excited, but she was more skeptical. *If it is true then he should take them to Brandon, or at least bring the documents home to sign. I'm afraid for my Harry.*

The problem had been brewing all summer and fall. Aweme's teacher, Mr. McNab, was not as easily put off as the ladies had been in expecting his full salary. As the amount owing climbed each month, he took his situation to arbitration in December and won his case. Mr. Criddle took the blow as expected, but he carried on to his night's card games and luckily won $9.20.[17]

Whether it was the bad news or good that sent Mr. Criddle back to happier days, Elise caught sight of him reading *Peg Woffington*.[18] She was instantly transported to their first romantic months in London. *Heads together, we poured over those pages . . . went to the play. A farce it was—reality and fantasy playing against each other. I was so gullible. . . .*

Isabel was home for a few days during hunting season. Then Minnie came for a rest and was there when Elise opened a letter and pulled out a card,

"Oh no! It's got a black border."[19]

Almost linded by tears Elise struggled to read:

Filled with pain and sorrow, we communicate to our Friends and Acquaintances the sad news that our beloved wife and mother, **Mrs. Marie Harrer, nee Bauer,** *today at 5 PM after a long and difficult suffering passed away gently.*

Friedrich Harrer, Mannheim, December 10, 1895. The interment Thursday, December 12, 3 PM from the funeral home, O 6 No. 3 and 4

---

16   The Dennys were William, Roland, Emma, and later, Mrs. Denny, Thirza and a younger boy.
17   School Board Accounts of 1895 show wages owing for several teachers. Archives of Manitoba.
18   Reade, Charles, *Peg Woffington*. (T. Nelson and Sons, 1850).
19   Marie Barbara Caroline Mathilde Bauer, born May 13, 1839. Card in private collection.

Overcome with emotion, she deserted her post at the stove, fled upstairs and dropped to her bed. She imagined the lifeless body, the loving hands stilled, and whispered, *"Dear sweet Marie." They should have written to warn me.* She covered her face with her hands and sobbed.

Minnie came up and sat with her, "You are so far from your family, Mama. You cannot go to your brothers to find comfort. We will do the best we can. And right now I will look after tea, so don't worry. I'll bring something up to you later on."

And so alone in the one small room she claimed as her own, her memories and tears mingled. . . . A few lines of poetry expressed her feelings.

Armes Herz, das mit dem Grame ringet,	*Poor heart, that battles with grief*
Der des Daseins Freude ihm zerstoert,	*Grief that destroys the joy of life*
Der zum Marke seines Lebens dringet	*Grief that enters the very marrow of life*
Und den freien Blick zum Himmel wehrt! [20]	*And hides the free look heavenward.*

I weep for my brother and his motherless girls . . . and myself. . . . Marie was like a sister, a link to one of the happiest moments of my life.[21] *Percy and I had been engaged three and a half years already, but our wedding kept being delayed. I lived for Percy's visits to Heidelberg, but each time he left me only another promise. That day as Marie and Friedrich stood before Pastor Zottel pledging their love to one another,*[22] *Percy took my hand, whispered, "Dearest Elise, we will marry soon. You will be mine. Never again will that dreadful English Channel come between us." He was to sing for the happy couple and I was to accompany him. He said with a kiss, "I'm singing for you too."*

Es muss ein Wunderbares sein	*It is a wondrous thing to find*
Ums Lieben zweier seelen	*Two souls by love united,*
Sich schliessen ganz einander ein,	*So close in harmony entwined*
Sich nei ein Wort verhehlen	*That life by love is lightened.*
Und Freud und Leid, —	*In joy and grief, —*
Und Glück und Not —	*in sun and show'r —*
So mit ein ander tragen,	*These two will cleave together.*
Vom ersten Kuss bis in den Tod,	*From love's first kiss to life's last hour,*
Sich nur von Liebe sagen.	*Two souls as one forever.*

I thought my heart would burst. I wanted Marie's happiness. . . .
But my betrothed was not like her Friedrich. . . .

The beauty of that day vanished. Elise was once more an old servant woman, alone on her little bed, powerless to stop the flow of her tears. . . .

---

20 *Poesie*, Poem # 27, author unknown. Family Collection.
21 Friedrich to Percy, 1906. "40 years ago we were all together for New Years, Mother, Elise, Carl and Wilhelm."
22 Married Sept. 7, 1865, St. Peter and Providence, Heidelberg. Karlsruhe archives.

From far away, she heard organ music. It swelled ever louder, surrounding her completely.

Aus tiefer Not schrei ich zu dir,	*From depths of woe I cry*
Herr Gott, erhör mein Rufen;	*to Thee in trial and tribulation*
Dein gnädig Ohren kehr zu mir	*bend down Thy gracious ear to me*
Und meiner Bitt sie öffnen!...	*Lord, hear my supplication...*

She stood before the resurrection window: "Come onto me... and I will give you rest."

***

In the days following, grief suspended Elise between the mundane world of a domestic—emptying chamber pots, washing clothes, feeding fires, baking bread, peeling potatoes—and the world of her childhood, parents and brothers, uncles and aunts, cousins and friends. Her daily drudgery mixed with happy memories and losses.

***

McManes was running for Municipal Council and came asking for Mr. Criddle's vote. And lo, they buried the hatchet over a common cause—Prohibition—worthy of Mr. Criddle's oratory.

Prohibition I abominate – its votaries are always supremely ugly old maids with big feet. Or dyspeptic men (reformed drunkards very often or gospel grinders) And loud voiced strong-minded wives with not too faithful lords. Intemperance either on the booze or teetotal side is not for me – both are hideous and I hate ugly things – so – as I say – I'll vote Conservative and so I guess will all of the boys.

Elise wouldn't be voting, and as an extra blessing her Minnie came home for Christmas. There were other guests: the Denny brothers, Miss Steer and her gangly young brother, Arthur.[23] Mr. Criddle mumbled, "He wasn't invited, damn him!"

When Arthur put himself forward as if he were the son of a gentleman and added a greater transgression by breaking the unwritten law—let Mr. Criddle win—the Christmas air rang with colourful profanities.[24]

After the games and tea, Harry played the mouth organ so Mr. and Mrs. Criddle could open the evening's dancing. Mr. Criddle took a turn with his daughters, right down to little Alma who danced, he bragged, like an angel. But once he sat at the organ, young Arthur stepped out with the older daughters.

---

23 Arthur Steer. 1878-1945. Born in Upton, Essex. Attended Middle Class School Christ Church, Battersea, won the prize in geography. Enlisted in Royal Canadian Dragoons, 1897, Yukon Field Force 1898. Lifetime military career: saw action in the Boer War, WW I and attained the rank of Lt. Col. during WW II.
24 Arthur Steer spoke of Mr. Criddle as a poor loser, and raged, according to granddaughter Carol Snell.

Daggers meant for him went unseen, especially by his sister, for she was danc-ing with Edwy. Elise, from the kitchen said to herself, *Edwy is happy tonight, but what's in store for the two of them when Percy realizes he has more than Arthur to worry about?*

Chapter Twenty

Winds of Change

On New Year's Day, 1896, the youngsters enjoyed a fun-filled afternoon on their new rink. Elise and Isabel, enjoying their time together in the kitchen, heard the laughter before the door burst open. In they came, cheeks rosy and bubbling with news for Mama Dutcheen. "Stuart is getting better." "Cecil does backward eights." "You should have seen Harry's fancy tricks."

After the Knights bundled up and waved goodbye, Elise carried on in relative calm until later in January when the Criddle youngsters came down with high fevers and nasty coughs. Hearing Edwy and Harry talking about going to a skating exhibition in Brandon, she told them, "It's a fine idea. Get away from all this coughing. Enjoy yourselves."

Mrs. Criddle, also unwell, said to her, "Huckey, I would so love a cup of tea. Write Minnie. Ask if she can send some out with the boys."

When Elise hesitated, Mrs. Criddle pressed her, "Minnie won't mind. She likes to help out."

So after cleaning up the evening dishes, Elise dried her hands and did as she was bid.

My dear Minnie!

Edwy and Harry are going to Brandon tomorrow to stay over night at the Grand Central. I take therefore the opportunity to write a few words to you. I am glad you are away from the Thorpes at your old place and hope you like it, though washing all day is by no means pleasant work. I suppose you will try to get in the dining room instead soon. Mrs. Criddle and I will make your dress as soon as possible. I suppose you do not want it in a hurry, or you would have said so. At any rate Papa [what Mrs. Criddle called him] will not go in to Brandon for at least a fortnight.

Now I want to ask you something that is, if you ever can spare the money, will you get us some tea, if only half a pound at a time, both Mrs. Criddle and I are so fond of it and can not often get it, as Papa only buys some now and then for visitors. It is miserable to have to eat your bread dry in the morning or evening; don't say anything to Papa about it, give it to Edwy, he will have to go more into Brandon to take loads of wood to sell.

I am glad you enjoy yourself sometimes, take care though with whom you make friends. Do you often see Isabel? Papa says that you look better, you are thinner he says. Have you heard anything of Mrs. Foulger? I am waiting for weeks for a letter from her. Maida was very pleased with the print for a frock for her. I am getting stronger, though I cannot do much hard work without knocking myself up.

Goodbye dear Minnie, with love from all,

I remain your affectionate Mama[1]

She paused nervously. *I've been too bold! It can't be wrong to say we are **longing** for some tea, but I should have left it to Mrs. Criddle. What if Percy finds out?* She added a line:

You'd better burn this letter at once.

Then she popped it into her apron pocket, ready to slip to Edwy.

After their excursion Harry told her, "McCullough's skating was brilliant. He did lots of new tricks we can try. But we also learned a dandy way to get a better price for our smutty grain. Mix it with snow and tramp on it to wear away the smut. Put it through the fanning mill to remove the snow and debris. Keep on until the wheat looks normal. We're going to give it a try."

Edwy took a doctored load to Treesbank and happily accepted 32¢ a bushel.

Meanwhile, Mr. Criddle joined the ranks of the unwell, and between coughs croaked, "I'm not far from kingdom come!"

His poor wife, already tired of the sound, said rather curtly, "Coughing is brought on by fancy."

But he held to his own theories. "It's queer and disagreeable smells that bring on a fit. Extra smoking of a morning – tea for breakfast. On the other hand singing seems to protect me."

❦

Edwy whistled or hummed through the winter days, no matter what was expected of him. His mother guessed the reason. At the end of January, Miss Steer was there as usual, only that night Edwy was at her side. Overflowing with love and confidence he asked Mr. Criddle for permission to get married.

Elise's joy was short-lived. Mr. Criddle exploded! ! ! ! x x x . . .

Her stomach turned to stone. *I clung to the hope that Percy would support the boys. Edwy works so hard . . . does his utmost to please. 'My Boy' this and 'my Boy' that!* Her knitting needles clicked and the sock lengthened. *Will this break his spirit? Will he give up his love? Will it drive Miss Steer away?*

Edwy, accustomed to Mr. Criddle's tantrums, stoically endured the onslaught. Elise's memory went back to their engagement in 1863 when Percy's mother re-

---

1 Letter undated, but according to the Diary it was February 1, 1896.

fused, said he was too young, and she couldn't support a family. *But he wooed me all the more, said our love would win her over, she just needed time. Edwy and Miss Steer can't see how hard this furrow will be to plough.*

For her part, Miss Steer was utterly confused. Hadn't Mr. Criddle supported her like a father and welcomed her into his home? Mrs. Criddle, now icily cold, suggested Edwy take Miss Steer back to her boarding place. Edwy tried to comfort Emily and said confidently, "Our love is steadfast. The worst will soon be over; he'll come around, you'll see."

And to his mother he confided, "We just need to be patient. Isn't Mr. C's favourite, *O rest in the Lord, wait patiently for Him and He shall give thee thy heart's desires?*"

She smiled sadly, "I guess I'm the one who needs reminding of God's providence.

Mr. Criddle saw a host of unsavoury flaws making Emily unsuitable as a wife. Edwy had heard the same things said of other less than perfect young ladies. 'Big feet' was a benchmark of poor breeding. And, he had many other undesirable attributes he expected Edwy to apply to Emily. When his attacks did not deter the 'Boy' he diarized his frustration:

> Miss Steer not been here for nearly 3 weeks – a match between her and the Boy is imminent – if not already arranged – and I signified my disapproval – so she's taken the huff. For the Boy to marry her would be ruin to him, as though she's a very nice girl and all the rest of it – she's too old – too big and clumsy – of the type that ages very rapidly – she's not healthy – her stock are very common – and lastly she's the most careless – destructive – pleasure loving idle thing I've set my eyes on for many a day – besides being by no means brilliant in talent and quickness. In short she's totally unfit for a Manitoba farmer's wife and would burn his house down for him before she'd been married a week.

Edwy and his brothers, hoping to earn approval, worked like slaves to bring home suitable logs to build another stable. Mr. Criddle looked over the pile, "Splendid fellows – 47 varying in size from 21 inches to about 13 at the butt."

When not logging, Edwy was on the road taking Mr. Criddle to ailing neighbours, school meetings, and Brandon. The latter always took two days, the first getting there and driving from business to business until being dropped off at the hotel to join his friends. One morning the news was a little different: Mr. Criddle boasted, "My whist friends were away, so I went to watch a new game called curling – made six dollars betting on the winner of each end."

Elise noticed Mr. Criddle's merry mood when he returned. *I hope the worst is over for Edwy.* Having eaten quickly, Edwy passed by his mother and told her quietly, "I'm off to see my girl."

His mother was making her last rounds with the sick children when he came in.

"Emily can't stay on at Two Rivers School. Mr. C agrees with the trustees to let her go at the end of the winter term."

She paused to let the impact sink in and then patting his shoulder said, "I'm so very sorry."

He replied wearily, "I'm turning in."

What will he do if Miss Steer leaves the community to take another school? There is so much against them, no money, no house, and Percy!

Stanley Köhler and his home.

Edwy had next to drive Mr. Criddle to a bachelor party in honour of Mr. Köhler's upcoming marriage to Lily Husband, the doctor's daughter. *My poor boy, Percy wants him to celebrate a neighbour's wedding, when his heart is crying out for his own.*

Another event to keep Edwy from courting came with an invitation, "We'd like you and the boys to sing at our Blythe concert. Do that laughing song again."

With coughing for accompaniment, Edwy and Harry rehearsed *Va Da Si Via.*

Home again, Mr. Criddle had important news: "Exceptionally good fortune – met an oldish man and we fell to talking. I'm surprised to find such an educated, well-travelled man in rural Manitoba – enjoyed each other immensely. He's been trying to make a living teaching French, German and Latin – says students are scarce. He'd have better luck teaching card tricks in this country. I've caught him up for our School – thirty-five dollars a month! He's glad – so am I – for he's full of reading – learning – anecdotes – music – and travel – and if he doesn't drink – why I shall have got a thoroughbred Highlander without clannishness – such as the wretched Scotch people round here are full of – and if I mistake not – a kindred spirit."

Elise pondered. *A well educated gentleman to teach in this little school. Kindred spirit? . . .*

❦❦❦

Alexander Clark

Nelson Clark and his mother

Alexander Clark, the Two Rivers postmaster died suddenly of pneumonia.[2] Shocked by the news, Elise asked herself, *did I ever see him? He was kind to Minnie the night she was so late and needed help to get across the river. A big loss for the Clarks, Nelson will be alone now, looking after the farm.*[3]

A few days later, Miss Steer finished the school term and found work in Treesbank at J. Clark's store, post office and grain buying business.[4] The lovers, now separated by the Assiniboine, would only have Sundays to see each other.

June 20th, '96
My dearest Edwy,
. . . I need not say that I would like to see you tomorrow but suppose you could not get over. I shall stay in Treesbank all day if you should come. . . .
July 3rd . . . I have borrowed a little cart and harness, without any trouble of Mrs. Adam Clark, so that unless I hear from you to the contrary I shall expect to see you on Sunday morning at the place agreed upon. . . .
August 14th . . . I think the best way will be for me to meet you near the turn to Jim Clark's and cross in his boat to Köhler's. Mrs. Arnold was here yesterday and they will see us across. . . .
October 2nd . . . My dearest Edwy, I think a better plan will be for you to get to J. Mair's say about 3. I will meet you in the flat, opposite Arnold's place, on the Main Road and we can go for a walk instead of visiting. D.V. [Deo Volente: God willing].

In the meantime, the prize pedagogue opened school and walked over. Once the gentlemen had their pipes drawing well, the learned discussion began. As the night wore on, Mr. Criddle's image of his catch became more and more tarnished. Mr. McPherson was older than first thought and suffered from chronic bronchitis.

On April 19, when Cecil sat down for breakfast, Elise whispered in his ear, "Happy twenty-first my dear boy. Too bad I have no gift for your milestone." [5]

---

2 Alexander Clark died March 20, 1896 at 76 years of age. Postmaster of Two Rivers 1881-'96. Nelson carried on the post office until it closed in 1897.
3 Nelson's sister Fanny was listed in Henderson's directory as Two Rivers Post master.
4 James H. Clark, son of Alexander Clark, moved to Virginia in 1909.
5 April 19, 1896. Twenty-one had to be whispered because Mr. Criddle maintained he was a year older than Norman.

A gift for her as well as Cecil came in the mail that afternoon. Violet May, Isabel's baby had arrived safely, on April 16th.[6] "Uncle Cecil, sounds first-rate. That's a jolly good birthday present."

She smiled, "And for me, 'Grandma' is first rate also. We must write and congratulate her."

⌑◦⊶◦⌑

The weather held cold and unusually wet that spring. Rain seeped through the straw roofs of the outbuildings, dripped on the animals; the ground under their hooves became muck. Brooding hens on their eggs were drenched. Elise's little house leaked so badly, the Denny brothers moved over to Edwy's shanty— dryer, bigger, and closer to their land. On learning a sister was coming as well, Mr. Criddle warned his boys: "She's of a common nature."

St. Albans didn't have a straw roof, but it also leaked. So badly, in fact, that during a downpour there weren't enough pots and pans to catch all the drips. A pool in Elise's room found a crack in the floor directly above Mr. Criddle's music collection. A bloodcurdling howl sent Elise rushing upstairs to mop up the offending puddle, while Mrs. Criddle feverishly blotted up the water on his pages. Elise got her comeuppance as she came down the stairs, "Look what you've done to my precious manuscripts! Dammed Dutchman! Careless, stupid woman! They're ruined! Look at these pie-bald watermarks – always be here to remind me."[7]

The fields too wet, Edwy was sent to Brandon for stores. Mrs. Criddle used the opportunity to send several hints to the lady with an income.

Aweme, Manitoba May 10th, 1896

My dear Minnie,

I suppose you saw the letter I wrote to Dido, so I need not repeat myself. We have almost finished the wheat seeding, in fact, Edwy would have done yesterday if there had not been heavy rain. There is water still standing in the swamp, a thing we have not seen for years.

If you have the money to spare, please give your Mama a pair or two of cotton stockings (rather big) because her foot, though much better still remains much swollen. My toothache has gone and we are all fairly well again. Edwy is looking tired and thin. You know he always overworks himself a little when seeding and harvest times come. Norman comes of age on Thursday. What an old party I am getting! Don't I wish I had a little money of my own? Anyway we mean to have a little extra for him in the cake and pie line if we can't do anything else.

When are you coming out to see us? I wonder if Dido will come out with Edwy. I suppose I must wait till he comes to find out. We have got into the everlasting egg season. No meat of course, but if we had cheese and sago or such like things

---

6   Violet May Knight, April 16, 1896. City of Brandon, Dr. McDearmid in attendance. Vital Statistics, Manitoba.
7   May 9, 1896.

would be more variegated. We have 69 chicks at present, two sittings have been spoilt by the rain, which came through everywhere and kept on dripping for days, making the buildings into regular quagmires. Miss Steer is working at Jim Clark's store. She is very busy and happy and has no time for visiting except on Sundays. I am very glad she has got the place, as it seems to suit her very well. I presume Mama and infant are well, lots of love to her and you from all.

> *Goodbye, keep well.*
> *Yours affectionately, Alice Criddle*

The Criddle's eldest son and heir didn't wish a twenty-first party. Norman, a quiet and meditative fellow, preferred solitary rambles and was happy with a birthday cake and the extra goodies Minnie sent in response to Mrs. Criddle's letter.

Elise worried about Edwy losing his girl, but her letters kept coming. One night he told her, "I know you liked Emily's little horse. You'll be interested in this:

> *What will you think of me I wonder! I have parted with Shepherd F. Knapp! This is how it was. A party of Indians came here yesterday from Shoal Lake to Oak Lake and (they had a letter of recommendation from a lady, which I read) to visit some relatives and one of their ponies was tired right out. The chief or boss took a fancy to Dilly and wanted to trade so after much persuasion I did. This I have got is only 7 years old and is quiet and gentle as Dilly. I rode on his back and he is faster. Poor old Dilly! I felt sorry to see him go but he trotted off quite happily drawing a little white covered two wheeled rig. I think he will be looked after. They seemed very respectable people. . . .'*

His mother thought a moment before saying, "I was fond of that pony, but I guess she did the right thing."

Edwy read on:

> *Had a long tiring day yesterday. Expect another today. Fridays and Saturdays generally are. Mr. Sutcliffe saw my flowers yesterday and said with a sly look. "You've had someone to bring you flowers."*

He left his mother to guess the rest of the letter.

One lovely June day Will borrowed a rig and brought Isabel and their new baby to St. Albans. Grandma hurried out and reached up for the little bundle. Lifting the blanket, she studied the tiny face, kissed the perfect little fingers. Then holding wee Violet May to her heart, thanked God, and oblivious of the others sang the wee girl a lullaby.

Hush, my babe, lie still and slumber, /Holy angels guard thy bed,
Heav'nly blessings without number, /Gently falling on thy head.
How much better thou art attended, /Than the Son of God could be,
When from heaven He descended, /And became a child like thee!

Looking up she noticed the others waiting to see the child. "I'm forgetting our dinner, I must get the potatoes on to boil," and reluctantly gave her up, "I hope we have time to visit a bit again after we've eaten."

Shortly after the Knights' brief visit Mr. Criddle agreed to Edwy's marriage. Like a captive set free, Edwy was away to Jim Mair's to borrow a buggy. Then under the stars, with the moon as witness, he proposed. The very next Sunday the happy couple officially announced their engagement. Elise's heart overflowed with happiness. *Thank God, Edwy's bad times are over.*

Spring rolled on to summer. Isabel and the baby came again; Miss Steer also came, but not for pleasure. She needed help for a large, painful abscess on her upper arm. Mr. Criddle gave her pain killers and Elise applied hot compresses. In a fortnight she was well enough to go back across the river. All seemed well.

Then Elise received a letter.

Carl Harrer

Mannheim, 28th of June 1896

Liebe Elise!

I received some time ago your welcome letter, as well as one for Carl, which I sent to him. You know, dear sister that our brother Carl often suffered from a bad cough, because of which he often went to resorts with hot springs. Lately the malady got worse and caused a heart problem, which during the last weeks became very serious. Four weeks ago I visited him in Karlsruhe and found him feeling fairly well; the doctor too thought it was not a serious illness and would pass over. Later there were signs of (hydropsie) retention of fluids. On the 25th of June he was freed from his eight-day suffering coming from a lung and heart paralysis. Amalie always had hopes of him improving, therefore did not write us how poorly off he really was, partly also because she thought the bad news would excite us too much and harm us. Yet the passing of dear Carl has shaken me up badly; I have lost much with his passing and I can hardly grasp it, that he would have to follow my dear wife so soon.

You too will be shaken up by this news, but it is our fate to see so many of our loved ones leaving us. Be strong and don't allow the pain

Amelie Harrer

caused by our brother's passing to affect you too much, for you also have duties towards your family.

The interment took place in Karlsruhe yesterday, where I was present. Participation was general, for Carl was well liked in Karlsruhe. Julchen and Elsa are still with Amalie. Amalie herself is quite composed; I feared for her. She sends greetings to you and will write you personally. Her life will change now. She will have to make adjustments in order to make ends meet with her pension. . . . She wants to keep Julchen with her until she has finished her examinations but how she will decide on a course of action in the future is not visible yet.

I and my family are, except for the mourning for dear Carl, fine. Farewell, dear Elise . . .

A kiss from your brother, Friedrich

Can it be? My loving brother . . . my big handsome brother – dead? Dear Amalie, you were so happy.[8] *. . . I'm too far away but your family will comfort you. . . . Dear Friedrich, your darling Marie gone and now our brother.* She broke into sobs. . . . *I feel so alone. . . . You ask me to be strong.* She took out her poetry book, turned to *Trennung* [Parting], and read through tears:

. . . Alle Freude scheint zu fliehen,	*. . . All joy seems to flee*
Und es bleibt nur bitt'rer Schmerz.	*And only bitter pain remains.*
Doch ein Engel schwebt hernieder,	*But an angel glides down*
Laechelt sanft in sel'ger Ruh,	*Peacefully and smiles*
"Weine nicht! O Kind der Erde,	*"Cry Not! O child of Earth*
Zage nicht!" ruft er ihm zu.	*Despair not!" he says to it.*
"Alles trennt sich, um vereint zu werden,	*"Everything parts, in order to be reunited.*
Unten oder oben wird's gescheh'n.	*Here or above it will happen.*
Trennung ist dein Los auf Erden,	*Parting is our lot in earth*
Doch im Himmel harrt das Wiederseh'n.	*But in heaven a meeting awaits us.*

Meanwhile in Germany, Amalie was visited by authorities to itemize the assets of Karl Jacob Wilhelm Harrer, Grand Ducal *Oberrechnungsrat*.[9] Since Karl hadn't left a will and had no children, his siblings were also legal heirs of his estate. Amalie gave their names: Karl Friedrich Harrer, merchant in Mannheim; and a sister, Sabina Elise Harrer, the 'wife' of Percy Criddle, Aweme, Canada. After verifying Friedrich and Elise's identity through their birth records, they were to be notified. Since the foreign name 'Criddle' might give rise to confusion, they wrote 'Criddel' as pronounced.

---

8 Amalie Franziska Burgweger and Carl Harrer were married in Heidelberg, May 19, 1881.
9 *Oberrechnungsrat*. Senior financial advisor. State Archives Karlsruhe, Baden-Württemberg. B 270/IV, Nr 28187.

Next morning Edwy said, "I've been asked to join a cricket team playing against Brandon today. Mr. C says I can go. I can take you to visit Isabel and the baby."[10]

She looked up, "Do you mean it?"

She glanced around the kitchen. *I've never gone anywhere for pleasure . . . but the berries are done—seventeen fresh pots of jam sparkling on the shelf.* Still she hesitated.

Edwy urged, "Ask Mrs. Criddle."

From deep within came a burst of courage, "May I go with Edwy?"

"Your work can wait a day."

Unbelievable! . . . I will see Isabel's home and baby Violet!

Edwy watched his mother untie her apron. A sparkle in her eyes sent him hurrying out to hitch up the team. Cecil helped her climb up and onto the wagon seat. There she sat, feeling like a queen beside her son. This time when he clucked to the horses, it was Elise who was going. *A holiday! A loving God is indeed in heaven!*

It was a bright day, if a little breezy. With so much rain that spring, the prairie was extraordinarily lush; white, blue and yellow flowers danced beside the road. Edwy pointed out the farms they passed and told her stories of his many adventures: fording the river in high water, losing his way in blizzards, getting soaked by rain.

Isabel was dumbfounded to see her mother at the door. She made a cup of tea and they chatted. When the baby awoke, Elise held her little granddaughter and enjoyed a special tête-à-tête, "My precious wee girl. Thankful, that's what I am, to be holding you. . . . Do I see a wee smile for your *Grossmutter*?"

It was special island-of-time, just the three of them. "I can hardly believe I am here in your home, my first holiday since we left our flat on St. George's Road."

They didn't say, but both thought, *it might be the only one.*

Edwy came in, "My cricket game didn't come off. I'm done Mr. C's errands, but I'm in no hurry to get back. Enjoy yourselves. Is Will around?"

"He's hauling today. There isn't much work in that line just now."

They talked: about the baby, Edwy's girl, Uncle Karl's untimely passing, and the crops looking good, but needing rain. Isabel made them supper, and then Edwy reluctantly went for the team and wagon. Elise's eyes were misty as she kissed little Violet May's forehead, "Come out to see us soon."

As the horses trotted steadily homeward, the sun sank in the west and darkness closed around them. The summer air was soft; the stars grew brighter and the sliver of a moon climbed higher. Its pale white light seemed to Elise to create

---

10 July 18, 1896.

an island of peace in the vast dark world. *Just the two of us, side by side, no need for words . . . travelling on and on, as if the end will never come. How blest I am to have this son and his gift of this special day.*

Her prayers were short that night; she slept soundly.

⸙

But Elise's peace was quickly swept away. Norman's cold and cough developed into another long bout of bronchitis. Miss Steer's abscesses flared up, and although it was clear she wasn't welcome, Elise nursed her back to health. Edwy's new frock coat disappeared from the peg outside the Criddle door and the housekeeper was expected to know its whereabouts. And then, a registered letter addressed to Mr. P. Criddle, Secretary of Aweme School, from the court in Brandon, ordered him to garnishee Mr. McPherson's salary.[11] Furthermore, disgruntled parents arrived claiming the above mentioned teacher partook too liberally of certain fluids in Brandon and failed to reach his classroom in a timely fashion. School problems should not have been Elise's, but when Mr. Criddle was frustrated, she and her sons bore the brunt of his temper.

The weather added to their troubles as day after day they watched the once promising wheat shrivel under the scorching sun. When at last the barometer dropped, Mr. Criddle announced, "Expect a storm ere long – if we get it – we can reckon on the crops pulling through."

Clouds built, grew black, and charged down upon them. Just as Mr. Criddle put the final touches to his new tune for *Love Knocked Softly,* all hell broke loose. Walnut sized hailstones walloped the walls; windows shattered; and ice, mixed with glass, littered the floors. Their roof, threatening to give way, creaked and groaned.

In the storm's wake, they found a changed world: the ground white, the flag-pole down, the new wagon rack at the bottom of the hill, and the precious thermometer broken. In those few minutes, Edwy's hope to marry that fall, like the crops had been pulverized.

Mr. Criddle made the rounds of the neigbourhood and described the devastation:

> . . . top of Little's house demolished – has 5 pigs and a lot of fowls killed. Lonsbury hailed out – Bruner ditto – Bellhouse ditto – Fortune ditto – McManus [sic] ditto – John Martin ditto and half his house destroyed (some of the logs and roof carried 150 yds). Marshall ditto – Ake ditto – Jim, Geo and Alec Mair ditto – J. Martin Jr. and Calverley escaped to great extent. No one killed or injured.

---

11 July 14, 1896.

Sara Jane Clark

He also learned that the Clark family, still adjusting from their father's death, had lost their mother that stormy evening.[12]

When Miss Steer's health improved, she went back across the river to the store. Still determined to be a farmer's wife, she bought a cow and calf from a neighbour, and sent them to Edwy. Nor had he given up, and told his mother, "Even considering the cost of twine, a little wheat is better than none." He set up the binder to salvage what he could. Harry and Stuart went to Douglas to scavenge scorched wheat from a burned grain elevator. [13]

"Needs must, when the devil drives," Mr. Criddle said as he hired out his workforce. Harry and Cecil threshed; Stuart went to Cooper's, and Edwy to Husband's. Evelyn worked a few days and brought home his own plus Harry's three weeks' pay. The boys' sweat kept the Criddles afloat until Mr. Tulk arrived.

Due to bad weather, Edwy went to meet Mr. Tulk's train alone. A new thermometer and a supply of gentlemanly duds for Mr. Criddle made for a warm welcome, "I was on the brink of having to wear handmade garments."

—◦◦◦◦—

While they celebrated Mr. Tulk's arrival, their closest neighbours were gathering around Mr. Bellhouse's sickbed. He passed away October 16, and was laid to rest in Millford Cemetery beside his daughter, Susannah. Sister-in-law, Mrs. Clara Bellhouse, would keep the post office.

—◦◦◦◦—

Elise came down to light the fire and found Edwy writing. Looking up he said, "Emily has another boil. Mr. Criddle agreed to go to Treesbank to advise her, but the weather's bad. He won't want to go."

Quarter to six Saturday morning
Aweme, Oct 31, 1896

My dearest Ella,

I did not intend writing to you at all as Mr. Criddle wrote to you last night but circumstances alter cases. I am afraid that last night's snow and frost will stop us from getting across the river tomorrow. I still have hopes however and if it was left to me I have no doubt that we should manage it, but it will not be left to me. Most likely Mr. Criddle will not even start unless the weather changes. What it is, to be afraid of everything? Perhaps he is right though, but I can't see it where you are concerned.

12 Sarah Jane Clark, nee Ake, 58, born Kent, Ontario. Died August 2, 1896, Treesbank, Manitoba, of brain fever, duration 26 days, Dr. Vanstone. Informant, Rev. H. Wigle. Manitoba Vital Statistics.
13 Harry Vane. "We were more than happy to eat scorched wheat."

However, be at Jack Mair's in time in case we come. I shall do my best you may be sure. If we don't see each other tomorrow it will be the first Sunday since we were engaged. We shall have to imagine we are together. . . . Well never mind it can't be helped.

So long as my dear girl is well and happy I can stand anything.

We finished threshing at Fortune's yesterday. . . . I expect they will get here sometime on Monday. I have been to bed late and up early the last three or four days, the consequence being the want of sleep. Will and Roland [Denny] here all one night and Marshall last night. We played cards till I was black in the face.[14] Confound the Dennys!

Of course I saw Miss Denny while at Fortunes. I have a strong objection to the way she shakes hands; she holds my hand as if it belonged to her. God help me if it did. I think you will have to box her ears. I suppose you will say poor fellow when you read this. He is getting particular! Miss Denny is supposed to be helping Miss Fortune. She as good as told me she is more nuisance than she is worth. She don't [sic] get up till eleven of a morning. I would throw a pail of water at her. Perhaps she would get up then. She isn't worth the paper this is written on.

It is pretty near time I was off to Bellhouse's [post office] with this. With my love to you . . . God bless my girl and make her happy, is my prayer.

Ever your own Lover, Edwy   I shall hope to see you tomorrow.

Edwy refused to see the writing on the wall

NO WEDDING THIS YEAR.

His mother could read it on his face the night they'd finished threshing. He told her sadly, "I promised Emily I'd let her know about our crop."

Aweme, Nov 5, 1896

My Dearest Ella,

I have just got home from McManes', 8 o'c where I have been threshing. We finished ours this morning after 3 days to thresh 760 bushels.[15] A handsome return for a lot of hard work! I am thoroughly disgusted. I can't help being rather downhearted about it. Especially as it is worse than I expected. Wet with beastly weather, having wet feet all the time and hardly any sleep lately I don't feel very well. If only you were here to cheer me up, I should be all right.

It is Mr. Tulk's birthday. The boys are making some fire works. I expect they are going to let them off in a few minutes. Blow the fireworks! I am off to bed. What are fireworks to me? Mr. Criddle and I are going to Brandon tomorrow. We won't get back till Friday night, I expect.

There are good many I s in this letter.

Friday morning. *Another beastly day! I have to go to Brandon directly after dinner whatever the weather. I shall have the pleasure of going alone, as the day is not good enough for Mr. C.*

I will try to get over to see you on Sunday, but shall run no risks for your sake.

Yours, as ever Edwy

---

14 Mr. Criddle needed four people to play.
15 Nov. 5, 1896. They sowed 205 acres so the average yield per acre was 3.7

Among the letters Mr. Criddle collected in Friday's mail were two from Germany: one from Elise's sister-in-law, Amalie, addressed as usual to 'Mr. Percy Criddle'.

The other, a registered letter addressed to 'Mrs. Elise Criddle, attention Percy Criddle, Aweme, Manitoba Canada, Northamerica.' He hastily signed for it while mumbling to Mrs. Bellhouse, "Stupid Germans, misspelling my wife's name," and slipped it between the other letters.[16]

On the way home he rested on a stump and opened the registered one. There were two enclosures, one a form, and the other, a short letter from a lawyer. He saw 'Karl Harrer' and 'June 25' so he knew it was the expected letter about Karl's estate. There were two amounts, '1,776 Marks' and '3,279 Marks.' He mumbled to himself. "Let's see – could amount to eight hundred dollars. A sizable amount! I could do a lot with that! Got it past Mrs. Bellhouse today. Mmm . . . but there'll be **more** registered letters and a cheque for Elise Criddle to sign. So – perhaps – all things considered – it's just too risky."

He examined the form. . . . He couldn't ask Elise to translate. Muttered, "Mmm, it needs the signature of Elise <u>Criddel</u> signed in the presence of a notary. Bloody bad luck that Bellhouse is dead. Can't go to Two Rivers – don't trust young Clark. Treesbank – another Methodist, and Miss Steer's there looking after the post office – don't need her in on this. How can I get the deuced thing back to Germany – without the Dutchman signing it? I'll ask Mrs. Bellhouse next week if she has the authority to witness signatures – got around her today."

He slid the form back into the envelope, stowed it in his inner pocket and walked on home. Handing Elise the lawyer's letter he said, "This came in the mail today. Read it – I want to be sure I understand."

Karlsruhe, 15 Oct 1896

Mrs. Elise Harrer, wife of Percy Criddel, Oekonom [business man] in Canada, N. A., Aweme, Manitoba.

Herewith I inform you that your brother Karl Harrer, 'Oberrechnungsrat' [chief financial advisor] in Karlsruhe, died on 25 June of this year, and ask you, in order to be represented at the division of assets, to appoint a representative and send me the letter of attorney as soon as possible. The assets consist of movables in a value of 1,776 Marks and active debts and ready money in a value of 3,279 Marks. [17]

---

16 Neighbours would only know the women as Mrs. Vane and Mrs. Criddle. She was Mrs. Criddle even to Mr. Tulk

17 "Active debts," obsolete term for money owed to the estate. State Archives Karlsruhe Baden-

Translating kept Elise from concentrating on the meaning, but before she had a chance to reread it, he exchanged it for a letter from Amalie and left her with it. The sight of pressed flowers took Elise to her brother's grave. Then blinking back tears, she saw a ten Mark bill. *Amalie's keeping Karl's tradition of sending a Christmas gift. But she will need it now. I'll send it back.* Elise felt calmer by the time she had finished reading the letter. *Amalie's facing her loss so bravely; I must try to do the same.*

⁂

Mr. Criddle posted letters the following week and asked Mrs. Bellhouse, "Are you able to witness an affidavit?"

"Sorry. I've applied—I expect it will be April before I have the authority. It took young Clark about six months to get his papers."

With that door closed he took a different tack. Approaching Elise later that evening he said, "About your brother's estate – I've written a letter for you to translate – must get it away in tomorrow's mail. You'll need to be alone to concentrate."

Elise longed for her bed, but after the dishes, took up her knitting. Mr. Criddle came from his room with pen, ink, and writing paper. He said, handing her a scribbled draft, "Translate this to German for notary Herr Stricker in Karlsruhe."

She scanned down the page:

Aweme, Manitoba, 15 Nov 1896

Honoured Sir,

I have received your letter dated 15 October and deeply regret that it is totally impossible to me to have drawn up a letter of attorney. My health is not good at all, and a journey of 150 miles would be necessary, for which I am completely incapable.

Gracious! One hundred and fifty miles! I hope Herr Stricker doesn't have an atlas. He wants me to lie to a notary? She read on:

I shall notify my sister-in-law and my brother Friedrich in Mannheim, and inform them with the circumstances, and hope they can settle the matter without my help, since I have no financial interest in the business of my deceased brother.
I remain with highest esteem
Your obedient servant,
Elise Criddle

Mr. Criddle cleared his throat. *I dare not change anything. I don't want Amalie's money but . . .* More throat clearing. *She dipped the pen and began.*

Württemberg, Germany. B 270/IV Karlsruhe, Nr 28187. Translated by Uwe Porten, genealogical researcher. All my information and correspondence are from Karl Harrer's file from the above archives.

Aweme, Manitoba 15ten, November
Geehrter Herr! . . . And wrote steadily to the familiar ending:
Ihre gehorsame Dienerin . . . . *Should this obedient servant sign 'Elise Criddle'?*
He glared. . . . She wrote,

Elise Criddle

She thought, *how easily it flows off my pen in spite of the many years since I left London.*

She added the recipient: *Gr. Bad. Gerichtsnotar, Herr Stricker, Karlsruhe, Baden.*[18]

Before she could lay down the pen he held out another, "For your sister-in-law."
She glanced at the page.

Dear Sister-in-law,
Your letter and enclosures I have received on November 8. . .

Yes, flowers and ten Marks . . . poor Amalie. But Mr. Criddle, not in the mood for reminiscing, growled, "I haven't got all night."

She began translating his English letter into German for Amalie:

Aweme, Manitoba, 15ten Nov, 1896

Liebe Schwaegerin!
Deinen Brief mit Inhalt habe ich am 8ten Nov. erhalten/as well on the same day the letter of Mister Stricker and I deeply regret that I am not able to have drawn up a letter of attorney, because we would have to travel 150 miles, which in this season in North America is impossible. You will remember that some years ago I suffered a heavy sickness and operation that I still have not recovered from. Always my legs are more or the less swollen. Part of the journey we would have to make in a sledge, and I would be exposed to the danger of freezing my feet. Last winter I had a very bad open wound on my leg that still has not healed completely. I never go out, the closest neighbours live only one mile from here, but I have never been inside their home. It is very lonesome here, often you do not see any house for miles.

She hesitated. *Nonsense! It's not the distance that keeps me from visiting.* He leaned over her.

Last summer I dared to visit my married daughter for the first time (she lives 25 miles from here) and returned so dead tired and sick, that I had to re-main in bed for several days. . .

My perfect holiday! How can I write such lies? He tapped impatiently on the table.

So you can see that I have to guard against dangers, particularly during winter-time. For eight days now it has been snowing continuously which makes the work around the house pretty difficult.

---

18 Elise's letters sent to Germany were all filed as part of the estate records.

She thought *who can believe that?* Tap, tap. . . .

*Our boys are very good and treat me carefully and help me in every way possible. Our boys, yes, **our** boys . . .* **Tap, tap. . . .**

> *I thank you very much for the dry flowers I wanted so much. I deeply feel with you that in all your sorrow you are burdened with unnecessary business and are plagued by them. We think it is so senseless, no one can lay claim to what is rightly yours. I give mandatory power to Friedrich, to do anything as it seems fit to him. And I send you the 10 Marks back. I even find it hard to write, and it makes me nervous,*
>
> *I close and remain always your true sister-in-law,*
>
> *Elise*

Hearty greetings from all of us to you and Julchen.

She had run out of space for the return address so she wrote it in the empty space at the beginning of the letter. He collected his pen and ink bottle and made off with her pages. Trembling, she sat thinking. *I do not want anything from Amalie . . . so many lies . . . I have sins to confess tonight.* Slowly getting to her feet, she made her weary way up the stairs. But even after prayers, her thoughts spun on. . . . *I was happy when our little son was born and Percy told me proudly, "Register the boy, 'Edwy' son of Percy and Elise Criddle." With that decree, we all became the Criddles of 131 St. George's Road.*

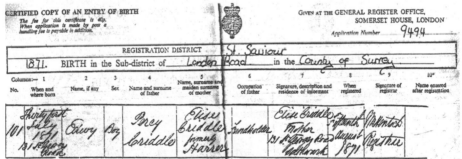

Minnie Isabel *But Percy didn't come home very often, said he was working on his music at George Nicol's place.[19] If I asked him to spend a night at home, he was quick to say, "Don't you want me to get ahead?" He must have been there when Harry was born. Later he couldn't be with us, he said, because his mother*

19 Alice Nicol's cousin George went to Heidelberg with Percy in January 1861, but George's parents called him home at the end of the year when the boys got into trouble. George went to Oxford and became a lawyer.

was so unwell. She needed her only son at home in Addlestone. At least he paid Mr. Wright the rent . . . until giving up his business entirely.[20] From then on I supported my family by sharing our flat, housekeeping,[21] and sewing. Yes, 'Mrs. Elise Criddle' built a good reputation with her needle.

"Emily's abscess has flared up again," Edwy confided to his mother. "And now she has a painful open sore on her nose. She's written such a brave letter. I'll read it to you seeing there's no one around."

> *The expected has come at last. I've got the sack. Mr. Clark told me this morn-ing that he thought he could manage alone what work there is here and Bert is coming to board and for that will do the chores and and help when he is not in school. I am not sorry, rather glad for I have been tired of it ever since the cold weather came on.*
>
> *I have been shivering all day, the store is as cold as Greenland (not in summer and it's no joke to get up and light the fire and fetch in your own wood, at least I think it isn't.) My face is still very sore and I don't feel extra well, I think I will go to the Doctor about it on Sunday if you care to take me. . . .*

"Isn't she a brave old girl? I'll take her to Dr. Husband on Sunday."

But Edwy couldn't get away. Miss Steer had many more hours in Mr. Clark's store the following week, getting business letters written and the post office books in order. When Mrs. Mair went for the mail later that week she was horrified, "You're much too ill to be here working! I'm taking you home with me."

Working at Mair's, Harry relayed her note to Edwy. All he could do was fret and talk to his mother. "Ella's worse, Mrs. Mair took her home on Thursday. Can't talk right now but you can read it," and he gave her the note.

In Care of John Mair, Treesbank

My dearest Edwy,

> *This is just a few lines. Harry can give you every information. I am feeling anything but right. My head aches, can scarcely see.*
>
> *Harry will tell you I have altered my plans of going to Sutcliffe's. I feel hard-ly able to move, let alone drive in this cold. . . .*
>
> *Your loving, Ella*

On Sunday, Mrs. Mair brought her to St. Albans to consult Mr. Criddle.

"I don't know what to do about Miss Steer. To send her to the hospital in Bran-don would be cruel – to have her here and let Dr. Husband attend her is almost as bad – in fact, looked at any way there are objections." So he sent her back with Mrs. Mair.

---

20 131 St. George's Road. April-June quarter, 1874. Occupier, Percy Criddle. Lease holder, Charles Wright. Corporation of London Rate Book, Bridge House Estates.
21 Census 1881 lists Elise's occupation as 'housekeeper'.

Elise worried and wondered. *Is it scurvy, or worry? Poor girl, so much in love, and so little prospect.*

"Something has to be done about our school," angry callers said.

Following a special meeting December 4, Mr. Criddle reported, "Jolly rumpus at School – in the course of two and a half hours I got things quieted down – all ended in an amiable compromise. Old Mac is an idiot."[22] Three days later, at the school's annual meeting, only four ratepayers turned out—himself, Fortune, Little, and Lonsbury. Harry, acting secretary, recorded the board's motion for each to continue in their positions.[23]

When Mr. Tulk left to catch the train for Vancouver, Elise watched Edwy and the gentleman disappear into the whiteness of falling snow. *I wish Edwy and Emily . . . she's not Miss Steer to me anymore. Anyway, I just wish they could climb aboard that train with Mr. Tulk and see the world.*

Edwy brought home good news: "Forest Cullen's back from Dakota. He and Jane are getting married in the new Presbyterian church in Treesbank."

His mother smiled. "That's splendid! I hope she is very happy."

Elise's letter reached Friedrich and he forwarded it to Amalie, his sister-in-law.

Mannheim, 5 Dec 1896

Dear sister-in-law,

Today I received from Elise the enclosed letter for you including 10 Marks. As you can see from Elise's letter, they do not have a notary right at hand like we do here, and the certification of a letter of attorney induces great difficulties and costs. Furthermore, I do not recognize why this should be necessary, since from our side nobody claims anything from Carl's assets, everything shall remain in your hands.

. . . Hopefully you take the decision to come and visit us.

With warm regards I remain your brother-in-law, F. Harrer

PS: The 10 Marks had no use to Elise, because there only Dollars or English Pounds have value, and in the loneliness there is no bank that wants to change German Marks. When I had sent anything to Elise, I always sent either American bills or postal payments.

Edwy had a load of chickens, pigeons, and beef to sell in Brandon. Elise sent along a letter to her daughter.

---

22 December 4, 1896. Mr. McPherson had become 'old Mac'.

23 The Vanes had no legal right to take part in Aweme school business. Elise's land was in the Two Rivers' district and Edwy's quarter, in the Municipality of North Cypress.

Aweme, Manitoba, 13 Dec 1896

My dear Minnie,

I wish you would come out on Christmas but I suppose it is impossible. If you did come, I guess you would miss some fun in Brandon. Take our best wishes for Christmas and New Year. Mrs. Criddle is very busy. We had Mr. and Mrs. Köhler, Harry Cooper, and another gentleman here. I hope you will come in the spring and take a good rest. There is no news to tell. Bobby is going to write to you. She was very pleased about the things you send her.

Goodbye dear Minnie, believe me ever,

Your affectionate, Mama

Handing it to Edwy, she said, "I hope you get the prices you need to purchase everything on Mrs. Criddle's list. Tell Isabel I'm looking forward to seeing her at Christmas."

The day before Christmas, Edwy went for the Knights and his girl from Mair's. Considering the hailed out crop, their dinner was abundant and the young lovers enjoyed being together. Next day Mr. Criddle looked directly at Miss Steer

and said crisply, "Mrs. Sutcliffe invited you."

In spite of a falling barometer, Edwy hitched up the team and left for the farm across the river. As the wind picked up and whistled menacingly around their house, Mr. Criddle paced the floor, "How I hate the Boy being out in such weather."

Elise worried also. *You told us the barometer was going down. Why did you send them?*

Fortunately, Edwy made it back in safety and as soon as the weather settled, he delivered the others home to Brandon. Little Violet May's going left a large empty space in her *Grossmutter* Vane's heart.

A hail insurance cheque for $14.02 arrived as the year ended. It might have cheered Mr. Criddle's New Year's Day, had he not been burdened by two problems: the first, 'Old Mac' was fighting for the rest of his salary; the second, the unsigned form he had stowed in his pocket the previous November.

Chapter Twenty-one

A Stave in the Wheel of Romance

The extra guests and busyness of Christmas left Elise exhausted. She had to drag herself out of bed to make breakfast and struggled through the day. Before falling asleep she thought of the past and lost dreams. *My youngest is twenty-one. Neither he nor Harry have land. Will they ever?*

One night Edwy, lonely and restless, perched on the side of his mother's bed with Emily's first letter from the Sutcliffes. "She's feeling better, but New Year's Day was not a jolly one. Mr. and Mrs. S. went visiting and left her to cook dinner for the hired man. She's knitting me a scarf. Will have it finished by Sunday when I go."[1]

The Criddle youngsters started making a skating rink. They leveled the snow, pumped a barrel full of water and pulled it over to the rink. After a first coating of ice, the flooding went more quickly and within a few days they were all skating, even Julia and Talbot. But keeping the ice clear took a great deal of shoveling because that winter, blizzard followed blizzard in quick succession.

Even the trains had trouble: passengers, newspapers, mail and freight were delayed. When a train did manage to get through, another storm blew its channel full again. An army of men kept shoveling; even the snow ploughs needed help. Edwy sat through a night in Treesbank waiting for the mail, but hearing nothing of when the train might get through, he gave up at noon and went home empty-handed. The boys dug pathways to the stables and the water trough for the horses and cattle, and Cecil clambered over the drifts carrying water to the fowl.

In spite of the weather, Mr. McPherson carried on his crusade to collect the rest of his salary. He sent letters to all three municipalities responsible for the school and then walked from farm to farm spreading his tale of woe. "I'm still owed $131 of my last summer's pay! How can a man live?"

Sympathy grew and fueled suspicion. "If Aweme School can't pay its teacher; the money must have disappeared into Criddle's pocket."[2]

---

1 Steer, Emily, letter January 8, 1897. There will be no further footnotes - letters are in the family collection.
2 Aweme School Financial records indicate that by each year-end, its teachers: Parrott, McNab, and McPherson received only part of their salaries. The men took legal action, Miss Parrott did not. Archives of Manitoba. School District Formation files: G 6316 H-14-15 and H 14-1- 6.

When the school board received an official 'order to pay,' two cheques amounting to $111.00 were written. Unfortunately, the gossip, like the drifting snow swirled on. When South Cyprus ordered Secretary-treasurer Criddle to have the school finances audited, he fumed. "McPherson has been telling a lot of lies about me. Why didn't my neighbours let me know?"[3]

To counter the rumors, Mr. Criddle also made visits, and on the way to Köhler's stopped at Sutcliffe's. Edwy, as his driver, had a few precious moments with Emily and later told his mother, "Emily is looking better. Mr. Sutcliffe is often away on municipal business and his wife likes to go too. So after tea Emily plays their piano and Charlie, their hired man, joins her. They sing all her favourite hymns. Harry saved some of his New Year's pudding for her. She'd like the recipe for future use. Emily thinks log houses are warmer than Sutcliffe's new house, even with a furnace." He lowered his voice, "I'm to tell you, she hasn't burned their house down yet."

They chuckled. . . . "I'll be driving her pony over to see her on Sunday."

But Edwy had to spend Sunday preparing a load of beef to sell next day in Brandon and by Wednesday, he was so fevered that Emily's image floated above his bed—her precious nose pressing against the window vainly watching for him to come up the trail.

Edwy's grippe swept through the household, Mrs. Criddle and Elise were seriously ill. Without the usual fire-stoker, the icy fingers of another blizzard reached farther into St. Albans than usual. Cecil, the only able man, dug out, watered, and fed the livestock, milked, and carried in the firewood. Mr. Criddle busily recorded the state of everyone's health and put stamps into albums. At night, he passed out whiskey and quinine, grumbling, "I have to keep up – there is nowhere for me to lie down."

The following week, Edwy, on his feet again, told his mother, "Staying cooped up here doesn't agree with me. I'm going to walk with Beatrice to Mair's, and then on to Treesbank to post a letter."

His mother guessed that by going to Treesbank for Criddle's mail, he hoped to see Emily, also there for mail. He got her letter, skimmed through it and added a few lines to his own: "I'm sorry to hear you are worse again. Don't worry about going to work in such a hurry, you old goose. I am writing this on your cutter. I hope you will get this tonight, my love to you, goodbye dear Ella." Then he dropped the envelope through the slot.

By the end of January, everyone but Mrs. Criddle was up and about. Mr. Criddle joined her in bed for a day, but had to be up the next, "Paperwork! Beastly school audit."

3 Criddle, Norman. January 19, 1897.

February 3 he walked to Sutcliffe's with the account book. Mr. Criddle received an all clear audit along with a $5 bill to the school. Then, still smarting from having to submit to the indignity, announced, "I'm sending notices to the Free Press and Tribune so everyone will know McPherson's accusations are totally false. That's going to cost the school too."[4]/ [5]

Although Emily was just beyond the frozen river, Edwy continued to work, write, fidget, and fret. His mother remembered her own years of separation. *Percy and I had a much greater distance between us and he managed to get across the channel as often as Edwy gets the three miles to Sutcliffe's.*[6] *If only Percy would give Edwy some free time. All I can do is listen when he feels like talking. Here he comes with a letter.*

"Emily was in Treesbank last week for the mail and found the Castles with a new baby and George down with the flu. So she stayed to help. She sent an application to Oak Creek School, fourteen miles southeast."

Edwy wasn't given time to visit his girl. Instead, Mr. Criddle sent him to Lonsburys to cut wood and do the chores while they holidayed in Brandon. Home again, he told his mother, "I'm about bushed—dashed hard cutting trees in this deep snow, and dragging the dang things out is worse."

WANTED—Teacher for Oak Creek school district, holding 2nd or 3rd class certificate, with Normal training, duties to commence March 1st and continue for ten months, with two weeks' holidays in midsummer. Apply stating salary expected to A. E. Abbott, sec.-treas., Stockton.   22-1

His next assignment: "Find some wheat for seed – **cheap**. There's none around here."

Feeling overwhelmed, he told his mother, "The roads are terrible, so hard on the horses." But by next morning he had a plan, "Sutcliffe knows a lot of people and might have a suggestion. I'll ask him."

Emily answered the door. They had a moment to exchange loving glances before Mr. Sutcliffe said, "I heard D'Orsay has some damaged wheat. He's out Banting way."[7]

Edwy followed the lead and arranged the purchase. Unfortunately, Sutcliffe's farm was too far off his route to stop by again. Edwy had to race against the weather to get the many needed loads of grain home before the winter roads turned to mush in the spring.

⌐◦◦⌐◦◦◦⌐

4 February 4, 1897. ". . . Am sending certif. for insertion to Free Press and Tribune. . ." School account, March 3, February 18, 1897, Free Press Co. Advt. $4.35."
5 Attempt made without success to find these announcements in Winnipeg Free Press and Tribune between the date of the meeting, February 5, and March 3, when the bill was entered in the school account.
6 Engaged February 1863, Elise's passport issued January 1867 to leave Heidelberg. Mabel was born May 20, 1867.
7 Railway siding between Treesbank and Methven, NE 2.8.17.

Firewood was becoming scarce. Mr. Criddle obtained permission to protect the trees on university land—south half of the same section he shared with Bellhouse. Evelyn posted signs: **KEEP OUT! WOOD CUTTING PROHIBITED.** He placed more signs along the trail through South Farm [Elise's quarter] to Two Rivers.

His father said, "Tell anyone you see I've got a letter from the archbishop and the university to prosecute anyone stealing wood."

When Norman checked next day, he found all their signs knocked down, tracks in the snow, and fresh stumps on South Farm.[8] He didn't carry out his father's threat.

As February slipped away, Edwy told his mother, "Emily's heard nothing from Oak Creek School and would like to go to Brandon to check on openings."

Fortunately, Isabel gave Edwy a legitimate cause to make the trip. "Minnie," she wrote, "was not well and needed a rest." Mrs. Criddle went directly to her writing desk:

Aweme, Manitoba Feb 14th, 1897

My dear Minnie!

Dico says you are not at all well. Can't you come home for a couple of weeks, if not for longer? It might just put you right again. You know I am all preaching about not overworking yourself; it is useless to work yourself ill, on purpose to make money enough to pay the Doctor.

Mrs. Payne must be on my side, I am sure; she has too much good sense to want you to ruin your health in her service. . . . It would be nicer to come in the spring perhaps, but they have a fine toboggan and a very good skating rink, so you might get some exercise out of them. Anyway—whatever you do, take care of your health.

We have got over the Grippe very fairly well, only feeling a little weak and having a general inclination to cough. Solomon is the only one who escaped it.

Many thanks for the dripping.[9] We are doing very well in that line just now as Dico is often sending us some and poor "Beauty" fattened into fat instead of into meat.

Goodbye, do the best for yourself – much love from all.

Yours affectionately, Alice Criddle

Elise added wood to the stoves and sat down at the kitchen table:

Aweme, Manitoba 14 Feb. 1897

My dear Minnie!

I hope you are better, if not it would be better for you to come home and take a good rest. Pray don't overtax your strength. You have now been 14 months straight on at hard work and it is time you stopped.

---

8 February 10, 1897. "The people are stealing green wood everywhere again, got 2 loads of mine without getting caught I regret at NE corner South Farm."
9 Dripping was rendered from beef and pork and used for baking and frying.

Poor Dido has lots of trouble now with her dear baby. I hope she gets safely over the teething. I have not written this time to her. Mrs. C tells her everything on which I always agree. Even if you are better, I hope to see you soon.
   With love from everybody, I remain,
   Your affectionate Mama

When Mrs. Criddle reappeared, Elise gave it to her saying, "I hope the weather warms up. It's dangerous for travelling and Minnie isn't well."

It was 39 below the Sunday morning Edwy fetched Emily, all bundled up in her fur coat. That afternoon neighbouring youths joined them for a winter party. When they left, Edwy took Emily to see her new calf, "I call her School Marm."

Emily rubbed its little head between the ears, and said wistfully, "I hope I find a school."

Next day, at the education office in Brandon she enquired.

"We're sorry, there's a surplus of teachers. We have nothing right now."[10]

With heavy hearts they got Mrs. Criddle's supplies and went for Minnie. As the ladies snuggled deep under the blankets, Emily shared her disappointment. Minnie had the perfect solution, "Why not apply for Aweme School? They need a teacher."

The girls were chattering when Edwy hollered, "Hang on! We've got to give way to a loaded sleigh." Then with a sharp "Gee" to the horses, he pulled hard on the right line and his team immediately plunged up to their bellies in snow. The other driver nodded as he passed safely by. "Now to get back up," Edwy said, and slapped their backs with the lines. "Haw!" His horses floundered, the sleigh tipped, his passengers squealed, but they didn't upset! And on they went. Minnie arrived none the worse for the cold drive.

They were hardly home before another gale whipped the snow into even higher drifts. In spite of impossible trails, Edwy returned Emily to Sutcliffe's, saying, "Take courage. We'll have a good crop this year. No more putting off our marriage."

He called from the door to Mrs. Sutcliffe, "Sorry I can't stop. Have to fetch another load. I'll have a dickens of a time if the weather turns and roads go to pieces before I'm done."[11]

Edwy had more early breakfasts and challenging drives. While his mother worried about him, he worried about his girl; "Ella is having a cold time of it. She asked to help around the house, but Mrs. Sutcliffe says she has to do her own work. It's the only way she can keep warm. Ella can't sleep for worrying about the future. She's ready to leave whenever I can go for her."

---

10 The Winnipeg Tribune noted 35 applications for one position advertised in its pages, February 1897.
11 March 5, 1897.

The snow kept falling and the drifts around the buildings grew higher. Apparently, it took four men and a girl at Bruner's all day to shovel out their horses. In spite of the weather, Harry and Cecil kept logging and Edwy joined them when he'd finished hauling wheat. They'd made 21 trips by the time the weather turned warm. On that last day the trail was so soft Edwy's heavy load upset twice.

At the end of March Emily came across the river just before Aweme's school board was to meet to hire a teacher. With good qualifications and Mr. Criddle's support, she felt confident. It came as a complete shock that afternoon, when Mr. Criddle said, "I recommend that you not accept the job. Mr Lonsbury is disagreeable on the subject of hiring you."[12]

Stunned and heartbroken, she nevertheless bowed to his recommendation.

Edwy was furious—believing he was betrayed by his friend.

Separation was now inevitable; Emily must leave Edwy, the family, little School Marm, and her pony to find work as a domestic in Brandon.

The warm spring sunshine made the drive very pleasant for Emily and the returning Minnie. For Edwy and his horses it was a terror. The packed snow on the built-up trails was soft. The horses' feet skidded, sometimes broke right through the track and the sleigh kept sliding sideways off the trail into soft snow. His passengers were constantly shifting their weight from the low side to the high side of the sleigh box. Luckily, they arrived without an upset.

Edwy tore himself away from Isabel's place next morning. His worry about Emily having to find a domestic position added to his troubles on the rotting trail. Home at last and having pulled off his boots, he told his mother, "I've been on the road since early morning. I hope never again to face such a trip."[13]

What could she say? "You'll feel better with something in your stomach and a good sleep."

Next morning, he was up before his mother, busily writing.

Aweme, March 31ˢᵗ, 1897

My Darling Ella,

I arrived home at a quarter to six yesterday evening after a long anxious day of it. The trail was simply awful, far worse than even I expected. I didn't think it possible for any trail to change so much in one night. I got along fairly well till I got to Waddington's[14] and from there home the trail went all to pieces and,

12 March 29, 1897. "Boy gone to Bdn with Minnie and Miss Steer – the latter having by my advice declined the Aweme School. . . . Am going across the river myself presently to look for a School marm – dam 'em all."
13 March 31, 1897. "Am getting preciously doubtful as to whether the Boy can get home – as the trails have gone all to pieces and the snow on the level is too deep and heavy to plough through. I wanted him to go last Thursday when all would have been right – but he put it off on acc't of Miss Steer and that infernal school . . ."
14 Thomas B Waddington, came from Ontario, bought CPR section 9.9.17 about seven miles from St. Albans. Owned one of the first threshers, built a cheese factory and then a felt factory in Brandon. Nelson Clark married a daughter, Sara Jane, in 1898. Waddingtons and the Uppers moved to North Portal, Saskatchewan. *Municipal Memories, R. M. of Cornwallis*, 1884 – 1984.

[place name]
March 31st 1897

My Darling Ella

I arrived home at a quarter to six yesterday evening after a long anxious day of it. The trail was simply awful far worse than even I expected I didn't think it possible for any trail to change so much in one night. I got along fairly well till I got to Waddingtons and from there home the trail went all to pieces and although I had no real mishap still it was touch and go all the way home I had to drive very carefully and very slowly the whole journey, my arms ache still from driving as you may well imagine and I think I was just as tired as the horses when I got home I hope never to have such a drive again but yet I feel proud of your boy for getting home without an accident, aint I conceited. They did not expect me home till to day, the horses behaved splendidly they seemed to know just exactly what I wanted them to do.

although I had no real mishap, still it was touch and go all the way home. I had to drive very, very carefully and very slowly the whole journey. My arms ache still from driving as you may well imagine and I think I was just as tired as the horses when I got home. I hope never to have such a drive again, but yet I feel proud for getting home without an accident. Aint I conceited?

The horses behaved splendidly. They seemed to know just exactly what I wanted them to do.

I am tired today and I miss my dear girl very much more than I care to write or think about. I would not mind quite so much if I knew you could get a nice place. I hope to know by Saturday. There is one good thing you have friends in

313

Brandon. It is not like as if you were all alone in a strange place. You must go and see Minnie and Dido as often as possible. They will cheer you up.

Next day Edwy was still feeling dull and low spirited.

April 1ˢᵗ Afternoon *Happy will be the day when we are united never to part again. If some kind Samaritan would just give us enough cash to start us in life we could jolly soon stop all this worry and trouble.*

I would work twice as hard if by so doing I could prevent you dear Ella, from that beastly drudgery. It is perfectly hateful to have you working like a slave and me not able to stop it. I feel very bitter against Lonsbury, I am not likely to forget or forgive in a hurry.

After giving your things a good overhauling with turpentine I just finished carrying them over to my shanty. They will be safer there from wet and they can stay there until we want to use them. Which box do you want your fur coat put into? Mama will hold out that it is the box downstairs and I say it is the box on the landing. There is no great hurry as there won't be any moths for a long time yet. But so soon as you let me know which box I will put it away at once and paste it all up tight. I will put the lock on your box directly Mr. C is out of the way and lock it.

Our quilt is getting whiter.[15] Shall I put it in the big box or put it with the coat?

I will finish this tomorrow good-bye dear, I enclose one dollar. Cheer up Ella the happy time is coming when I will prove my love for you.

Friday afternoon *I hate this kind of weather. I have got nothing to do but think of you and it don't agree with me, at least when i can't think without worrying.[16] I have had so many disappointments lately that i quite expect not to get a letter tomorrow. I don't know what to do if i don't. I know what it is to be anxious about the mail now. I used to laugh at Dido before she got married about her anxiety to get a letter, but this is no laughing matter, Ella. I hope you are settled by this time to your satisfaction. And remember that your health is everything to me. If you can't stand the work, don't be afraid to tell your boy. He won't let you ruin yourself (and him) for a few paltry dollars.*

I would like to walk to Brandon while there is nothing important to do but I suppose everybody would kick up such a row. I don't see why I shouldn't do as I like. . . .

For ever and always, your loving Edwy.

Edwy was so encouraged by Emily's Friday letter that he hurried to his mother, "You'll be happy to hear that Emily is doing fine. She was at Dido's place and your girls were teasing her so much she could hardly write for laughing." He paused. "Emily made several enquiries and the next morning Mr. Jay Fleming, the chemist, came asking Emily to see his wife.[17] She went straightaway, and got the

---

15 Cotton flour or sugar bags were bleached white by the sun.
16 Edwy sometimes used the lower case 'I' when it was not the first word in the sentence. An indication that his mother taught him since German pronouns are not capitalized within a sentence.
17 Dr. Alexander Fleming was one of Brandon's first doctors, organized the first school board. Fleming

job. Mrs. Fleming had an accident last summer with a runaway horse. She's in bed and has to lie on her side. There are two school children. Ella won't need her seeds this summer, so the boys can have them. They are in her box on Mr. Tulk's trunk.

"Now how's this for a coincidence?" He unfolded Emily's letter and read, "I met a boy with a telegram from Rounthwaite for Miss Agnes Smith. I suppose about Aweme School." He sighed, "Emily was really disappointed, but now she's going do her best to be happy with the Flemings." As he turned to go, he added, "Minnie's back to work. Dido's baby is fine again."

The snow gradually melted, the meadowlarks and blackbirds returned, the hens began laying, and by April 7 the sleighs were put away and the box mounted on wheels. Edwy had the pleasure of driving Mr. Criddle to Fortune's to meet the new teacher. On the way home Edwy controlled his anger with difficulty when Mr. Criddle said, "Miss Smith is apparently a pleasant young lady – says she knows nothing – which is quite fresh and novel."

Next mail and Edwy had more news for his mother, "Got a postcard. Emily has her own little room and plenty of good plain food. She's up at 6:45 to make breakfast. Lunch is at 12, dinner at 6. She has to wash, iron, make the bread, and everything. She says it's jolly good practice for future days. And listen to this," he said with a grin, "Emily wants to buy a heifer, **if I let** her."[18]

Elise smiled. Then asked, "Did she say how Minnie is?"

"Minnie is still not entirely well. Dido is alone nearly every night, but she's always cheerful. She had tea with Emily on Sunday. They all send their love."

When a second Sunday passed without Edwy seeing his girl, he wanted to strike out on foot for Brandon. Instead, he set off to check the fields and make plans for seeding. Harry borrowed a horse from McManes so they had three on the seeder, two for the harrows, and Norman ploughed with the oxen. The cows picked up fast in both appearance and milk, and the hens were laying well. A fall wedding looked so promising, Edwy told his mother, "I'm thinking of fixing up my homestead shanty. Emily is dreaming about a chicken house—wants Barred Rocks. I'll take her to see the place next time she comes. It's not far, but enough to be independent.

Edwy's plan lasted until it reached Mr. Criddle. "Balderdash! Bunkum! I want you **here!**" and pointed to the floor. I can't be walking over **there** to tell you what's to be done. . . . **This** is your home!" He stopped to catch his breath. "I don't want you wasting valuable time digging a well over there, or building a fowl house.

School was named after him. His son John William joined him as druggist. Brandon-Souris Community News Edition, August 31, 2006, by Fred McGuinniss.
18 Emily later decided to put her money toward other things.

Bally nuisance!" He stormed into his room and slammed the door. Edwy muttered to the closed door, "We can't live with you and Mrs. Criddle and a dozen others."

Harry took him aside, "Mr. C is trying to keep you from getting married. Remember how we used to stick a log in the wagon spokes on that steep hill at Upper's ferry. It was a good thing to have a stave in the wheel there. But he's doing the same thing to you. It's one thing after another and I'm fed up with his manoeuvres."

At the first opportunity, he spoke up, "Edwy needs a house of his **own** and a good one. Why don't we use the logs we hauled home last winter to build it? We can get more logs next winter for the barns."

"**Bosh, I tell you!**"

Harry came back with, "Then what?"

"**Then** . . . then, Edwy can use my 'E'[19] house right here beside us for a year or two. I'm not using it for concerts. These infernal Canadians don't appreciate good music."

"Edwy needs his **own** house. Besides, your E house is too close."

Edwy's heart ached, but he'd been well trained to obey. Once again Elise felt the pain of betrayal. *My sons have given all these years to him and his farm. They're men now; if they get too angry they might just give up and walk away . . . with nothing!*

Mr. Criddle did some thinking too. He depended on Edwy. . . . And if he left, he could take Harry. And even Cecil. He'd had grand plans for his 'E' house, but his choral society hadn't got off the ground. It would be better to give up his concert hall than the new outbuildings. He'd let the boys take it down, and rebuild it farther away. But he wouldn't say anything yet; he had to keep them guessing, at least until after seeding.

❦

Having promised Emily a visit as soon as seeding was done, Edwy worked like a man possessed—his letters were written before the others rose. He worked late, and went directly to roost. By the end of the week he had more news for his mother, "Mrs. Fleming says Ella's tea biscuits are so good she'll not wish for better. She asks me not to be angry with Lonsbury about the school. Thinks now this is for the best, but I'm not sure **I** can forgive him. But you'll be interested in this: Mr. Fleming bought a gramophone for his wife. She can listen to reproductions of songs, recitations, and all kinds of instrumental music." He paused, to let her think about it. "Wouldn't you like one of those? You'd have it playing all day!"

"It's hard to believe. I'll ask Emily more about it."

---

19 Short for East. Built in 1892.

Emily is doing fine. I'll read you what she says:

*I get on better every day and Mrs. F. sent me down word tonight that her dinner was first class. Isn't that worth something! A little praise is very good to have sometimes. I hope to stay here until **you want me.** (I shouldn't say that, I should say) till **you can have me.** It's only a few months now, cannot be more than 6 or 7 and then as Mr. C said, "It will be all over."*

Thinking he should have stopped a little sooner, Edwy glanced at his mother. She didn't seem to mind and smiled back. Both knew "**it**" depended on a good crop.

⸺◦⸰◦⸰◦⸺

All the while, unknown to anyone in Mr. Criddle's household, the unsigned affidavit concerning Elise's brother's will was still hidden in the locked drawer of his desk. As long as he kept Herr Stricker's form in his possession, he worried about a follow-up letter concerning his Dutchman's inheritance. Each and every Friday afternoon he had to be on hand when the mail arrived because he couldn't risk anyone else seeing a letter addressed to 'Mrs. Elise Criddle'. He wanted that affidavit signed, witnessed, and mailed to Germany. Mrs. Bellhouse's six months were up, so he asked her, "Have your papers naming you as our postmaster come through?"

"Yes, my position became official the first of April."

He thanked her and mumbled as he walked home, *I could have dispatched this job a little sooner. . . . Never mind can't be helped. I'll tend to it now.* He waited for Mrs. Criddle to be out of their room giving the children their lessons. Unlocking his desk drawer, he took out the form. Placing it strategically above a scrap of paper, he practiced writing *'Elise Crittel'* exactly as was written in Germany. When he felt satisfied, he dipped his pen and wrote it boldly in the space for Elise's signature.[20] As the ink dried, he congratulated himself; "That was easy!" Into the waiting envelope went the form. Taking up his practice paper, he walked over to the stove, opened the door, and watched the evidence burn. He addressed the envelope to Herr Stricker and placed it back in the drawer. *Tomorrow's Good Friday, I'll visit Mrs. Bellhouse on Saturday.*

That afternoon he saw smoke billowing into the sky not many miles west. With the wind from the southwest it posed no immediate danger. This, Mr. Criddle decided, would be a fine time to approach the postmaster and walked over. He

---

20 Hawkeye Studios, Grapho-Lab Services. "There is no correlation to the exemplars of Elise. The questioned signature though conscientious and deliberated in execution, does disclose some stroke correlation to the exemplars of Percy Criddle. It is the opinion of this analyst that there is a reasonable possibility that the questioned signature was written by Percy Criddle." Calgary, February 5, 2010.

found both Bellhouse ladies outside looking worried, "Devil of a fire," he said, "If the wind changes we could be in for trouble."

He moved toward the door, "I have some business for you, Mrs. Bellhouse."

Handing the form through the wicket, he said, "Now that you can witness this for us, I want to get it away. It's already signed. She saw the smoke and didn't want to leave the children."

Mrs. Bellhouse, proud to be able to make use of her new position, only glanced at the name. In a clear firm hand, she signed, '*C. C. Bellhouse P. M.*', pressed the postal stamp on the pad, and thumped it down on the form—'Aweme, Manitoba, AP 17, 97'.[21] "There you are. Do you need a stamp?"

He nodded as he slid the form into the envelope, handed her a penny, licked the stamp and stuck it on. Sealing the envelope carefully, he handed it back. With another thump on the stamp pad and envelope, the letter dropped into the bag of outgoing mail.

"Thanks, I'll have some more business for you one day."

Outside again, he surveyed the sky and added, "Might get deuced lively if the wind changes. I'd better check on my boys . . . . Might need your team."

He left the women studying the ballooning smoke. Later that night the wind did swing to the northwest and everyone, including the Bellhouses, was out ploughing fireguards.

⁂

Unaware of Mr. Criddle's deception, Elise continued to enjoy Edwy's chats; "Do you remember when we passed that big green house with stables on Victoria and 4ᵗʰ Street? Not far from the hospital? That's where the Flemings live. . . . Emily was feeling lonely so I sent her a pansy for her birthday.[22] Anyway, she's preparing some jolly good meals. Here's her menu.

Breakfast: (haddie[23], toast, porridge)
*Lunch: (cold beef, **my** biscuits and bread, roast apples and cold pudding)*
Dinner: roast duck and onion stuffing, and mashed potatoes, gels, bread and custard. Pudding, cream.

"Doesn't that sound grand? She's getting so confident she'll not mind Mr. Criddle saying she can't cook potatoes a hundred different ways. She's allowed to eat the same food after she's finished serving. Emily gets more nourishment in one day than she did last year, in a week. Want to hear about her day?" He didn't wait for her answer:

---

21 Exhibit #151 re Carl Harrer's estate. See Appendix 6.
22 There were many pressed pansies in Edwy's letters.
23 Haddie: haddock cured with smoke of green wood, turf, or peat, originated in Scotland.

Go down at 7. Lit fire, swept dining room, kitchen, called up everyone, dusted dining room, made porridge, boiled eggs, etc, etc. Laid the cloth, had my breakfast and swept over bedrooms, made the beds, swept hall, veranda etc. ... cleared breakfast things.

Dusted all over, washed up, folded down ironing.[24] Did a little ironing and then got lunch etc. etc. Cleared away, washed up, swept up kitchen and dining room, finished ironing by 4 o'c.

Peeled potatoes, minced beef, made pudding, cooked duck liver and heart for Mrs. F., laid the cloth etc, etc. for dinner. Also set my bread during afternoon. Cleared away, washed up by 8 o'c.

Sat down for awhile then kneaded down my bread and now I'm in my room writing. Still have to make Mac Matheson's bed on lounge downstairs and . . .

"She got her first pay, ten dollars and lots of praise. She says, 'I shall be vain Ella as well as Ella Vane.' She's a plucky one, isn't she?"

His mother nodded. *Love is a wonder. She doesn't know half of what's in store for her.*

"I guess you want to know if she sent news from Dido. I hate to tell you, but her baby's sick again, the croup this time."

"Poor little Violet May. Her first birthday is coming up. I must send congratulations."

Elise's drudgery continued to be the foundation of every enterprise. She fed and wished them well each morning, and was there with a meal at day's end. Jack Mair had sick children and needing to tend them asked for Cecil.[25] Others herded the cattle, did the chores, and gardened. Beatrice, the poultry lady, offered to give one broody hen with its setting of eggs to Emily for a wedding present.

Without rain that spring, any fire started for burning unwanted scrub easily got out of control. As smoke billowed skyward in several directions, Elise recalled her days on the front line. *I couldn't do it now, but I'm willing to feed the lads any time of the day or night.* Mr. Criddle had some anxious nights sleeping with one eye open, receiving reports, and entering pertinent information in his diary. Edwy told his mother, "You've heard enough about the fire but I need to write Emily. She'll want to know what I've been up to."

There had been a fire up towards Chater and Douglas two or three days, but we didn't think we should have any trouble. However we did, as you shall hear. I had just got home from work rather late (being 8 o'clock) when the wind changed to the North West and you should have seen the excitement.

The fire came along on two or three lines with a rapidity that was grand to look at but not very pleasant for us to contemplate. It was the awfulest fire we ever

---

24 "Folded down the ironing." This included sprinkling the clothes with water for ironing.

25 P. Criddle, May 16, 1897. "Harry home from Charleson's where he has been 4 days – Solomon home from Jk Mairs where he has been 24 working days."

had since we have been here. We got two ploughs ready as quickly as possible and off we went to meet it. Mr. Criddle went to Buns to get his team and Stuart went to Bellhouse's for their team. We were only just in time. The fire had already got to the end of North Farm. Harry with one team ploughed from North Farm to Little's and about half way met Bellhouses' team as fore arranged. They ploughed together while the Littles and Nicolson, with our boys burnt along the furrow to make it safer as they went. The excitement was intense but they managed to get their fire broad enough before the real one met it. The wind was blowing a gale and the fire was going faster than a team could trot. While they were making it safe from that direction Evelyn and I were ploughing as hard as we could go from North farm.

Luckily the wind changed a little more to the west again taking it more north, but still the fire went past us at an awful rate. We couldn't have had the least chance beating it out. By the time we were done so were the others and everything was safe by 11 o'clock if the wind kept where it was. The poor horses had it pretty hard. Fancy them racing all over the prairie after their day's work and nothing to eat all that time.

The whole prairie as far as you could see was nothing but a vast ocean of flame. It was perfectly light. You could see just as well as if it was daylight. I can tell you I was glad when everything was safe, though if the wind had changed to the North East it would have been worse than ever. We had still to watch it. By 3 in the morning, it had got about 10 miles east of us. At half past three owing to a smart shower of rain the whole thing was put out and we were not in the least sorry to go to bed in safety.

⤐⋙⋘⤏

Winds lashed the seedlings and carried off their soil. Edwy wiped the dirt from his face, and told his mother, "I don't need a lot of food tonight. I've swallowed plenty of sand."

Yet, when she put a plateful before him, he dug in. *How does he keep up? He's had a tooth pulled, worked long days in the fields, and chases around the prairie at night fighting fires.*

He told his mother, "I promised Emily a visit. I'm a lucky boy, to have such a darling plucky girl. The rest will find out after a bit that I have some brains after all. If I haven't, Ella has enough for both of us." May 6 he left for Brandon and his mother imagined their happy meeting and walking that evening along the river.

⤐⋙⋘⤏

Edwy told his mother, "Mrs. F's brother brought them a cow from the farm." She looked up as if to ask . . . "Don't worry, Ella doesn't have to milk her—they've hired a boy. But she has other troubles: her pudding went lumpy and the bread got chilled over night and didn't turn out.[26] She thought Isabel would cheer her

---

26 The Flemings must have had yeast. The Criddle bills included baking powder, not yeast. Mrs. Sara Clark wrote some years later to her son. "The Baking Powder to make bread is in the . . . "

up but the baby was teething and she'd been up all night. It's silly she says to say, 'Absence makes the heart grow fonder.' Absence makes one wretched."

A week later Edwy had another edition, "Emily was feeling blue; thought going to church would help. But she felt like a moth beside a butterfly when Minnie wore a lovely pale blue silk with velvet trim. Isn't jealous though, likes to dress to please me. Knowing Mr. C has a bad opinion of homemade things, she wants to know if I will wear the silk tie she's sewing. I'll be proud to wear anything she makes. Anyway, she went shopping after all and bought a new hat, black with lace and a feather. . . . Oh, nearly forgot; Dido has a pain in her big toe and Will got hit with a baseball—his arm's in a sling. That's your news for this week, Mama."

The Queen's Birthday at St. Albans was low key. Elise prepared a picnic dinner for the younger generation, and being in charge of the little ones, went with them to the river. Tolly caught his first pike. Harry headed up a tree-digging crew for a windbreak around their buildings. They had 22 young maples in the wagon when dark clouds appeared above the trees on the riverbank. Elise rounded up her young charges, got them into the wagon, and Cecil raced for home. The older boys stayed, daring the rain to come their way. Edwy had driven Mr. Fortune to Brandon and was almost home again when the storm hit. All the boys got a precious ducking.

⸙

Emily's 24th of May holiday came to Elise via Edwy. "Union Jacks flew all over Brandon. Emily was busy—baking, roasting—served a real feast to the whole Ingram family.[27] She got lots of praise for her plucky efforts. By the time she'd washed up she was good and ready to go to her room and put her feet up. She listened to the new gramophone through the wall.

"Oh, and while they had extra people about, Ella helped carry the cook stove out to the shed for the summer. Keeps the house cooler, but it's lots of work carrying everything in and out, up and down the steps." He paused, but he had more to tell her. "Monday being a holiday, Emily started the wash at six Tuesday morning and had everything on the line by nine. Then, guess what? The sheets blew down and they had to be washed again, poor old girl. You've had that happen a few times, have you not?"

His mother nodded, "I have indeed."

⸙

Mr. Criddle kept grumbling about Edwy wanting his own house. But, with Harry's backing, Edwy held firm, "We can't live in your E house."[28]

"You boys have better things to do than build a house."

---

27 Mrs. Fleming's family, the Ingrams, lived in the Northfield area south of old Millford and Treesbank.

28 Emily Steer, letter May 30, 1897. "Tell Harry not to incur Mr. C's wrath about our house."

They didn't have to be reminded: ploughing, sowing, harrowing, haying, gardening, chores.... Plus his building list for the summer: granary on 'One',[29] root cellar, another layer of sod on all the outbuildings, and a new fowl house. But for the first time in their lives, the brothers didn't cave in. Elise marveled at their tenacity. *There is too much at stake to give way. The young couple will have difficulty enough without living in the shadow of St. Albans.*

Two nights of heavy frost the end of May added another spoke in the wheel of Edwy's hopes for a good harvest. With wood to sell in Brandon, he talked to Emily and told his mother; "Emily and I agree. We're getting married after harvest, no matter what!" Then to lighten the mood, he produced a coconut, "She sent this for the youngsters."

Not able to see his girl on their first engagement anniversary, Edwy received a sad letter. "Ella's finding it hard," he told his mother. They teased her at church. She doesn't want to dress up like a guy as all the girls do. Likes the country where she can dress to please me. Anyway, she ends her letter with a joke. The boy got the sack and Emily had to milk the cow. She sat down on the wrong side." He paused for his mother to anticipate and added, "Of course the cow kicked." They enjoyed a good chuckle imagining the flying milk pail.

Edwy wanted to sit right down and comfort his girl, but work on the granary came first. He hoped to write Sunday morning, but Norman used the table until noon. Directly after dinner, the lovely Miss Denny and her brothers turned up, and he had to be a gentleman. More company came in the afternoon and stayed for tea. Then, having an audience brought out Mr. Criddle's urge to perform and he warmed up his voice.

My pretty Jane! My pretty Jane!
Ah! Never, never look so shy....
But name the day, the wedding day,
And I will buy the ring ...
The Spring is waning fast, my Love,
The corn is in the ear.

The Summer nights are coming, Love,
The moon shines bright and clear;
Then pretty Jane, my dearest Jane,
Ah! Never look so shy,
But meet me, meet me in the Ev'ning,
While the bloom is on the Rye.[30]

Elise felt sorry for Edwy. *He's stuck here while his thoughts are on meeting his own pretty girl in the cool of the evening.* But encouraged by applause, Mr. Criddle announced the *Erl King*.[31] Elise was taken aback. *I like Schubert's music, but this strange poem of Goethe's always gives me the shivers. What will they make of it? Does **he** know what the song is really about? Life is hard here, but a father losing his infant son to a king of the underworld?* She was still thinking about a shadowy figure flitting from

---

29 'One' was the quarter section recently bought, supposedly for Norman and Harry.
30 *My Pretty Jane!* Effie Adelaide Rowlands, 1894.
   http://www.youtube.com/watch?v=ZfVhaOGioio Viewed, December, 2011.
31 *Erl King*, Goethe. A dark poem based on a Norwegian legend of the Elf King and set to music by Schubert.

tree to tree in the Black Forest when the polite applause called her back to hear him announce, "My next two songs are *Deeper and Deeper*, and *Waft her Angels* from Handel's *Jephthah*.[32]

Elise's thoughts wandered back to biblical times with an anxious Jephthah swearing an oath: *"Help me defeat my enemies and I'll sacrifice the first one I see when I return home." And who came dancing out to meet the victorious general but his beautiful little daughter. She had to die for her father's vow! I'm glad Handel changed the ending.*

Mr. Criddle went all out to help his audience visualize the scene of the innocent girl being wafted heavenward in the midst of angels.

He ended with *O Rest in the Lord.* Edwy wafted back to the night, when smitten by love, he knew for certain that if Emily wouldn't have him, no one else would ever take her place.

It was Monday night before Edwy could respond to her unhappy letter.

> *Don't you care one bit what the people (in the dirtiest hole in creation) say or think about what they please to call style! Tell them they can all go to blazes. At any rate you can go among people and hold your own when the most of them can't. Miserable lot of snobs. You are quite right to dress nicely for me and hang everybody else. Minnie dresses rather nicely sometimes but she is hardly an authority on the subject. And she has to make the best of her opportunities. I love you for yourself—not your dresses.*
>
> *Naturally I am very proud of you and like to see you well dressed. Still there is something else besides dress. Don't worry my **Queen**. . . .*
>
> *Getting dark can't see. Good night my unselfish Darling.*

Edwy got back to the letter the following night with happier news.

> *I have some news for my loving old girl that I know will do her good. You know, don't you, that I have a patch of ground down by the pond in among the poplars about two hundred yards from the house. It was given to me in 1884 as a birthday present. Well, it is nearly certain (**not quite**) that somewhere close there is where our house is going to be. There are lots of places for a good garden as well. Won't that be jolly?*

By six next morning Edwy had shaved, eaten, and was off to Treesbank to buy a few cents worth of nails to complete the granary roof, mail his letter, and pick up what he hoped to be a very long letter from his girl. He was not disappointed, and since his horses knew the road home, he feasted on Emily's words and her longing to be with him.

"Emily adds to her letter each night," he told his mother. "Helps take her mind off the heat. She found this in the paper, and thinks it will fit us to a T next winter."

---

32 From Handel's last work, *Jephthah, 1751*, based on the story in Judges 11.

In his best, cultured, high-brow voice he read:

The blessed antidotes that sweeten and enrich domestic life are refinement, high aims, great interests, soft voices, quiet and gentle manners, magnanimous tempers, forbearance from all unnecessary commands or dictation, and generous allowances of mutual freedom. Man wears a noble allegiance not as a collar but as a garland. Love makes obedience lighter than liberty.

"And guess what Emily said then! . . . '*So I mustn't order you to milk the cow. Boo Hoo!*'"

Edwy went off to bed, chuckling. Elise knitted and remembered a lovesick young woman embroidering silk roses on linen pillowcases. *I had fantastic fantasies as I longed for my life with Percy to begin. Emily is more realistic, gets right to the point, "I can't ask my husband to milk the cow."* And she also chuckled.

⟿⟾

One hot Thursday, Edwy and Harry worked until noon and then left for a football practice at Treesbank. By nightfall they hadn't returned. Elise lay in her hot, little room listening for their return. The hours crept on. She heard Mr. Criddle pacing the floor below and then an outburst, "**It's 12:55! Damned Football. Might have capsized the boat.**" She heard him go out, and then come up to get Cecil out of bed. She heard a few shouts and then all was quiet. An anxious hour passed before she heard them returning. Fearing the worst, she wrapped herself in a blanket and went down. In they trudged, heads down, wanting nothing to eat, and headed for the stairs. Mr. Criddle waxed philosophical, "'All in a lifetime' as Dido would say. All's well that ends well. But, I think the Boy ought to give Mr. Nelson Clark a damned good licking and shove his head in the river. He's a miserly lout at best of times and wears false teeth." [33]/ [34]

Elise concluded: *my boys are alright, it's 4 AM. I'd better follow them to bed . . . catch a couple of hours sleep before my day begins.*

⟿⟾

When she came down in the morning Edwy was writing at the table. *I'd like to look over his shoulder. I'll just have to be patient.*

My Darling Ella,

Harry and I got home this morning at four o'clock after being out all night. I will give you a short account of our night's work. We left the horses at McManes' and then went to the river opposite Clark's. After yelling a long while, Nelson came and put us across. (George Clark had taken Bellhouse's boat away) We could see that Nelson was mad all right enough, so I offered to pay for taking us over. But he wouldn't take anything.

---

33 June 18, 1897.
34 Nelson Clark, Edwy's age, had lost both parents the previous year and had all the family and farm responsibilities. He likely took a dim view of interruptions from others who should, in his opinion, have their own boat to cross the Assiniboine. Nelson's children, Carol and Ruth, claimed their father didn't have false teeth.

We went on to Treesbank and after a good game we got back to the river and then the fun began. We couldn't make anyone hear us at Clark's. They were either all away or didn't want to put us across and so didn't take any notice of our shouting. I thought it best to go back to Bob Mair's and get him to put us across, while Harry stayed with the boat in case anyone should come. About 5 minutes before Bob and I got back Harry heard a shot up at the house [Clarks] and went up to see who had fired it. We came down the hill in one place and Harry up the hill in another direction. So we missed each other. We got down to where the boat had been a few minutes after Harry had got to the house so that the boat had been left 10 minutes. But in the 10 minutes, Nelson had sneaked the boat away after throwing our things out. I couldn't make out where Harry and the boat had gone to. I shouted and Harry came from the house at once. He enlightened me. "The beastly sneak Nelson has taken the boat away on purpose so that we can't get over."

Here was a pretty go! We were properly fooled. However we went back to Bob's and had something to eat. It was now 12 o'clock and we hadn't eaten anything since our dinner at noon.

We started for John Mair's as soon as we had done eating. The next thing was to wake Martin up. Which we didn't succeed, but Mr. Criddle heard us at home. (Fancy hearing all that way). And he and Cecil started off for the river not knowing what was up. They got pretty nearly there and not hearing us anymore (we had given up yelling) they supposed that we had got over all right and went back home. Just as they were nearly home I happened to give another yell and they again heard me. This time they came right to the river shouting as they came and we answering.

We were not sorry to get home I can tell you. We were pretty tired and soaking wet up to the knees. So much for playing football!

Nelson will likely hear something before I have done. You can laugh as much as you like dear girl, it will do you good. We called ourselves all the names we could think of, being done by a Methodist. The dirty sneak.

Edwy signed off, gulped down his breakfast and called to his mother as he went out, "I'm off to the post office before we start work."

I'll have to wait for Harry. He'll tell me what happened.

On June 22, everyone gathered at the flagpole to celebrate the sixtieth year of Queen Victoria's reign. Edwy left immediately for Brandon to purchase the commemorative stamp for Mr. Criddle. "Be worth a fortune someday."

The builders waited for Edwy to get home to head up the roof raising on the root cellar. Elise slipped out of the sweltering kitchen and marveled as she watched.

My boys used to struggle just to lift a log. Now they're accomplished builders. "Almost done," Edwy said, "it's a first-rate roof. No leaking when this is finished."

When the boys came in for tea, Mrs. Criddle took Edwy aside and told him, "Mr. Criddle says you can take down his 'E' house, build it on the other side of the bushes below the children's gardens."

The dismantling began first thing next morning. Edwy told his mother proudly, "We'll build it straighter and three logs higher than this house."

"I'm happy for you, my son. It will be lot of work, but you'll have your own home."

But still she worried. *Will they be far enough away?* Before she slept, she added an extra prayer. *Please, God, may things work out for Edwy and Emily.*

Chapter Twenty-two

A Palace for a Queen

Edwy endured another night of socializing when Miss Denny came to say goodbye. As a parting gift, Mr. Criddle ended the evening singing, *Oh, Rest in the Lord.* Edwy gazed longingly at Emily's photo above the organ and when the guests left, he asked his mother for a lamp. "I don't care how many times Mr. C hollers, I'm not blowing it out until I've finished my letter."

Handing him the light, his mother sympathized. *I remember how I longed for Percy and his letters. He and Emily certainly love each other. I should never have worried that it wouldn't last.*

The young man's work and love flowed word by word onto the paper:

. . . . Evelyn and I have been road working all day with the team. The rest of the boys went off to dig a wolf out. They failed to get any young ones as usual. . . . [For bounty]

Wednesday evening: *We have been sodding all day. Beastly hot, beastly dirty and precious hard work. That horrid root cellar is finished at last. What a lot of trouble it has given us. I have just come up from the wood. I wanted a good wash so I took a pail of water into the wood, stripped off and had a jolly good wash. Rather sensible of me wasn't it?*

One thing I am sure, I did have brains when I picked my girl and fell in love and captured her. Wait a minute, you captured me didn't you? You don't like being teased like that do you?

*I wish I had a **palace** for you to live in. My wishes are easily made, but nothing ever comes of them. . . .*

⁂

Harry and Edwy played with the Treesbank football team at Methvin's First of July picnic. Their mother had wished them well, but was alarmed when they came limping home. "Never mind the bruises," Harry told her. "We were treated like heroes even if we didn't win. They fed us loads of lemonade and stuff."

Nor did Edwy care. "I have far greater worries on my mind," and he sat down to write.

St. Albans, Aweme July 2, 1897

My Darling Girl,

Another terrible hot day. I would give anything to know how you are standing it. You may be ill with the heat. The suspense is a terror to me . . . I get nearly mad sometimes. I am afraid the whole time that something will happen.

Two more days like today will ruin the whole crop. I feel very downhearted and want my girl badly tonight. You always have the power to cheer me up my dear loving girl. I know I am a coward, but can't help it. I have been building such castles in the air. Are they all going to vanish?

We finished the log part of our house yesterday morning. I am going to peal all the logs. It will be a big job but it will look a lot better. 78 logs to do and got to be done with a chisel. I have been at it all day in spite of the heat. I shall be at it all the spare time I have. I like to be working alone. Then my thoughts are not interrupted.

*. . . I never asked you when you were going to have the lizence [sic]. Let me know a little before hand won't you, because I shall have to get my trousers ready. Unless you will take me, as I am, in which case, my **queen**, I'm ready at any time. Don't forget the ring. . . .*

Chuckling, he went up to roost. By next evening he'd made some decisions:

I think you will be pleased with the place I have chosen although I wish you had been here to see for yourself if it was all right. We shall have bush nearby all round us with an opening here and there so that we shall have a pretty good view. And at the same time we shall not have everybody spying on us. All along the north side we shall be protected from any blizzard that chooses to blow. It will be much warmer in winter than up here and cooler in summer.

Where I propose making the well is 35 yards from where the house will be. You will be able to have a garden pretty near by. I think you will be pleased and satisfied. I hope so. To please you is all I live for. Our house will be about 200 yards from this house. Is that far enough? We shall be able to see the roof of the other one. That is just right isn't it?

I am the devil to give description <u>ain't I</u>? You mustn't mind my grammar; it would rather spoil the effect of my graphic way of putting things. . . . I am always ready to learn from you if you will teach me. Tell me when I make mistakes, both in writing and everything else. There are so many things you can improve me in and I have brains enough to know it. I want to be as near as I can your equal when we are married, so help me all you can like the dear old girl you are. . . .

Elise heard whistling before Edwy opened the door and told her, "Emily got Will to hire a team and they're coming Sunday. I want her to be in on the plans for our house."

"That's wonderful. You will get your Emily and I will get my little grand-daughter and Isabel."

A shower Saturday night settled the dust, cooled things off a little, and lifted everyone's spirits. When they arrived Elise slipped out and Isabel handed her little one to her proud grandmother. Elise held the child out at arms' length; "What a big girl you are!"

Edwy helped Emily down and as soon as the hands had been shaken in welcome he said, "Please excuse us, I want to show off our future home."

Elise said to Isabel, "The sun is so very hot. I'm sure you're thirsty. We've just carried up a pail of cold water."

Next morning, as the buggy faded in the distance Edwy and his mother lingered side by side until they also, went back to work. *Lovers suffer doubly, but parting is always difficult.*

Later that morning Julia came running in, waving a watch, "Look what I found on the trail!"

"It's Isabel's," Mrs. Criddle said with surprise. "I'll write. Let her know we found it."

That night Edwy's pencil was busy again:

I was very late home from ploughing tonight. Just had tea, nearly nine. Time is flying; it won't be long to wait for our union. Our parting will be over; we'll have just one long happy time, all sunshine, peace and rest. . . .

Elise was almost as anxious as Edwy for the mail that week. Sure enough, he received his letter and told her, "Isabel was terribly upset to lose Mr. Tulk's gift, but they couldn't turn back. Didn't have time."

"Did she get Mrs. Criddle's note?"

"Yes, she cried with happiness. Emily's trip was miserable too. She faced backwards and by the time she got to the Flemings' she was decidedly **woozy**. Not too dizzy though to see the mess in the kitchen. Mr. Fleming wouldn't let his wife do the dishes, and, he didn't. The tables were stacked full. Not a pan nor a bit of crockery washed. They were glad to have her back. Emily's not planning any more holidays."

Another hot dry week dragged by. There were showers to the north, and to the south, while their fields grew ever more parched. Mr. Criddle trotted out to the rain gauge after every sprinkle and reported—two; nine; and five hundredths of an inch. Such comments as "The wheat is thinking of going up the spout and trotting off to a better world," continued day in, day out. It got on Edwy's nerves so badly, he told his mother, "I gave Emily leave to knock my head off if I was such a nuisance." They exchanged a wordless glance before Edwy changed the subject.

"I've been thinking of working out with my horses this fall, threshing. Get enough money to go up north to visit Emily's family." And he settled down at the table to write.

*(July 8) **My darling Ella**, I am looking forward to that trip. I can tell you I mean to thoroughly enjoy myself. I know you will. Won't it be jolly going together! Bet it will. . . .*

I expect when we get up there we shall not be in a hurry to come back. Do you think they will be able to kick us out? We will go skating on the lake among other pleasures. We can make things lively up there. I bet. I don't intend (like Mr. C) to keep quiet for one minute when up there. I will show them whether your boy has got any energy. We must take a football with us. You and I with Dolly [Agnes, younger sister had worked for the Mairs] will play the rest.

We must go there when they are all at home if possible. What a lot there will be of us, enough to make a small army. I will make Harry drill me.[1] That will be sport. . . .

For her part Emily pleaded with every passing rain cloud, "Please, please—water our crops." She had her dark times and troubles to share with Edwy.

Are our castles coming down smash again? I think my heart will break if they do. I cannot look forward to another years' waiting. It will be a case of my buying the license after all. Dido was arguing with me about the folly of getting married if crops are not good. I always think of Minnie's words. They think I am robbing the family of you. I know they do. I can't help it. I _can't_ and _won't_ give up my life. And you love me. That settles it.

Edwy shared that part of her letter with his mother, but she could tell something was amiss. At breakfast the next morning he was even more on edge.

Now I have to go to breakfast. What a thundering nuisance that fellow is! Instead of writing a lot this morning I had to look after him, for he was up as soon as I was in spite of my rising early. I have been up late four nights running, somebody here every night. I am happier dreaming of my love than playing cards . . .

Elise saw Edwy off to Lonsbury's, "I've not seen him since Emily gave up Aweme School on his account. I can't forget it. But our horses need to be reshod and he owes us."

He was late home and said, "Sorry if you waited supper. Lonsbury shod the horses while I ploughed in his place. I had supper there and he took me to see his crop. He was very nice. So was Mrs. Lonsbury. Now can you keep a secret? Emily might have another holiday. Mrs. Fleming wants to visit her mother if the doctor gives her leave."

Mr. Criddle's nerves were better with visitors. One night he invited Miss Smith, his new teacher, two Miss Mairs, Miss McManes, and Miss Bellhouse. A note from the last mentioned explained her absence: "My sister's husband has been killed on the track somewhere out Bradwardine way."

---

1 Harry, Eddie, and Arthur Steer all enlisted.

Edwy soon had more details and told his mother, "Poor Marion, her husband was a brakeman on the railway. He lost both legs and died within hours. Emily says if something like that happened to me she would die. She is going over to see her on Sunday."

The following Friday morning Elise rose before 5:30 to get Edwy breakfast before he left to market a fattened calf. When he hadn't returned by dark, Mr. Criddle fussed, "There's nothing to prevent his getting home that I know."

Elise had kept her secret and Saturday wore on with no sign of Edwy. The barometer dropped and by late afternoon clouds ballooned up the western sky and the wind strengthened into a gale. She began to worry. As conditions worsened she reasoned: *if he's bringing Emily, he'll surely have the sense to stop in somewhere.*

Mr. Criddle, desperate for rain and fussing about the boy, noted:

5.15 PM Barometer falling (now 28.429) but bar a few heat drops now and again – no rain. Strong SE wind blowing and air stewing hot, though there's been no sun. Max temp 91°F. Boy not home from Bdn yet – getting anxious about him as well as the weather . . .

6.40 PM Great dust blowing down S from E of Treesbank to Bdn Hills – suppose we are to be blown away for a grand finish.

6.55 PM Gale very bad – nearly S – slight spatters of rain – dust everywhere.

7.15 PM Wind gone to SE again- full gale. No boy yet – can't imagine what he can be up to.

About eight o'clock the door flew open and Emily blew in. "Gracious! It's a wild night!" She went upstairs to repair the effects of the storm. Elise stirred up the coals in the stove and added a stick to reheat the stew. Edwy explained more calmly, "We got along fine until the wind caught us at the river. I wasn't too worried and told my girls, 'Let's go!' You can see they got us here."

The storm dropped a measly six hundredths of an inch of rain. Evelyn and Stuart were having trouble finding grazing for the cattle because the prairie was so dry. "There's one advantage," they joked, "The mosquitoes are as scarce as the raindrops."

Finally, July 21, a splendid 1.22 inches of rain fell. Mr. Criddle checked his crops. "Now I have strong hopes that no material damage is done – except of course that the crop will be short and deficient in stools."

Seven more hot days and the crops were parched again. Elise worried about Edwy. *He's so desperate for a good crop. I'm glad Emily is here to help him stay positive. But the way Percy growls I think he's not pleased to have her in his room with Edwy to discuss the day's work.* She wasn't surprised to overhear, "You'll have plenty of arrears to make up for this lost time."

The young couple enjoyed themselves; Emily took in some football matches and celebrated Edwy's 26th birthday. She departed August 3rd when Edwy and Harry went to Brandon to purchase a new binder. After negotiating the deal, they loaded the heavy machine and headed home late in the afternoon. When Elise was out early the next morning she was surprised to see them in the yard. *How did they manage that? Did they travel all night?* They came in, ate their breakfast in almost total silence, and went out to hay. Still no wiser by evening, she watched over her knitting needles as Edwy bent over the table writing to his girl:

Aweme, Wed. August 4, 1897

My Own Darling Girl,

I miss you . . . . We didn't leave Brandon till 6:30. . . . I wouldn't risk coming across the river with such a heavy load in the dark. We left our wagons on the other side and rode the horses to Denny's where we stayed the night. Twelve o'clock when we got there. I had the nightmare, a thing I never had before. I don't feel well yet. I was sleeping by myself. Harry and Will were sleeping in the kitchen and Roland in the bed in the next room to me. I scared Harry and Roland pretty badly. They didn't know what was the matter with me. I guess it was some of their bread did the mischief. I gave them an exhibition of my yelling powers anyway. They woke me up and I rose and dressed myself. This was pretty early in the morning. However it was the means of getting home in good time. I don't want any more nightmares. I warn you against making bad bread. You wouldn't make bad bread if you tried.

Aug 5th *Just had tea by lamplight. I am making up for the two weeks. What a time we had! I was awfully happy and content with you. I can hardly write it. I shall always remember those days as long as I live. Tomorrow is another 6th, 14 months since you said, yes.*

He stood up and yawned, "I'm off to bed. We'll be a man short tomorrow with Cecil gone to do Lonsburys' chores while they're at the fair. He wants to check out the machinery and Mrs. Lonsbury enjoys seeing who takes the prizes in baking, pickles, and jams. Good night Mama."

Elise was still puzzled. *The boys usually tell me when interesting things happen. Did something happen I'd worry about? Perhaps I'll find out by and by.*

Next evening Edwy had news for her. "Mr. Fortune had been to the fair. They say he'd been drinking, but was almost home when something spooked his team. The wagon tongue jabbed into the ground and he was pitched out on his head. Mrs. Bruner saw the whole affair and ran over with a pail of water. She got him partly revived before help came. He was shook up pretty badly, but the only real damage is a broken knee bone."

"Poor Mr. Fortune! Poor Jane, She does have a time with that father of hers."

"Do you remember Harry, Emily's brother? He stopped on his way to Winnipeg and gave Emily a photo of her three handsome brothers in uniform.[2] She, Gertie, and Dolly decided to have one taken too. Emily felt extravagant and ordered six! Mr. C tells me she's not to be trusted even with postage stamps."

They exchanged glances.

Harry, Arthur and Eddie [Edwin]   Emily, Agnes [Dolly], Gertrude [Gerty]

Edwy changed the subject. "Emily saw black clouds out our way and was so worried; she cleaned all the downstairs windows."

His mother nodded, "Many a task gets done when we're anxious."

The hot, dry weather quickly ripened the wheat. Edwy and Harry dressed in their Sunday best before leaving for McManes' to borrow a horse to speed up the harvesting. Elise noticed Edwy's silk tie. *Emily certainly has a flare for sewing, I'm sure he's proud to wear it.*

Next day he was up long before his mother and it was late when he came in that evening. "I haven't had a moment's peace since I got back from Douglas. Norman and Stuart were haying all day with the oxen and we didn't finish till dark. Harry was cutting wheat. I wish the men had come sooner to put the new binder together. I'll see you in the morning."

His mother watched him climb the stairs, *He's wound up; I hope he sleeps well.*

She didn't hear him call out in the night, but he certainly had a restless night. One he could only share with Emily.

---

2   Henry William (Harry) Steer Sgt. 90th Battalion of Rifles, later known as the Royal Winnipeg Rifles. Ernest Arthur Steer, Royal Canadian Dragoons, Edwin Pachett (Eddy) Steer 90th Battalion of Rifles.

My dreams last night were rather horrid. . . . The confounded binder would not go in spite of all I could do. I kept waking up with a start. I sit [up] with the intentions finding you there looking at me with those dear old eyes. Finding you not there, I would go to sleep again and then the same performance would ensue over again. . . . If you were there when I did wake up, I wouldn't mind. Some of my dreams will come true, won't they? I shall wake up and really find you, my darling wife.

The cutting is going fairly well. Will drove into a badger hole yesterday with the big wheel. He and Harry had quite a time getting the binder out. Will and Roland are excited about their Uncle coming and go to Brandon for him on Sunday. I would like to send this by them but can't bring myself to trust them or anybody else with my letter . . . .

Good bye my Darling

While his horses munched on their oats at noon, Edwy added to his letter:

Another frightful hot day. I suppose we shall have a storm tonight. The barometer is about as low as it can be. If we had hail now, good-bye you, and everything. It won't bear thinking of. I seem to be in constant dread of something going wrong. . . . .

Edwy's worries were magnified by Mr. Criddle's constant harping; "a sickly wife is the devil." He told his mother, "I'm sick with worry about Emily in this heat. I begged her to keep her hands out of boiling water. I told her to take the dishes outdoors and turn the hose on them!"

His mother laughed, "I don't think Emily would do that! I know she was ill last year, but now she has good food. I think she will manage."

Edwy went off to bed and left her thinking. *He doesn't notice how hot it is in this kitchen. It seems all young people take their mother's sacrifices for granted. I know I did. It's my turn now—for my children's future. Minnie seems happy. Isabel has a home of her own and a lovely little daughter. Edwy has Emily. Harry and Cecil . . . I have to trust they will find their way too.*

⋯⋯

Next afternoon Edwy was so preoccupied with finishing the field he didn't pay enough attention to the sky. What happened next he described to Emily.

We started for home, but the dust was frightful. Couldn't see 10 yards. We got about half way home when it caught us full force. We ran all the horses into the first bush we came to till the worst was gone and then started for home again. I was really scared for the first time in my life. I expected to see the house gone when we got up here, but no, it was all right. We found everybody in the root-cellar.

Can't tell what damage is done. I expect all the stacks of wheat are blown down. Here the damage is two stacks of hay gone to the devil, each broken, and the garden knocked out pretty well. When it stops raining we shall be off to see what damage is done. I had a foreboding of this storm. Good thing it was not worse.

Would give anything to know whether you were safe. Stopped raining. I must see what's up. We shall work till dark. No more today. Good Bye.

Working frantically to repair the damage, the darkness came too soon. Elise had a hot meal waiting for them and they said, "We'll be up early. It looks like rain. We'll try to get at least one haystack back up before breakfast."

They kept on working even in the rain. "It's no use grumbling," Edwy told his mother later, "I'll write a bit and take my worries to bed. I'm counting on a letter to tell me Emily's alright."

Next morning he felt better until Evelyn came in; "A cyclone has gone through North Farm. The stooks are scattered all over and the wheat badly shelled out."

His mother watched him write. *I'm thankful he has a girl to love. So many discouraging things can break a young man.*

So long as nothing happens to you, I can stand anything and everything. Without you, I won't live. That I am sure of, so you had better take good care of yourself. You are my life and my hope. My life before you came was only an existence. In fact, I have many a time imagined that my living was not at all necessary, but for my darling to be my wife, I should feel like it now. . . . No more tonight. . . . Perhaps I will feel more like myself tomorrow, if there is a cheering letter from you.

Throughout the following wet, dreary day Elise had a houseful of restless farmers. Mr. Criddle measured nearly an inch of precipitation and it kept right on raining. The garden was the bright spot—flowers were blooming, wondrously revived by the rain.

Edwy counted on Emily's letter to tell him she survived the storm. When no letter came, he stewed all night and told his mother in the morning; "I'm worried sick that something has happened to Emily. Dennys are going to Brandon to meet their uncle. I'll walk over and ask Roland to take her a letter."

"Sure thing," Roland said, "I'll deliver it in person."

That afternoon his mother watched him fret like a caged animal.

"I'm entirely miserable from worry. Guess I'll write and let her know how I feel."

St. Albans, Aug 15th, 1897

My Darling Girl, This is one of the most wretched and Dull Sundays in my life. I can't find anything to do that will keep me quiet. I am as restless as it is possible to be. I cannot even sleep it off. Everybody wants to know what's the matter with me. There is nothing wrong with me, I am only very anxious about you. Why did I not have a letter? Surely somebody would let me know if anything was wrong with my girl. But there is doubt. I must wait till Denny gets back.

What a fool I am! Why don't I walk to Brandon and settle this suspense. I was thinking this morning, of telling them here that I was going to Sutcliffe's, and go to Brandon instead. But second thoughts wouldn't allow it. I can't write anymore till tomorrow night. I shall then know what's up, if anything is wrong.

Goodbye Ella. I am sick at heart without you.

He picked up his letter and plodded up the stairs. *I hope he catches up on his sleep. . . . He's been working too hard.* But Edwy had something else in mind. He reached under the bed for his box of treasures and found the verse Emily had sent him in June. Walking over to the window he held it in the light.

Because I love you, dear—
Because my heart sings all day long
A song of love, a new sweet song,
I find I love the whole world more.
Because I love you dear—
I love the little ones I pass
And see in each dear lad and lass
The flower of love like ours, dear heart.
Because I love you dear—

I'm tenderer than I've ever been.
The thought of you comes in between
Me and an impulse less than true.
Because I love you, —
Ah! What in all the world is there
I cannot suffer, cannot dare?
Because you're all the world to me.

from E.L.S. Sunday, June 27, 1897

His lovesick heart basked in Emily's love, so tender, yet courageous in trusting her life to him. His resolve returned, and he began to dream of the happy home they would make for each other. *Our love is deep and true, but it is not only between us. I too am tenderer; Ella has given me a reason to love the whole world.*

Next evening his mother noticed a change as Edwy came through the door. "All my worrying for nothing! Emily told Roland, 'I'm right as a trivet'. Brandon got the storm sure enough. Nearly everyone's brick chimneys blew down. The Flemings were away, but Mrs. Webster was with Emily and they went into the cellar. Dolly came for the night. They half expected me to show up at the door next morning with bad news. By the time she got her work done it was too dark to write. No electric lights since the storm, and they had no coal oil."

"Did she hear from Minnie and Isabel?"

"They're fine. Minnie is busy. She saw Isabel. Will was working again."

When Elise came down to light the fire next morning, Edwy was writing:

Roland brought me your letter yesterday morning. Oh wasn't I glad! Words are not in it! I would rather starve for a week than go through the same suspense again.

I haven't many minutes for writing. We start work at ½ 6 and go on till we can't see. Then it is two miles home so that we don't get home till pretty late. There is always something to fix. Every bit of spare time is taken up. I guess we shall have a rough time at Denny's, as there is no place to sleep. Good Bye, My own Darling girl

Thursday morning 5 o'clock. *We didn't quite finish last night. We tried hard but it was no good. It got dark an hour too soon. We cut seventy acres in two and a half days, not bad for boys.*

And then feeling very optimistic he opened a door of hope:

I have estimated the crop at 2600 bushels and as apparently the prices are go-ing to be good. I guess we can be married. When that will be I can't tell at present. I expect it will come off the next sixth of June. Will that do?

He chuckled, *she'll catch on that I'm teasing.*

The boys were all away harvesting when Mr. Criddle's card-playing lawyer buddy and friends drove out from Brandon.[3] Elise was too busy preparing din-ner to wonder what had happened to her young helpers, but they were watching from afar as the gentlemen, without a livery boy, figured out what to do with their team. Edwy passed a shortened version of the performance on to Emily.

Mr. Kirchhoffer was here today. He and Mr. C just took two hours to get the horses unhitched and put them in the stable, neither of them knowing anything about horses.

Mr. Criddle was to return the visit August 23rd. Before Edwy went for the team, Elise said, "You will have some time to see Emily, I hope."

He wanted to badly enough, but Mr. Criddle kept him on the go. He told his mother. "We only just saw each other. Emily thought I looked thin and tired. She wants me to take care of myself as much as I can. And, suggests I take Thorley's food for cattle!"

"That's a new one! I wonder is that what her chemist recommends for farm-ers." They both chuckled.

"Chemist Fleming gave Emily tickets to the Opera. I wasn't there so she took Dolly."

His mother looked expectant, "Did she enjoy it?"

"I'm sorry; she didn't have time to tell me any more."

I loved going to concerts and the opera was even better. Went with Percy to "Robert de Diable" [Robert the Devil] in Mannheim. Everyone was talking about it.[4] The costumes, the music, the sorcery, the dancing nuns, and all the romance . . . it was splendid! . . . I'll ask Emily more about it when she comes.

Harry and Edwy ran old and new binders to cut the wheat and then the borrowed horse went back to McManes. Mr. Criddle noted the days in his diary, "Came on morning of 12th – so we've had him (or her) 11 working days." Then

---

3 August 20, 1897. "Mr. Kirchhoffer and Mrs. and Dr. and Mrs. Kirkland and Miss Kirkland here for lunch."
4 Percy's letter to his mother November 20, 1861. Meyerbeer's *Robert de Diable* is regarded as the first grand opera.

a few days later noted how he paid for the horse: "Boy home from helping Mc-Manes stack: 1 boy – 4 days; team and 2 boys – 1 day."

That afternoon, he hosted a cricket match while his workforce hayed, hauled, and stacked. Having the stooks stacked in one location saved money by having

the threshing go more quickly. Criddle's setting had a ring of 19 stacks.

Another afternoon Mr. Criddle and Beatrice walked to Denny's, to greet the uncle from England and a new Miss Denny. When he finally got to Mair's to arrange for his threshing, Mrs. Mair broke the news, "We're not going out threshing this autumn."

Seeing his disappointment, she asked, "Would you like to taste my butternut squash?"

He did.

"It's delicious isn't it? I'll give you seven seeds to plant next spring."

Next morning Edwy was sent across the river and arranged with Elders to thresh their crop.

Elise was as busy as the harvesters. The girls dug the potatoes and carrots, but she was the servant responsible to get the food on the table. If anything went amiss, it fell to the 'Dutchman' to make it right. And feeding the family was only part of her job because Mr. and Mrs. Criddle and their guests had to be properly served. Submerged as she was in drudgery, Elise looked forward to her visits with Edwy and his news from Brandon.

"Emily helped serve at a fashionable wedding for Mrs. Fleming. She didn't see the ceremony but could hear everything. It was all over in ten minutes. The bride and her attendants surprised everyone by wearing white."

"Are you sure they wore white?"

"Yes, she said they looked lovely. But she didn't care for the groom. Acted like a big overgrown boy, instead of a man of twenty-three. Emily wouldn't trade me."

His mother smiled, "I agree with her there. I wouldn't trade you either."

"Emily's mother invited us to be married up there. She could make arrangements with their clergyman. It's proper, Emily thinks, for a bride to be married at her home. But, she feels at home here too. She'll leave it up to me to decide."

Elise held her tongue. *The wedding will be at St. Albans, or not at all.*

Edwy hadn't told his mother, or anyone of Emily's plan to leave Brandon at the end of September, or that Mrs. Fleming hoped for the go-ahead from the Doctor to go to her mother's. Nor had Edwy told his mother about Minnie advising Emily to put off their marriage as money was so scarce. And he had especially not shared Minnie's upsetting remark that the family thought Emily was stealing him from his family. He was just thankful to read Emily's reaction.

I'm not one bit scared, if we have to live all year on porridge and potatoes. Shall we get that? . . . . Well, I'll pull through. I want a month in the country before the wedding. After a short time at St. Albans, I'll go to Lizzie Mair's to have my dresses sewn, spend a day or two with Mrs. Sutcliffe, and then home to prepare for November 10.

In the meantime, I have to vanquish Mrs. Fleming's fall cleaning.

His mother noticed Edwy's pencil wasn't moving when he tried to write. *It must be hard on him trying to find a way to keep both Percy and Emily happy.* She soon learned that Emily was not happy. "Cleaning is hard work," Edwy told her. "Every carpet must be taken up, carried outside and given a good beating. She has to empty every cupboard, clean them thoroughly, scrub every floor. Emily's so tired after fourteen and a half hours that even her teeth hurt."

His mother was sympathetic, "It's a good-sized house, if I remember."

Edwy wasn't finished, "She had six sets of blankets and sheets to wash. Wringing them by hand is very slow work. She started at six and didn't get done until three-thirty. Remember that windy day last week. Emily said, 'Hanging the dang things on the line was enough to try the patience of Job.'"

She nodded, "It can be very trying. I've had those struggles."

"Emily's thankful that the evenings get dark early now and she can't work past eight."

Elise didn't mention her own long days. *Edwy takes my services for granted, but Emily is, after all, the Flemings' servant. . . . They expect no more than others. In fact less, for Emily has free time—even on Sunday afternoons. She also benefits from their generosity especially in the food line. It's unusual for a servant to be allowed to eat the same food she prepares for them.*

Edwy ended by saying, "Emily's collecting enough wild cucumbers to stock Manitoba. She wants me to stick up poles to make a summer house and says, 'Won't there be times!'"

They both smiled. *There will be times all right,* she thought. *When will the new Mr. and Mrs. Vane have time to relax in a vine-covered bower?*

Edwy went to Brandon on July 3rd expecting to fetch Minnie home for a rest. But she had persuaded Will to come out and to everyone's surprise they arrived just before noon. Elise went out to welcome her daughters, but couldn't visit. "I'll add a few potatoes to the pot, we can talk later." But, since Will wanted to go right back, grandma had only enough time to hold little May on her knee for a song.

Minnie unfolded a letter that evening as her mother darned socks. "I have a letter from our dear old friend in England. I'll read it to you."

24 Sheepcote Lane, Battersea, S.W. July 27, 1897

My dear Minnie,

I was very pleased to hear from you and that you are all quite well. I am better but not very well. I wish I was near you as I am very lonely. I have hardly any one I love. They are all dead or gone away. Perhaps you may come to England some day.

I do not get much time like you for wrighting [sic]. I am glad you have had a holiday as it gives great rest and pleasure to all. I have not had a holiday for years to go on a visit anywhere.

We have had grand doings in London but I was not well, so did not see it.

Give my love to Mama and to all and kisses. I wish I could pop in and see you all. I often think of our happy times together. Love to dear Isabel and dear May. I hope she [will] have her teeth.

With love, my dear, Goodbye, Your loving Olger

Looking at her mother, Minnie said, "I'm glad I wrote her. Poor Olger, she and Mr. Foulgar were so good to us."

Her mother agreed, "I must write to her just as soon as this busy time is over."

<hr>

Meanwhile Edwy reached Brandon and rushed through Mr. Criddle's business hoping to spend some time with Emily. The few precious minutes he had simply added to her longing to get out of Brandon and be with her boy. In her next letter he told his mother, "Emily is lonesome; her news is full of sore feet, toothaches, and fall cleaning."

Elise concluded that whatever else Emily wrote was for Edwy alone and she was right. He still didn't tell her, or the others, that Emily hoped to be away from Brandon by the end of September. But by her next letter things had changed and Mrs. Fleming was back in bed. Emily was counting her money and thinking she wouldn't mind staying on. But, she absolutely did not wish to go to a different place to begin cleaning another house.

Minnie's presence at St. Albans gave Edwy something other than their house to tell Emily.

Minnie seems fairly and cheerfully well, especially when last night Harry put the chair on her toe, of course by accident. It woke her up. Anyway I was wondering how she liked sleeping with Miss Smith and whether she disliked it as much as when she slept with you. Fancy anyone objecting to sleep with such a darling.

But Edwy didn't get any further with his letter:

Mr. C up—What a row he does make! Where's the Boy? Is the first words he utters. I wish he would leave the Boy alone for a few minutes. I suppose I must go. Confound everybody.

Then having received his day's orders, Edwy joined the others for breakfast. He added a few lines before leaving for Treesbank to purchase his first load of lumber for their home.

> *Mr. C is going with me as far as Mair's. The boys have gone off ploughing on One and took Miss Smith.[5] I no longer scheme about taking girls home.*
> *God guard and keep you from all harm.*
> *For ever your own loving boy, Edwy Vane*
> *PS Save all the jubilee stamps you can get hold of. They might be worth quite a lot some day.*
> *Good-bye my darling Queen.*

Edwy counted on seeing Emily on his next trip to Brandon to fetch Mr. Tulk September 16th. But his business didn't go smoothly and his time with her shrank to a measly 15 minutes before train time. Then, as he loaded Mr. Tulk's trunks, he missed the two greatcoats and his precious scarf he'd brought along in case of inclement weather. He searched and asked in vain. When they finally drew up to the door of St. Albans, Mr. Criddle pounced, "Why so late?"

Edwy confessed the loss, but due to Mr. Tulk's presence, he escaped the full punishment. With tea over, Mr. Tulk presented each boy with a fine knife and a watch for Beatrice.

Had Elise not been so preoccupied, she might have worried more about her son, because that was only the beginning of Edwy's trials. He was sent to fetch a load of sheaf oats to feed the threshers' horses. He had to pay a frightfully high price to get them and expected to be held to the wall for it. But worse was to come. He began his tale of woe to Emily with 'if'.

> *If things had gone well I would have been home soon after dinner. But everything went wrong. Coming up McManes' hill from the river we broke down. We were half way up when the reach broke and of course the load came down then and there. We had a job (Evelyn was with me). Besides the reach, one of the bolsters got broken, also some irons. But, however, eventually we got home with load and all, but in a pretty dicky[6] condition.*
> *The accident did not improve my temper . . . On arriving home I found Mr. C in a bad temper and very nearly had a row with him before I had been in the house two minutes.*

---

5 Aweme School, where Miss Smith was teaching, was another mile beyond their field..
6 Fluttery, queer, shaky, unsteady.

And then Roland came over with the upsetting news.

. . . seems to be Elders plan (and most of the other people were in it including Lonsbury and Fortune), to leave us unthreshed. Everybody seems to have a ban on us and for no reason that I can see.

I am mad. Perspiring all over with excitement. I shall be all right in the morning. McManes and Lonsbury are coming to help put the roof on. Lonsbury had better be careful what he does or else I will fly at him like a wild cat. I haven't forgotten about the school yet nor am I likely to. The least thing will set me on fire.

It is just as well I have you to love and look after. If it was not for you I don't know what would happen to me. Tonight I feel more sick of life and its burden than ever before, I tell you straight if my love for you was not as it is I believe I should go mad and death would have no terror for me. Whether it is wicked or not my brain seems to be on fire. Everything has gone wrong since I left you yesterday. It serves me right for disappointing the dearest girl in the wide world. I am not worthy of you. I shall go to bed and try to sleep my misery away.

Elise's heart went out to him. *Others are coming to work on his house tomorrow. I hope it cheers him up.*

Edwy didn't get back to writing until eleven o'clock Saturday night.

We started with the rafters and finished them by half past three. Then we put the gable posts up and boarded up both ends. That done we went on boarding up the rafters. We got nearly half of them done. I hope to finish the roof today ready for shingles. The shingles we shall not put on for some time yet. We cut out the East window. It is about 24 by 12 inches.

. . . We worked till dark tonight and I couldn't get out of playing cards with Lonsbury and Mr. Tulk. Lonsbury just gone. I certainly didn't enjoy myself, but I feel better than I did yesterday.

Early next morning*. I was disappointed at seeing you for so few minutes. As yet I don't see my way for getting to you. But the first chance I have, I will take. You believe me, don't you? . . .*

We got on Splendidly with the house yesterday. With the roof on it looks far bigger and better in every way. It certainly will be the best house around here. Even Lonsbury said so. Talking of him I feel sure he has nothing against us. He was as jolly as could be yesterday and stayed till late. Mr. Tulk is very jolly, seems glad to be out here again.

I can see our house from here. It looks fine and I think you will be pleased with it. Now the next job is to make a cellar. You will want one won't you? Answer next time you write.

Good-bye, dear heart. True as Steel.

—◦◦✧◦◦—

Roland's news that Elders weren't planning to do their threshing completely dumbfounded Edwy. He'd walked all that way earlier, and made a firm commitment. Mr. Criddle hadn't said anything about the deal he'd struck with R. Coon a few days later, but Elders must have heard about it, and thought Edwy's agreement had been overruled. In any case, Mr. Elder had taken Criddles off his list and now Edwy was being sent to repair the damage.

Sunday. I must go to Elders to see about threshing. There is no doubt that some person or persons have been telling lies about us and have given others the impression that we won't have them thresh us at any price. Naturally we would just as soon have them as anybody else so I will go to them and explain.

Edwy had a few words with his mother before he set off, "I'm worried about Emily. She walks like a cripple."

"She must be nearly done the fall cleaning by now."

The long solitary walk gave Edwy time to consider his good fortune. *There is no girl living that combines everything like my girl: love, truth, honesty, unselfishness, always ready to help others and a woman above everything.* That evening he wrote:

I feel more jolly tonight. I have just had tea after coming back from Elders. They are perfectly willing to thresh for us if we want them.

Mr. C and Mr. Tulk are playing Dummy. There is one continued succession of "Damns!"

The racket was too much for Edwy. Tired enough to sleep through anything, he went to bed. Next morning, he approached their wedding date as diplomatically as he could.

You have your heart set on being married 10th of November. Well. For several reasons I can't promise to have it on that day. Suppose the house is not ready. I hope it can be the day you want.

Tuesday morning he found a substitute for a table.

Writing under difficulty on my knees with an old box. I can never get into the other room because of Minnie. She don't [sic] get up till 9.

Cheer up and keep up your spirits. You must be in perfect health for our wedding day. Tuesday night. Mr. Tulk, Mr. C, Harry, and I at the house this afternoon and there is an awful lot to do. We finished boarding the roof and put a lot of buttresses up. Tomorrow the roof has to be run straight from end to end and the cross pieces for the upstairs ceiling will be put up.

You need never be afraid of your house blowing away. You should just see the way we nail everything. Even Mr. Tulk says it is tremendously strong. And you know what he's like. . . .

I did intend doing the walls and floors with common boards but I have changed my mind and we shall use tongue and groove boards instead for everything excepting the downstairs floor. I got the lumber this morning for that, splendid boards, but not quite as good as tongue and groove. The latter stuff will cost more but it will be much warmer and look nicer and it won't matter whether we paper the walls. . . . So far everything is nice and straight and I am well satisfied. Everyone takes interest in the house . . . You and I are all they talk about.

Minnie, I think, is envious but she talks very nicely about you all the same. I am a lucky boy to have everybody make such a fuss about me and our future.

Being so busy with their house, Edwy had less time to worry about his lonely girl. On top of the **too** short visit, she had other troubles he shared with his mother. "Emily was in a devil of a bad mood. And I don't blame her. She broke a cracked jug; knocked her finger nail with the hammer; Bert Ingram's two little dogs disappeared; and she has five cats and three dogs under her feet the whole time. Lets her know she has big feet." They laughed at Emily's expense.

But his mother didn't know Emily had written something else to burn a hole in his pocket.

Now cheer up, and if you're <u>very</u> good you can fetch <u>me home on</u> the 1ˢᵗ [Oct]. Mrs. F. is going away and wants to shut up house. She told me yesterday morning. Is that good news?

I may have to go down and make the fire on, if Mr. and Mrs. F want hot water. I hope not, for I'm tired, and they don't get up on Sunday till about 11, always breakfast in bed. We won't be lazy as that will we? We'll have Mr. C watching the smoke!"

Edwy knew his feelings weren't shared by Mr. and Mrs. Criddle, or Minnie, who would have to share her bed. Furthermore, their home was a long way from being finished. He had no money for lumber, nails, and shingles and wouldn't have, until some grain could be sold. They were still waiting for the threshers. Yet, he had to tell them Emily expected him to fetch her October 1ˢᵗ.

St. Albans, Thursday night Sept. 23, 1897

My darling Ella,

I have had no time for writing today till now. We have been at the house all day, only 20 minutes for dinner. I told Mrs. Criddle this afternoon that you were coming home as soon as I could fetch you. Well, she has written you, advising you to stay in Brandon for a while longer for reasons, which she has not told me. One thing I am sure Mrs. Criddle has nothing but our future happiness at heart. At present we must be content.   Courage Darling. Don't cry.

Edwy thought he had softened the blow. He posted it and received hers.

This is probably the last letter I will ever write you from Brandon. Next Friday night I hope to see my boy. . . . Goodnight dear."

PS "Isn't it cold tonight? Winter will soon be here. Mrs. F says not long till Christmas. We'll have a jolly Christmas won't we?

"You and I together, love. All the way together, love. Never mind the weather, love . . ."

When Emily opened the letter from Mrs. Criddle, she expected loving words of welcome.

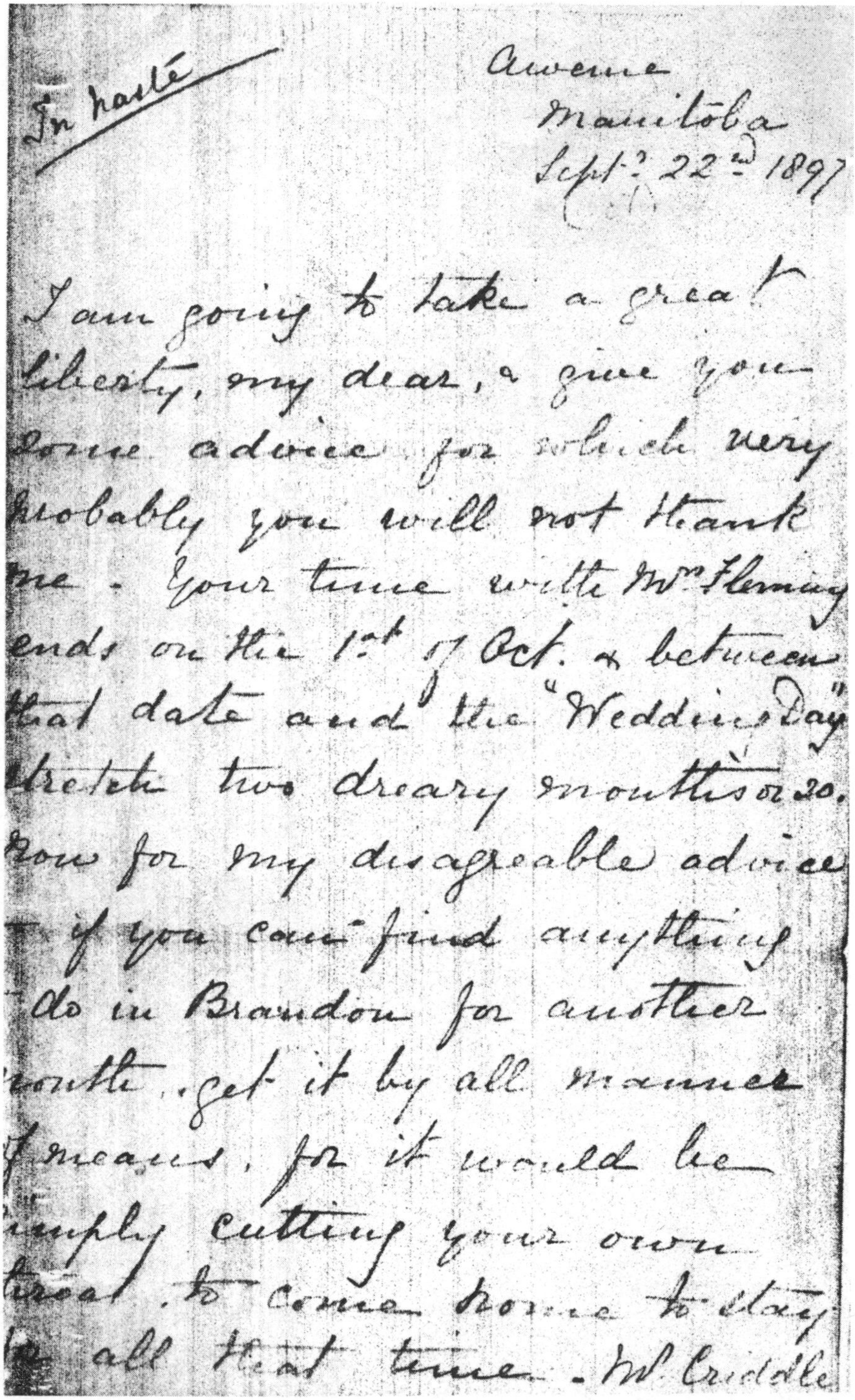

In haste

Awenne
Manitoba
Sept.ʳ 22ⁿᵈ 1897

I am going to take a great
liberty, my dear, & give you
some advice for which very
probably you will not thank
me. Your time with Mrˢ Fleming
ends on the 1ˢᵗ of Oct. & between
that date and the "Wedding Day"
stretch two dreary months or so.
Now for my disagreable advice
— if you can find anything
to do in Brandon for another
month, get it by all manner
of means, for it would be
simply cutting your own
throat to come home to stay
for all that time. Mʳ Criddle

Aweme, Manitoba. Sept 22, 1897

In haste

I am going to take a great liberty, my dear, and give you some advice for which very probably you will not thank me. Your time with Mrs. Fleming ends on the 1st of October. Between that date and the "Wedding Day" stretches two dreary months or so.

Now for my disagreeable advice. if you can find anything to do in Brandon for another month get it by all manner of means. for it would be simply cutting your own throat. to come home to stay for all that time.

Mr. Criddle wants you to be here for two weeks before this "Event" to get things straight and ready. I know that he does not expect you to come before. Brutally frank? But you know I love peace and a "flair up" just at this time would be very undesirable. Also the joy of having a few extra coins of your own, when cash is scarce is great – also, if you are on the other side of the river when the ice is not firm my Boy will be trotting over continually and "worriting"⁷ his family with anxiety. Not for myself do I speak, only for you –

Yours lovingly,
Alice Criddle

Edwy has not seen this.
Show it if you like.

❧

---

7   Alice Criddle's letter to Emily Steer, September 22, 1897. B. J. Becker, B.A., SCAN. Linguistic Consultant, Winnipeg, 2009. "If Mrs. Criddle had used the word **worrying** his family with anxiety, the meaning would be straightforward — causing concern. However, the archaic "worriting" carries hidden meaning because of the context surrounding it. It is a dialect, sometimes thought to be an 'illiterate' dialect. Thus the quotes could indicate that she is talking down to Emily — in an illiterate manner so that she will understand. OR: it can be a form of *worrying* that carries an attitude of pestering or annoying. 'Quit *worritting* the cat.' In other words, sort of a willful misbehaviour. Again, a criticism of Emily's actions and their implied outcome."

Chapter Twenty-three

Mr. Tulk Works His Magic

Elise saw disappointment on Edwy's face when Mrs. Criddle told him, "Emily must stay in Brandon. If the Flemings don't need her; she'll have to find another situation for a month."

Having lived under that firm hand for 15 years, Elise knew that her words felt cruel to the recipient no matter how pleasant they seemed to others. *She runs her household with the firm hand of a general and isn't to be questioned. I'm afraid Emily will learn soon enough who wields the power behind the throne at St. Albans. Thank goodness Mr. Tulk is so jolly and presses on to get the house finished. Percy can't entice him away from the project even for hunting. I shudder to think what might happen if Edwy's wedding plans don't work out.*

Edwy had grown up accepting the Criddles' decisions about his life, and tried to gloss over the troubles he and Emily faced, and would face, living under a pretentious Victorian umbrella. Without fully understanding how the coldness and lack of support had hurt her, Edwy carried on filling page after page of news about their house:

I believe the house will be practically finished by the 1ˢᵗ of November and a jolly, happy, warm, comfortable house it will be. . . .

You wouldn't believe the work there is to do. It is simply astonishing to me. The cellar alone will take two or three days to do besides getting the logs for it. Harry and I have been chopping and siding the logs inside the house most of the day. Another good half day and we shall be ready for the siding inside which we shall fill up with mortar as we go. . . . We will start boarding the cellar as we have no lime yet. Can't get any at Treesbank. . . .

I am happy all day long working on your house. I repeat the old cry, I want my darling.   *You and I together, Love*

                              Shall be our world together, Love

                                      Who shall dare to part us, Love

                                              Hand in hand together, Love

Breakfast 6:30. *We are going to the Spruce for floor joists. I am afraid we shall have trouble in getting them but must have them if it takes from morning to night. Mr. Criddle is very jolly and is working hard at the house. He must take a great interest in our future welfare in spite of what he used to say. Those were bad times for me. . . .*

⤚⟡⤚

Meanwhile in Brandon, Emily received two letters. She set Edwy's aside and opened Mrs. Criddle's, expecting to be warmly welcomed. As she read, she exclaimed, "Gracious! I can't believe it!" She read it again. "You will be cutting your own throat to come home to stay." Her happy expectations had been cut from her heart as a cook slices a bad spot from a potato. . . . *What a thing to say! Home should not be the place to have my throat cut. . . . It looks like Edwy's queen has been building a castle in the air . . . and it has crashed. . . . We've been patient . . . worked so long waiting for our wedding. Mrs. C calls it an* **Event**. . . . *It will be an* **event** *alright! But two* **dreary** *months come first. She's right on that. . . . She orders me to stay here "by* **any manner of means.** *" . . . Am I to go begging! Doesn't she care what manner of work I do?*

Emily visualized herself surviving on stale bread; on her knees scrubbing mud from an unfinished wooden floor; up to her elbows in a wash tub of filthy woolen underwear; milking skittery cows morning and night. What a comedown for the educated eldest daughter of an English builder! She burst into tears. . . .

But not one to give up easily, she gathered herself together. There were words scribbled in the bottom left-hand corner of the page. "Edwy has not seen this. Show it if you like." Her temper flared, *"Show it* **if** *I want." You bet I want; I'm his girl. Why didn't* **she** *show him? There's more to this than meets the eye. . . . Will I be to blame for any and all flare ups?*

For all her questions, Emily still found it hard to associate such words stemming from the lady who had appeared so loving: she wrote:

I can't help thinking Minnie has something to do with it. I don't often feel rebellious but I do not like the thought of staying in Brandon another month. I would not mind if it were here, but to get another place is too much. I know you wouldn't ask it. I am tired right out with house cleaning, washing and ironing and do not fancy getting into another house and having the same performance.

She looked over Mrs. C's letter again. '**My boy**' leapt out. *Is my beloved Edwy* **her boy**? *My soon-to-be-husband: does he belong to Mrs. Criddle? Furthermore, my Edwy does not* **trot** *about like a horse,* **worriting his family.** *. . . I'm his family. Would I want to put him in harm's way? And what kind of an expression is "worriting"? It sounds most unsavory.*

She dipped her pen and continued:

Mrs. C's words "What a nuisance you are" have been running in my head quite a lot today and that's just what I feel I am and I'm sure if I had the money or hadn't promised you otherwise I would go straight home and make you come and fetch me. (I was going to add if you wanted me, at this the tears come. I know you do, but I cannot help the rebellious feelings.) I went down to Dido's tonight with

Eddie and I am a regular cripple. I daresay I'll feel better in the morning. Just as I'm counting the days for me to leave, I am asked to stay another month. It might just as well be another year, one sounds as formidable as the other.

I need not be at your place. I never intended to. I'm just as much, if not more scared, of any trouble as Mrs. C. I have other places to go to and am going. So there, but I'll wait to see you and go to bed now and sleep off my discontent and misery.

Good night my loving Boy. Forgive me.

Sunday morning after Emily got Mr. and Mrs. Fleming their breakfast and saw them off to the farm for the day, she added to her letter:

Well! I can't say I feel any better about staying in B. than I did last night. I have longed so for this month to end. Two months is a desperately long time to wait yet. . . . Now I'll get to work and straighten up the house and I'll be done for the day. I'm going to see Mrs. Evamy, Dido, and make a regular round of calls. . . .

I have just read your letter for the 4th time and Mrs. C's too. She evidently thinks I was going to stay there for all the time and she is making a mistake. I did not and would not if I could. I knew your wishes long ago on that score.

I wish you were here to talk things over. They always seem much easier from your point of view and suppose I ought not to say it, but I can't help thinking that we shall never be allowed to do as we like. It will always be in fear and trembling of Mr. C. I feel this more than you do. You are so used to it. I know Mrs. C means in all kindness and love to me, but all the same there's a rankling notion that I shall be expected to obey. You shall read her letter when you come and this too. You will see if I am not right. We shall be looked upon as children who want supervision and looking after.

I am going out now after this long lecture. Suppose now you're entertaining Mr. C. . . .

Emily went first to see the grieving widow Marion, now packing to move back to her mother's at Aweme, and ended at Isabel's for supper. Her brother Eddie walked her home at 9:30. When the Flemings returned, she made them supper, carried their hot water upstairs, and spent a few final moments with Edwy:

Am still bothering about what I am to do. I daresay you will make my mind easy and settle things for me. Of one thing I am sure and that is your love for me and mine for you will never change whatever may happen. Good night, Ella.

By morning she had recovered some of her former gumption:

I think our marriage will be made in heaven if some are not. We'll both try to make our home a little heaven or haven of rest, won't we? We, us and Co. but without the Co.

I spend a lot of time scribbling when I ought to be doing something useful but shallow empty minds can't settle to anything (à là Mr. Criddle). You don't think mine is empty? Well that is one of your present privileges. You'll find out one of these days (also à là Mr. Criddle)

Think anyway we will give up any idea of the Dauphin trip and go next summer. I shall be expecting you. . . .

—◦⊙∽◦—

Elise had enjoyed having Minnie home, but appreciated her decision to return to work on Monday. *It will give Edwy a chance to see his girl.* He left others working on his house and drove his sister to Brandon. That evening, in spite of Emily's crippled feet, the lovers walked down to the Assiniboine and took a path along its edge. An old log caught their eye, they settled on it, and Emily took out her letters. Her eyes filled with tears watching Edwy read, first Mrs. Criddle's note, and then her own troubled reactions. As he finished and looked up, she said, "You see how my castle has come crashing down?"

Edwy kissed her tears away, "You're my queen and you shall have your **palace**. We're using first-class materials, real tongue and groove boards to line the inside walls. Mr. McVey says it will be the best house in the settlement and the warmest. I've told you many times, nothing is too good for **my queen**." He hugged her so long and so tightly that she had to struggle free to catch a breath. With another kiss he said, "Everything will work out in the end if we have patience. Just a little longer." And sang, "You and I together Love." Emily joined in, "shall be our world together, Love. Who shall dare to part us, Love? Hand in hand together, Love."

After a moment of silence, Emily said firmly, "I'll try to see Mrs. Criddle's letter in a more positive light. She said her advice was for my own good."

It was late when they parted.

—◦⊙∽◦—

By the time Edwy got back to Denny's next day their wheat had threshed out at eight bushels an acre. A disaster for them, and for Edwy, since his wouldn't do any better. His mother had hoped her son's little holiday had lifted his spirits. Instead he was even more down in the dumps. "Wheat's turning out badly and gone down five cents in the last two days. Perfectly beastly! I'm not feeling so well . . . will be off to roost as soon as I've written a note to Emily."

He knocked on Mrs. Criddle's door and handed her Emily's note. She read it quickly and said, "She's a dear girl. Will have all the visiting she wants when the month is over."

Finished eating, Edwy sharpened his pencil and sat down to write:

My dear Girl,

I am lost without you. Did you enjoy being with me last night? Everybody in the settlement . . . believes that we are to be married on the 4ᵗʰ of November. . .I wish it was true.

He listed the work done on her palace while he was away: finished the gables; set the floor joists; built the stairs.

Thank you for going out with me the other night. Words are no good to express what I thought about it. Those poor old feet, how terrible sore they must have been and to please me you went for a long walk, when every step must have hurt like the deuce.

Your Palace is a priority. One day, five, including Mr. Tulk, worked hard and the next, it was four, with only Norman ploughing and two away threshing. With help from Cecil, Harry and Stuart, I tar-papered the roof. It was a beastly job. There was nothing to hang on to. We were nearly off two or three times but then a miss is as good as a mile.

The next step required plenty of stamina: sand, dug from the cellar was lifted out and mixed with water and grout to make mortar. Working from the ground up, they filled every crack.

It is a slow job and hard work but we made a first class job of it. It will take at least four or five more days with a full gang of men. The mortar disappears so perfectly surprising. It ought to be warm. . . .

I would dearly like to know how your feet are. You must have been on your feet all the time for them to get so sore. It is a beastly shame and there's Dolly too working like a slave and only sixteen years old. She will be old and worn out before she is thirty.[1] . . .

Edwy got plenty of ribbing next day from the threshing gang.

They are bound to have a dance at any cost. I guess we shall have to manage somehow or other. I don't see how we can get out of it as all the people reckon it is settled. If we don't have a dance inside our house on the day we are married there will certainly be one outside, in spite of all we can do to prevent it, so there.

I hope your poor old feet are better and you don't have any more toothache. God Bless you.

At the Flemings meanwhile, Emily was writing to Edwy:

This time last night we were walking home from Dido's. My chum the tooth-ache is giving me fits. Am I not a daisy! Mrs. F very sick today. She had to call Mr. F last night as soon as he had gone out. I wonder when the doctors are going to cure her. She is quite losing heart.

She managed to finish the fall cleaning by the end of the month and carried the scars to show for it. She walked like a cripple and had three blistered fingers from ironing all the curtains. With the satisfaction of a job well done, however, she packed to begin her new position with Mrs. Hall.

Then, Mrs. Fleming called her to her room, "Please, please stay until I'm better."

---

1 Dolly married Joseph Slugget and lived a long, happy life in Vancouver. They sent holly to Emily and Edwy every Christmas—a branch given to my parents was one of the wonders of my childhood.

Edwy wanted to be working on his house. Instead he was driving the countryside searching for sheaf oats to feed the threshers' horses. "I am awfully sick of being short of feed," he told his mother. "Day after day wasted hunting up oats without the least idea of where to go."

He managed the oats. His next assignment brought even more sympathy from his mother, when he came in black and sweaty, covered in dust and said, "I was at the straw, threshing today. Can hardly see, my eyes are so full of dirt."

He didn't tell her what he wrote his girl. "If you were here I would ask you to take some of the dirt. I am hanged if anybody else shall." And thinking she had begun her month at Mrs. Hall's he encouraged her.

Is she nice and kind to you? She ought to be. I don't see how anybody can be anything else to such a darling as you are dear old girl. . . . Keep up your spirits and courage. You will need it next month. Four days gone nearly.

⦿⦿⦿

Elise noticed Edwy's restlessness after Emily's letter. He pulled a chair over beside her that evening as she was darning socks, "Emily doesn't know what's up. Want to hear the story?"

His mother nodded.

"You knew Emily had given up all thought of getting away from Brandon and was moving to Mrs. Hall's. Well, she didn't. Mrs. Fleming was unwell again and asked her to stay. But then the next day, she said they were moving to rooms over the store and needed her only a week, instead of a month. That left only three weeks with Mrs. Hall and Emily decided not to go to her at all, but come out to stay with Lizzie Mair."

"Is that definite?"

"Well, the plan lasted a day. Mrs. Fleming had to call the doctor and was ordered to stay in bed. Emily felt so sorry for her that she cooked a good roast beef dinner, with cauliflower and sauce, potatoes and roly-poly pudding. After they'd eaten, Mr. Fleming told her privately that they wanted her most likely for two or three more weeks, depending on his wife's health. And that's where this letter ends. I won't be going for Emily this week, anyway. I'll write her."

Seven of us at it this afternoon. We made things fly, I can tell you. I shall be glad when it is finished. I wonder whether you will be pleased with it. I very much hope so. I do want so badly to please and make you happy. It is all I shall live for. I must succeed, failure would break my heart. I know I do owe you such piles and piles! It will take a long while for me to pay some of it back.

I'm not afraid, my love is strong and unending and will surely take us to our journey's end. May that end be long in coming, aye Darling? Think we shall ever get tired of each other? I say, "No, it never shall be."

Emily's next letter was more cheerful.

> *My own dearest Edwy, I had resolved I wouldn't count any more, but here I am reckoning ¼ of the month gone and now I know this is positively the last month I shall spend here.*
>
> *On the whole I am having an easy time now. What did you make out of my last letters? You must have thought me crazy. I am settled now, until you fetch me.*
>
> *While I am sorry for the necessity of my staying with Mrs. Fleming I am glad for my own sake. $10 will help get us that easy chair we want.*
>
> *If we can't get out of giving a dance, why we can't. But for my own part I would rather not have it in our house. Why not have the school like Forrest Cullen for their wedding dance?*

Edwy chatted with his mother, "Emily's work is easier now that the cook stove is back in the house. The house is more comfy too. Mrs. Fleming was up again and played some lovely tunes that set Emily dreaming. She hasn't given up on me, says we'll pull through somehow. Her brother Harry sent $15. It will help us a lot."

The western sky threatened rain as the threshers pulled away. Elise breathed a sight of relief. *Even if the crop is meagre, it's safe in the granary. It's another bad year[2] but at least Edwy can buy shingles for his house.[3]*

Only a few days later an excited Edwy told his mother, "There's a change; listen to this."

> *Oct 11, Monday 2 o'c. Well, this is a world of change! Mrs. F told me this morning that she thinks they will manage without me after Friday. That makes me 1/3 of a month. I am not sorry. It's getting pretty cold now. I want to be home. Your letter says you will be in the later part of the week. Can you put it off till Friday and go out on Saturday morning?*

"She sends her love. She's getting paid for the whole month and went downtown to shop."

Elise was serving him an early breakfast Friday morning, when Mr. Tulk joined him, "I can't stay for the wedding, though I'd very much like to. I'll keep you company and see how Isabel's getting along."

It was music to Elise's ears. *Does Mr. Tulk know how helpful his support is to Edwy? Today, he's taking a big risk by fetching Emily.* Emily was already at Isabel's, so apart from a little shopping, it was time to enjoy each other's company. They spent the evening recounting hilarious stories of the early days in Manitoba. That drive home on October 17 would be a treasured memory for Emily. Her heart

---

2 October 13, 1897. Criddle *1,812*, Little 467, Fortune 1680, Lonsbury1340, Bellhouse 470, Jas. Martin 198.
3 Mr. Criddle's two homesteads plus Elise and Edwy's homesteads. Edwy's land was sandy, most of it pasture.

sang, *Goodbye servanthood, goodbye Brandon! I'm in the best of company: my Edwy and Mr. Tulk.*

When they arrived at St. Albans, Emily saw no scowls, no obvious danger of having her throat cut. As soon as Edwy had the horses stabled, he took her on a tour of her Palace and pointed out the tongue and groove walls and Mr. Tulk's carefully fashioned windows. Monday, Edwy dropped her off at Mairs' to help Lizzie bake for a harvest dance they were planning for Saturday night. Now that the ferry was operating, he hauled some wheat to Treesbank. Getting a good price of 76 to 80 cents a bushel meant he could pay for the shingles.

Edwy, no longer looking for letters, was surprised to receive one stamped Ochre River. *From Emily's family, but who?* He opened it and checked the signature. His heart skipped a beat on seeing, 'Emily Steer'. Then he remembered that his Emily was named after her mother. He was surprised again when he saw, 'Dear Sir'. *By Jove that's a change from Boy! What does she say about our not going there for our wedding?*

Ochre River P. Office Oct 20ᵗʰ 1897

Dear Sir,

I have often thought of writing to you but never seem to have the time for it. If you make up your minds to be married up here, we shall be pleased to have you for a visit as long as you like to stay. If on the other hand you don't come now, come between seeding and harvest next year.

Our house will be finished this month. The plastering etc. won't be done till next spring. We had some rain every week all summer and kept the cement from drying quickly. So could not get the work all done this year.

We have an abundance of vegetables and a good cellar. Everyone says the vegetables are not up to the average this year but we have nothing to complain of. Our cellar is full.

I suppose it is usual to congratulate you on the coming event. I hope you will both be happy in your new life and that you have health and things to enjoy the good of this life and may it be a preparation to meet the life to come.

With my kind regards and best wishes to all your people,

I am yours Truly,

Emily Steer.

He was pleased. . . . *Stay as long as we like . . . hospitable, like Emily. Yes, we'll go and have a good long holiday. Emily will be pleased to know her mother has taken our decision so well. I'll see her tonight.* Before leaving for the dance he showed his mother, "Look at this. Emily's mother calls me Sir. Ain't I moving up in the world!"[4]

---

4   Oct. 22, 1897. "Boy, Bobby, Stuart and Evelyn gone to Mair's dance."

As Mr. Tulk's departure approached, they pushed to finish the Palace. By the fourth of November, the window frames—both downstairs and up—were completed; all glass installed and puttied; the stovepipes up; the well dug. It was all but completed by Guy Fawkes Day. Before Elise ventured down to the bonfire, she made sure her kettle was filled and hot, the stove well banked. She met Talbot running toward the house, "Mr. Tulk asked me to fetch a box under his bed."

Cecil made room for her on a log and she looked around the circle of faces. *So many changes over the years since our first campfires back in '82.*

Mr. Criddle stood up and asked for silence. "On the commemoration of this historic event – 'tis most appropriate that we honour you, my gentleman friend, on the achievement of something we all aspire to – another year of life." Everyone joined in to clap.

Mr. Tulk stood up as if to make his usual reply. Instead he beckoned to Emily and Edwy, "Please join me." They hesitated a moment before stepping forward. He looked at all the faces in the firelight and then began, "My birthday this year is special indeed. A most fitting occasion to congratulate this fine young couple, Edwy Vane and Emily Steer, on their forthcoming marriage. I have received great pleasure in taking part in the construction of not only the strongest, but also the warmest home in this great Northwest. I concur with you Edwy; The Palace is indeed, a most fitting name for your future home."

Talbot hurried up to him carrying a heavy box. Mr. Tulk smiled and said, "Thank you Talbot. Give it to Edwy."

Then, smiling at Emily, he said, "Open it."

With only the light from the fire, everyone strained to see what it could be as Emily untied the string and carefully pulled away the brown paper. The children were no wiser as she lifted up a heavy cast iron object. But she knew, "Oh, Mr. Tulk, how perfectly splendid! We shall have waffles for our very first breakfast! If you could stay, I would be pleased to serve you."

Mr. Tulk had not finished. Facing the couple he addressed them: "It becomes me to wish you many joyful years together. May your well-crafted palace keep you warm through the long, cold winters. May you be blessed with healthy, happy children. And may your home be one of peace and happiness, welcoming to all." He shook their hands. Everyone clapped and broke into singing, "For they are jolly good fellows. . . ."[5]

⋯⟋⟍⋯

Mr. Tulk had worked his magic. Elise waved as he departed the following Wednesday on one of the two wagons loaded with wheat. He caught the noon train and then, Mr. Criddle, with four hundred dollars in his pocket, paid some

5 Originally a French song sung the night after the Battle of Malplaquet in 1709.

debts, purchased a new stove, and winter stores. Only to his diary did he relate his activities that night.

> Met no end of people in Brandon – a frightful consumption of whiskey and cigars. Stayed at Palace Hotel . . . 'tis the best and brightest hotel in Brandon.

Travelling home the next day, Edwy found himself wondering. *Is this fine big cook stove a wedding present for Emily and me, or will he keep it and give us the old one? In any case Emily will be able to cook her waffles.* Mr. Criddle said nothing about the stove, but announced, "Kirchhoffer had to leave for Winnipeg – missed out on our cards. I promised I would go back for our rubbers[6] Saturday night."

Thus Edwy, who now had no desire to spend a night in Brandon, would have to do so. Winter arrived and the day was so bitterly cold Mr. Criddle borrowed Lonsbury's buggy for more protection from the wind. They found the river frozen over, yet the ice broke under the horses' weight and the wheels rammed against the ice. Midstream a singletree snapped. "Whoa!"

And there they sat, marooned. For a moment Edwy questioned his role as livery man. But he couldn't turn back, so he handed the lines to Mr. Criddle and jumped into the icy water to adjust the traces. Then he waded ahead and jumped up and down until the ice gave way. Little by little he broke a trail for the wheels to the western shore. He stopped at the first farm to borrow trousers and a pair of socks.

Mr. Criddle's outing was not the success he envisioned. Had his hardworking family known how he spent the night they would have been disgusted. But because of his position, only his diary knew to whom he blamed his losses.

> My play all through the evening was I believe very bad—couldn't remember the cards— something wrong with me—and—I ascribe it to Joe McDonald having mixed me an overdose of whiskey and water. I told him it seemed mighty strong but he said no—and I drank it unwittingly— damn him.

❧❧❧

Edwy obtained the wedding license and had enough cash in his pocket to write the Church of England Incumbent to officiate his wedding. He showed the reply to his mother, "See this, The Reverend also calls me sir."

> *Rounthwaite, Nov 9ᵗʰ/97*
>
> *Dear Sir,*
> *I will be at Mr. Criddles house by 11 a.m. on the 24th as desired,*
>
>   *Yours truly,*
> *Mr. Vane, Aweme*   *James Kimberley*

❧❧❧

---

6   Best three of five in a series of hands.

Having waited so long for their union, the date now rushed toward them. The bride and groom made a shopping trip to Brandon for supplies for their home. Presents arrived nearly every day.[7] Mrs. Criddle, capable hostess that she was, listed the guests and settled who should sleep where. She decided the menu and calculated the quantities. Elise heard her sigh, "So much extra work!"

Elise did her best to do everything asked of her. *I often worried. How will my sons ever find themselves a wife, working as they do from dawn to dark? I'm celebrating for Edwy. I like Emily, and she fits in well with the young folks. I know things will change for me; I have enjoyed our conversations, but he'll still be coming to get his daily orders. Will Harry and Cecil spend their evenings at The Palace? . . . I must not think of myself. Rather I must thank God for granting my wish to see my boy happy.*

As the wedding approached many of Elise's old memories resurfaced. *Surely, I'll be able to attend <u>this</u> wedding. And since Rev. Kimberley is Church of England, I will hear the ceremony Percy promised me. We had planned to be married in Heidelberg, and I went to interpret for him at the 'Bürgerliche Standesheamts' (Registry Office). He paid the three kronen for the Baden marriage application and I watched the official stamp thump down on the page. My heart thumped too with happiness. My long wait was over; we were getting married. Just like Emily, I was very excited. Filling my bride's portion of the application was straightforward. But when we got to the groom's I discovered a different Percy. First, they wanted his home address verified from his town's registrar and proof of his profession. "Stupid German regulations. None of their damned business!"*

I pressed on. Until the age of 25, a groom required written permission from his parents and an 'excuse' for his 'underage' marriage. Percy was incensed. I knew his mother had not agreed to our marriage when we were engaged five years earlier, but now with our baby on the way, I expected her approval. Was he angry with his mother? Or with the child in my womb? I was the one who had to go to the local authorities.

---

7   November 10, 1897. "Sundry presents coming in for boy – Expect he'll have a grand lot of people for his wedding if the night prove fine – A favourite everywhere."

Hateful as it was, I'd have to be examined to obtain their certification of the child. But Percy stormed, "Bah! They have no right to interfere!"

I kept on: What was the place of his last residence and how long had he resided there? "Bah!" After the marriage, where would his future residence be? "Damn them all!"

I thought he was going to tear up the form. I picked it up. "I don't care what you do with the idiotic thing. Won't need it. . . . I'll take you to London."

He took me, but I didn't get the promised wedding. Still have the form in my trunk.[8] I'm happy for Edwy and Emily . . . but it doesn't heal that old wound. Her tears were close. . . . *He caught Mrs. Criddle the same way, but she got both the baby and the wedding. . . .*

After all these years I'm going to hear the service, and, being the mother of the groom, I might get a chance to talk with the Reverend. In the meantime, I won't have an idle minute.

Sunday night, the happy mood was interrupted by the Dennys. Roland had been stabbed in the eye by a sharp spruce twig. Mr. Criddle sent them post haste to Brandon.

Monday, the first guests, Emily's brothers, Harry and Eddie, came by train from Winnipeg to Treesbank. Edwy went to Brandon Tuesday for the Knights and Emily's sisters, Dolly and Gertie.

November 24th, dawned bright and almost 30 below with a sharp west wind. Would anyone blame the Reverend if he opted to stay warm in his study rather than face a ten-mile drive? But he arrived as promised with a fine team of drivers—bodies steaming, white with frost. Cecil took the horses, cooled them down, and stabled them. Meanwhile, Mr. Criddle pulled the gentleman in and pushed the door shut to cut off the wave of cold air sweeping across the floor. Mrs. Criddle took his frost covered greatcoat and called to Elise, "Pour Father a cup of hot tea."

While savouring his drink, he and Mr. Criddle commiserated about the hardships of travelling in such weather. Warmed by the tea, he asked for the groom, "I'd like to meet the young man. We have some formalities which need attention."

Elise took his cup and carefully wiped the table.

"I'd like to use this table if I may," he said as he arranged his books: *the Holy Bible, Book of Common Prayer,* and the *Record of Marriages.*

Having been sequestered in Mr. Tulk's room, Edwy and his best man nervously approached.[9]

---

8 Official form for application for marriage in the Dukedom of Baden. Groom's portion blank. Private family collection.

9 Criddle, Norman. November 27, 1897. "Edwy and Miss Steer were married this morning (just before dinner) by Rev. Mr. Kimberley. Harry was best man and D. Steer was bridesmaid."

The Reverend quickly put them at ease, "I'm pleased to meet you, Mr. Vane. Edwy is it?" shaking his hand. Then extending his hand to the best man, he said, "Harry? You're brothers I understand." Having covered the formalities, he said, Mr. Vane, please sit down. You need to fill in these forms," and he slid the record book to Edwy pointing to the spaces. Edwy carefully wrote his name, address, and occupation as well as the name of his parents, 'Harry Vane' and 'Elise Vane'.

"Your bride is Emily Steer?"

Edwy nodded.

"She can fill in her parents' names when she signs after the service. "Marriage is a big step, but one you will not regret. I am sure Miss Steer will be a very capable and loving wife."

As the family gathered, no one seemed surprised to see the mother of the groom dressed as usual. She was after all the housekeeper. Elise had not broached the subject of a dress for the occasion in fear of running the risk of being banished from the ceremony. She looked about. *My, Emily's sister, Gertie, is a pretty girl. Isabel is wearing her lovely dress again. Mrs. Criddle's new dress is just right for this occasion. The young ones are feeling so special, their tresses shining, and their Sunday dresses stiff with starch. And just look at little May! Isn't she a caution sitting with the big girls? I wonder what Minnie will wear? I hope she arrives soon. It's not like her to miss her brother's wedding.*[10]

Minnie still hadn't arrived when the Reverend asked everyone to take their seats. Elise brought her chair from the kitchen and placed it at the back. The men faced Father Kimberley on his right and little Alma was dispatched to Elise's little room, "Tell them it's time."

A hush fell over the gathering as bridesmaid Dolly came down the stairs. *No wonder everyone calls her Dolly instead of Agnes. Her features are as delicate as a porcelain doll.* Then Emily stepped into view. Elise took in a quick breath. *She looks so lovely. That's the perfect hat! And the little red chemisette sets off her jacket. Her skirt turned out well. She and Mrs. Mair have done some fine sewing. I'm glad she decided to wear her Grandmother Vincent's cross.* Emily had come down the steps and took her tall brother Harry's arm. He led her to the groom. For a moment their eyes met and then she too faced the priest. *It does my heart good to see them so happy.*

The Reverend Father cleared his throat and, in a practiced, clerical tone, began, "Dearly beloved, we are gathered together here in the sight of God, to join together this Man and this Woman in holy Matrimony; which is an honourable estate, instituted of God in the time of man's innocency, not by any to be enterprised, nor taken in hand, unadvisedly, lightly, or wantonly, to satisfy men's carnal

---

10 Criddle, N. November 27, 1897. "Minnie and another fellow got out from Brandon just to (sic) late for the wedding."

lusts and appetites, like brute beasts that have no understanding; but reverently, discreetly and in the fear of God; duly considering the causes for which Matrimony was ordained."[11]

"First, it was ordained for the procreation of children, to be brought up in the fear and nurture of the Lord . . .

"Secondly, it was ordained for a remedy against sin, and to avoid fornication; that such persons as have not the gift of continency might marry . . .

Elise gasped, *so that was my role! The remedy for Percy who had not the gift for continency. Woe to my trusting heart.*

The priest droned on. "Thirdly, it was ordained for the mutual society, help, and comfort, that the one ought to have of the other, both in prosperity and adversity. . . .

"I require and charge you both, as ye will answer at the dreadful day of judgment when the secrets of all hearts shall be disclosed, that if either of you know any impediment, why ye may not be lawfully joined together in Matrimony, ye do now confess it. For be ye well assured those not joined together by God; neither is their Matrimony lawful."

He paused, then added solemnly, "If any man do allege and declare any impediment, why they may not be coupled together in Matrimony, by God's law, or the laws of this Realm; the solemnization must be deferred, until such time as the truth be tried."

Elise held her breath. *Why did no one speak out at Percy's wedding to Alice? Was Mr. Tulk present but said nothing?[12] Percy told us that morning before leaving, "I'm going to see my Mama in Addlestone. She's not well." We expected him. The children watched for him to come down the street. They cried so.*

The Reverend had already moved on: "Edwy, wilt thou have this woman to be thy wedded wife, to live together after God's ordinance in the holy estate of Matrimony? Wilt thou love her, comfort her, honour, and keep her in sickness and in health; and, forsaking all other, keep thee only unto her, so long as ye both shall live?" Edwy answered, "I will."

Then the priest turned to the bride, "Emily, wilt thou have this man to be thy wedded husband, wilt thou obey him, and serve him, love, honour, and keep him in sickness and in health so long as ye both shall live?" To which Emily, never thinking that there would be a time when disobedience would cross her mind, promised, "I will."

---

11 Abridged from Solemnization of Matrimony: Book of Common Prayer, 1662. Church of England.
12 Marriage Certificate, Sept 8, 1874. Percy Criddle, bachelor, 131 St. George's Rd., to Alice Nicol, spinster, 52 Thornhill Rd.

Whereupon the minister asked, "Who giveth this woman to be married to this man?" At which her brother Harry Steer stood and answered with a smile, "I do."

Addressing Edwy, the Reverend continued, "Take the bride's right hand and repeat my words. I, Edwy take thee Emily to be my wedded wife . . ." Elise drifted to a time long before—*I loved him so. . . .*

Edwy ended his pledge, "and thereto I plight thee my troth."

The minister turned to the bride, "I, Emily take thee Edwy to be my wedded husband to have and to hold from this day forward, for better for worse, for richer for poorer, in sickness and in health, to love and to cherish, and to obey, till death us do part and thereto I plight thee my troth."

The priest then held open the Bible and Harry carefully laid the wedding band on it. Taking the ring, the Reverend delivered it to Edwy, who, ever so lovingly, slipped it on the fourth finger of Emily's left hand. Holding it, he was led to say, "With this ring I thee wed, with my body I thee worship, and with all my worldly goods I thee endow . . . Amen."

Elise thought wistfully, *all my son's worldly goods . . . so few, yet Emily loves him.*

The couple kneeled; and the Minister prayed over their bowed heads: "O

eternal God . . . as Isaac and Rebecca lived faithfully together, so these persons may surely perform and keep the vow and covenant betwixt them. Amen."

The Reverend looked about, paused and then declared: "Those whom God hath joined together let no man put asunder. Forasmuch as Emily and Edwy have consented together in holy wedlock, and have witnessed the same before God and this company . . . I pronounce that they be Man and Wife together, In the Name of the Father, and of the Son, and of the Holy Ghost. Amen."[13]

---

13 Book of Common Prayer. The minister would have read Psalm 128 or 67 and delivered a short sermon regarding the duties of the husband and wife according to Ephesians 5, and Colossians: "Wives, submit yourselves unto your own husbands, as it is fit in the Lord."

Elise breathed a sigh of relief. *This is the perfect occasion for Mendelssohn's "Oh rest in the Lord, wait patiently for Him, and He shall give thee thy heart's desires."*

The minister led the way to the table. Emily took the pen, noticed Edwy's name already at the top of the page and signed. It would be absolutely the last time she would write *Emily Louisa Steer.* She filled in her parents' names, *Henry William Steer* and *Emily Steer.*[14] Dolly wrote, *Agnes Violet Steer,* but the best man, Edwy's brother, held back. Instead, Emily's brother came forward and signed William Harry Steer, Winnipeg. The Reverend took out his fountain pen and completed the document—*Church of England,* married by *License* and finally his own signature, *James E. Kimberley, November 24, 1897, St Albans, Aweme, Manitoba.* But before he closed the book, Mr. Criddle bounded forward. "As head of this household I must witness the Boy's wedding." With his usual flare, wrote *Percy Criddle, Aweme* between the two names already written.[15]/[16]

❦

Elise moved quickly to the stove to get the kettle boiling for the wedding breakfast. Minnie arrived just as the honourary servers, Maida and Julia, began. Mr. Criddle occupied the clergyman by discussing world events—each man predicted the outcome of the Spanish-American conflict. Emily didn't mind having no wine for toasts. She and Edwy had other priorities, and Mr. Criddle had not thought it a necessity. This 'Event' had cost him far too much already.

That evening, in spite of the cold, neighbours came bearing gifts. Not wishing to be awakened for a chivaree in the middle of the night, the happy couple stood at their door welcoming all.[17] The Palace was packed to the rafters. They danced, paused for supper at midnight, and then danced until sunrise.[18] Elise tried to stay on duty at St. Albans where Mr. and Mrs. Criddle held sway and card playing was the activity of choice. Shortly after midnight she slipped away to her little room. *I am content. . . . Thank God I lived to see this day.* She was drifting off to sleep when a thought flitted into her consciousness. *Today was my birthday. Dear God, I forgot all about it in the excitement. Nothing could make a better gift.*

The housekeeper could be forgiven for lying in bed longer than usual, especially since no one seemed to be clamouring for breakfast. It was already light when little May tapped on her shoulder, "Grandma, are you awake?" Elise stretched out

---

14   Henry William Steer, born 1846 in Petworth, Sussex, England. In 1881 the British Census records his family living in Surrey. He was a builder, employing 24 men. Emily was born 1871, in Kennington, England.
15   Diocese of Brandon. Married, November 26, 1897, by J.C. Kimberley of Rounthwaite. Record No. 147. Account is based on the original Marriage Record in which Percy Criddle's signature is between and overlapping the other two.
16   Vital Statistics, Manitoba, Registration # 1897 –06-001412, December 1, 1897, Form 10. Mr. Sutcliffe, Secretary of the Municipality did not forward Mr. Criddle's name as a witness. The two witnesses are Agnes V. Steer and Henry W. Steer. Question: Why did Harry Vane, the groom's brother as best man, not act as witness?
17   A noisy mock serenade (banging pans and kettles in the night) until the newly married couple invites them in.
18   Criddle, N. Diary. November 27, 1897. "There was a dance in the evening which lasted all night at which there were 105 people including us. A good many of them brought presents."

her arm and drew her under the covers. But they hadn't snuggled long before the little girl whispered, "Sing me a song, Grandma."

Elise missed Edwy's greetings at breakfast, but she took comfort in seeing the smoke from The Palace. *They have their own home, God be thanked.* Cecil came in later that morning and told her, "Minnie gave them crockery and a handsome chair, large enough for two. Gertie is helping to cover the old chaise lounge with cretonne. It's not safe there for me."

The Palace: Note the lace curtains & geraniums on the window sill.

Emily's family left the following week. Isabel stayed until her birthday on the 29th. With the shuttling of wedding guests ended, Edwy came over to show off a pretty black teapot he had bought for his new wife. Mr. Criddle held it up admiringly, and said, "Well, this will make a fine wedding present for Archie Cooper."[19] And with that, the teapot was Emily's no more.[20] Elise saw Edwy's colour change, his mouth open, but no words slipped out. *What a shameful thing to do! How will he explain this to Emily? She could have given up one of the six water pitchers.*

A few days later, as if to consolidate his authority, the traditional ritual of weighing and measuring the family took place as if Emily didn't exist.

Wednesday, Dec 15, 1897.

Height in stockings:

Edwy	5.7 1/8	Harry	5.3 ¾	Cecil	5.1
Stuart	5.8 3/8	Evelyn	5.7 ¼	Maida	4.8
Julia	4.5 5/8	Bobby	5.7 ¾	Alma	3.5 ¼
Talbot	4.0	Norman	5.11 ½		

Weight – ordinary clothes – no boots

Edwy	152	Harry	136	Cecil	120
Stuart	146	Evelyn	146	Maida	73
Julia	69	Bobby	145	Alma	33
Talbot	53	Norman	148 ½		

19 December 13, 1897. "The youngest Miss Husband [Amy] married to Archie Cooper last Friday and – they've gone to England for the honeymoon."
20 Emily writing to Minnie, December 10, 1897. "Edwy got me a pretty black tea pot yesterday and behold! He took it to the house to show them and they bagged it to send as a present to Archie Cooper."

Elise gradually recuperated from the wedding while the young folks enjoyed themselves twice over, first in making a rink and then skating and hockey. Norman spent his time painting. Stuart, with Evelyn's help, mounted deer heads. Harry was sent away to work. Cecil did the chores. Edwy was kept busy driving. A few days before Christmas they butchered old Rose and Moira—kept the front quarters and sent the larger hind quarters to Brandon for Edwy to purchase supplies for Christmas dinner. He also brought out the Knights. Minnie wasn't coming. Edwy and Emily had Dolly as their first Christmas guest.

Mr. Criddle took great pleasure in counting 18, not including May, around the table Christmas Day. That night, an exhausted Elise thought of her faraway brother. *Does he feel the advancing years as I do? My nieces, are they making their way in the world?*

Thank God for my dear children. May the coming year be kind to us.

Chapter Twenty-four

If They Could But See Around the Corner

After Christmas, while the weather continued mild, the men went hunting and the youngsters played outdoors. Little May was bundled up, and Alma and Talbot had great fun pulling her around on their skating rink. Later there were thrilling rides down the big slide. Their happy squeals, shouts, and laughter filtered in to Isabel and Elise, baking in the kitchen. *They've been out for hours without getting cold. I cannot remember such weather at this time of the year. It's extraordinary.*

But visits end, and on December 28 Elise hugged her granddaughter tightly, kissed Violet May's little nose, and handed her up to Edwy. "Bye-bye my little one. Look after your Mama." Isabel helped the little hand blow grandma kisses as the sleigh pulled away. *I never had a chance to take my children home to my mother. But I mustn't think of that now. Better to count my blessings that Isabel comes and I can enjoy her dear little girl.*

Mr. Criddle gave his usual year-end summary:

It was not a bad year. Got some old scores from the hail of '95 rubbed off. The Boy's house got built, furnished and paid for – but for that we should be quite flush of tin – as it is – we are not. New and greater comforts have been added to the daily curriculum – and more pleasures with less work. We have also considerably increased the values of the farm – stock – machinery – and power to make money.

Not everyone included in Mr. Criddle's '**we**' would agree with his assessment of more comfort and less work. Elise had just as many plates to fill, clothes to wash, socks to darn. But, with his boys so capable, Mr. Criddle left more and more to them while he engaged in more gentlemanly pursuits. As Justice of the Peace, 'sundry' people arrived at his door for assistance in minor legal matters. He called on ailing neighbours with medical advice and railed against anyone who questioned his treatment or sought a doctor. Aweme School's enrolment was too low, but he kept it open and continued to collect his yearly stipend as the board chair and secretary.

Winter being party season, Elise watched the young folks happily set off for the dances. *Edwy and Emily look so happy; I hope the coming year goes well. And now that more of the young folks go along, I can listen in on their morning-after chatter.*

I like to know who attends and who plays for their dancing. Beatrice is the best for telling me what is served at midnight and notices what the girls are wearing. All was well until Mr. Criddle went along to Lonsbury's party. The following morning, as Elise enjoyed the usual banter, his door opened and all eyes went down. She knew something was amiss as he marched across the floor and stood over them. "She is the silliest chatterbox I ever saw – religious – totally insincere – ignorant – full of airs and graces – stupid, dull – don't seem to possess any garters – at any rate her stockings are generally all awry – hanging down around her shoes – or rather – some horrid galosh arrangements called shoes. She's thinking of learning the violin! Yet, she hasn't learnt to sew or cook yet. Bah – how I hate inane chattering fools. You have better things to do with your time."

Is he talking about Miss Denny? He's entertained her with obvious pleasure. . . . Sounds a little like the speech he made the night Edwy asked permission to marry Emily. Was one of his boys enjoying her company? Which of the lads is it? Evelyn, Stuart, Harry? If it's Harry, I hope he doesn't do anything rash.

The crew put on their coats and went out without a word and worked on the new fowl house under Mr. Criddle's watchful eye. Mrs. Criddle kept up her social connections through letters.

St. Albans, Aweme Jan. 16th, 1898

My dear Minnie,

Have you ever seen such lovely weather for January? We are all enjoying it thoroughly and only hoping it will last a little longer – and a little longer. . . .

I had another Post Card from Louisa Nicol. She is very much better and asked me

to send her such Canadian Stamps as I could get for a little boy she knows who is not at all strong. So I have packed her off as many as I could lay hands on.

I have plenty of work on hand and lots to last a long time, but I (and all of us) are very glad to have some books to read and it is very good of Mr. Parkes to lend them. I took the liberty of mending "Cleopatra" as she was going to pieces pretty badly.

Mrs. Kohler has a son and they are both doing well.

I thought I wanted to write something very special but I do not know in the least what it would have been so I won't.

Solomon had a very bad cold and has got nearly well again. Talbot has a number of sore spots (gatherings) just the same as he had last year. Otherwise we are all respectably well.

Mr. Clay has come over for a night and has brought us a nice hindquarter of pork; we have been looking after his trees for him.

Lots of love from all.

Yours affectionately,, Alice Criddle

Edwy delivered the letter to Minnie at work, and stopped at Isabel's. She was overjoyed to see him and held up little May's arm. "Look at these dreadful sores. Do you think I should take her to Mr. C?"

"He's as good as a doctor. It's a fine day . . . Get your things. . . . I'll take you."

Home again, Edwy felt in his greatcoat pocket for the five-dollar bill Minnie had given him for Mr. Criddle. It wasn't there. He searched his clothing, the sleigh box, the grocery box.

Eventually calm prevailed and little May's sores got Mr. Criddle's attention. Talbot had ugly spots too to show his papa. "Why didn't you show me these before? You have the same squamous covered swellings. We'll just treat them with that old nostrum for scurvy.[1] A dose of chlorate of potash twice a day should do the trick."

Getting up in the night to tend her boy, Mrs. Criddle fainted. A dose of sal volatile brought her around, but she was still rather shaky in the morning. Elise was concerned; *I hope she is not in the family way again. . . . It's not for me to say, but she's had eight babies and is no longer young. Nor am I. Do I have the strength for another of her delicate years? I dare not think about it. Keeping up with the regular work is quite enough the way I am feeling these days.*

Cecil faithfully continued to support his mother with firewood—sawed, split, and carried in. In spite of the unusually easy winter he found the chores unpleasant. They were so short of fodder, the hungry animals strained at their ropes and bawled for more. Still, morning and evening, he carried in a pail of milk for the girls. It was second nature to them now: cool the milk, skim off the cream, and wash the pans for the next batch of fresh warm milk. When the cream was cold and properly aged, the churning went quickly. The dasher moved up and down to the chant:

Come butter, come. Come butter, come
Peter's standing at the gate waiting for a butter cake.
Come butter, come.

Once the little droplets of butter had gathered into a solid mass, it was spooned out of the churn into a bowl to be washed, salted, and worked. Finally, pressed into a crock, it went to the cool cellar. Not only was making good butter hard work, it was also an art.

---

1   Lemon-juice as a preventative and cure for scurvy had been known since 1636. An Order in Council in 1795 systematically introduced lemon juice into the diet of seamen and the disease disappeared. Furthermore, he and others became aware of the value of potatoes as both food and medicine. "Its anti-scorbutic virtue lies in the vegetable's acid tartaric, partly in a free state and partly in combination with potash and lime." Thomas Watson, MD, *lectures on the Principals and Practice of Physic.* (Lea and Blanchard, 1845) p. 1027

One mail day Elise received a letter from her old friend from Southwark, Mrs. Foulgar, and filled with warm memories, she sat down to read. Her joy soon turned to sadness—*the poor dear, such a cruel world. I'll write her soon. In the meantime I'll ask my girls to write their Olger.*

Aweme, Manitoba, 28ᵗʰ Feb, 1898

My dear Isabel!

    I will not give you any reason for saying that I never write to you, although I have nothing particular to say. I hope you are well and little May got rid of her nasty sores.

    I had a letter not long ago from poor Olger. She is not well and feels very lonely. She speaks of the happy Christmas when she and Mr. Foulgar tried to make you all happy. It would be kind of you if you would try and write to her sometimes. She wanted to know if Minnie is still engaged and I had to tell her that it was broken off by you long ago.

    When shall we see you and Minnie for a long holiday?

    With love to all of you, I remain,

    Your affectionate Mama

⋄◦⊂⊃◦⋄

When the boys completed the fowl house, Elise wondered, *how is Percy planning to keep the boys happily at home now?* What a surprise when she heard, "We could do with a billiards table. All we need is a small table – sides on it – felt the surface – cues and balls."

Ten busy days later, the project was finished: several cues, three carved wooden balls—1¼ inches in diameter and a surface 5.8 x 2.10. While his boys took turns learning the game, Edwy drove Mr. Criddle to Brandon to find a teacher and enjoy his usual tea and music at Mr. Rose's, followed by whist at the 'Club'.

That March marked a watershed for Norman. Mr. Boger, a well-known butterfly specialist, came from Brandon and for two days examined Norman's collection and drawings. They talked of nothing but Lepidoptera and when the expert departed he took 217 drawings to send to the Department of Agriculture in Ottawa. Elise watched from the sidelines, *I hope something comes of this. There is not much I can do to help him anymore but the boys help by watching for interesting specimens.* Her boys collected; but the gentlemanly activity of mounting and drawing was Norman's domain. Whenever he ploughed, he also collected flowers to paint. He was striving to complete as many as possible to enter in the Brandon fair.

⋄◦⊂⊃◦⋄

Edwy came up from The Palace one evening and sat down by his mother who was mending beside the stove. "You wondered about Emily's brother, Eddie. He had stomach trouble last fall."

She nodded, "Yes, how is he?"

"We got a letter today. He says he's getting better . . . seems in good spirits. He asked me to tell Mr. Criddle that he can't follow his orders to get weighed every week. Their nearest scales are nine miles away at Ochre.[2]. . . Had other news too: young Reg has 860 posts cut to fence his quarter. And his Uncle George is going back to England; he can't get on in this country."

"I'm not surprised. . . . Many of our neighbours have gone. There are only the two Lonsburys at school now that Littles have moved to Treesbank." Then she lowered her voice, "Why not let our youngsters attend? They'd enjoy it. . . . She'd have five students with Maida, Julia, and Tolly. That's the number they need to qualify for the grant, is it not?"

Edwy nodded, "Well, I must be off home. We're having a surprise party. Hope the weather stays mild so everyone can come."

His mother was still thinking about school. *My mother wanted me to be a teacher. . . . Mrs. Criddle enjoys her children, I expect she will keep them home as long as she has someone to do the cooking and washing.*

The new teacher didn't measure up to the previous one in Mr. Criddle's estimation. "She's not as ladylike. The people will go on trying new teachers, because the brats never learn anything – which of course they can't do – having no learning capacity."[3] Elise thought back to Miss Smith's coming to pick up her salary the previous year. *I didn't hear her say anything negative about the children. But she did wish ours would attend. As for others wanting to change teachers—who would they be?[4] Percy is chair of the board. There's Lonsbury and now Harry has filled in for Mr. Little.[5]*

The sun climbed higher. Tolly, Julia, and Alma played their first game of cricket. Seeing the geese flying northward, Harry and Stuart took their guns to bag some for dinner Easter Sunday.[6] Although the river was on the verge of break-up they still expected Cecil home from Mair's. *I'm glad I have plenty to do or I'd worry myself sick.* She had a hug for him when he came in and said, "I know you're careful, Cecil, but that river! Thank God you made it!"

The family played cricket in the afternoon and after tea, card games extended into the night. Next morning, Elise learned the Mairs wanted Harry for spring seeding so her worry shifted to her second youngest. "Don't worry," Edwy told her. "We'll take that long plank. I'll come back as soon as he is across to let you know he's safe on the other side."

2 Eddie Steer's letter, February 18, 1898, Makinak, Manitoba. Private collection.
3 April 5, 1898.
4 August 23 1898. "Miss English asked to be released. Lonsbury objected to a change so, she'll have to stop."
5 Archives of Manitoba. Aweme School Minute Book P336A. H. Vane: Trustee in 1899.
6 April 8, 1898. "Harry and Stuart just brought home the 1st gooses (sic) of season – shot through the head at 500 yards!! Weight 11 ½ lbs"

It seemed like hours before Edwy returned to tell her, "It was like Cecil said, only more open water along each bank this morning. The ice in the middle still looked solid enough. We used the plank for a bridge to get onto the ice—carried it across—then found a narrow enough spot to reach the other bank. Harry got over all right."

Edwy didn't go into detail about rotten ice or the swift flowing water below the plank. He calmed her fears by saying, "By the time he's done seeding, the ice will be gone."

Snow still lingered in the nearby bluffs as Edwy began seeding on South Farm. Mr. Criddle soothed him about having so little seed by saying, "We'll come out ahead. There'll be moisture from the snow to get started – fewer plants will have larger heads – fat kernels."

Meanwhile, the boys found a yearling heifer stuck in a snowdrift, but were too late and it died. When another went missing, Mr. Criddle came down hard on them. "You knew Faith was weak – you've had to help her get up most days! The beast ought never to have been let run without watching. In a few days with outdoor grass it would have picked up and got all right again." In late April, Ivy, about to calve, died. There were two more stillborn calves.[7] Elise, not overfed herself, wondered. *Am I going to be like them? . . . Get weaker and weaker and then one day not be able to get up?* Her fears were closer to the truth than she realized when a cold went first to her throat, settled in her chest, and developed into a roaring fever. She was allowed to go up to bed. Had it not been for Harry's wages and advance payments for herding other farmers' cattle, there would have been even less food on the Criddle table.

⋯⋯⋯

Some days later, Edwy dropped by to see his mother. "Just got a letter from Eddie. He seems alright, but his writing looks shaky. I'll read it to you. Tell me what you think:.

Turtle River, Makinak P.O. May 3/98

My dear Emily,

I was very pleased to get your letter last Saturday and I had one from Gertie the same day she is at Elder's and likes it immensely.

We have two heifer calves one on my birthday and one on the 21st. May's heifer has turned out a dandy, quieter than the other cow, the two give a large tin pail and a fifth of milk twice a day and no grass yet. The hens (13 in number), are laying 9 eggs a day average. Reg and Frank went to McRea's fishing about three weeks ago and got 137 Jack (actual count) and one of them was the biggest McRea had ever seen, it was a monster.

---

7 According to a veterinarian it is not unusual to lose poorly fed livestock in early spring before the grass can replenish the animals' stamina.

I don't think I will be able to do any hard work next summer but might herd cattle or something light, mother thinks I had better stay home till the fall anyway. But I don't know it all depends.

With love to you I am,
Your affectionate brother, Eddie Steer

They chatted about Eddie's prospects and then Edwy said, "You're still feeling poorly, aren't you? I'd better go and let you get to bed. We'll talk again soon. Goodnight, Mama."

He had no idea that within the week he'd be hurrying back, "Mama I have bad news from Emily's mother. Better sit down."

Turtle River, Makinak PO May 9th 1898

My dear Emily,

You will have received Eddie's letter before mine. Treasure it as his last effort at writing. He began it one day and finished it the next and Gertie's. He got up early and wrote as the mail had to go. Poor boy he had a little outdoor exercise each day and sat in the sun and out of the wind. He was looking forward to riding. He reminded me so much of Auntie Maria ever since he has been ill. Cheerful all through, patient and grateful for all he had done for him and gave as little trouble as possible. On Thursday he got giddy when moving out the door and I had to assist him. On Monday he did not go out but laid down as his head, he said, was too full of blood and his heart was thumping at a great rate. His veins had been very full for weeks past. No matter what nourishment he took he lost weight all the time . . . he has been comparatively out of pain.

On Saturday May 8th a hemorrhage began and continued up to the last. He was not delirious but for a few seconds together once or twice, but before he had finished a sentence he recovered and knew all he said. But he did not speak of anyone, only asked to be moved or something to drink . . . . . he asked for a drink of cold water half an hour before he passed away. He died very quietly at 4:15 on Sunday May 8th.[8]

We had a letter from Harry and Arthur to Eddie but he said midday Sunday don't read it, it hurts my head. So he never knew what either letter contained. It was Arthur's last before he left for the West. The funeral is on Wednesday May 11th at one PM. All the neighbours are calling and offering to do anything they can for us.

With love from your,
Mother E Steer

"Emily wanted to get home, but with such a poor crop, we put our trip off. Never thought he was so ill. His letters were always cheerful." He paused, then changed the topic. "Young Arthur's off to the Klondike. Sixteen horsemen from Winnipeg's Royal Canadian Dragoons have joined a lot of lads from Ontario. They're called The Yukon Field Force. Canada wanted help for the Northwest

8 Edwin (Eddie) Patchett Steer born April 26, 1875 – died May 8, 1898. Buried in Turtle River cemetery.

Mounted Police because of all the American gold seekers.[9] I sure hope he gets home safely. Emily's mother can't help but worry. . . . Well, I must get back; losing her brother is hard for Emily."

Manitoba Contingent. Arthur Steer is seated centre middle row.

Minnie, Isabel, and little May came for a brief visit in early June. Although they were good medicine for everyone, Elise, still weak from the high fever, was especially thankful. Little May was content to sit on her knee and while they chatted, Edwy mentioned he was starting on Emily's fowl house. He was surprised to hear his mother's enthusiastic support; "I'm pleased for Emily. Having to beg for every egg she needs hasn't been easy."

When Mr. Criddle heard of it, he had a different opinion. "Awful folly, not wanted – spoil the look of things – the fowls will probably all mix in with mine. The logs might have profitably been used elsewhere."

As spring passed into summer, trouble erupted in the Denny family. Left alone on the farm, Roland came for Cecil to do a day's ploughing. The door had barely closed when Mr. Criddle exploded! Cecil explained to his mother later, "Mr. C is afraid Roland won't be able to pay. But I promised; I'll go."

Cecil did his day of ploughing, but Roland soon gave up—without money he couldn't buy seed or hire help. "I'll get work in the coal fields at Estevan. Will you keep my gun and mare 'til I get back?"

---

9 The force was made up of 203 volunteers. The troop travelled an all-Canadian route by train to Vancouver and up the coast to the mouth of the Stikine River in Northern B.C. After a disastrously difficult jouney, they reached Fort Selkirk [former Hudson's Bay Fort] on the Yukon River, 180 miles south of Dawson. Some of the group helped the NWMP maintain order in Dawson. Law and order was maintained, and the Yukon remained Canadian.

As another year of drought threatened, Mr. Criddle was so distraught he paid no heed to headlines in the news, LOCUSTS DESTROY DAKOTA CROPS. The heat and tension took its toll on everyone. When Edwy received an invitation to play football against Stockton, he accepted, explaining to his mother. "They're a tough team. But we need something else to think about besides the weather." The fellows practiced, strategized, and put up a noble fight. The excitement carried them through another hot, dry week until at last rain fell and eased the tension.

By July Norman had 127 flower paintings ready for Edwy to take to Mr. Rose who had agreed to enter them in the fair. "With heat like this," Edwy said, as he scanned the western sky, "we could get a storm. I wish you or your Governor would go along to oversee this business."

As he carried the precious bundle past his mother, he said, "My life depends on getting this package delivered safely."

All went well, and Edwy was soon back haying. He'd purchased another set of harness so they had four teams, including Norman's oxen, in the field. *It's not for lack of workers that we go hungry,* Elise thought. A day later she watched Edwy and Evelyn head off in the moonlight, leading a couple of steers to sell in Brandon. *Better that they travel in the cool of the night. Tomorrow will be another hot, dry day. The kitchen's an oven from boiling all this jam.*[10]

Edwy's predicted storm burst a few days later. Luckily, St. Albans escaped with only one broken window. The next morning Mr. Criddle made a westerly tour and reported, "I find things out that way more serious. Have lost a quarter of my best wheat. Happily all my Home Farms are practically uninjured."

Then to add insult to injury, the temperature dropped so low overnight that frost nipped some vegetables. "It's a pretty state of affairs – fried, hailed, and frozen all within 60 hours."

At tea one evening Mr. Criddle shared a newspaper clipping Mr. Tulk had sent. "My cousin, Sir Chaloner Alabaster, died the end of June.[11] You should be proud to know you have such an important relative. Had a great opportunity

10 July 13, 1898. Started 1.25 AM – 10 ½ hours. "Shade temp. 100.5! One of the hottest on record."
11 Four years before Percy's birth in 1840, his mother's brother Chaloner Alabaster and wife died of TB, leaving their three young boys, Charles 7, Henry 4, and Chaloner 1½. Percy's parents were named to administer their lucrative Straw Hat business until the sons came of age. Within a short time Harry Criddle had sold the business and for one year was listed as a voter. (Only male property owners could vote) The cousins attended school (no free education in England). By 1858, when Percy's father died, the money was spent. But the three industrious lads were already on their own: Charles, a clergyman in New Zealand, Henry in Siam, and Chaloner in China, in the employ of the British Consular Service. All sent money home to help their now impoverished Auntie and young Percy; Chaloner £100 per annum plus the income from a house. Charles died of TB leaving a widow and two children. Henry fell on hard times in 1878. Chaloner married in 1875 and with a family could no longer spare 1/3 of his income for Percy, who, he said, should at the age of 38 be self-supporting. This severed his relationship. Percy, Alice, their children, and his mother, had to move into a small cottage on the Tulk estate 1878/9. Compiled from extensive research in England, family letters, documents and The Alabaster Society.

for a 16 year old – King's College recommended him as an interpreter to go to China.

When the Chinese refused to open their ports to British traders we had to use force. They gave Chaloner the China Medal for his courage and in the end he became Consul-General of Canton. Queen Victoria made him a knight at her Birthday Honours in '92."[12] Looking at Norman he said, "When you get to be a famous artist, the Queen will honour you – have KCMG after your name – Knight Commander of St. Michael and St. George. We'll have to call you Sir Norman Criddle."

Watercolour of young Chaloner Alabaster

Elise glanced at Norman. *He tries so hard, Is his father teasing?*

For Norman to receive a knighthood from the queen for his paintings was about as likely as Edwy's chances for success as a farmer. No matter how hard he worked, he couldn't make it rain. But he'd made a plan and told his mother, "The swamp is dried up. I'm going to put up as much hay as I can and sell all we can spare. I promised Emily I'd take her to the fair next week. Do you think she'll like travelling on a load of hay?"

His mother smiled, "She's a good sport. You do enjoy teasing her."

"Anyway, we've got Gertie—her infected finger is improving. She wants to go too. And I'll invite Norman to see how his pictures have made out with the judges."

But Norman declined, he wasn't well enough.

❦

On returning, they hurried up to the house, "Norman, you should have seen them! Your pictures looked first rate. Won first prize—a big red ribbon . . . and another ribbon was even fancier—in gold letters 'Judges Special Mention'. No end of people standing around talking about them. You even made the *Brandon Times*, only four lines, but you were the only one they mentioned."

Elise said to the happy young man, "Congratulations, your hard work has paid off. Keep on."

They celebrated Norman's success until his father came in, ranting, "They've begun operations on that ferry down by Nelson Clark's! I blame old Calverley – and I'm determined to upset the scheme. Cost $1000 – and no use. I guess I shall spoil him as I've done on a few previous occasions. "[13]

---

12   Chaloner Alabaster, knighted for his service in China, died June 29, 1898, Bournemouth, England. Obituary of Sir Chaloner Alabaster, *North-China Herald*, July 11, 1898, p. 59.
13   July 25, 1898. Treesbank Ferry operated nearly 90 years.

Mr. Elder came looking for Gertie, the end of July. But three days later she reappeared, "Can't do the work."

Then another disgruntled servant turned up: Minnie also needed a rest.

As harvesting began, Mr. Criddle estimated the crop on South Farm, "Sixty-five acres – very poor – had it been thicker – been more rain – less weeds!"

Elise thought sadly, *my homestead . . . my dreams of land and riches for my boys.* When the harvesters moved to Criddle's fields his optimism surged, "Crop generally in very good shape and the heads are big – ditto the grains. . . . I expect 3700 bushels."

Then midway through harvesting the sky opened and the moisture needed in July came down in torrents. St. Albans' roof leaked like a sieve and pots and pans were scattered about to catch the drips. Unfortunately under cover of darkness, Norman's floor chose to channel its water directly down to his parents' bed!!!

Minnie helped with the cleanup and then along with Gertie—who'd given up on the Elders—caught a ride to Brandon with Edwy.

⟡

Things finally dried out. The men got back to stacking and discovered a new problem. They couldn't fork the sheaves onto the rack because of broken twine. Harry complained to his mother, "It's a confounded nuisance! Have to tie them up by hand. I'm going to write the Department of Agriculture. They should know something."

Reply in hand, Harry told Mr. Criddle, "It's not crickets cutting the twine; it's grasshoppers."

Harry started corresponding with Dr. James Fletcher, Dominion Entomologist and Botanist and since Mr. Criddle wasn't interested, and the others were too busy, he chatted with his mother. "I got a report from California about using poison bait against the hoppers.[14] Dr. Fletcher says he authorized it three years ago in Ontario.[15] If we have hoppers again next summer, I am going to try some experiments. But first, we have to get this crop threshed."

Mr. Criddle held to his predicted 3700 bushels until forced to accept the actual tally of 1,560. "The bushelers gave jolly good measure – had the machine thrashed better, there might have been 150 bushels more. There's a most deuced lot of grain left in the straw."

Edwy made use of the ferry and started hauling grain to Treesbank. With money in his pocket, he and

14 Coquilett, *Locusts of the San Joaquin Valley, California,* Calf- A Report (US) Commissioner Agriculture for 1885-86, 00 289-395.

15 Fletcher, James, *Report of Deptartment of Entomology and Botany,* 1896 p. 236. J. E. Richardson in Brant County, Ontario, had used a very similar formula as early as 1896.

Emily prepared to drive north to visit her family. At sunrise October 25, Elise went out to see them off and handed Emily up a package of fresh biscuits to add to her picnic basket. "Thank you. I'm excited to see my parents, but I'll miss my brother."

Edwy jumped down, put his arm around his mother's thin frame and told her, "Take care now, Mama, I want to see you well when we get back." Then up again beside his wife he clucked to the team; Emily waved and they were off on their long awaited trip.

❧

Mr. Criddle also had 'wheat' money and told Harry. "I can't wait for the Boy to get back. I've got business to see to in Brandon. You'll have to drive."

And so Harry, some days later, had the honour to overnight in Brandon. They were only just back again when the children shouted, "We see Edwy and Emily coming." Alarmed, Elise hurried out and waited anxiously with the others for the wagon to pull up. Everyone talked at once, "You aren't supposed to be back. What happened? Are you sick?"

Emily was teary-eyed as Edwy explained, "The roads were nothing but mud and water. We had only 40 miles to go, might as well have been a hundred. We couldn't get through."

Mr. Tulk had watched the scene and as soon as there was a lull in the conversation, he said, "I have 25 dollars for you. Try again for Christmas. Take the train."

The gentleman had stayed longer than usual, hoping for a trophy deer. But having failed yet again, Edwy drove him and Minnie, who had been home again, to Brandon.

Just before Christmas, Elise was out in the frosty predawn wishing Edwy and Emily well on their trip to have Christmas with her family. "Take good care of yourself, Emily. Remember me to your mother. . . . Enjoy yourself, Edwy!"

Returning to the kitchen, she heard Mr. Criddle mutter, "Thirty dollars wasted going to that God-forsaken country – at least it wasn't all my money."

For Christmas that year, St. Albans got a badly-needed kitchen floor and tough beef—old Bruce. Mr. Criddle grumbled, "No Dido – can't come. No Minnie – at Winnipeg. No Boy – at that beastly Dauphin." Elise felt differently. *It is always wonderful to have them but I have Harry and Cecil. Edwy and Emily deserve a holiday and my girls have to look to their own interests.*

A visitor came by Christmas Eve with upsetting news. "We hear *The New England* was sighted in distress off Ireland." Elise felt her stomach tighten. *Tell me, God, it's not true. What would we do without Mr. Tulk?*

❧

Chapter Twenty-five

A Princess and the Generals

Mr. Criddle attended several 'bachelor' parties and decided to host one. Mrs. Criddle kept to their room while Elise and her young helpers prepared the night's fare for the guests and set everything out in readiness. Then the three girls, Beatrice, Maida, and Julia, schooled Harry and Cecil for their role as servers. Their laughter followed Elise as she headed up the stairs. *I'm fortunate, indeed. It's a rare treat to be let off on a party night.* The young people's fun ended when the first guests were heard approaching. The girls, fortified with a well-filled lamp, disappeared upstairs to enjoy a night of reading beyond their usual curfew.

Elise cleaned up after the party and Monday morning prepared for wash day.

 *I used to be able to do this but couldn't manage now without Cecil's help. He already has the snow melted and helps me set up and fill the tubs. Minnie's scrub* 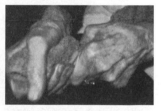 *board certainly makes the job easier.*

On good days she had the clothes wrung out by noon for the last time and pegged on the lines in the frosty outdoor air. Late in the day, she carried them in and enjoyed the fresh clean smell as she lifted each garment. It softened enough to be draped over the drying rack, and she raised it to the ceiling above the stove. Next morning the girls took over; sprinkled, rolled, and packed everything into the basket and were eager to do the ironing in winter. It was warm beside the stove, and irons reheated quickly and were always hot enough when the one they were using got too cool and they needed to exchange it.

Elise missed having Edwy stop by, but their holiday passed quickly and Harry set off in the predawn on December 28 to meet the train in Brandon. The children spotted the team at sundown. By the time the couple pulled up at the door there was a chorus of greetings. "We missed you!" "How was your holiday?" "What did you have for Christmas dinner?"

"My gracious," Emily exclaimed, "We missed you too! But wait. We'll tell you all you want to know as soon as we unload and make sure our fire is going."

Elise had biscuits ready, and moved the kettle to the hottest spot on the stove top. She thought happily, *I can tell by their faces they had a good time. . . . Emily looks well.*

The couple faced a bitter wind from the northwest as they walked up from The Palace. Handing over their coats, Edwy said, "Good thing we got here today. That wind is cold! Looks like the end of our mild weather."

As soon as they were settled, Edwy began, "I'll start by saying we had a jolly good time of it all through. Reggie and company were waiting for us at the Makinak station. We had a beautiful ten-mile drive in the moonlight. Everyone was very kind and made much of us. Plenty of good things to eat, including a fine Christmas pudding. The weather was mild and we had any amount of good skating. I missed it badly by not taking my skates. Reggie lent me his, but they were poor after mine. Besides, he couldn't skate with us."

"I enjoyed myself," Emily added. Mother was just the same, busy with everything. She likes her new house, so much more space. My baby sister, May, is growing tall, almost up to Mother." And so it went on. The young couple enjoyed their holiday again by sharing it with eager listeners from beginning to end.

As Edwy predicted, the next day was a holy terror and the extremely bitter weather held on. In spite of all Elise's efforts, St. Albans was unpleasantly cold and drafty. Mrs. Criddle sent word, "I'm feeling poorly – lying in today – buzzing in my ears and pain in head – a little feverish too . . . I'd like some toast and tea."

Meanwhile Norman dug out his grandmother's old paints and tried his hand at copying a portrait.[1] He struggled awhile before confiding to Elise, "Painting a person is difficult."

"Don't give up. I too had trouble. I like the way you did the hair. It takes practice to get the highlights and shading."

---

1 Mary Ann Rebecca Alabaster Criddle began painting in the 1830s and struggled to gain recognition, but it was a man's world, and she settled for painting children's portraits for rich patrons. Her paintings supported herself, Percy, and his family, especially after Henry and Chaloner Alabaster's support ended. She died December 29, 1880.

Harry and Edwy Vane, Charlie Bellhouse, Fred Calverly, Stuart Criddle,
Billy Martin, Evelyn Criddle, Edward Bellhouse, Cecil Vane

The cold couldn't keep the young man from playing hockey on the river. One day walking home, Edwy picked up the mail. There was a letter from Minnie postmarked Minneapolis, USA. He hurried home and read it to Emily. Then, knowing how his mother was fretting, walked up to the house. "Got a letter from Minnie. Guess where she is?"

"Is she not in Winnipeg?"

"No. But you'll never guess. Minneapolis, that's where."

His mother was alarmed, "How can she be? If I remember rightly we came through Minneapolis on our way here? It's a long way south. Gracious! My Minnie, so far!"

"Don't fret, Mama. She's pleased with her situation. I know you'll worry about your little girl in the big city, but she's enjoying herself." He passed her the letter, "Here, you can read it as many times as you want."

Everyone had an opinion about Minnie. When the dust settled; Edwy wrote a newsy reply:

Aweme, Feb 2ⁿᵈ, 1899

My dear Minnie,

I was very glad to hear from you. Now that you are so far away, one is more anxious. Poor Mama, she frets all the time about you. Write her a nice long letter and cheer her up will you, there's a good girl.

It must be a big place after Brandon. I think you had much better not go out after dark by yourself. You were lucky to pick up with such a good friend right on the start. It is a pity the wages are not bigger isn't it, but so long as you are contented, what's money.

I have got some seeds for you which I enclose if I don't forget to put them in. They are all ready in little packets. Harry gave them to me for you.

***Friday morning.** Another beastly day, 26 below zero with a delightful Nor'Wester.*

. . . The boys do nothing but play billiards these days. They often talk of you and you can expect a letter now and again from them if you are still determined to stay at Minneapolis.

Lonsbury gave us [Emily and Edwy] a nice pig a while ago so we shall have some pork in the spring. I divided the fowl house and put the pig in one half with the hens in the other. The hens were a little too cold before the pig was in there, now it is quite comfortable. We have averaged two or three eggs a day all through the winter and have sold several dozen at a good price.

Jack Mair's eldest girl, Emma, is staying here. Emily is boarding her and giving her a few lessons for 2 dollars a week. She is very good and gives no trouble. She helps Emily with some of the work.

Everybody is well except Julia. She has got a kind of low fever and doesn't look at all well. Hoping this will find you well and in good spirits.

Love from all. Your loving brother, Edwy

(You never mentioned Mama or Emily in your letter)

As Mr. Criddle made his morning rounds each cold morning to check the temperatures, Elise thought, *he's still grumbling . . . 17 degrees of frost in his room. What, I wonder, is our temperature upstairs without a stove? Being cold is miserable enough, but I'm worried about another problem—the bottom of the flour barrel will soon be showing.*

The extreme cold hung on until Valentine's Day. Mr. Criddle summoned his Boy, "We've a famine in the land – no backy – no matches – preciously little flour – here's a list of stores we need.[2] Take Stuart to sign for Tulk's box – sent new rubbers for a proper billiard table."[3]

Three weeks later they were playing on the improved model.

Emma Mair came up from The Palace to visit with the Criddle youngsters and stopped at the stove. "Mrs. Vane, you're just like my mother, always busy. She's helping Emily sew for her baby: little shirts, binders,[4] nightgowns, and lots of diapers. I folded them last night, twenty-four little ones and four big ones for night. I'm knitting soakers."[5] Another day she said, "They made little blankets. . . . Everything is ready. Lizzie's coming to take us home tomorrow."

Museum, Glenboro Manitoba

Emily expected another week or two, but it was not to be. She walked out to the stable where Edwy was fixing a manger. "The way I'm feeling . . . you'll be needing your team."

---

2 February 14, 1899. "Stuart's 1st journey there!"
3 March 4, 1899. "Length 6.4 ¼.
4 A four inch wide strip of cloth wrapped snugly around the new infant's body to prevent the tummy-button from protruding.
5 Knitted woolen panties worn over the diapers for added warmth and absorption.

"Are you sure?"

"I'm quite sure. Will you ask your mother to come down?"

Edwy went directly up to the house. Elise stowed her knitting in her bag, gathered a few garments, and returned with him to the Palace. She chatted with Emily and then said to him, "Your waiting will soon be over. You can fetch Mrs. Bellhouse?[6] Tell her not to rush. It's not urgent."

Then Elise turned to Emily, "Mrs. Bellhouse has plenty of time to get here. Our first usually takes time. Are you feeling nervous? . . . You'll be fine. Take some deep breaths whenever you feel uncomfortable. . . . There now. . . ."

Elise put another stick in the stove and the kettle began to simmer comfortingly.

A short time later Elise welcomed their neighbour and hung her coat on a peg. Mrs. Bellhouse sat down beside Emily and as they talked Elise thought, *it's so good to have a friendly woman like Mrs. Bellhouse. Emily is more at ease already.* The women arranged the things they would need; more to help Emily feel everything was in order than for immediate use. That done Mrs. Bellhouse asked, "Would you like a sip of tea, Emily? I think Mrs. Vane and I will enjoy a cup. This is not something we can hurry. Your little one will decide the right time. In the meantime, we can have a good visit. It's not something we get to do very often."

Feeling so much more relaxed, Emily lay back on the bed semi-dozing as the women talked and finally drifting off to sleep. Mrs. Bellhouse sent Elise upstairs to catch some rest, "You'll be on duty once our little one arrives. I'll sleep when I get home."

In the early morning Mrs. Bellhouse called up to Elise. "No hurry, Mrs. Vane, but things are progressing . . . we need a good fire and some warm water. I didn't want to disturb Emily, but it's getting rather cool in here."

Emily was a healthy young woman, and in Mrs. Bellhouse's capable hands everything went well. For this grandchild, Elise was on the frontline and accepted the wee girl from Mrs. Bellhouse. Examining the newborn's face and perfect little fingers and toes, she exclaimed, "You're beautiful . . . a precious miracle." When the two women had tended to both mother and infant, they placed the tiny bundle in bed beside Emily. Edwy had said the night before, "If it's late I'll make use of your bed, Mama. Just give me one of your good calls."

He was already in the stable when he heard his mother's high-pitched, "Yoo hoo," and he appeared at the door with a pitchfork. She called across the yard, "Good news! You can come home." He hurried over and pulling off his coat took in the scene. Smiling from their bed was his beloved Emily, a bundle by her side.

6 Community midwife - her name given on this and other births.

"We have a daughter. How do you like that?" She held the blanket away from the little face and Edwy took a first peek. Elise would never forget the look on his face—wonder, pride, and thankfulness. . .

Mrs. Bellhouse broke the spell, "What about something to eat? I'm sure Emily's ready for a good cup of tea. How's your appetite, Edwy?"

"To tell the truth, I have a better appetite than usual. They miss you up there, Mama. No sign of breakfast."

Elise and Mrs. Bellhouse set about preparing it, and while they worked, Emily brought up the next hurdle. "What shall we call her? We've had fun thinking about names. Now we need to be serious."

Edwy nodded, "It's a girl . . . you choose her name."

Still riding an emotional high, Emily plunged right in, "I've always loved my name, Emily Louise. Our firstborn should have two names, don't you think? One from each side of the family? . . . My mother and yours? . . . Emily Elise? Sounds pretty together, don't you think? But what would **they** say? I can almost hear Mr. C." She paused and then rhymed off her sisters, "Gertrude Margaret, Agnes Violet, Edith Grace, May Victoria. But, if I choose one, her other aunties will feel left out."

Mrs. Bellhouse interjected, "The child doesn't have to be named this minute. You've done well, Emily. Don't be fretting. Be thankful for a healthy baby."

They chatted as they ate and then Mrs. Bellhouse said to Edwy, "I'll check Emily again. You can get the team. I'll be ready to go. I'm sure everything is fine, but if you need me, I'm not far." On the way out she assured Emily, "You couldn't be in better hands than with Edwy's mother."

Emily was still excited and anxious to give her little one a name. "I've been thinking, Huddock,[7] the royal family might be the place to start . . . should please everyone. Not Victoria, there are too many Victorias. . . . The Princess of Wales, Alexandra? I think not, too imposing for my little one."

"What about her youngest sister, Princess Thyra?[8] She's known for her kindness."

"I've always liked her. Thyra means child of God in Danish. Wasn't there a Saxon princess with that name?"

Emily held her daughter up to the light. "Should we call you Thyra? She looked into the tiny face and repeated softly, "Thyra . . . Thyra. . . . I think she likes it. It's the perfect name for our little princess, firstborn in our Palace. We'll see what her daddy says when he comes home tonight."

---

7 Emily refers to Edwy's mother as 'Huddock' in the letter following.
8 Princess Thyra married the 3rd Duke of Cumberland (one of many titles) and was well known to the British public.

Reactions at the big house were anything but favourable. "Can't you find a normal English name?" But Emily held firm, and Edwy made his way to Mr. Sutcliffe's to register his newborn daughter.[9]

Elise stayed on at the Palace through Emily's first days of motherhood. Her gentle confidence and lullabies set a peaceful atmosphere for the new mother and infant. The pleasure went both ways, for Elise found their home very snug compared to St. Albans. "Thyra should have come during the cold spell. My chilblains were so troublesome."

Emily tried to get her letters written before she was left on her own.

Aweme, Manitoba April 9ᵗʰ, 1899

My dear Minnie,

Doubtless you have heard that I am the mamma of a little girl. She was born on March 27th rather unexpectedly but nevertheless I am glad it is all over.
Ma Mair only went away the Friday before and I thought to have at least two weeks to myself.
Mrs. Criddle got your letter on Saturday and everyone was pleased to hear from you, that you were well and getting on.
Huddock is going to sleep at the house tonight for the first time since 27th. She is now waiting to go up and sends her love. She will write to you soon.
We had some difficulty in settling on a name to please ourselves and everyone else and finally she was registered Thyra Vane and I think, pretty. What do you think of it?
I must now bring this to a full stop.
With love, your affectionate sister,
Emily L. Vane

⁓⁓⁓

Minnie's sudden move to Minneapolis was a setback for Mrs. Criddle who benefited from Minnie's generosity and was hoping for some new fabric and more novels. She tried to be diplomatic in her response.

St. Albans, Aweme Manitoba April 21st, 1899

My dear Minnie,

I had your letter just two weeks ago tomorrow, but as Harry was writing I thought I would wait awhile. You certainly seem to be getting on nicely and to be enjoying yourself as much as can be expected. As you say, the money flies very easily when you have so many opportunities for spending it, but it is the way of the world.
The prints must go — you could not send any from the States, duty and carriage would make them dearer than if bought here, so if we can't afford to buy any for ourselves (which I don't expect to do), why, we must just manage with what we have got and make the best of it.

---

9 Thyra Vane, born South Cypress, March 27, 1899. Manitoba Vital Statistics, Registration 1899-06-005209.

Emily is going on finely, the little daughter is a very good baby at present, rather on the small side and fairly good looking. We're all glad the affair is over and everything all right. Of course, the new Papa is able to tease the new Mama a little more than usual so that is a great advantage.

Alma has a troublesome cough for three or four weeks, otherwise most of us have been very well through the winter, owing very likely to the quantity of cabbage, etc, we had, and there are still some left.

We have one hen sitting and expect more very soon, the Gobbler is as big an idiot as turkeys generally are and is pretty big. The Hen is rather small and has not begun to lay yet. If you have any books, we should be glad to have them, but don't bother.

Love from everybody, Yours affectionately, Alice Criddle

Elise looked about. *I'm behind in my work. . . . But I must take a few minutes to tell her how relieved I am to hear from her:*

Emily and baby Thyra

Aweme, Manitoba, 21st April 1899

My dear Minnie!

I am so pleased to hear that you are so happy and comfortable. Now I don't worry any more and think it was for the best, as you are in much better health and spirits. I had a letter from my brother. He was pleased with your photograph I sent him some time ago and thinks you are like his youngest daughter, Julia.

Emily is getting on, she has a pretty little baby, she finds quite a difference in the work. We help her along as much as we can. I must say goodbye now.

With love from everybody, I remain,
Your affectionate Mama

When spring arrived, the young folks worked full out—seeding, gardening, fencing. One afternoon the door opened and there was Harry, face covered in blood. Evelyn helped get him to a chair. "The beastly fence wire broke. An end got his eye."

Elise, initially shocked, determined the eye itself was not injured, set about cleaning and bandaging his wound. "You can thank God, Harry. It's not as bad as it looked when I saw you in the doorway. Time will put you right again."

Harry's next big push was planting trees around their buildings and the windbreak along the fields. He, with help from Edwy, Norman, and Evelyn, dug hundreds of little maples from the river flat and transplanted them to the open prairie.[10] "This is only the beginning," He told them. "They'll need lots of watering to survive."

---

10 Criddle, Norman. May 15, 1899. "260 maple trees along N side of One."

As Harry watered the transplants, he noticed tiny grasshoppers leaping away from his boots. He tried to raise the alarm, but his warnings weren't welcome; "Don't talk about a few measly insects, our real threat is drought."

The boys finished seeding by the 24th of May and were ready for an outing. Lizzie joined Emily and Baby Thyra for a picnic with the young folks at a little lake up north. Everyone enjoyed themselves in spite of the mosquitoes.

A few mornings later, Mr. Criddle explained that Mrs. Criddle was giddy and faint, possibly from 'the thundery weather.' But it wasn't the only rumbling at St. Albans. Mr. Criddle's fight against 'Ferguson's Folly' had failed. South Cypress Municipal Council had the hated 'scow,' lengthened, made more watertight, and put into operation. "Terrible waste of municipal money – a bridge would have cost them far less and been fifty times better."

He put his own little army to work taking down and replacing his outbuildings. On completion, he crowed with pleasure, "Granary measures inside 24 x 20; cow house 24 x 17.6; fowl house 24 x 15; sitting house 10 x 5.9; and pigeon house 5.9 x 5.9 – all well put up and, I may say, the handsomest range of log buildings I have seen anywhere."

❧◈❧

Father Kimberley had come the previous December to consult Mr. Criddle on a new church in Treesbank. Mr. Marmont, his driver that day, was a keen insect collector and returned in June with a Brandon enthusiast. They poured over the butterfly collection and Norman's drawings. On Sunday they went to the Tamarack for more specimens.[11] Elise was philosophical about the extra work. *It's so encouraging for Norman; I don't mind preparing picnic baskets.*

The two men had barely driven away when Edwy returned from Brandon. Elise was startled when Minnie threw open the door, "I'm back, Mama! I've lots to tell you about Minneapolis. But first, come and see what I brought!"

Edwy lifted a shiny bicycle from the wagon and stood it on the ground. The children chorused, "Is it for us?"

Spectacular tumbles and gales of laughter were the order of the day until Mr. Criddle was pressed to take his turn. He'd told them many a tale of his bike-racing days in England. They expected great things. But as the machine raced him downhill to an unpleasant finish, no one laughed. He struggled back up the rise and handed it over, "I have not the nerve I once had."

When the excitement died down, Minnie went indoors to talk to her mother.

"You used to tell me, Mama, about the opera and wished we could see one. That's just what I did. It was fantastic! "How do you say in German?"

"Woonderbar."

---

11 June 19, 1899.

"I tell you, Mama. Dame Nellie Melba was Woonderbar! She sang. . . . I can't describe it. I felt shivers up my back." Elise was captivated by Minnie's adventures in the city.

⸺∽◦❦◦∼⸺

As the familiar pattern of drought, sandstorms, and hail played out, Mr. Criddle's anxiety kept everyone on edge. Minnie brought his emotions to a boil by asking for a ride to Brandon Fair, "It's time you boys had a holiday! You don't know what you're missing."

Minnie had seldom heard 'no' from Mr. Criddle, but on the fair he wouldn't budge. Fortunately for her, the Knights came out Sunday and she had her ride. She chided the boys, "You don't need me for an excuse to get to the fair. Take yourselves later in the week."

They promised, but their request hit a brick wall in spite of compelling reasons: the fair was the place to see new machinery; the latest grain varieties; prize winning vegetables.

"Rubbish! Bally waste of time!"

By the end of the ugly 'set-to,' the boys had accepted Mr. Criddle's rule once again.

The vanquished were still licking their wounds when Edwy came up from The Palace to consult his mother. "I guess you know Emily has a bad abscess. It's worse today and she can't manage the baby. She feels comfortable with you. Can you come?" Mrs. Criddle could hardly object, so Elise gathered up a few things and went with him, thinking as she walked, *is she not eating well? Is it too much tension?* Painful memories swept over her as soon as she saw the poor girl and without hesitation said firmly, "This is serious, especially for a nursing mother. Take Emily to Dr. Husband. I'll look after the baby."

Edwy, Cecil, Norman, Evelyn, Talbot [Tolly], Harry

His mother's alarm gave Edwy courage to approach Mr. Criddle. "If it's all right, I'd like to take Emily to Dr. Husband. I'll tend to your errand tomorrow."

The doctor treated Emily and she was soon on the mend. Elise was back at her post the following Sunday and serving dinner when Mr. Köhler offered to take a photo of all the boys. Elise's heart skipped a beat. *What if they want a photo of **everyone**?*

As the drought continued, things went from bad to worse. The drama of life and death played out on the stage of the 'estate'. More calves died and the grasshoppers multiplied. Harry worried and read everything he could on the subject of grasshopper control, but his hands were tied. Mr. Criddle did not want him wasting time on insects.

"What damage they are going to cause has already been done. What we need is a good rain."

Summer passed and the binders were set in motion. Edwy spent Harry's birthday cutting oats; "They're good," he reported, "what there are. But the beastly grasshoppers have thinned them out."

Then, to make a bad situation worse, the rains came. With harvest on hold, everyone with the exception of Mr. and Mrs. Criddle, Elise, Norman, and Evelyn spent a day chasing butterflies in the Tamarack.

In the weeks following, Elise fed two important guests: Mr. Fowler, politicking for a bridge further north between Oakland and Cornwallis municipalities; and Father Kimberley with an update on his church at Treesbank. "Our building is almost completed," he said with pride. The Bishop of Rupertsland will be in attendance for the dedication on October 15, only six weeks away. When I came last Christmas, I asked if you would play the organ and be our choral director for the dedication service. My hope is that you will begin training the choir."

His words triggered Elise's memories of worship long ago at their church in Heidelberg: *the organ, the choir and the hymns we sang so lustily. Wouldn't I enjoy some familiar hymns! I'm sure the people are thankful for their new church. She hummed the line, "Now thank we all our God with heart and hands and voices. . . ." Crüger wrote so many beautiful tunes. That used to be my favourite verse but now that I'm not well I find the next one means more. She sang it quietly to herself:*

Der ewig reiche Gott	*Oh may this bounteous God,*
Woll uns bei unserm Leben	*Through all our lives be near us*
Ein immer fröhlich Herz	*With ever joyful hearts*
Und edlen Frieden geben	*And blessed peace to cheer us,*
Und uns in seiner Gnad	*And keep us strong in grace,*
Erhalten fort und fort,	*And guide us when perplexed,*
Und uns aus aller Not	*And free us from all ills*
Erlösen hier und dort.[12]	*In this world and the next.*

---

12 Poetry by Martin Rinckart, 1636. Tune by Johann Crüger, 1647.

Will Percy allow my boys to sing in his choir? He said, "I intend to write a brand new Full Choral Service," and went straightaway to the organ. There he 'slaved' while five boys with two teams went stacking wheat.[13] The music had to be set aside the day Edwy drove him to Brandon to meet Mr. Tulk. And a memorable day it was, for he also met the breaking news of war in the Transvaal.

And so instead of the music Elise longed to hear, the gentlemen talked of nothing but war.

"Appears the Boers dare to oppose us."

"I rather fancy we may get some temporizing and fiddling and compromising and arbitration – and so stop on the brink – instead of taking the damned country and hanging Mr. Kruger and his gang – as we ought to do."

On September 8th Mr. and Mrs. Criddle celebrated their silver wedding anniversary with a flag-raising ceremony and dinner. Rev. Kimberley was their guest, having come to go over the choir music yet again.

❧

On the last Sunday of September, Harry drove Mr. Criddle and the Bellhouses to Sutcliffe's for a further lift to Treesbank and a first meeting with the choir. Arriving home at dusk, Mr. Criddle was exuberant, "About 20 young people there ready to put themselves under my direction – several of 'em with good voices – and – I think everything will rapidly get into shape despite some monotonous croaking. Practice again next Sunday." After tea he went to his room and his diary:

> I shall have a lot of traveling about and trouble but I don't mind that if they will condescend to learn to sing respectably and that I think they will do. The Organ is a regular beast – but perhaps we may improve on it later on.

Between the war and travelling to Treesbank, Mr. Criddle was well occupied. The morning of the dedication service Edwy came up to the house, "We had a deuce of a lot of snow during the night. Be hard walking. Can I give you a lift to Treesbank?"

"No, I'll walk – but as I said last Sunday, owing to muddling and altering of my music, only half my people came out to praise. Between that and the wretched organ I am likely to be pretty well disgusted." And with that, he put on his coat and set off.

Edwy lingered with his mother, "When I saw all that snow this morning, I thought he'd like a ride . . . guess he doesn't want any of us around."

"It's too bad, you're all good singers. You would have enjoyed it."

"Anyway, I'll have a day at home."

---

13 September 12, 1899. "Boys just home from Mairs where they have been helping stack (five of 'em and 2 teams) – 5 days. They also helped A. Ellis – 5 boys and two teams 1 day and 3 boys and 1 team one day. . . stooking done 2 ½ days and they are yet to help a day or so . . . so they will have made quite a lot of money. . ." Norman's diary, "the boys earned $120.00."

Elise couldn't get the church service out of her mind. *Wouldn't I love to be singing! . . . I wonder if I know anyone in the choir. His music wasn't familiar and sounded difficult. . . . They had so few rehearsals. Will Percy be flying high or in a funk when he comes home?*

Well after dark, the man stormed in. Mrs. Criddle had waited tea, and as Elise served them, she overheard, "A sea of mud – ferried myself across the river – about eighty people at church. Choir broke down over one of my chants – wretched instrument – I couldn't keep them together. Not impressed with His Grace, the Archbishop – tall, beaky Scotchman. I fancy not very long for this world."[14]

His stint as choir director ended on Mr. Tulk's birthday, however the two men were just getting going as the armchair generals to the British forces in South Africa. Since all the boys and teams were busy threshing, the gentlemen walked to Treesbank for the newspaper. "Delighted to see the Boers got a big hiking at Glencoe last Friday – they showed the white feather too."

The faraway brass was not in the least affected by their advice, yet every success or failure affected the home front. Too preoccupied to concern himself with slaughtering an animal to feed the threshers, he arranged meals at Lonsbury's and told Elise, "Will save you a lot of time and effort. I'm sending Bobby to Mr. Lonsbury."

It will be a relief. But wouldn't it be Mrs. Lonsbury needing Beatrice's help?

When the crop of 1,786 bushels fell far short of his projections, Mr. Criddle rationalized, "The cattle got into the stacks up north and the fowls ate a lot of stuff round home."

Harry shrugged and said sadly to his mother, "I still haven't got through to him about the hoppers."

Elise wasn't asked to bake a birthday cake. Mr. Tulk was in no mood to celebrate after reading about the disaster at Ladysmith:

2000 BRITISH TROOPS CAPTURED.

Furthermore, the Boers on the heights put the entire force in danger. The next news buoyed them up somewhat, for the situation was not as desperate as they first thought. The cause of the defeat, being only that the general had allowed his wing to go without cavalry, and the mules—loaded with ammunition had stampeded.

At that crucial point in the war Mr. Tulk took his leave. Always the gentleman, he paused as he passed the kitchen, "This has been a topsy-turvy kind of year. I've been so preoccupied with the war I have paid little heed to your efforts, Mrs. Vane, to keep me comfortable. I do, indeed, appreciate most sincerely all you have done for me."

---

14 Archbishop Robert Machray, Archbishop of Rupertsland from 1893, and later, first Primate of Canada.

Mr. Criddle went to see him off on the noon train and then joined his friends at 'The Club'. Once again Edwy learned on the way home that he wanted to return a week later for a grand three-day bout of whist. The others took advantage of his absence and moved the stove in the sitting room to the north wall. They explained to Elise, "We're tired of putting it out because of the smoke whenever we have a north wind. Now we hope for two things; he doesn't make us move it back, and the room is more comfortable this winter."

When he got back, he railed; but not about the stove. "We need more troops in Africa. Our government, with true English wisdom, has selected all the dullest old tubs it could find as transports."

Meanwhile the lymph Mr. Tulk had brought from London for the purpose of vaccinating the youngsters waited until the end of November. Starting with the 'Boy's baby', Mr. Criddle moved on to Maida, Bobby, Tolly, Alma, Julia, and Solomon. He checked seven days later and reported a good 'take' with Alma, but only fairly well with Talbot, Maida, and Solomon, and not at all with Bobby, Julia, and Thyra. He told them, "I'll try again later in December."[15]

Large brining crock

While Mr. Criddle directed the war, Elise matched her days to the family's needs. A successful hunt meant a great deal of work for her as each trophy had to be dressed, cleaned, cut up, and what wasn't cooked in a day or two, salted or frozen. That year Cecil shot two deer—one a fine four-year old stag; Stuart and Norman got one each.

With few farmers remaining, Norman chaired the School Board's annual meeting and Harry was re-elected a trustee. Next day Mr. Criddle took his boys to Treesbank to vote against the teetotalling Methodists' candidate and boasted that evening, "We had a solid phalanx[16] of seven to plump for Henderson and the conservatives."

Unfortunately, his troops weren't sufficient in numbers to swing the vote.

◦◦◦◦◦◦

Mrs. Denny, an older daughter, and young son, came out from England. As soon as she paid Rowland's debts, St. Albans' door opened and the families once again hunted, skated, and partied together.[17] They also provided Mr. Criddle with an audience for his opinions on the war. After a particularly unfortunate loss of

---

15   December 17, 1899. "Vaccinated 4 Lonsburys – 5 big boys, Julia, Bobby and Thyra." January 1, 1900. "The late vaccination was a complete success with the 2 elder Lonsburys and Harry – Partly so with Norman, Evelyn and Stuart, and a complete failure with Bobby, Julia, Thyra, the boys and 2 younger Lonsburys."
16   Military term derived from the Greek word *phalanx*, meaning the finger—formation of an army's troops.
17   December 13, 1899. "2 Miss and 2 Mr. Dennys here yest'dy afternoon – to skate – and they stayed and danced till 1.15 this morning – evidently enjoying 'emselves."

British troops, he told them, "Guess someone at the War Office made a stupendous blunder – Probably overdrunk himself at afternoon tea. I'd shoot the beggar and let him get his tea for the future in Hades."

Emily's brother Harry spent a few days at The Palace before going home for Christmas. He'd seen his brother, Arthur, in Winnipeg, so Edwy had fresh news for his mother, "Arthur got home from the Yukon, and upset his parents by saying he had volunteered for Africa. He's in Toronto now, training and will sail in the New Year."

Elise didn't like the idea of him going either. "Mr. C says we need more troops to the Cape. But he doesn't have a good word for the thousand young Canadians already on their way. He certainly thinks poorly of Arthur."

Edwy shrugged, "I can't say we're pleased, but I don't blame him for not wanting to farm."

⁘⸎⸛⸎⁘

As news of the Boers' victories reached St. Albans, Elise did everything she could to help the little ones stay cheerful. When Mrs. Criddle learned her cousin Louisa was sending a big box, the atmosphere improved. *She is not one to show excitement, but I can tell she is really looking forward to new clothes and there's sure to be something for the youngsters.* Then Norman received an encouraging letter about the drawings he sent to Professor Fletcher in Ottawa. *It is easier now to be positive and those nineteen bottles of chokecherry wine mellowing in the cellar will add to the festivities. Grossvater Haarbarth would be proud of my efforts to help the lads.*[18]

Christmas arrived on schedule, in spite of the bad news from the front. Elise's daughters hadn't come, but with 10 Criddles, Harry, Cecil, and Edwy's family, Elise didn't have a chance to sit down. In place of the usual beef, there were turkeys. Mr. Criddle carved them ceremoniously at the table. The meal was topped off with nuts, figs, apples, two bottles of homemade 'champagne' and the '**best pudding**' on record for Manitoba.

Next day Edwy and Emily hosted a post-Christmas skating party. Cecil told his mother, "Too bad you couldn't go, Mama. After tea, Emily brought out a very funny old play called, *Box and Cox.* Did you ever see it in London?"

She shook her head; Cecil carried on. "It's about a greedy landlady. To make double the money she rented her one room flat to two men—James Box and John Cox. Box, the hatter, worked all day. Cox, a printer, worked nights. Mrs. Bouncer thought Box could use the fire, dishes, and bed overnight and then Cox would come home in the morning after Box had gone to work. But one morning, Box's boss gave him a day off and he went home to enjoy his holiday. When he opened

---

18   Friedrich Wilhelm Haarbarth, Kupfermeister in Heidelberg. "Cellar man (wine maker) a very common profession in Baden wine country." Archivist, Dr. Eker, Freiburg im Breisgau.

the door to **his** room, he found the other man cooking breakfast on **his** fire. The scrapes they got into! . . . Jolly good fun. Everything came out alright in the end. Emily will let you read it.

"Anyway, Mama, we had a jolly time. I'm not much for dancing. I played my whistle along with Harry on the violin. We kept on 'til morning. I hope we didn't wake you when we came in."

And so the year of 1899 drew to a close while the bloody Boer War raged on.

Chapter Twenty-six

A Prince For Elise

The 20th Century dawned clear and cold. Elise was up early to get the fire going, the goose stuffed and into the oven before breakfast. By noon, everything was ready, right down to the hard sauce for the pudding. The family was happily feasting when there was a knock on the door. Mr. Criddle motioned for them to keep still while he went to check. There stood Jack Mair, his wife, and three children. "We usually go across the river for the day, but we thought we'd start the new century with you! Your boys often talked about playing billiards and the big slide."

Mr. Criddle thought quickly. *How preposterous to come on New Year's Day. But Mair's money has put food on the table and might well do so again.* He let them in and they all had a taste of the New Year's pudding.[1]

The Boer War continued to go badly for the British. Being anxious, Mr. Criddle sent his Boy to secure newspapers—Treesbank was the closest, but he sometimes went as far afield as Douglas or Brandon to obtain them. Mr. Criddle kept the family abreast of developments. More and more, the Colonials,[2] first expected to be only a hindrance, were deployed against the unorthodox manoeuvres of the Boers. Elise kept her ears open for anything Canadian to pass on to Edwy and Emily as Arthur's letters took a very long time to come from the front.

Mrs. Criddle and her girls were waiting anxiously for the coming of 'the box'. As soon as the notice arrived from the customs office, Edwy, given money to pay the duty, set out for Brandon. Just before dark, a lookout spotted him in the distance and shouted, "He's coming!"

By the time Edwy pulled up at the door, the family had gathered. Eyeing the huge box, Mr. Criddle wanted to know, "How much was the duty?"

"None this time," he said as he handed over the money and newspaper.

The box was large and so heavy it took all Stuart and Evelyn's strength to lift it from the wagon and manoeuvre it through the door. Once inside, their mother pointed toward the Criddles' room. The expectant parade passed by Elise, the boys

---

1 Criddle, Norman. Jan 1, 1900. "The new century begins with a disaster—we had just prepared for a good dinner (goose, plum pudding, etc.) when J. Mair and his wife (the commonest woman anywhere about here) came with a lot of children."
2 Troops went from Canada, New Zealand and Australia.

weighed down by the box, followed by Mrs. Criddle, young Talbot, and all four daughters fairly dancing with excitement.

Fine wool.

Elise's feelings were more of resignation. *If there is any new underwear, my boys need combinations.*[3] She heard an anxious, "Take care, Stuart; I want this box. It will make a fine cupboard!" and imagined him prying up the cover under his mother's watchful eyes. Hearing nothing more, Elise assumed they were unpacking, checking, and assigning the garments.

Edwy came in with a smaller box and not seeing any of the Criddles, he told his mother, "Minnie sent a gift for their 25th anniversary. She says it's better three months late than never. Sure is heavy. I'll just leave it on the table. Good night, Mama."

When Mrs. Criddle came out to open Minnie's package, Elise, curious to know what her daughter sent, joined the circle. *Must be breakable, packed in sawdust.* Mrs. Criddle rummaged down and pulled out a beautiful teacup. There was a collective, "Oooh!" Everyone watched, fascinated as one piece after another appeared. Mrs. Criddle was absolutely delighted, "A real tea set, after all these years of having to drink tea from common cups." With a little more digging, she found another small box with a miniature set of china. Little Alma squealed, "Look Mama Dutcheen, we can have a tea party."

Elise felt proud. *How very thoughtful of Minnie. She and Isabel have happy memories of the little set Mr. Tulk gave them in London. Her new position must be going well if she's able to send such extravagant gifts.*

Two weeks later Mrs. Criddle wrote:

St. Albans, Aweme Manitoba Jan 19, 1900

My dear Minnie,

I ought to have written sooner but have been so dreadfully busy that letters seemed quite out of the question. Many thanks from Papa and me for the tea things, they are a great addition to the stock and look very much nicer than the heavy white cups and saucers. The children are delighted with their set, and had a grand party as soon as possible. They are quite a little size and the tea (pours) out nicely, so they all say that Minnie is very good and send her lots of thanks and love. You will be pleased to hear that I got Harry to fix up my <u>Box</u> as a cupboard and as it is larger than any of the other ones we have we have much more room than we had before, though we manage to fill the shelves very fairly full.

Edwy told you about the box, I suppose, as you speak of it in your letter to him. I wish you had been here to enjoy the opening – there are so many beautiful things that I don't know where to begin. The grandest dress is of openwork brown

---

3   Full length suits of underwear with a trap door in the back.

canvas over brown watered silk and trimmed with coloured bead . . .[4], it has a front of beautiful figured white satin (little coloured flowers all over it) and the collar and cuffs are lined with the same. My silver wedding dress and no mistake. Louisa Nicol says it is of no use sending out a few things at a time, as the freight costs so much, so she has sent plenty of things this time. 2 Serge dresses, a cape and jacket to match, a . . . fur-lined cloak, a good . . . proof, a black and yellow silk bodice and black skirt, a grey alpaca and a blue linen dress, four wool shawls, 13 pairs stockings, 12 pairs socks, 6 prs trousers, 3 coats; and waistcoats, a coat and knickers to fit Talbot, 3 over Jerseys for men and 5 under-vests, an overcoat, 2 bonnets, 1 hat, 10 combinations in cotton and 3 in wool, 4 petticoats, 1 woollen dressing gown and 2 cotton ones, a black cape, kid gloves, darning wool, mending cotton, brush and comb, odds and ends and some very pretty cards of which I send one to you, and 21 cloth bound books with our names written in . . . 3 for me and 2 for the rest each.[5]

I am glad you are getting some skating, it will do you good, only today we are having spring! I suppose we shall pay for it soon and be nearly perished with cold. The children have had a good deal of skating and a good deal of dancing and have enjoyed them both. I have two other letters to write today so must end.

Lots of love from everyone. How is the hair getting on?
Yours affectionately,
Alice Criddle

———❦———

On February 22 Edwy handed over the newspaper and chatted with his mother. Mr Criddle re-emerged from his room, "There's been a battle at Madder River between McDonald's Brigade of Colonials and Canadians, and Joubert's force trying to get to Grange. The result seems pretty foggy – but McDonald is reported dangerously wounded and the Canadians are said to have lost eighty men–killed and wounded."

Edwy's face fell, "Oh, oh. Our fellows have been doing some hard fighting. Their horses help to get around that rough country. I'm not sure if Arthur is fighting yet. I'd better tell Emily. I'm glad her sister Dolly is here."

Arthur Steer.

Most of January and through February, many of the family, but especially Harry, were severely ill. When Edwy succumbed, Mr. Criddle walked to Treesbank for his paper. "Bloody bad news," he told them, "even Tulk's letter is pessimistic."

As soon as the boys were well, Edwy challenged Rounthwaite to a hockey game. The locals excitedly gathered at the river for the big game but the

---

4 Missing words due to torn corners of the letter.
5 As there are nine other Criddles, the Vanes were not included.

opposition didn't show up. Mr. Criddle gloated; "Pretty good for a whole district to be afraid to play five of my boys, helped out by a couple of almost duffers."[6]

The young folks didn't feel too let down, for they had another social event coming up—Miss Thirza Denny's surprise party. Elise worried. *Denny's house is small, but does Harry have anything to do with having her party here? It's good Percy's preoccupied with doctoring and the war. I hope he doesn't notice anything untoward and put a stop to their fun.* All went well, however, and the party was in full swing when she climbed the stairs. *I enjoy seeing the young people having so much fun. Harry plays as well as the other fiddlers. He'll be fine. This will be my first time to be lulled to sleep by four fiddlers and two mouth organs.*

⤞⤝

Along with discouraging news from South Africa, Elise learned that the McManes were leaving for the Belmont area, and Mr. Tulk was going tiger hunting in India. According to Mr. Criddle, they were equally unwise decisions. He added, "If Tulk saw a tiger, the chances are higher for the tiger to get Tulk, than for Tulk to get the tiger. He's the last man in the world to go in for a game that requires sudden and decisive action. He was never ready for a deer." Elise smiled to herself, *I'm afraid we'd go hungry if we depended on Percy's trigger finger.*

By April the tide of the war had turned in favour of the British and Mr. Criddle was tiring of the business. Furthermore, he had crises of his own—two close calls with prairie fires. One swept down suddenly from the north. Only with everyone's frantic ploughing and beating, combined with a change in the wind, did they save their buildings. The second, despite their fighting like demons, was rapidly sweeping past their line when an area with no grass cover, due to an infestation of grubs, slowed the flames momentarily and the fellows managed to get the upper hand. Norman came in mopping his brow and told Elise, "Evelyn has gone north with the Bellhouses to fight it. We've saved our place. It's the closest we ever want a fire."[7]

Between the emergencies Mr. Criddle announced, "Got a school teacher at last – coming Saturday."

She arrived with her brother, a law student, and made a good impression on her new boss. "Miss Helen Cain is very pleasing," Elise overheard him tell his wife. "She's bright and smart – plays tennis and hockey – wants to learn cricket – is fond of music – especially Chopin and Wagner. She's a good bicyclist and not pious. I've arranged for her to board at The Palace."

When Mr. Criddle entertained her, Emily recalled her own good times before she and Edwy announced their engagement.

---

6 March 3, 1900. Calverley and Jackson played when they won over Stockton earlier.
7 Criddle, Norman. April 18, 1900.

Late one evening a distraught Harry came in to talk to his mother, "I'm disgusted. We didn't do enough last summer to get rid of the grasshoppers. Now they're hatching . . . hordes of the beastly things. I'm going to fight them. I don't care what Mr. C says."

He wrote to the Department of Agriculture asking for a supply of Paris green.[8] Before it arrived he talked to the neighbours.[9] "The grasshoppers are hatching in the millions, destroying our crops. If we start right away, burn the grass, we'll get rid of the eggs and young hoppers." They set about burning the road allowances and then he and Cecil ploughed under the edges of their fields where the young hoppers were thickest.

While the Vanes fought the grasshoppers, Mr. Criddle and sons sorted out a large batch of postage stamps. Stuart told Elise, "We got 155 different stamps this time, and that's not counting duplicates."

Mr. Criddle was celebrating the British capture of Willow Grange when he read the next headline: VICTORY PREMATURE. As the Boers retaliated with guerrilla-style attacks, the colonials on horseback were proving their worth. He stormed, "The Boers will never make loyal subjects of the British Empire. Wipe out the whole race and be done with it."

Edwy and Cecil, checking for grasshoppers as they travelled, drove to Brandon May 11 with a load of hay. Their mother overheard their report to Harry.

"The beastly things are everywhere! Looks bad."

Harry muttered, "I wanted to build a 'hopper dozer' last spring to destroy the eggs. I read about it way back in '98. They were used south of the border."

Edwy said, "We'd better try something, or we won't have a crop to harvest."

"I've tried! McKellar from the Department of Agriculture sent me the information last year."[10]

"I think Mr. C is beginning to see that grasshoppers are as big a problem as the drought. When you talk to him we'll back you up."

---

8 Paris green, an arsenic-based chemical identified by its colour, adopted because of its low price and high toxicity.
"Poisoned bait was first used against grasshoppers in Manitoba during the outbreak of 1900- and this is probably the first occasion in which bait was used on a large scale for the protection of grain crops. The mixture then used was very similar to the one mentioned above employed in California excepting the sugar was omitted and the bait was broadcast instead of being placed in heaps. The initial credit for this improved poison bait application belongs to Mr. Harry Vane who was then working in close cooperation with the writer on the farm of Percy Criddle six miles south [sic] of Treesbank." Collected works of Norman, Volume VI Manuscripts on Orthoptera, Department of Entomology, University of Manitoba.
9 Criddle, Norman. May 11, 1900. "Locusts are doing no end of mischief . . . everybody is in a funk . . . Harry is practically superintending the works connected with them here." And again, May 15, "Harry and Cecil went ploughing grasshoppers under about 7 p.m. and got home about 2 a.m. today. The results seem satisfactory."
10 H. McKellar, Chief Clerk, Manitoba Department of Agriculture.

Harry dug out his picture of the grasshopper dozer. He could make everything but the steel for the scoop and kerosene for the burner. With the diagram behind his back, he knocked on Mr. Criddle's door, "The fellows say the hoppers are eating our wheat on One. I've an idea to save it. It's been used in Dakota and other places." He held out the picture and added quickly, "Won't cost much. I'll build it. Two horses can pull it."

Edwy and Cecil nodded. With some haggling, Mr. Criddle mumbled, "Well, go ahead — if that's what you want."

The 'rig' was to slide along the ground and burn the eggs and newly-hatched hoppers in the grass.[11] Harry made a model and then constructed the rig—sheet iron, 2' x 10' with 8" sides, and a 12" back. The following week he improved it by adding bars for a grate to burn the grasshoppers below, as well as those that jumped into the fire.[12] It definitely cut down the numbers of eggs and the newly-hatched, but larger ones were already feasting on the crops. Harry received the Paris green and wanted to get started. But the recipe called for sawdust, salt, and sugar. He was short on sawdust and had no money to purchase salt or sugar.

Stumped, he talked the problem over with his mother.

"Well, Harry," she said, "when I don't have what I need, I try to substitute something I do have. You want something damp and fibrous? Do you have anything like that? Look around, maybe you'll come up with something."

He found his 'something' in the stable—the horses' fresh warm droppings. He scooped them up, added what he estimated to be the right amount of poison, mixed it with water, and spread it along the edges of the fields. Even without sugar, the grasshoppers swarmed to the bait like bees to syrup. Harry talked the neighbours into following his example. "Do what I did. Write the department and ask for Paris green." Harry wrote to Mr. McKellar describing his experiment and asked them to send more poison for the farmers willing to use it. Mr. McKellar replied, "I will come to the district to meet with the farmers. Keep records of your experiments and especially the proportions you use for the poison bait. If you determine that it's effective, we'll publicize your innovation."[13]

Mr. McKellar came to Aweme Thursday, May 18. Mr. Criddle put in an appearance and boasted, "My boys are already fighting the pestilence — burning, chasing, ploughing and trapping. You'll do no good among the stupid dolts of neighbouring farmers who just sit down and suck their thumbs."

---

11 Gives the date as 1898 for Harry Vane leading the local fight against grasshoppers. Bulletin of Entomological Society of Canada, Volume 37, Number 1.
12 May 29, 1900.
13 Continuation of the manuscript previously quoted. "On the following year still greater improvements were made. It was noted at this time that grasshoppers were greatly attracted to horse dropping, and mixing Paris green with this, a bait was obtained that proved in every way superior to the bran bait. . . ."

Having had his say, he left the meeting and went home to preside over a lawn party he'd planned for the afternoon with Miss Cain, the Sutcliffes, the Dennys, and Ellis. The two latter neighbours, seeing no need to learn about grasshopper control, had skipped the meeting.

On the 24th of May the young folks took a break from the doom and gloom. Others joined them and their cavalcade drove north to picnic at their favourite little lake. "Be back by six o'clock," Mr. Criddle told them, "We'll have tea and entertainment."

The weather was fine as only May can be on the prairie; the happy hours sped by. Suddenly someone noticed the slant of the afternoon sun and raised the alarm, "We'd better get back." The girls grabbed their picnic baskets and raced for the wagons; the fellows untied their teams and headed home as fast as their heavy workhorses could trot. Unfortunately it was seven o'clock when they arrived at St. Albans. Mr. Criddle stood angrily on his doorstep, "You're late! Mrs. Criddle and I have eaten. You're out of luck." Chastised, the Criddles climbed down and disappeared inside. Everyone else, including Miss Cain, continued down the hill to The Palace where the friends agreed, "It's been a good day. We'd better get home. See you soon."

Next day the Vane boys were back fighting grasshoppers and scanning the sky for signs of rain. It appeared to Mr. Criddle that the insects were not gaining on his crops and he kept his spirits up during some dreadful dust storms by taking account of the neighbours' losses. He calculated for the boys: "Martins have lost at least 80 acres. Denny 30 acres – Fortune no end – and Lonsbury is one of the greatest sufferers."

It shouldn't have surprised them when that longtime neighbour, dropped in to say, "I've had enough of this country's wind, dust, drought, and hoppers. I'm selling out."

Mr. Criddle didn't mind, and said to Norman, "You'll be spared from patrolling the woods to save the trees." No thought was given to the fact that Lonsbury's children were the only students in Miss Cain's class. Perhaps he was distracted: "Got my papers for reappointment as J.P. This is my third commission – under three different governments."

The prospect of that income was offset by a severe frost which took everything except the potatoes which, because of the drought, hadn't come up. Elise, captive in the kitchen, was inundated with melancholic speeches; "We've had four successive bad seasons – two hails, two droughts – but this one bids fair to beat 'em all – drought – gales – grasshoppers – frost – and – what's to be done I don't know. . . . No sign of rain – no taters – no turnips – no hay – no wheat – no oats - no straw – will be quite a record."

It was depressing for Elise to think about another year of hunger. Unpaid taxes, she learned, were another reason why neighbours had given up. *If we can't pay ours again this year, we too might be moving.*[14] Although Mr. Criddle grumbled about the poor prospects, his enthusiasm for entertaining never wavered. He sang excerpts from the Messiah one Saturday night with Miss Cain and the Dennys until midnight.

Mid-June the Calverleys hosted a picnic. Miss Cain, Maida, and Beatrice planned to walk until Mr. Criddle insisted on driving. On their return, he stomped in and marched straight to his room while the girls bubbled enthusiastically about their outing. "Miss Cain is great fun. She took part in everything, played tennis and football, sang along with all the popular songs."

The girls had just gone up to bed when Elise heard, "I shouldn't have gone. There was the usual collection of louts and females – some dreadful singing and recitations. One girl had a good voice but sang vulgarly – some very so-so tennis and a poorish football match."

Elise thought sadly, *He finds it hard to share Miss Cain.*

Norman, who didn't enjoy socializing, escaped one guest-busy Sunday with Roland to the Tamarack and came home late in the day with bunches of lovely flowers for them. As new neighbour Ellis [15] was leaving, he spoke to Mr. Criddle, "It's been great sport. But thinking of next week, I have a fortnight's ploughing for one of your boys."

So Harry, in spite of his ongoing work with the grasshoppers, got his orders, "Ellis wants you tomorrow – two weeks worth of ploughing."

Harry wanted to say, "Send one of **your** boys. I'm fighting grasshoppers."

That evening he sought out his mother. "I have to leave my hopper business and slave for Ellis. Norman says he will superintend my work here. The worst is that Mr. McKellar wrote that he'd be back to meet with me. I was to explain what I'm doing and show him my experiments."

Elise sympathized with her son, but Harry went ploughing.

Sure enough, two days later Mr. McKellar arrived with Dr. Fletcher, the Dominion Entomologist, and asked, "Where can we find Harry Vane?"

Mr. Criddle invited them in, "Harry's not here. Norman can tell you all you need to know."[16]

Elise served them tea and noticed how carefully they listened as Norman showed them the diagram and explained the mixture of Paris green poison, horse

---

14 Tax records from South Cypress Municipal Office, Glenboro, Manitoba.
15 Ellis, a single man, was no relation to the former neighbour, John Ellis, who had moved back to Ontario.
16 Dr. Fletcher's reports are condensed in *Ministry of Agriculture in Manitoba*, 1971.

droppings, and salt. She wanted to tell them it was Harry's innovation and grieved for her boy. *Harry will be so disappointed. Why don't they send for him? He's only a few miles away. Please, Percy, give the gentlemen directions to the Ellis farm.*

⌒◦⌒◦⌒

The disastrous spring of 1900 ended in an equally dry, dusty summer. Sundays were more demanding of Elise's energy than weekdays, with so many visitors adding their appetites to those of the already large household. No longer able to endure the endless hours on her feet, she was grateful that Beatrice and Maida began to leave the games early to assist her with tea. She tried to get away as soon as the dishes were done.

News from the Boer War hadn't improved and new trouble made the headlines: the Boxer Rebellion in China—Britain's ambassadors murdered. Unfazed, Mr. Criddle turned his telescope on the night sky—Saturn, Jupiter, and nebulae—for the benefit of Miss Thirza and Roland Denny.

Harry returned from his stint of ploughing, handed over $15 to Mr. Criddle, and asked, "Did McKellar come?"

"Yes, he has been and gone – Norman looked after the business."

Elise could tell from Harry's face and the set of his shoulders that he was terribly frustrated. "What's the use of trying?" he said. "I just can't get anywhere here."

Her heart went out to him. *My dear Harry. . . . He does all he's asked and more. Planted all those trees, and if we have a crop at all this year, it's because he knew what to do.*

Grasshoppers slipped in importance for Elise when Roland walked over: "My family are all away in Winnipeg. I've trouble with my blind eye."

Mr. Criddle had Edwy drive him to a doctor in Brandon, and there he remained while Emily coped on her own.

Aweme, Manitoba Wed. July 25, 1900

My dearest old Boy,

 It's lonesome without you - been expecting you all day and now I hear Tom Farrow is here and that you are not coming. I haven't been to the house since you went away and Miss Cain has been away both evenings so the days seem very long especially when I am looking for you every minute.

 Monday night Tol [Talbot] came down and helped me water the tomatoes. Last night he came down again to see if I was all right. Harry was down also.

 As usual our little daughter is playing general hobb. Fell downstairs yesterday afternoon, no harm done. Now she is bothering me every way she can think of— gobble, gabble—a message for daddy.

 Very hot, as I suppose you know, not a sign of rain, barom. very high Harry says, but going down.

401

Plymouth hen sat for nothing, eggs all bad . . . I churned this morning and a nice time I had of it. Was up at 5 and didn't get done till 10. Thyra had to get up too of course.

Hudduk not well, staying in bed since yesterday afternoon. I am about the same—cranky as usual . . . Kiddy coming with a cup making a noise of it—little monkey . . .

Mrs. Bellhouse heard Emily was alone and invited her and her boarder, Miss Cain, for supper Friday night. Emily, heavy with child and carrying Thyra, was ready to walk the short distance when Edwy drove up. They all went and enjoyed the evening. On leaving everyone said, "We should do this more often."

They'd not considered Mr. Criddle, left high and dry on a Friday night. Only to his diary could he express his displeasure: "Miss Cain gone to tea at Bellhouse's with the Vanes – very much against my wishes – Like their infernal cheek to invite her."

⋘⋙

It rained 'Old Billy' during harvest time. Elise mopped up the puddles from the leaking roof and baked a birthday cake for Miss Cain. During the meal, Lonsbury showed up. "Came to say goodbye. Young Cullen's bought my place. He's welcome to take what he can of my crop."

Lonsbury was taking Miss Cain's last two students.[17] If Aweme School were to stay open it needed the Criddle children. Mr. Criddle gave his teacher a week's holiday.

Elise felt she was in a war zone. *Can he change his wife's mind in a week? He's desperate to keep Miss Cain. I'm sure our children would enjoy her classes. She could teach them music and art, ever so much more than reading, writing, and arithmetic. On the other hand, I can't blame Mrs. C for not wanting her. . . . It's been a difficult few months. I'm quite sure his wife will win this one. Miss Cain will go.*

Already in a funk, Roland came by and made it worse. "I'm buying Fox's farm on the other side of the river for $3000."

"Paid far too much" Mr. Criddle said after he'd gone, "didn't ask for my advice. Far too clever and self-reliant to consult anyone with brains – if there is ever a wrong way of doing anything – by Jove the Dennys find it."

Harry's birthday, August 25, slipped by as usual without fanfare.[18] *My Harry,* Elise thought sadly, *Percy has overlooked him from the beginning. He was never home and didn't seem to care that he was going to be a father again. We always paid our rent to Mr. Wright, yet that year he persuaded the gentleman to put Criddle instead of Wright in the rate book.[19] Then after our baby was born, he turned up and insisted*

---

17 Aug. 17, 1900. ". . . if we don't keep the place open why we lost Gov't and Municipal Grants."
18 Aug. 25, 1900. "Aug 25 – Harry's supposed birthday."
19 The lease owner of St. George's Rd was Mr. Charles Wright from 1868. Percy Criddle's name appeared

on naming him Harry. [20] *I wondered—for Harry Smith, his partner? His father, or Lord Harry a patron of artists. In any case, my Harry never had a father's love, unless it was dear, kind Mr. Tulk.*

No.	When and where born	Name, if any	Sex	Name, and surname of father	Name, surname, and maiden surname of mother	Occupation of father	Signature, description, and residence of informant	When registered

REGISTRATION DISTRICT Saint-Saviour
1873. BIRTH in the Sub-district of London Road in the County of —

| 152 | Twenty-fifth August 1873 St Georges Road | Harry | Boy | Percy Criddle | Elise Criddle formerly Harrer | Wine Merchant | Elise Criddle Mother 131 St Georges Road Southwark | Second October 1873 |

At the end of the week, Miss Cain returned from Oak Lake and came up from the Palace after breakfast to talk to Mr. Criddle. Elise heard arguing. Then with her head in the air, the lady walked right past Elise, and out the door. Gone like the wind. Everyone kept a safe distance from Mr. Criddle to avoid becoming a victim of a flare-up as Mr. Criddle ranted about her foolishness.

Elise shook her head. *He must have promised he would send his children to school. She came 80 miles expecting everything to be arranged, only to find out that Mrs. Criddle was not going to give up her children.*

Pining for a letter the following week, Mr. Criddle crossed the river in Marten's boat and walked to Treesbank.[21] He came in just before tea time, his boots caked with mud, his clothes soaked. "Alice, help me get out of these confounded clothes. Some beggar stole the boat so I had to ford the river – jolly deep and not over warm – was nearly afloat. Fifteen miles for nothing."

His wife guided him across the room to their quarters and shut the door. *How strange, such a long way around. Why didn't he take the ferry? Was he afraid Mr. Palmer would ask about his teacher going away so soon?*

Emily's young sister Edie [22] came to help Emily. When they sat down to tea, Edie read the latest letter from their soldier-brother.

---

the year of Harry's birth. Rate books, for Southwark, UK.
20 August 25, 1873. Re Harry. Name and surname of father, Percy Criddle. Name, surname, and maiden name of mother, Elise Criddle formerly Harrer. Occupation of Father, Wine merchant. Informant, Elise Criddle, Mother, October 2, 1873.
21 "I miss Miss Cain horribly – She used to come up for music or cards nearly every evening – to say nothing of Tennis, etc, on Sundays. She was very lively – full of fun – I miss her horribly – especially as I now think it was almost all my fault that we quarrelled."
22 Edith Steer, born July 5, 1882 in London, England.

Edith [Edie] Steer.

Middleburg SAR August 7, 1900.

Dear Dolly,

I got your letter dated the 21ˢᵗ of June and some from home and some from Emily and Edwy. They seem to be the same as ever on their sand hills. This year it is grasshoppers and the usual scarcity of rain. I suppose it will continue until the end of the chapter.

Edwy looked at Emily, "So that's what your brother thinks. . . . Well, he's right about this year. Looks like the worst crop ever . . . no money to pay our taxes again."

Edie finished chewing, swallowed, and read on:

I am entirely sick of this country and only wish we could get the Boers to take a stand and get it over but they won't do that and keep horsing around all over the place and constantly on the move with occasionally an hour or two of running fights thrown in. As for the country itself it isn't worth anything for farming. The only thing that grows is maize or Kaffer corn and the soil is all sand and rocks. I expect we shall be on the road home by the time you get this or near it as they don't seem to be giving us any more horses and we only have about 20 left in our squadron and about the same in "B".

There is a rumour in camp today that Dewit and several thousand men are captured but you can't believe all you hear out here but anyhow you get the news before we do, I suppose you have heard we have had several sharp fights and have lost two of our best officers so I won't tire you with stories of the bravery of Canadians.

Emily broke in, "Mr. C's news was true. Thank goodness Arthur's safe."

. . . I sent some Transvaal money home and I have got a Kruger Sovereign for you but I don't like trusting it to the post so will bring it home with me. It will make a pretty broach.

. . . I was a month in hospital at Kroonstad with enteritis but am all right. I rejoined the regiment at Pretoria. I hear the CPR are giving free Tickets when we get home to the men serving out here. If they do I will look you up if it is only for a day. I must close as I am wanted at office. I forgot to tell you I am under arrest, so good-bye.

P. S. Just back from orderly room—got reprimanded. Write soon and send all the news.

Your loving brother, Arthur.

There was a moment of silence around the table and then Emily said, "Well that's my little brother . . . likes to keep us in suspense. I wonder what he did this time."

Edwy chuckled, remembering the fun they'd had at New Year's. "Such a daredevil. Sure got under Mr. C's skin. Do you recall that, Emily? Or were you so much in love with me you didn't notice Arthur kicking up his heels?"

Edie folded up the letter and added, "I hope he brings more than one Kruger Sovereign. I'd like to have a necklace, too."

Holding out his hand, Edwy said, "Can I borrow the letter, Edie? I'm sure Mama would like to read it. She often talks about Arthur, remembers him as a 16-year-old. I guess he's not old yet, but I expect he's a good deal wiser."

Edwy came home late after a long week of threshing on September 29, covered in dust, looking for supper, and longing to 'hit the hay', Emily heard his footsteps and was ready when he opened the door, "It's going to be tonight. I'm told a second child can come quickly. Thyra's asleep upstairs and will be fine. Will you go for your mother? Edie went earlier for the evening. Ask if she can sleep over. And, I'd feel better if you went for Mrs. Bellhouse right away." She gave him a little peck on his sweat-streaked cheek and added, "You'd better sleep in your mother's bed tonight."

At two in the morning Emily gave birth to a healthy baby boy. After she and the wee one were cared for, the three women chatted over their tea. "Let's not waken Edwy. He's had a hard week. Tomorrow is Sunday, no threshing. I hope Mr. C doesn't want to be driven anywhere. A father should be home accepting congratulations. He'll be proud—a son to help him plough."

Mrs. Bellhouse changed the subject, "The last time I was here, Emily, you chose Thyra's name. Is this Edwy's turn?"

Elise interjected, "I'd like to suggest a name for my first grandson. Can we wait 'til morning, when Edwy's here?"

Emily looked up at the clock. "Gracious, it's almost morning. You must be tired. Huddock, you can snuggle up beside Thyra. Take care on those steep steps. Mrs. Bellhouse, there's another bed up there. I'll call if I need you."

At the first sound from the baby, Mrs. Bellhouse came down and picked him up. "You're a fine little fellow. Just want us to know you're here." She tended him and his mother, while Elise started the fire and put on the kettle and porridge. Edwy must have been watching for the smoke because he was soon knocking on the door. "Is it safe to come in?"

And so Daddy met his new son. Not feeling quite so awkward this time round, he picked up the little bundle and looked down at the tiny face. "I'd forgotten how little they are." He sat on the side of the bed and was chatting with Emily when Thyra made her presence known. Grandma met her at the top of the steps, "Good morning to you, little Princess. We've got a surprise for you. Come see what Daddy has." Edwy held the baby down for her, but the toddler wasn't interested. Thyra just wanted to climb into bed beside her mother.

They were soon enjoying breakfast. Mrs. Bellhouse looked at Edwy, "Emily says it's your turn to come up with a name for the baby. Your mother has a suggestion for you."

Not used to being put on the spot, Elise hesitated a moment. "Yes . . . I do. We have Princess Thyra. Now I have a suggestion for a prince. How about Prince Rupert, the first governor of the Hudson's Bay Company?[23] What do you think?"

Being a quick thinker Emily responded, "Gracious, we never even thought of Rupert when we discussed boys' names, but I like your idea. . . Prince Rupert . . . Rupert."

Teasingly Edwy countered his mother's suggestion, "I think Mr. C is going to want the baby called Harry after **my** father, Harry Vane." He looked at his mother—she looked down at her bowl. . . . "Well then," he went on, "Harry, after his uncles, Emily's brother and mine. . . . You still want to try for Rupert?" Emily nodded.

"Alright, I might have a better chance of getting it past Mr. C if we put Harry first, even if he doesn't approve of two names."

Emily added, "I prefer two names . . . and Harry Rupert sounds fine. One is ordinary and the other royal. Would that please you, Grandmother Vane?"

Elise, with the baby in her arms, nodded.

That evening, Mrs. Bellhouse had gone and Edie was back. Grandma brought up the baby's name again. "I have another reason why the name Rupert is special to me. I haven't talked about my homeland, but I'd like to tell you now. Rupert, Ruprecht they say in German, is a very important name in Heidelberg. A long way back in history, Ruprecht the First built the oldest part of our castle, and being a learned man, he also founded our University.[24] Men came from all over to study and discuss new ideas. Have you heard of Martin Luther? It was there he defended his beliefs. But later on we had centuries of oppression, one war after another. Our wonderful library was carried away to Rome, our castle destroyed. Our Grand Duke of Baden in 1803, gave the university back its freedom to teach modern

---

23 Prinz Ruprecht von der Pfalz, 1619-1682, persuaded King Charles 1 (his uncle) to fund Radisson and Groseilliers' expedition to Hudson Bay. They were successful and Prince Rupert became the first governor of the Hudson's Bay Company. He's buried in the crypt of Westminster Abbey. His nephew became King George I of England. http://www.british-civil-wars.co.uk/biog/rupert.htm Viewed 12/09/2010.

24 Ruprecht I, Count Palatine of the Rhine founded the University of Heidelberg in 1386. Known for freedom of thought until the Thirty Years War in 1618 after which its teachers were suppressed by political interference. In 1803, Prince Karl-Friedrich, then Elector and later Grand Duke of Baden restored its intellectual freedom. Thus its name, Ruprecht-Karl University of Heidelberg, commemorates both its founder and later champion. http://www.uni-heidelberg.de/university/welcome/history.html Viewed 09/10/2010

thought and sciences. Once again it became a centre of learning important to Heidelberg and all of Gemany."

She paused for a moment and then continued, "When I was a little girl, our family sometimes went to the Church of the Holy Spirit. I asked Mama why there

was a stone man and woman lying on the floor. Mama told me they were Ruprecht the Third, and his wife Elizabeth. He started building the church way back in

1400. It's a beautiful church. I wish you could see it."

They had never heard her talk so passionately! But she wasn't quite finished, "Rupert is a special name for me. I'd be very happy if you name your son Rupert. . . . But, he's your little one. I'll accept whatever you decide."

Emily added, "Well, we can't just have Harry. I don't want anyone calling our son, Young Harry. Harry can be his honorary name. Your name is like that, isn't it Huddock? Edwy told me you were named for your grandmother Sabina. You went by your second name, Elise."

She nodded; Emily continued, "Rupert is unusual, but I like it already, Harry Rupert Vane. Don't you like the sound of it, Edwy?"

Edwy hesitated, "I guess Mr. C will get used to it." Then wanting to please his mother he said, "If we're going to call him Rupert we had better get in the habit right away."

Edwy's days were filled with threshing, hauling what little grain they had, and then he took Mr. Tulk to the train. It was over a month before Mr. Criddle agreed to the baby's name and Edwy walked across the frozen river to Sutcliffe's to register his son, Harry Rupert.[25]

The following day he drove Edie to Douglas to catch the train to Makinak and the next day walked to Brandon to see Dolly before she left for home. The Steers were worrying about Harry. He had not regained his strength as they hoped and they faced the growing reality that they were going to lose him. They needed young Arthur to come home safely from the war.

25　November 15, 1900. Birth date, September 30, 1900. Manitoba Vital Statistics.

The Criddle household was also in for some tough times. The lack of funds in the district was so severe Mr. Criddle couldn't collect the money people owed for the boys' work. Their crop was worse than '96, after the great hailstorm. And the price was disgustingly low. Due to drought and grasshoppers, they had very few potatoes, cabbages, and turnips. The boys slaughtered two animals hoping to sell the beef in town to get enough cash for the usual winter stores plus treats for Christmas dinner. Unfortunately, their strategy came up short. Brandon was inundated with meat from other farmers hoping to do the same.

Mr. Criddle called the annual meeting of the Aweme School Board, accepted the honorarium for his work, and took on another term as trustee. *I'm not surprised,* Elise thought, *the school was his idea . . . he's going to hold on.*[26] Hope for future students ended when Jack Mair came by, "I've had enough of this country. There's no future here for my children." Elise thought sadly, remembering their New Year's visit, *his children won't be climbing on Harry's lap for a song again.* A few days later Bruners slipped away from their farm and, as the snow fell deeper and deeper, they realized winter travel would be difficult—no other teams to break and pack the trails.

That Christmas, there was no mention of plum pudding or late night parties. Mr. Criddle wrote in his diary, "The very worst year on record for us so far as money is concerned." Elise thought of all the years she'd skimped on food, *I've always held out hope that someday we would have plenty for everyone, and I wouldn't go hungry so the youngsters could have a little more on their plates.*

On New Year's Eve after her prayers, Elise crept into bed. Her body cried out for rest, yet her thoughts had first to make a stop with each of her dear ones: *Friedrich . . . his girls . . . times are tough there, too. My plucky Minnie . . . dear Isabel, lively Miss Violet May. Edwy and Emily—happy in their Palace, in spite of the poor harvest. . . . Little monkey Thyra and our wee Prince Rupert. . . . My Harry, I think he's over the doom and gloom of last summer. And dear Cecil, always kind in this cruel world . . . May God in heaven watch over my Cecil.*

---

26   December 3, 1900. "Elected Trustee for the 6th time consecutively – now had 15 yrs of it. . . ."

Chapter Twenty-seven

More Cracks in the Empire

Harry waited for his mother to be alone in the kitchen and then, scarcely above a whisper, said, "Thirza has promised to marry me. Keep it quiet. You know what Mr. C is like. I've told Cecil and they know at the Palace . . . . We've no plans just yet."

She hugged him, and said, "I wish you every happiness, my son."

He went out whistling. *Harry's a changed boy from last summer. But Percy's going to oppose him, when he finds out. He treats him like a boy instead of a man of 28. I'm fond of Thirza, but, is she suited to life here? She is used to her mother's money. What does Harry have?*

Two weeks later neighbours let the 'cat out of the bag'. As Harry expected, Mr. Criddle criticized Thirza, her mother, and the 'whole damn Denny outfit'. Harry no longer whistled. It was a bleak winter. There was no cash; potatoes and turnips were scarce; and almost everyone, including Elise, was ill. When Minnie's parcel included a pair of hand-me-down slippers, Elise was very thankful to have something warm for her feet.

Aweme, Manitoba 1901

My dear Minnie,

I find that Bobby [Beatrice] is writing to you so I take the opportunity to thank you myself for the nice slippers you sent me. It was very kind of that lady to do that for you. Don't you think, my dear, that I should ever refuse anything that you choose to send to me; of course Mrs. C can't help herself.

I am not very strong yet, but thankful to be able to move about. Everybody is so good to me. Bobby has a great deal to do, Mrs. Criddle being laid up, but she is so good to me and will hardly allow me to do anything, so are all the children who work well. Now I have to say goodbye, write soon again. I am thinking of you and Harry all the time.[1]

With love,
Your Mama

Harry's Thirza was also having trouble. Her oldest brother, Fred, turned up unexpectedly and the family, squeezed into Swaisland's old shanty, erupted. Fred sought out Dr. Husband, wanting to have his entire family locked up in the luna-

---

1 Minnie had taken a position northeast of Brandon at Hamiota.

tic asylum. In return, they declared Fred insane. Elise thought, *Thirza should get away—marry Harry. But they wouldn't be welcome here.*

As suddenly as Fred had come, he vanished and all appeared well with the Dennys.

News of Queen Victoria's death, January 22, spread like wildfire. The morning of the royal funeral Mr. Criddle gathered his family at the flagpole. Everyone stood stiffly at attention as he raised the Union Jack to the top, held it there for a minute, and then lowered it to half-mast. He cleared his throat, "All true Britons grieve her loss." He went on at length, listing England's glorious achievements during her illustrious reign and concluded with an appropriate period of silence. Then his words rang out: "The queen is dead. . . Long live King Edward VII." Having warned them earlier of the necessary word changes, he led the singing. "God save our gracious king, long live our noble king . . . . Send him victorious, happy and glorious . . . . God save the king."

Their patriotic duty done, everyone went back to work. Elise had extra meals to prepare due to the Justice of the Peace's involvement in a case the Dennys brought against Mooney, for stealing wood. After several days of legalities, Mooney was let off on condition that he pay for the wood, plus costs.

Things had barely settled down when one of their best hockey players, Fred Calverley, told his teammates, "I'm off to join Baden Powell's forces in South Africa." That was followed by another bolt from the blue: Mrs. Denny announced, "I'm leaving for England in a fortnight, taking Thirza and my youngest."

Elise was shocked. *Life will be dull without Mrs. Denny, but to lose Thirza! Oh! Dear God! My Harry!"*

Mr. Criddle gloated, "I'm jolly glad; neither she nor her mother is any good."

Elise's heart sank as Harry bolted for the door. *This is not going to end well.*

Elise had another young man to console. Norman had come to the absolute end of his Grandmother Criddle's painting supplies. "You can't help me anymore; I've run out of colours and paper. My whole trouble is CASH. The sum of one dollar would help me enormously. In fact, the sum of two dollars would overcome all difficulties. Yet, it's as far off as the moon."[2]

"If I had a dollar, I would surely give it to you," she said sadly. Nor could she provide anything to relieve his toothache.

Meanwhile, to raise cash to pay an urgent debt, Harry and Cecil cut wood and Edwy hauled it to the customers. Emily with the two little ones, was on her

---

2 Criddle, Norman. March 11, 1901. "This is the hardest time of my life. . . . My stock of colours is now at an end and I have no means of getting more."

own with the chores, the woodpile, and the fire to stoke. When a man came looking for Edwy, she left the washtubs to get him dinner, and while he ate, she scribbled a note for Edwy

My dear Edwy,

Thought you might like a few lines when you get back to Brandon as Norman McCrum has been here to dinner and I will send this with him. . . . . washing is very much behind, will take me the best part of afternoon. We are all very well, Kids especially. When's Daddy coming home is heard pretty often. Mr. C came down Monday afternoon and Maida and Bobby slept one each night.

I went a crack on the ice soon after you went away and feel it yet pretty sore. The baby is fretting and such a noise from Thyra. Must stop.

Hoping you will soon be home. Miss you awfully,

Your loving Emily.

Thirza spent her last weekend at The Palace and confidently assured them, "Mother insists on my going with her, but never mind, I'll be back in six weeks."[3]

After she was gone Harry sought solace with Edwy and Emily, who knew from experience the pain of separation.

They comforted him, "Your love is genuine. You'll get through."

Emily had more on her mind than Harry's lovesick heart. Her own brother, Harry, had been a patient in a Winnipeg hospital the previous autumn, and while there, had been chilled by a draft from an open window. A few weeks later the doctors sent him home, assuming he had consumption. His family hoped he'd improve, but following Christmas he rapidly went downhill. *Poor Emily,* Elise thought, *little ones to look after and sad news from home. It can't help her to have our Harry moping around.*

Edwy confided to his mother at the end of February, "Emily's terribly downhearted with the news about Harry. She's losing her closest and dearest brother and wants in the worst way to go home. It's a bad time of the year to travel with children, but she can't leave them behind."

"If you can manage it, send her. Families need each other at times like this."

The following week's letter brought word that Harry was fading quickly. Edwy told his mother, "Emily wants to go, even if she has to walk. I'm going to see Billy Marshall. If he goes to see his family, Emily could travel with him."

Edwy came back in the morning, "The weather is improving. I'm picking up Marshall and will put them on the train in Brandon. If you have any letters I'll take them."

---

3 February 24, 1901. Also mentioned in a letter from Emily.

Mrs. Criddle wanted to get a message to Minnie about some fabric, but not feeling up to the task, asked Elise.

My dear Minnie!

As Edwy is going to write to you, I must also enclose a few lines. Mrs. Criddle has a bad cold or she would have written today. She is going to write soon. The pattern of the print we have, but it is rather difficult to judge from a little piece what it really looks like. We shall be delighted to get the things you send Dido the money for, and thank you beforehand very much.

I am much better now, but have to take care, as I am very easily upset. I shall never get so strong again. I am getting old. Mrs. Denny and Thirza are going to England but Thirza is supposed to come back in 4 months. The boys are playing another hockey match in Treesbank tomorrow.

With love from all, believe me ever

Your affectionate Mama

Emily packed, gathered blankets to wrap around the children, and, in spite of very heavy going for the horses, they set off. Marshall joined them and Edwy managed to reach Brandon. The next day he put his little family on the train and reported that night to his mother, "So far so good. I hope Emily gets there in time. She was terribly anxious. Poor old Harry."[4]

He waited anxiously for the mail and was quick to share it with his mother. "Emily started the letter in Portage. You can keep on knitting; I'll read it to you."

March 1, Hotel Portage. *The first thing Miss Thyra went out of the room to look for Daddy and has been galloping all over the place ever since, thoroughly happy.*
. . .

Just looked for her, she is with one of the girls making the beds. . . . Thyra was quite at home at breakfast, had a high chair and the girl carted the baby off to the kitchen while I had breakfast. She said he was making love to the cook, and did not want to leave her. True to his manly nature eh! A gentleman gave Thyra another ten cents so she will soon pay her own expenses. Billy [Marshall] is so kind and nice as he could be and we have had no trouble with the children. We got the same room with the kitchen stove pipe and so comfortable for the baby. He is sound asleep on the bed. . . . Thyra has discovered an imitation pony in the sitting room. I have been giving her a ride. She is very good, even the girl says it is nice. Nearly all the children who stay here cry all the time.

On the train. *I had a cake and cold wafer lunch. The mug I bought has come in very useful. Both babies are now asleep. Thyra is good as can be walking up and down the car inspecting things and people generally. The car is hot and full of people and children and other babies—but ours beat them all.*

His mother smiled, "I am not surprised Emily thinks our babies are the best."

---

4   March 4, 1901. "Hear Mrs. Edwy Vane is going to Dauphin tomorrow with all her children – Hope she'll like the journey – madness to take young children for long drives in such weather."

But Emily's next letter was more somber. "Harry is terribly changed . . . eats almost nothing and is not able to help himself. Arthur is home on leave and says there was never a better nurse than mother. Mother says Arthur is a godsend. They have the French doctor, a very kind and patient fellow, who warns them that Harry had gone too far. Yet, they seem confident that he looks better today."

But it was a false hope. Another short letter sent Edwy back to his mother, "It's over, Harry's dead. Emily can tell you better than I can, I'll read it to you."

> *Poor Harry passed away peacefully today soon after noon. He was delirious all yesterday. He became conscious this morning. His last thoughts were for his family and he bid us all goodbye and was at peace. But he rapidly sank. Arthur is dreadfully cut up. I can hardly realize it at all and I have the babies to look after so have my time and thoughts occupied. They had not really ever thought he could live, but while there is life there's hope. Apparently he had suffered much all the time. He had never recovered from the pleurisy. . .*
>
> *Poor mother and poor all. Harry said to me on Monday, "It's hard for me, but it's harder for the rest."*
>
> *His funeral is to be on Sunday. Oh Edwy! I cannot write any more.[5]*

Elise wiped her eyes and Edwy said gently, "Harry was kind and good, a favourite with everyone. Emily found it hard, but in the long run, she knows she did the right thing by going. Thank you for encouraging me that day." Then more cheerfully he added, "Harry gave me his football jersey and pin; Emily, his pen and ink bottle with a screw stopper in a case. Arthur is sending me a pair of woven woolen khaki leg bandages . . . true things for cycling."

⋅⋅⋅⋅⋅⋅⋅⋅⋅⋅

Mrs. Criddle continued poorly, and in the middle of March began complaining of a crippling pain in her lower back. Elise was struggling too, but with stomach trouble. One day she didn't get out of the kitchen fast enough and her retch was brought to Mr. Criddle's attention.

"Why didn't you tell me? How can I give you the right medicine if you don't tell anyone?"

I cause such a fuss when I complain. I find hiding my condition is best for everyone.

Harry stuck it out in the bush cutting wood for another four weeks. He told his mother one evening "I've got to get away. I hope to get married in a year or so. I can do better on my own. As a start, I'm going to work with Roland."

Seeing the stricken look on his mother's face, he said, "Don't fret. I'm not going far. Thirza will soon be back. We'll let you know what we decide."[6] And out he went to tell Mr. Criddle.

---

5 Henry William Steer, born Feb.2, 1874 in London, died March 14, 1901. Buried in Turtle River Cemetery.
6 April 1, 1901. "Henceforth he's on his own hook to work out – foolish fellow giving up all his chances here and his many pleasures because we've had bad luck the last two or three years with the wheat."

He was back within minutes looking like a thundercloud. "I'm not going to be bullied into staying!" Up the stairs he went and came down with a few clothes stuffed into a grain bag. With a quick kiss on his mother's cheek, he was gone. Teary eyed, she thought of the phrase, '*Off to seek his fortune.' But I'm losing a piece of my heart.*

Mr. Criddle came in ranting, "I warned Harry what it would be if the girl went away - showed him the old hag's game - offered him the money to get married right away."

Elise collapsed on a chair. *Talk like that doesn't help, my Harry has gone.*

⚬⚬⚬

A rather nervous census official came to the door on April 16. "I'm James Erratt, here to take your information for the 1901 census. Mr. Criddle said curtly, "I heard you were making the rounds. Come in, we'll get the job done and you'll be on you way." They sat down at the kitchen table. Mr. Erratt took out his pen and ink bottle, unscrewed the lid, and laid out the long form. Elise thought, *Percy hasn't noticed me; I'll hear what he tells them.*

Mr. Erratt dipped his pen. Mr. Criddle, with his eye on the column headings dictated. "Criddle, Percy: male, white, head, married, born 21st November, '44, age 56, born in England, came in '82, I'm of English origin and I'm Canadian. We're all Canadians – you can ditto that for the rest of my family." He looked back at the form and said, "Religion? I've none of those common ones; write deist, **d-e-i-s-t.**[7] Farmer, I'm an employer. No income—a bad year. I can read, write, and speak both English and French."

Next row: "Criddle, Alice: female, white, wife of head, married, born 24th November, '49, age 51, born in England, came in '82, Scotch heritage, deist, can read, write and speak English and French."

Next: "Norman: male, white, son, born 14th May, '75, age 25, born in England. English origin, agnostic, **a-g-n-o-s-t-i-c.**[8] Occupation – farmer's son. Reads, writes, and speaks English."

And so they continued, Evelyn and Stuart . . . "deists, farmer's sons."

Beatrice, Maida, Julia, Talbot, Alma . . . "Deists." *They have no occupations.*

On he went: "Vane, Elise: white, female, lodger, widow, November 25, '40, Age 60, born in Germany, immigrated in '82, is German, Lutheran and a farmer. She can read, write, and speaks English and French."

I'm a lodger. I'd say domestic farmer is closer to the truth.

"Vane, Harry. Single, lodger, 25th August '72, age 28, born in England, came in '96, is German, Lutheran. Can read, write and speak English."

---

7 Belief in the existence of a god without accepting revelation.
8 Belief that nothing can be known about the existence of God.

Elise shook her head. *Harry's not here! He has no occupation? I guess a lodger doesn't work. Mr. Erratt should catch Harry at the Denny's and get the correct information.*

"Vane, Cecil. Male, white, single, lodger, born in England, 19th of April, '73." . . . *Goodness that's Harry's year of birth, my Cecil's aging fast, now he's two years ahead of his time* . . . "born in England, is German and Lutheran." *How can my boys be German, with Vane for a name?* "Immigrated in '96", *Gracious, he and Harry came together! Would I have left my little boys behind? Doesn't Percy appreciate the 14 years they have worked on his farm?*

He's also doing Edwy! "Male, white, head, married, 31 July 1871, born in England, German heritage." Elise blinked. . . "He came in '82 and is English Church." *Emily's church and he's a farmer. And they're on to Emily . . . she's away with the children.* "German heritage, came in '82, reads, writes and speaks English and French." *I never thought of speaking French to Emily. And the children?* "Thyra—born in Manitoba, German." . . . "Harry." *So our little Rupert is still Harry. What a pack of lies . . . This Justice of the Peace doesn't speak the truth, the whole truth, and nothing but the truth.*[9]

Mr. Criddle didn't order tea. He simply ushered the census taker out, and shut the door. "Confounded questions! A waste of money! They're bound to be filled with mistakes with the way the process operates."

⚜

Elise could no longer do heavy work, but she liked to be in the kitchen darning or knitting. Edwy found her there. "This will amuse you. Emily says she celebrated her birthday pleasantly enough if nursing babies constitutes it."

She smiled; "Emily does have two lovely little ones."

"Here's the latest news. Arthur wanted to be stationed in Winnipeg but he's been called to Toronto. They miss him terribly. Emily asks about our Harry. She still feels Thirza was genuine, but is letting herself be overruled by her mother." He saw her look up and added, "Your worry, Mama, won't help him. We'll just have to wait and see."

The following week Edwy had more news from Turtle River. "Emily sent some pages from Eaton's catalogue. She's been making out an order: a good pail for 33 cents, some strainers, and a watering can. She wants to paint our floor and thinks she can do it for a dollar." Edwy glanced down at the board floor and said, "You've managed to keep this floor clean without paint."

His mother understood well what it took to keep the floor presentable—men's boots walking in from the fields and barns. She'd done her share on her

---

9   1901 Census, Province of Manitoba, District No 18, Macdonald, S District No C, South Cyprus, Man. (T) 8 & 9, N 16, W 1st P M, 13-16 April.

knees scrubbing those rough boards with all the elbow grease she could muster. "I'm sure a coat of paint would be a great benefit for Emily. She's by herself with so much to do. But you know best about the money."

"Emily also wants a brown teapot and an oval baker to replace our cracked pudding dish. Money's as scarce as hen's teeth. Anyway, you'll be glad to know Emily and the babies are the picture of health. Her mother sees me in every line of little Rupert's face. He's good tempered and jabbers all day, 'Mam-ma-mam-ma.' Emily's teaching him to say, 'Dad-dy.' They're coming home the 24th of May."

⌒⌒⌒

Harry appeared suddenly one morning, "I'm going to Hamiota to see Minnie. She has a friend who will lend me the money to go to England. Will Denny says I can help on their big farm. Where's Mr. Criddle?"

Too shocked to say anything, his mother nodded toward their door. She heard some sharp exchanges and "You're crazy – to give up all your good chances here – on a perfectly wild goose chase with heaven knows what consequences. I told you Thirza was no good, just like the rest of her family!"

Elise got a hurried goodbye and Harry was gone. She was still reeling a few days later when he reappeared with a suitcase. "I borrowed $150 from Jim Brandon and Minnie gave me this," holding up the case, "for my clothes. Everything is worked out. Edwy's going to take me to Brandon to catch the train. I'll be in Montreal in time to sail on the S. S. Numidian for Liverpool."

Mr. Criddle lashed out at Minnie for helping Harry as he worked every angle to prevent the departure. Only at the last minute did he say, "I hope you'll come through this fiasco and get home again in safety."

Elise couldn't hide her tears. *Will I ever see my boy again?* She wanted to hang on to him, but he gently eased her arms away and sprang up to the seat beside Edwy. Her teary gaze followed the wagon until it disappeared.

Harry, on the other hand, was in such a state of excitement he noted the newly hatching grasshoppers and told Edwy, "I'm done with the whole pesky business. Norman can take charge. Come harvest, remember my scheme to keep the beggars from chewing the twine to pieces. Soak the balls in a solution of two pounds of bluestone to 12 gallons of water for half an hour. Make sure it's dry before you use it." [10]

While Edwy was seeing his brother off, Dr. Fletcher and Mr. McKellar came to check on the grasshopper infestation and noted that in the fields where Harry had worked the previous year, the grasshoppers weren't going to be a problem.[11]

---

10 Criddle, Norman. Quoted in Annual Reports, Manitoba Department of Agriculture 1888-1912, Legislative Library, Winnipeg. MB. ". . . found very successful in preventing locusts and crickets from eating the binder twine. Introduced by Mr. Harry Vane of this place"

11 Department of Agriculture, Dr. Fletcher. Seasonal papers (No. 10) 1-2 Ed. VII "fine crops of wheat which

Convinced the method worked,[12] they hired Norman at two dollars a day to instruct farmers in the use of the Paris green mixture.[13] Edwy drove him in style from farm to farm with the exception of a two-week period when he, with his team, worked on the railway bridge at Millford for $2.25 a day.

⁂

Elise struggled to keep going until the hot weather robbed her of her strength.[14] Beatrice and her younger sisters took over cooking breakfast, in fact, most of Elise's household work. The girls also cared for their mother. They were worried that her continuing illness was some internal, unfixable ailment. When the pain localized at last into an abscess at the bottom of her spine, Dr. Husband was summoned. Once lanced, the pain subsided and Mrs. Criddle's road to recovery was assured.

Elise longed for news from her son. *Has Harry seen Mr. Tulk? Is he at Will Denny's farm? Does Thirza still love him? Surely he will soon be home. If only I had a letter.*

Harry must also have been on Mr. Criddle's mind for he told them one morning; "I had a strange dream – Harry had come home – in red trousers or undercoat – somehow his back seemed to be turned to me – but I knew his voice. Suddenly I awoke in a kind of alarm – and at that moment the clock began striking midnight."

Harry's longed for letter came at last. Elise's hands shook with excitement as she examined the envelope. "It's Harry's writing sure enough! Mrs. Vane, Aweme, Manitoba, Canada. Where is he? The postal stamp says 'Chigwell Row' . . . that doesn't help."

"Open it, Mama." Edwy said, "He'll tell you where he is."

And so they learned that Harry was, as planned, working for Will Denny on Brownings Farm[15] and Thirza was still the apple of his eye. He had looked up Olger and told her all the family news. Mr. Tulk had taken him to the theatre in London. Now he was settled at the farm. Harry's news satisfied everyone but his mother.

Harry with Thirza on the Denny farm.

had been saved by Paris green mixture on land where everything had been destroyed the last year."
Excerpt from Dr. Fletcher's 1901 report is included in the appendix.
12 July 5, 1901. "Dr. Fletcher, McKellar . . . are now converted to Norman's Paris green treatment for grasshoppers and are disseminating his doctrines everywhere on Gov't authority."
13 Criddle, Norman. May 29, 1901.
14 May 30, 1901. "Dutchman still very feeble hot weather tries her."
15 An ancient farm, with house built in late medieval times. The central section rebuilt in 16th century, extended in 1800 in typical Essex timber-framed and plastered construction. Loughton and District Historical Society.

Having deceived her own family, she didn't feel certain about Harry's happiness. *If I were sure, I could bear having him so far away.*

⋅ᢒᡝᡝᢓ᙭᙭⋅

Wind without mercy swept up the topsoil and blotted out the sun. Edwy told his mother; "Emily said in her letter they noticed what looked like smoke in the sky to the south. They thought it to be dust, and knew we were catching it on the plains."[16]

Sand filtering into their house was miserable enough, but it was nothing compared to the havoc that followed. A gale, combined with heavy rain, found so many ways through St. Albans' roof that its dripping into pails and pots made about as much racket as the wind and thunder outside. Surveying the scene next day Mr. Criddle downplayed the damage: "Three panes of glass blown out – perhaps 150 shingles from roof and a shed door blown away – nothing else."

The boys didn't let the storm keep them from a championship cricket match. The final between Millford and Ninette was at Cooper's, just along the road from Sutcliffe's, close enough for Bobby and Maida to attend with their Papa. Millford captured the Challenge Cup and, to Elise's joy and Emily's pride, Edwy attained the highest batting score in the league.[17]

⋅ᢒᡝᡝᢓ᙭᙭⋅

Norman was giving out poison in the neigbourhood. They read the label, "Paris green treatment for grasshopper eradication, Norman Criddle."

"You didn't invent the treatment! Harry told us about people in Ontario using Paris green years ago. He wanted to use it then, but your father wouldn't let him." And they kept on, "We know Harry changed the recipe to make it cheaper. It should be Harry's name on the bag."

"Harry's gone to England. Do you want the poison?"

That night Norman made an unusually long entry in his diary.

It seems marvellous [sic] to relate that at least 2 people or families in this settlement are jealous because I in company with Harry Vane developed a simple remedy for killing locusts—Paris Green, salt and horse manure which has been used by themselves and lots of other people with lots of success. They are jealous because I sent down a recipe to the Dept. of Agriculture of how to mix it, which the Dept, has copied and sent with each package of Paris Green, with my name attached. . . . But why they should be so bitter against me I cannot find out.[18]

⋅ᢒᡝᡝᢓ᙭᙭⋅

---

16 Emily to Edwy. May 5th 1901.
17 July 14, '09. ". . . the Boy wins a bat for the best batting average, Stuart coming 2nd and just missing it by a fraction of a run."
18 Criddle, Norman. July 27, 1901.

Elise, still very unwell, thought about Harry constantly but hadn't answered his letter. *Harry can be proud to know his grasshopper method is helping so many farmers. But to know Edwy is driving Norman around the country with his name on the mixture might upset him. I'll not mention it. I miss him terribly, but Percy says things are better because Harry is not here stirring up trouble with foolish ideas. . . . The words will come if I make a start. . . .*

Aweme, Manitoba 24th July, 1901

My Dear boy!

I was very pleased to hear from you, though it is not satisfactory. I am anxious for you to come back again and don't see the use of your staying there, when here at this time you might earn a lot of money. You say that you are as fond of Thirza as ever but you don't say she feels the same, however you can put up with it I can't understand.

I wish I could see you once more happy, this is my sincere wish. I am glad you saw Olger looking so well, I meant to answer, but you tell me she is going to move, so I better wait till I know her new address. Please tell her so, when you see her. I am glad you are going to see Mr. Tulk again, and thankful he is so kind to you. You don't say what you thought of the theatre, was it in London?

I wonder what you think of Emma Denny marrying Mr. Ellis, who would have thought that! [19]

I am much better in health and if I had nothing to worry me, I might feel quite well, it is all very well to tell me not to worry. [20]

There is nothing more to say, love from all. I hope to see you soon again . . . With the best wishes for your happiness, I remain always your, Affectionate Mama

❦

During harvest, Edwy was stricken with excruciating abdominal pain. Mr. Criddle tended him for two days and nights and then sent for Dr. Husband. The problem, they concluded, was a bowel obstruction and administered large doses of castor oil. Next day the stoppage gave way and after a dose of laudanum, Edwy slept.[21] Mr. Criddle came up to the house and told his worried mother, "Edwy is going to make it. Am very tired after three nights watching and three days maneuvering – practically only four hours sleep all through. But – the battle's won – and I'm all right."[22] Three days later she had an update, "Boy getting on pretty well – toddles about a bit and is feeding up – but he's still mighty weak."

---

19 Emma Denny was an older sister of Thirza. Ellis was the farmer who asked Harry to plough,
20 Becker, B. "This sounds positive, but it is clear she knows she has a serious problem that those around her don't want to take seriously."
21 Drink of 10% opium and 90% alcohol, flavoured with cinnamon, used as painkiller, sleeping pill, or tranquilizer.
22 August 27, 1901.

Harry's letters, addressed to each of the family in turn, kept arriving and everyone followed his adventures. He didn't mention getting married, but the overall happy tone pleased his mother.

Aweme Manitoba 11ᵗʰ Oct 19 [1901]

My Dear Harry!

Your letters give me much pleasure, they are more cheerful. I can put up with it much better that you are so long away from us. Will, Dido and May are out here since a week ago. Will enjoys the hunting, he has shot quite a few chickens, but not a goose yet. The boys have shot a good many geese, we used up six for threshings alone. They had 8 one morning. The boys have been hard at work threshing, in a few days it will be all over.

Edwy is all right again for some time, he was very ill for a few days and was in great agony, even Dr. Husband said it was touch and go with him . . .

I am sorry you don't see much of Olger. She has never answered my letter, I wrote a few months ago. I shall have to write again, poor old girl. I am glad you are so much thought of. You must be of great use to Will Denny as you always were to all the Dennys. The wheat has not nearly given out as much as was expected and much wheat at some places has suffered by the rain. Bobby is gone to the other side of the river to pay visits and will stay away the night.

Everybody sends their love to you including Will and Dido.

Goodbye my dear boy, be happy, this is the dearest wish of
Your Affectionate
Mama

Edwy, concerned for his brother, confronted Roland, "Thirza is not keeping her promise to marry Harry. It's very dishonourable of your family." Their friendship ended in the bitter quarrel.

Two unrelated, but happy announcements caught Elise by surprise that

Arthur seated, wearing the Queen's South African medal. Carrie standing.

harvest season. Mr. Criddle announced, "I'm going to have our roof reshingled – it needs it badly enough."[23] The second, from Edwy was even more surprising. "Arthur's found the girl of his dreams and snapped her up before she had a chance to change her mind. Her name is Carrie. She's a wee bit of a thing, but makes up for her size in looks and personality. She suits Arthur to a T."[24]

23 October 28, 1901. Four years later, July 2, 1905, the roof is mentioned again. "Rain and the roof is leaking in every direction – deuced mess on the floors – the organ and a dozen other spots-large quantity of pots and pans and clothes all over the shop."
24 Ernest Arthur Steer married Caroline Mary Hephzibah Bragg, at Holy Trinity, Toronto York, October 31, 1901.

"My gracious, that was fast! That's what Harry should have done!"

Edwy left her deep in thought. *But Harry couldn't get married so quickly. . . . Percy and I had to wait, too. His mother couldn't provide for a family. She wanted him to get a profession first. . . . I must write Harry.*

Aweme Manitoba, 20ᵗʰ Nov. 1901

My dear boy!

I am so glad you feel pretty comfortable. I know Mr. Tulk would be very kind to you, but he will soon go to India and you will be sorry. Remember me kindly to him. Everybody is very busy today, the boys are killing the pigs and a lot of fowls have to be sent to Brandon tomorrow. Mr. C went to Brandon with Cullen on Tuesday and Edwy is going in tomorrow. The usual things are bought before the winter sets in. The weather is still fine and warm and Edwy takes his trips to Douglas every other day. The river is not safe yet to cross and the price of wheat low.

I think you must spend a little fortune in postage stamps, we agree that we should be contented for someone to get a letter once a week. I have written to poor old Olger and I hope soon to hear from her. It does not seem much chance to see you before winter and perhaps the work in winter would be pretty hard for you here. This letter will not arrive in England, so much before Christmas, so I may as well wish you a Merry Christmas and Happy New Year.

Everybody sends their love and is so pleased to hear from you. Letters are always eagerly looked for. All are well and will miss you on Christmas.
With fondest love always,
Your Affectionate
Mama

⁓⦁⟩⦁⁓

Elise helped prepare the poultry and pork for sale in Brandon, but the extra lifting and long hours on her feet proved too much.[25] In bed just before Christmas, wonderful aromas from the kitchen floated up the stairs and carried her away to a happy, long-ago Christmas. Her old Grossmutter had come by mail coach to visit her oldest son and family. At first, she and Wilhelm held back, a little afraid of the wrinkled old woman dressed in black. But before long they cuddled up beside her for stories. *Grossmutter Harrer knew how to keep our fingers out of the batter while mama and the servants did the Christmas baking. I remember it all so clearly.*

"Long, long, long before your papa and your Grossvater were born, there was a baby called Franz Joseph. His mama and papa lived in a beautiful village, a long day's journey by the Postkutsche from us here in Donaueschingen. Stockach was an up and down kind of a place with a castle watching from the hill. The only road went right through the middle of the villiage. A Postkutsche came from the East." She pointed

---

25 November 29, 1901. "Dutchman not well again"

her crooked fingers toward the east. "All the way from Wien and Ungarn." [26] *Then she pointed in the opposite direction, "From Spanien, way over the mountains." Pointing to the south she said, "And from the city of Rom." With a nod to the north, she added, "all the way to the Nordsee. How much farther . . . I don't exactly know. Your papa will know. Ask him when he comes home.*

"Und so it was. When the people heard the horn, 'Tootooraa, TooRaa, TooRaa',

they knew the Postkutsche was coming. Everyone cleared the way to let the horses gallop by. Curious children stood on their tippy-toes to see the passengers and if they hurried to the Gasthof they might see a grand lady or gentleman step down. The coachman changed his tired horses for a fresh team and as soon as his passengers had climbed in, they were off . . . down the hill on the other side of town and away. It was exciting!"

Grossmutter bounced Wilhelm on her knee and sang:

"Hop, hop, hop, Pfärdchen lauf gallop!	*Hop, hop, hop, little horse gallop!*
Über Stock und über Stein,	*Over stick and over stone,*
Aber brich nur nicht den Bein	*But do not break your leg*
Hop, hop, hop, Pfärdchen lauf gallop!	*Hop, hop, hop, little horse gallop!*

Wilhelm wanted to keep galloping, but Grossmutter said, "Not now, our horse is tired. Did you know, Elise, that a real princess stayed overnight in Stockach? Our beautiful Princess Marie Antoinette was on her way to France to marry the prince. Yes, Stockach was a busy village.

"One day the people heard there were bad soldiers coming. 'Gott im Himmel!' What should we do? What should we do?'

"'Hide, that's what. Hide in the forest until the trouble is over.' So Mama and Papa Harrer and their family gathered up their clothes and blankets, and all the food they could carry. Mama carried her new baby Franz Joseph. They walked and walked, deep into the forest. They all got very tired. At last they said, 'We will be safe here. When the soldiers go away we'll go home.' They stayed there until a man came to tell them the soldiers were gone. All the families hurried out of the forest thinking of their warm homes. But—ach, mein Gott! What a shock! All their houses had been knocked down and burned. Arme Leute, so sad. . . . There was nothing but sticks of charred wood sticking up from heaps of stones. . . . Winter was coming, all the papas and

---

26 Vienna and Hungary.

mamas and boys and girls worked very hard to build their homes again. Papa Harrer was helping everyone because he was a Maurer and knew everything about building with stones. They made Stockach a good place to live in again. The mail coaches came, boys and girls went to school, and the people went to church to thank God for helping them through the hard time. Jah, jah, so war es . . . That's how it was."

Grossmutter groaned and said, "I must get up, meine alte Knochen strecken."[27] Wilhelm liked his warm spot on her lap and I liked her stories, so it was not long before we were back under her shawl.

"Baby Franz Joseph grew up to be a fine man and the villagers chose him to be their Ammann. Do you have a Bürgermeister? Franz Joseph was the same as a Bürgermeister, but in those times he was called the Ammann. He had a big job. Wilhelm, hold out your hand. See, you have four fingers and a thumb. Your fingers have a hard time without the thumb, nicht wahr? Is that not so?" Wilhelm and I agreed that our thumbs helped us eat and tie our shoes. "The Ammann was like a thumb and helped all the people of Stockach. If they needed soldiers he must find them. If a man charged another person too much money for his milk, or potatoes, or wine, he made that man pay back the money. He made sure people kept the forest laws about cutting trees. If a teacher told him a student didn't come to school, the Ammann found him. Sometimes poor families needed their children to help with their work, but there was a good rule—every boy and girl must learn to read and write. Jah, everybody's problem was the Ammann's problem!

"Franz Joseph was most happy about building a hospice to care for very sick people. And you'll like this, Wilhelm, he always wore a sword. Franz Joseph stayed on as Ammann of Stockach until he was a very old man, older than I am . . . 86 years old! Jah, you can be proud of your Gross-Grossvater Harrer." Grossmutter patted Wilhelm on the head and said. "That's enough stories for today mein Kinderlein."

Next morning Wilhelm tugged at Grossmutter's big skirt and begged for more stories. She wrapped her shawl around us and continued, "Jah, Franz Joseph was a fine man. He and his Frau Maria Eva had children and the littlest one was a boy they named Andreas. . . . I'll tell you about him in a minute. Remember yesterday, I told you that Franz Joseph was the Ammann for a very long time, but even after that, he didn't stay in his house. He kept on walking around the village visiting. People said, 'Maybe Franz Joseph will live to be one hundred and see the new century, 1800.' But no, he died in 1795. Elise, you have a good head. Can you tell me how many years he lived? . . . The baby in the forest in 1701 until 1795. . . . You say 94. You are right. Sehr gut!"

---

27 My old bones to stretch.

Elise's mind wandered for a moment. *Ninety-four! Wunderbar! I feel old and I'm only 61. Grossmutter Harrer lived to be 71[28] and mama lived to be 77. I think I can't arrive at so many years.*

Elise and Wilhelm were back under their grandmother's shawl, and the story continued. *"Andreas liked music. He played the violin and organ. He studied and studied and became a master teacher. He taught big boys everything they needed to know so they could be teachers. But after his papa died, Andreas decided to leave Stockach and go to the town where his sister Maria Anna lived. Radolfzell was on the shore of a beautiful lake, Bodensee. Boats laden with good things came from far away and*

people traded with the merchants. Radolfzell was my town so that's where we met, your Grossvater and me. He asked me to marry him and we soon had a beautiful little girl with dark eyes like you, Elise. We named her Maria Apolonia, but I called her, my Annastasia. Next year we had a baby boy. My Carl grew up to be your big papa.[29]

"But trouble came to Radolfzell. Ach du lieber! My goodness! Very cruel soldiers with hundreds of horses rode into our town. We couldn't hide. They took our food. They made us feed their horses so we had no hay left for our cows. The soldiers didn't go away

School House, 1658-1824.

like the bad soldiers in Stockach. We didn't like the new laws they made for us, but we had to obey. We had to get permission from the soldiers for everything we wanted to do. They took all our school books and made a big fire in the square. They said, 'No more Austrian books. You must have French books.' But we had no money and couldn't buy new books. Poor Andreas, so many students and no books! And, of course, the children's families couldn't give their teacher any food, so we had nothing but rotten potatoes. It was terrible! We were hungry. . . At that time your Uncle Friedrich was born."

Grossmutter stopped talking . . . .

28 Catharina, Harrer nee Reuthemann, age 71 widow of Andreas Harrer of Radolfzell, died in Mannheim, January 15, 1851. Family Page of Andreas Harrer from the rectory in Radolfzell. Her will provided same information.

29 Carl, born October 2, 1805. Friedrich, born June 19, 1808. Records obtained from the archivist Achim Fenner, Radolfzell, who had published a book on the history of education in the town and was familiar with Andreas Harrer. Fenner obtained other information from the Catholic Church protocols in Radolfzell.

Was she asleep, we wondered? Wilhelm wiggled and Grossmutter remembered us. *"Everyone was upset. Many people got so very hungry they died. My sweet Anastasia died too. It was a very sad time. At last the bad soldiers went away and the Grand Duke of Baden became our ruler. He was good and kind, but our troubles were not over. We had more bad years because our crops and the grapes failed. But your papa and Uncle Friedrich grew up and went to Stockach to start working for the Post. And now, here I am with you in your big house. Gott sei Dank! Thank God! We cannot say it too many times. . . . Do you smell something good? Maybe your mama will give you a little cake now."*[30]

Elise's little room was dark when Cecil brought her tea. She was not as anxious to eat as she was hungry for company. He lit the lamp, she nibbled a little. But she really wanted to talk. "I've been whiling away the hours remembering my grandmother's stories. You missed out on having a grandmother to hug you . . .to tell you stories of the olden days. Perhaps, one day you'll have time and I'll tell you. Grossmutter Harrer came to visit us for my ninth birthday and soon after she went away our papa died and . . ." Elise's voice failed. Cecil knew she was remembering and waited until she said, "It seems like only yesterday, I loved my papa."

Cecil took her hand and said, "I know, Mama."

"Before I'm gone, I have so much to tell you about my mother's family in Heidelberg, Uncle Friedrich Harrer, your great-uncle, and my cousins. Great-uncle knew all about the Harrers from long ago when they were nobles in Styria, a part of Austria. He had their coat of arms on his wall. I see it clearly—a springing golden lion with

Graz, Capital of Styria.

30 Sources: Wagner, Hans. *Aus Stockachs Vergangenheit.* Other sources: papers, pictures and pre 1900 history book from Hans-Eugen Harrer. Catholic Church records, archivists in Stockach, Freiburg, Donaueschingen, and Radolfzell.

a red tongue and above it a visor with long plumes. Out of the helmet sprang another lion." Cecil looked confused. "I should draw it for you sometime. Yes, Uncle Friedrich was very proud of it. He told us, 'You children have something to live up to.' Your ancestor, Matheus, town judge in Wels, received it way back in 1453 in recognition of his honesty and pure moral values. And you, his rightful heirs, are entitled to its "Schutz, Schirm und Salva Guardia."[31]

"I want to listen, Mama, but I can't keep my eyes open."

"I'm sorry. I've been lying here in bed all day and I have so much more to tell you about our Ritters [knights]. . . . It's hard to think of Christmas without Harry. Minnie thought it was for the best to help Harry, but it certainly got her into trouble with Mr. C. I miss her and her letters." She held out her hands, "I have you, my dear boy. A mother could never have a better son."

❦

The dust from the girls' sweeping before Christmas touched off Norman's bronchitis. So with him not well, and no jokes from Harry, and not even a letter from Minnie, a noticeable shadow hung over their festivities. Elise felt thankful, nonetheless. *Isabel has her own responsibilities. I have Edwy's little family with Thyra's chatter and Baby Rupert to sing to sleep. I feel a special bond with our little prince. And Cecil, I mustn't forget Cecil.*

Harry's Christmas greetings included a card for everyone but Tolly. Elise noticed and said, "Harry didn't mean to miss you. I'll write him. He'll send you a special letter."

Aweme Manitoba, 27th Dec 1901

My dear boy!

Your letter and nice Christmas card has given me so much pleasure, you seem to have thought of all but poor Tolly, he did not say anything, but seemed to feel it very much, that there was no card for him. I am sure it must be a mistake; you

---

31 Harrer, Hans-Eugen, Lörrach, Germany. His Grandfather Harrer's letter and sketch. *'Adelstand und Verbesserung des ihren Voreltern de dato, 1453, verliehenen Wappens für alle.'* It outlined the nobility, with a coat of arms, bestowed upon Matheus Harrer in Graz, Austria, in 1453, and amended in Vienna in 1630 to "Joachim Harrer, Town Judge, Wels, Austria, and also to Michael and their sister." GOD IS MY HELP AND SHIELD

never meant to leave him out. I hope you spent a happy Christmas and will find the new year brings you all the luck you want. Christmas here was rather dull after the dinner, everybody was so quiet, everybody thought of you and we drank your health with the boys once again in the evening.

You want me exactly to tell you how I feel, my feelings are very mixed, sometimes I feel it very much, that I can't have you all round me, other times I try to comfort myself that things might have gone worse.

. . . I am glad you don't give up all sports, they pretty soon found out you are a good player. I have had a very sad and mysterious letter from Olger, that something or somebody [has] been unkind to her, poor soul, who always was such a good friend to me. I was in hope, you see her more, but you never mention her name. How is it, surely you might find time to see her.

I can quite understand that you miss Mr. Tulk, I suppose you will get some letters from him from India. Mr. Denny [Will]was so kind as to send me a pretty card, you must thank him and Mrs. Denny for me. I don't think I thanked you yet for mine.

I have to close now with the best wishes for you my dear boy,
I always am your Affectionate Mama

Between Christmas and New Year's, the triumphant cricket players travelled with the rest of the Millford team to Ninette for the club's annual celebration. Edwy brought the bat he had received for the highest number of runs to show his mother. She ran her fingers over Edwy Vane so beautifully engraved on the brass nameplate. "You've done well, my boy!"

"I won't get an award for my other statistics. The last couple of years I've written down each night how far and where I went on family business. I thought you'd be interested to see how the miles add up. Last year I walked 1,579 miles, and with the horses drove 2,598 miles.[32] This year the driving is about the same, but my walking has gone up to almost 1,900. Stuart and Evelyn are doing more field work so they take the horses. I don't wonder that Harry is not in a hurry to come home, he'll be getting soft over there."

Noticing tears in his mother's eyes he added, "I know you miss him, but don't be worrying. He's enjoying life while he's waiting. He won't be back as long as he has hope for his girl."

Edwy picked up his bat and went down to The Palace to celebrate with Emily. His mother, with her feet on the oven door, reflected on their conversation. *If Edwy thinks I can stop worrying, he doesn't understand a mother's love. I will worry until I take my last breath. Each and every day I pray: Gott im Himmel watch over my children.*

---

32   Vane, Edwy. Yearly Records. Family collection.

	June
	Driving

8	Treebank	13
4	Home	
7	Belmont + Back	42
8 Sun		
9	Half way to Douglas + back etc	17
10	Treebank + back	13
14+13	Home	
14	Treebank + back	13
15	To Ferry + back	7
17	Home wet day	
19	Putting out Pow's Green N	4
20	etc To I + back	5
21	Treebank	13
23+24	Brandon by Chater + Hills	56
25	To River very high water, highest since 1832 + still rising ferry stopped cable broken by log raft	8
26+27	Haying on I	15
28	" " "	14
29	Pateleys + Martins	9
		229

	June
	Walking

Sun 1st 2	Plays? putting in corn etc	12
3	Sutcliffes from Treebank + back	7
5+6	Seeding at Plays etc + coopers	440
7	Home from Belmont from cooper	8
12	Martins + Treebank	16
14	Treebank to coopers + back	6
16	Pateleys + I	6
18	" " etc	7
20	Ploughing on I etc	8
21	Coopers for cricket	8
22	Bellhouses etc	4
23+24	Brandon	15
27	Haying on I River at ~~~	9
30	~~Ploughing~~	
30	Pateleys etc hunting horse	10
		156

Chapter Twenty-eight

Hans Kuony's Advice

The winter of 1902 was unusual. For the first time since their arrival, there was not enough snow to make winter roads. No sleighing meant no grain hauled to the elevator. So, for the needed cash the boys were sent to the bush to cut stove wood—40 cords at 40 cents per cord.

A snowfall in mid-February finally allowed the transfer of the wagon box from wheels to sleigh, and Edwy's daily 26-mile marathon began. He'd load wheat for Treesbank, sell it, and drive on to the mill in Wawanesa to purchase weed seeds for horse and chicken feed. His mother worried less now that Emily welcomed him in from the cold with a hot meal. *It's a tall order for her to keep their clothes washed and mended, the bread baked, the butter churned, the chickens fed, the eggs gathered, with two busy little ones at her feet. But she does it.*

The municipality paid the Criddles 15 cents an hour to build a new road south to the ferry. It was necessary now that McManes' old farm was being fenced for Mooney's cattle.[1] Mr. Criddle, still grieving his bridge, told them, "Had the precious Council helped, all the money they've been wasting these last years would have been saved. We would have a real good road at all seasons, whereas now – there must always be a week or two spring and autumn when there's no crossing the river for love or money. But such are councilors ever – dull heads and boodlers."

Elise shook her head. *Why didn't he run for Council and get his bridge? But bridges can fail too. I remember our Neckar River overflowing its banks. Many Heidelberg bridges were washed away. Only our Alte Brücke survived.[2] And Major Roger's bridge in Millford was gone as soon as it was built. At least ferries can be pulled up to high ground until the danger is over.*

---

1 Feb. 12, 1902. ". . . Municipality has to brush and grade a new one . . . a nice little job as there are several hundred rounds of muskeg and swamp to obliterate."
2 'Old Bridge' built in 1786-88. Our travels to Heidelberg showed flood levels and dates on an abutment. One very high water level was in 1845 when Elise was five and lived probably just above it.

Edwy kept hauling until a warm, windy day spoiled the roads. The wagon box went back on wheels and he told his mother, "I have to keep going even if my poor bones rattle right out of their sockets." He rumbled over the frozen roads, like a train crossing Millford's railway bridge.

Edwy gave his mother a letter one evening that really set her hands trembling with excitement. "A letter from Minnie! At last! It's almost a year since the trouble over Harry." Edwy waited as his mother read her short note and looked up with a smile, "Isn't it wonderful of Minnie to write. I'll answer right away. Will you post it for me?"

Aweme, Manitoba Feb 14, 1902

My dear Minnie,

I am glad to hear you enjoyed the dance the other night and have not quite so much work to do. I had a letter from Olger the other day, she has seen Harry at Christmas time and says he looks quite well. She will send you her photograph as soon as she looks a little better.

I have worn the slippers you gave me last year and wore the soles right out, but the tops are quite good yet and perhaps I can get a sole like it in Brandon to put on.

Harry was at a dance the other night and seems quite happy again. I am so pleased and will be contented.

I hope we shall hear from you soon again, goodbye now dear Minnie, with love from us all, I remain,

Your affectionate
Mama

March came in bright and cold, but without snow. Folks worried, "We're bound to pay for this good weather later on."

In mid-March their fears came true when the country was brought to a standstill. Mr. Criddle recorded the blizzard's progress.

March 14: Deuced heavy gale and a lot of snow (2 in. or so) in night.

11.20 AM – Temp got down to about 1 degree above zero. 'Twas something like 44 degrees at this time yestdy! Wind still blowing hard (force 7) – cloudy – Barom. has got up to 28.64.

7 PM – Wind worse this last half hour – force 8 – still cloudy – Barom. falling.

8.40 PM – A very beastly evening and house jolly cold. Barom. still falling – now 28.634. . .

Mar 15 – A very beastly morning after a very beastly night – snow – blizzard (One can't see much more than 30 yds) N.E. gale – our room last night 38 degrees; sitting [room] min. 10.5

9.15 AM – Storm pretty bad – at times the flag pole is half obscured – snowing still – as well as blizzarding – Barom. falling.

9.50 AM – Barom. falling rather fast – now 28.368. Storm if anything worse.

10.25 AM – Storm very bad – almost a record – Barom. still falling fast – Temp in Sitting room only 42 with a good fire going!

10.55 AM – Things as bad as ever – but I have a notion that the Barom. has begun to rise.

11 AM – No change – unless for the worse – Barom. down to 28.312 – house damnably cold.

Noon – Barom still falling and storm worse than ever – and still snowing.

12.35 PM – Barom. still falling - 28.308 – storm about the same as at noon.

12.45 PM – Barom down again 28.295. Storm certainly worse now – Flagpole decidedly foggy at times and we can seldom glimpse over 30 yds.

In spite of the storm the livestock needed food and water. Elise watched as Cecil dressed to go out and couldn't resist saying, "Do take care. It's so easy to lose one's way in a storm."

"I'll be back with the milk, Mama. Don't worry. I won't get lost."

Later on he blew in with a blast of wind and snow and pushed the door shut. "It's beastly out there alright. Edwy was out, milked their cow and helped me pump water and get the horses and cows to the trough." The rest of the day Cecil struggled through the snowdrifts to the woodpile. They stoked the fires to red hot, but couldn't get the temperature above 61°. Poking his nose outdoors later, Mr. Criddle reported: "Bad as ever, hardly able to breathe – snow in one's eyes – ears – everywhere. Great drifts in front of house – fowl house – and Heaven knows where else."

As the wind whistled and the log walls groaned, Elise wrapped her shawl more tightly around her shoulders. *I'll never forget that first cruel winter when we went out to find wood. The children were so brave. . . . It's a wonder we survived.*

At 3:40 and then again at 4:00 the weatherman reported, "Can still see the flagpole." Ten minutes later, "Six or eight feet of our flagpole out of sight – Barom. still falling – 28.240." And so it continued, every few minutes—another report: "Barometer down from 28.221 to 28.220. It goes down – down." Twenty minutes later; "Rose to 28.226." By 5:25 he was overjoyed: "28.244 and rising at last. I think I may now safely say that this is the worst storm that we've ever had in the shape of a blizzard."

The family drifted off to bed leaving him with his barometer and the wind, until he wrote:

1.50 AM – No really bad gusts of late and generally speaking – matters are improving – so as it's getting cold, I shall go to bed.

He picked up his diary again in the morning:

Sunday, Mar 16 9.15 AM – A very disagreeable morn – semi-blizzard – Wind NNW force 6 – slight snow. Norman has been down in Wood to measure snow — he makes out that about 11 inches have fallen since Friday evening — I've knocked off an inch.

The blizzard blew itself out late that afternoon. They found their cattle, but a yearling had already frozen and a second calf died soon after. On Wednesday Edwy was in Treesbank hoping for mail and heard tales of hardship from the alighting passengers. He had no letter for his mother but told her the news. "Friday's train came today. It was clean snowed up near Treherne. The travellers had a miserable walk to town. I heard too that a 14-year-old boy, south somewhere, went to the stable and didn't come back. They haven't found him yet. Cecil said you were worried about him. Binder twine comes in handy for weather like this for guiding his way."

⚜

Elise's winter cold settled in her head, throat, and chest, but she was determined to get a letter away to Harry and asked for paper.

Aweme, Manitoba, 21ˢᵗ March, 1902

My dear boy!

I ought to have written before, but I have not been very well lately. Mr. C says it is catarrh.[3] It is nothing serious and must not worry you, only it is very uncomfortable. I feel stuffed up and must breathe through my mouth all the time. Mr. C does not exactly know what is good for it and will write to Dr. Husband about it.

I am sorry Olger was ill, poor old girl seems never to be very well. She was delighted you came to see her at Christmas time, she sent me a card, and I sent her one that Norman painted for me.

I am glad you enjoy yourself with your friends. I have not heard you mention anything about taking land. I suppose you gave it up. We have had a two day's snow storm, mails are therefore delayed, a train was buried 30 feet in snow.

I will write to you again very soon.

Love from all,

ever your affectionate

Mama

⚜

A few weeks later Edwy was in again and called from the open door, "Mail! Two letters for you, Mama. I can't stay, have the horses. You can tell me later."

Harry's were never long so she opened his first, and smiled. He'd gone skating and everyone cleared off the ice to watch his manoeuvers. Then she opened Minnie's.

---

3 Inflammation of the mucous membranes associated with colds and chesty coughs, but can also be found in patients with infections of the adenoids, middle ear, sinus, or tonsils. The phlegm produced by catarrh may either discharge or cause a blockage which may become chronic.

"My dear Mama,

I have a surprise for you. I'm getting married to Jim Brandon on April 2nd. . . ."

Elise blinked and read it again. *Gracious! Can it be?* She looked at the date. *Gott im Himmel, that's past already. . . . My Minnie is married!* She tried to keep calm as her heart raced. When Beatrice, through habit, reached for the letter, Elise passed it to her. There was a moment of silence and then a scream. **"Minnie's married!"** Everyone within earshot came running. Such a hubbub! What a shock for everyone! Minnie hadn't given Mr. Criddle a chance to prevent the calamity. He snarled: "I might have saved her! She's gone and married a Canadian! A Methodist! And Irish to boot!"

But for Elise, it was important that her daughter was happy. *My Minnie is thirty-two years old. Surely she can be trusted to make her own decisions.*

Elise would have been surprised to know her daughter's answers to the clergyman's questions. "Religion?" "Episcopalian."[4] "Father's name?" "Percy Henry Vane."[5]

She responded to her daughter joyfully:

6 April, 1902

My dear Minnie,

I cannot express enough my delight at the news, which came so very unexpected as we had not even an inkling of such a thing. The idea that you have a home of your own makes me very happy. I have the greatest wishes for your happiness and know that you deserve it.

With fond love, I am your
Affectionate
Mama

Nor did Mr. Criddle dampen his wife's enthusiasm:

St. Albans, Aweme Apr 6, 1902

My dear old Lady,

We did not get your letter till yesterday, so I presume by now you are Mrs. James (is that it?). Our very best wishes are yours for health and happiness, and you know you have our love. It is good you have found a loving husband and a home of your own. Please give him my congratulations for he has got a first rate wife. Write again when you can. Lots of love and good wishes.

Yours affectionately,
Alice Criddle

---

4   The Episcopal Church was the former Church of England in the United States.
5   Henry: proper form of Harry. Marriage record: Minnie Vane and James Falls Brandon married at Kinsmore in the evening of April 2, 1902. Her mother, Ellise [sic] Harrer, and father, Percy Henry Vane. Witnesses, Matthew and Mary Brandon, Jim's brother and sister. Information from Minnie's granddaughter, Myrna Vane Brandon Paquette as recorded by Manitoba Vital Statistics.

In the spring of 1902, the river ice was exceedingly thick due to the lack of snow. Then, the blizzard's huge dump of snow was immediately followed by warm weather. The resulting runoff set in motion such a course of events that people talked of nothing else. Gullies flooded the creeks; the creeks filled the rivers and all that water lifted the still solid centre ice. On Thursday, March 27, the Clarks looked down from the bank above the Assiniboine and witnessed an incredible sight. The ice heaved, buoyed upward by the force of the rising water. Then with thunderous grinding, the solid ice broke into huge blocks and, borne on the raging water, rampaged downriver. Trees were mowed down like matchsticks and their floating trunks joined the wreckage already on the move. Everything in the water's path gave way, until downstream, north of Glenboro, blocks of ice and debris jammed the channel. The backed-up waters flooded low lying farms.[6]

Elise was in the kitchen when Edwy brought news of a tragedy. "A young English couple saw the water rising and were driving as fast as they could to safety. But the water was so deep the wagon box floated off the wheels. In spite of the farmer's best efforts, his dear young wife died in the freezing water."[7]

Elise remembered fording the river—clutching the side of the wagon box as the water came higher. *Edwy told me, "Don't worry." I had reason to worry. How many times have my boys escaped the clutches of that river? Thank God I still have three living sons.*

Edwy continued, "I'm sorry to say, but I've got more bad news. Just southeast of Millford a fellow, I don't know him, was driving young Arthur Hibbert further west to work next morning. His horse stopped at the bridge over Oak Creek. In the darkness they didn't see the bridge was gone and urged the horse ahead. Down they went into the raging water. The driver got out, but his horse and the young fellow drowned."[8] Elise gasped in horror.

"Bloody awful isn't it! But he forced his horse. Don't worry; I won't be falling into the creek. I trust my team. If they stop, they have a reason."

With all the flooding, St. Albans' mail waited. Edwy, anxious to wish his sister well, told Emily, "Minnie will be looking for our letters. I'll try to get across tomorrow." So Emily put the potatoes on to boil and wrote a note.

---

6   March 29, 1902. "Water rose 10 feet – Lots of wreckage, etc, floating down – the Souris rose 15 ft – and they say all the Bridges are gone – bar the railway at Millford. Flats everywhere under water – a pretty to-do. . . ."
7   Edwy's diary and Manitoba Free Press, March 28, 1902 re Mrs. Thomas (Maude) Hopkins. "*The Hopkinson Saga,*" in *Beneath the Long Grass* gives more detail.
8   The Gazette of Glenboro reported: There was a large attendance at Mrs. Hopkinson's funeral considering the state of the roads, over forty rigs being in the procession. The Gazette, Glenboro, Manitoba. April 4, 1902. Vol. XI, No. 14, page 1.

April 10, 1902

My dear Minnie,

Your letter was a great surprise to me. We are all very pleased with the news, especially your Mama, who looked happier last Sunday than I have seen her for many a day. She told me then that she has never been happy at the thought of your working so hard.

Your letter is so very incoherent that we are anxiously awaiting further news. Edwy has been waiting to get to Treesbank but the ice is still going down the river in chunks and it is hardly safe. However, this will let you see he has managed it. We had a nice letter from Harry. We are all very well.

In haste, with love, Yours affectionately, Emily

Edwy, on whom everyone depended to boat safely over the swirling waters, had written earlier.

Aweme, April 6th, 1902

My dear Minnie,

We only got your exciting letter yesterday so that by now you have been married four days.

Well, old girl, if good wishes and congratulations count for anything in the future, your happiness ought to be complete.

Your husband is a deuced lucky fellow and must be a rattler to deserve you. As a Sister you can't be equaled and at any rate you have heaps of love in return for all that you have done in years gone by for your own people, that is Mother, brothers and sister. In a kind of a way we feel that we are losing you, at the same time, I don't see how we can see less of you than of the last few years.

I will go to Treesbank tomorrow specially to get (I hope) a letter from you. Everyone is very pleased at the news and Mama looks a great deal better since she got your letter.

Edwy's good intentions came to naught. He got to the river and wisely decided to turn back. Later, when he made another attempt to post Emily's letter, he added to his own:

Thursday, April 10th, Emily's birthday.

I have not had a chance of sending this but will try and make Treesbank this afternoon.

Treesbank:

No letter from you so with heaps of love to you both,
I remain,
Always your loving brother,
Edwy

<hr />

Each of Minnie's letters gave her mother fresh reasons to celebrate. *My daughter has a home of her own and a housekeeper! And water that doesn't have to be pumped from a well where the animals drink and be carried across the yard. I wonder if Percy will hold on to his grudge.*

Minnie's home. Errecting a windmill to pump water.

She wrote again:

Aweme, Manitoba 24th April, 1902.

My dear Minnie,

Your letter to Edwy and Bobby has given everybody the greatest joy. The idea that you have everything to make you happy is such a blessing. It is not very often that my wishes get fulfilled. I never thought I should have them gratified and feel so thankful about it. How pleased Harry will be.

I had a letter from Harry the other day, it is undecided, whether he will come back in August, or take up a little land. He says he will know more about it when Mr. Tulk comes back, so I suppose he has hope of his help. I hope he will, though of course, I should dearly like to have him back here, but it won't do, to be selfish. My only wish is to see all my children happy.

. . . . Have you written to Olger? I have been waiting for a letter from her since January. I hope she is not ill with smallpox which is very bad at Battersea. I want to send her one of Edwy's photos but don't like to till I hear from her.

I need not tell you how I wish to see you and husband. I suppose it can't be till the seeding is over. Write often now you have time. Give my kind regards to your husband.

With fond love from everybody
Your affectionate
Mama

❦

Elise heard the whip-poor-will and her heart sang along. *Minnie is writing again. Harry is seeing Mr. Tulk.*

But the birds' songs were more of a dirge for Mr. Criddle. Six calves had died for no apparent reason; his rheumatic shoulder was so painful he couldn't play his organ; too many weeds had come up in the wheat; and the 'skeeters' were the worst he'd ever known. He put it all down to 'damned bad luck'.

Edwy, though, was just as pleased as his mother. He and Minnie had always been close and now that she'd opened the door, he picked up as if they'd never been separated.

May 10th, 1902

My dear Minnie,

Cecil got your letter this morning and of course we all read same. Many thanks for photos and newspapers. . . .

Well like all the rest of the girls, when they first get married you seem very happy and I don't wonder at it. You are mighty lucky but there you deserve everything that is good. You have got a lovely home by the look of it but, of course, that is nothing compared to Jim—any old shanty would do so long as he was there. We are all looking forward to seeing him. Will Jim let us call him Jim? I guess he will, anyhow it don't matter for he will get it anyhow.

Does he smoke and is he fond of sport, though I should rather imagine with the big Farm he has that he finds all the sport he wants looking after same.

I am glad you live 14 miles south of Hamiota instead of 14 North for it gives me a chance of going to see you. I am getting fairly good with the bicycle now so if I can make time, expect me some time hence. I will take all your things to Brandon as desired which will be I expect in about a week or ten days.

You say Jim and you are going there. Is there any chance of meeting you? Bobby is crazy to see you and if I knew when you were to be there supposing the weather was decent, I would make a point of going the same time. Your letters arrive somewhere about a week after being written. I don't know how long ours take, perhaps it can't be managed.

You must let us know what you would like for a present. We would like to give you something that you haven't got. Be sure in your next letter to tell us what you would fancy.

Bye the bye, now you have got Jim you won't have any use for your stamp collection. If I am right, just hand them over to yours truly and I will remember you in my dreams. Our wheat is all in and most of it up. Looks fine for we have had lots of wet. . . .

Thyra was writing to Auntie Minnie yesterday, but I am afraid her letter is both lost and unreadable. She has not forgotten you in the least and has got a memory like yours, hot and convenient, also very inconvenient some times, little monkey.

Wishing you both all the happiness and success in and for the future, I remain always,

Your loving brother,

Edwy

Wagon boxes full of love from everybody. Bobby has just asked me to tell you that it is now time to plant all flower seeds. Treesbank in the morning to post letter, Bye Bye.

Edwy gathered his sister's belongings and as soon as the girls arranged the date, they met up with Minnie at Isabel's. They chatted about the wedding, their gifts, and her new home.[9] Finally Beatrice brought up the subject of their mother's health—stuffed up, congested chest, stomach problems. Minnie was surprised, "I've been wrapped up in my own happiness. Mama's letters were so cheerful. I never thought her so poorly."

Beatrice added, "Papa's been to Wawanesa and talked to the doctor, says there's little he can advise.[10] I'll tell your mother about your wedding, but you should come out soon. She'd be so pleased to see you."

No sooner was Edwy home than Norman wanted to be driven to Douglas, where he expected a job teaching farmers about grasshopper control.[11] The job had evaporated, and frustrated, Norman arrived home to an angry father. To regain his composure Norman walked west of the stables to check the trees they'd planted and found 11 maples hadn't leafed out. To that news, his father was more sympathetic, "Your trees were doing splendidly last year – at least ten feet high. I fancy blight at the roots caused the mischief."

Elise remembered Harry watering the little trees night after night before he went away. *Harry wasn't here.*

Everyone's attention shifted to the news from South Africa: bloody fighting and heavy Canadian casualties. But what really soured the milk for Mr. Criddle was the generous terms the British were offering to end the war. He almost howled, "Canadians are giving £3,000,000 to rebuild farm houses!"[12] It was all too much. Complaining of shortness of breath, he moaned, "I shall perhaps decease on the jump some fine day."

Again he turned to his diary:

Could I listen to my heart, I'd jolly soon know what's wrong. As for submitting to an examination from a local doctor – why – I might as well send for a chimney sweep. Sometimes I fancy the whole business has something to do with the nervous system. I've been getting more or less mentally nervous – get dazed and brought to a standstill – for instance – at Whist – can't remember what are trumps – or what was my partner's original lead – or say whether the King of a suit is still in. Next hand perhaps I may be playing 1st rate again – but nervous excitement (playing with outsiders for dollars – for instance) is the keynote to the situation.

---

9   May 21, 1902. ". . . Bobby is going too – her very 1st trip to that ancient city since we came out here."
10   June 4, 1902. "Sundry chats with the Doctor – also sundry libations."
11   May 28, 1902.
12   June 4, 1902.

The flooded river subsided and the ferry opened for business. Then the sky opened and rain poured down. The river rose so quickly during the night that the rising water snapped the ferry cable. Clark's boat went down the river leaving the St. Albanites completely cut off from Treesbank again.

Fearing for Brandon's bridges, Edwy was dispatched to the customs office to fetch another 12-cubic-foot box for Mrs. Criddle.[13] And since Jim Brandon's fields were wet, he acted on Beatrice's advice and brought Minnie and Isabel to see their mother. Tears of joy trickled down her boney cheeks as she greeted first Minnie, who introduced her new husband, then Isabel, Will and little Violet May.

Mr. and Mrs. Criddle invited them not only in, but to the sitting room for a cup of tea. Little May ran off to play with Alma while Isabel boiled the kettle and visited with her mother. As the tea steeped, Isabel suggested, "You should go in and enjoy the visit.

"I've never sat with the guests. What if I'm not wanted?"

"Minnie brought Jim to meet you, Mama. I'll serve the tea and join them too. We needn't say anything."

So with Mr. Criddle's low opinion of Canadians ringing in her ears, Elise did as Isabel suggested. *I do so want Minnie's husband to make a good impression.*

Jim Brandon

The conversation was rather strained at first, but the men soon took over from Minnie and Mrs. Criddle. All went well. When Jim announced it was time to go, Cecil brought the team to the door, handed Jim the lines, and took his place as header. Elise watched the Knights climb up to the rumble seat, while Jim assisted Minnie. He stepped up and, seated beside his wife, nodded to Cecil let go his hold on the bridles. Jim flicked the whip, and off they went amid a chorus of goodbyes. Elise's eyes were teary, but her face glowed with pride and thankfulness. As the dust settled, Mr. Criddle commented, "Seems to have seen a lot of the world – got a goodish head – but wets his whistle, I fancy, a little too much!"

I needn't have worried. Minnie's husband seems a bit too forward, but she is happy and that makes me happy. She was anxious to pass the good news on to Harry.

Aweme, Manitoba July 21, 1902

My dear Harry!

No doubt you heard that Minnie and her husband was [sic] here and actually at the house. Everything is all right here between P.C. and her, is it not wise.

---

13 June 24, 1902. "Old clothes – 3 very nice dresses for her – 5 coats (2 great), 5 breeches, 4 westcoats – all wearable. One of the Greatcoats (for Norman) is excellent. Sundry skirts, bodies, etc, several hats and bonnets – A suit for Talbot – a variety of boots, etc, and some books – 5 of 'em A-1. also a variety of lace, odds and ends etc. etc."

I wish Minnie's husband had more manners. He is pretty rough, but of course Minnie thinks so well of him that I would not like to undermine her. Dido and Will were here also.

Mrs. C has her box and as usual good many things. The heat was very great lately and I did not feel well at all. I never do in this weather.

I shall have to say goodbye now. With fond love and best wishes for your welfare, I am

Your affectionate
Mama

The Criddle/Vane cricket players had to boat themselves across the flooding rivers for their league games. As soon as the water level went down they helped get the ferry back on the river. In the process the ferryman's rope caught the main cable and pulled the unfortunate Palmer into the drink. He'd have been a goner, had the rope not let go.[14] Unfazed, the players carried on and played so well Millford retained the cup for another year. The money for the team photo was given with muted pride, "You could have played less cricket, put more time into fighting the hoppers."

Will Knight, concerned about his health, drove out with his family to consult Mr. Criddle. Their overnight stay meant little May could pay her Grandmother Vane a bedtime visit. "I'm not able to sing, but I can talk. Would you like a story, Violet May?"

Up she climbed and snuggled under grandma's shawl. Isabel said, "I've not heard your stories for a very long time," and carried in a chair. So, propped up in bed, Grandma Vane was ready. "Ever so long ago, my little granddaughter, when kings lived in castles, there was a jester called Hans Kuony. He wore a suit of bright colours and a hat with a long tassel. If you saw him at the fair you would call him a clown. It was a jester's job to sing and tell stories to keep people happy. One day the duke—same as a king—the duke called him to the hall in his castle where he was eating with his friends. He told his jester; 'Tomorrow I am going to fight against the Swiss people. Sing me a song and say something to bring me luck.' Hans Kuony thought and thought. He did not like the idea of his duke going into the mountains to fight. He said to himself, 'It is a bad idea. Something awful might happen to our duke.' Anyway, he had to do as he was asked. He sang one of his master's favourite songs. Then he said, 'If you want to have luck against the Swiss listen carefully. This is my advice: *Ihr ratet wohl, wie Ihr in die Schwyz hineinkommen wollt, nicht aber heraus*'" The little girl looked puzzled.

---

14 July 15, 1902

Elise said, "I know; you don't understand. He lived in Germany. Do you want to know what he said?"

May nodded. "Hans Kuony told the duke, 'You have thought carefully about how to get into Switzerland, but you haven't thought about how to get back out.'

"The duke was angry. 'I don't care, for your advice. I'm going anyway.' Next morning he said, 'I'll soon be back.' He lined up his soldiers and they marched away behind the duke on his beautiful white horse.

"The Swiss soldiers were expecting the duke and his army. They came out of their hiding places and mowed the duke's army down like grass." Elise swept her arm from side to side like a scythe. "They all died, even the great Duke Leopold himself. I know because my family came from Hans Kuony's town, Stockach.[15] Too bad the duke didn't listen. We should think about what **might** happen. Do you like your mama's china teacups?" May nodded. "You might like to climb up on a chair and take one out of the cupboard. If it should fall and break, then what? Would you say, 'I didn't mean to break it?'" The little girl nodded. "Your mama knows you didn't do it on purpose, but she would be very sad and cross. Hans Kuony would say, 'Try to think carefully about what might happen. Stop before you get into trouble.' It's a good rule for grownups too. Yes, Hans Kuony can save us a lot of trouble.

"Now, my dear little one, I think it's bedtime. Come back in the morning. I have another story." They had a big hug, and Isabel took her daughter off to bed.

Next morning May came with her mother carrying a bowl of warm porridge. Elise tried a spoonful and handed back the bowl, "Thank you, but I'm not so hungry this morning. Do we have time for another story before you go?" May climbed up on the bed and snuggled up beside her grandma.

"My papa told me this story when I was little like you. It happened in Radolfzell, the town where he was born. The people liked to have a big party, the night before Lent. Everybody enjoyed Fastnacht. All the grownups, all the boys and girls dressed up in fancy clothes and put on horribly scary masks." Elise screwed up her face and stuck out her tongue. The little girl giggled. "They had a big parade. Then everybody danced and sang and ate up every pancake they had made to use up all their fat. Well, one year things were different. Bad soldiers came. They said, 'You have to stay inside your house. No visiting! <u>No</u> parties!' **No Fastnacht.**

"People were very sad. They begged, 'Please, **please**, can we go out, just **once**? We always celebrate **Fastnacht**.'

---

15 A tradition instituted by the Archduke's brother continues each year since 1352, when a current Jester has the privilege to conduct a mock trial of an important politician of his choice at the annual 'Karneval Fastnacht.'

"The soldiers said, '**No**, you can't go out. You want to celebrate **Fastnacht** outside your house? You'll have to lean out your windows.'

"They all grumbled, 'What a terrible time this is—we can't celebrate Fastnacht.'

"A clever young man looked at a window frame leaning against the wall of his kitchen. 'I have an idea. I'll put my head through it and play a trick on the soldiers.'[16]

"He put on his clown costume. The he picked up the empty frame and stuck his head through. They told us 'If you want to celebrate Fastnacht put your head out your window.' He said, 'Jah, jah, that is what I am doing.'

"Then he walked out his door. He sang and danced all up and down the streets. People heard him and leaned out of their windows. They sang too and pretty soon all the people were happy. Even the bad soldiers laughed.

"You are clever too, little Violet May. If you have trouble, think about what you can do. Maybe you'll find a way to be happy. When I'm feeling sad, I say to myself. 'Is there something I can do about this?' Sometimes I find a way. Sometimes not. And then I sing a song, or say a poem, and I feel better. I hope you will do that too.

"Well now, that's the end of my story. I think your papa is getting the horses to take you home. I am happy you came to visit. Please come back. Have you a goodbye kiss for your grandma? . . . And my dear Isabel, I can not thank you enough for coming to see me."

❦

Elise had put on a brave front, but it was clear to Isabel that her mother was no longer the strong, resilient woman everyone depended on. She wrote to Harry; "Please write to Mama often if you're not coming home, and be sure to make your letters cheerful."

❦

Elise's days downstairs had shortened, yet she liked to feel a part of things. She peeled potatoes to help the girls or kept her needle weaving up and down darning holes in socks. The summer's hot, dreadfully windy days soon erased the memory of too much rain. The promising grain shriveled until the boys thought it was too late for rain to do any good. Mr. Criddle watched the clouds, counted the raindrops, and mourned the loss of yet another crop. "My luck is damnable and always was. Forever everything taking turns in the wrong direction."

Cecil packed his inlaid boxes and picture frames to go to Brandon to be entered in the fair. His mother felt sure he would be as successful as Norman. When Edwy took the boys, she imagined Cecil's joy. *His eyes will grow big when he*

---

16 Memorial statue for the "Deutsche Revolution in Baden, 1848-49," in Radolfzell town square.

sees the golden letters, 'First Prize' on a big red ribbon. Everyone will congratulate him. She waited expectantly for their return.

Cecil came in quietly and said, "Don't cry, Mama. No prize. They gave me a notice; my entry was disqualified . . . 'not properly entered'."

After tea on August 24, Mr. Criddle stood up and cleared his throat. "It would be remiss not to call attention to the importance of this day." Everyone looked puzzled. "Twenty years ago we established ourselves here in the great Northwest. We haven't got on very well, but might have done worse. We've lost nothing – are worth one thing with another, eight or ten thousand dollars – and are all alive and kicking. . . . "

Elise stopped listening. She was remembering ever so many brushes with death: *freezing, the river, accidents, whooping cough, abscesses, falls, hockey pucks, and barbed wire. . . . I am still kicking, but how much longer?*

Mr. Criddle had suggested during the Knights' earlier visit that Will's health could benefit from a holiday in October. He could go hunting; Isabel could help feed the threshers. It was arranged and Elise had a letter written for Edwy to post when he went to fetch them.

Aweme Manitoba Oct 2, 1902

My dear Harry!

    Your letters are now always cheerful and very comforting to me, if I had you only not so far away, I should feel really happy. Mr. Tulk will be gone by now and you must miss him very much. I am not in correspondence with him or I would like to express my heartfelt thankfulness, as it is I hope you will thank him in my name. Mr. C and Edwy will go to Brandon tomorrow and will bring Will and Dido out and I hope to see Minnie soon, when their hard work is over. She wanted Bobby to come to her and help her but our own threshing is so uncertain so that Mrs. C could not let her go. Jim Brandon and his brothers have a machine between them. The machines here are all afraid to raft the river. . . . I was very pleased to hear you had a watch given to you on your birthday, a very nice present indeed.

    Bobby is looking very much forward for a letter from you, she does like so a letter to herself. I am glad you did not go into partnership with Mrs. Denny, it is better for you to be independent and have all the profits to yourself. . . . Mrs. C is quite well again, fortunately she could do without the doctor this time. I hope Olger will be able to write to me soon. I have written again to her. I don't know if she ever got Edwy's photo I send her.

> *Goodbye dear old boy, write soon to your*
> *Loving mama*
> *Love to all*

The Knights stayed almost a month and Isabel cheerfully spent her days with the girls in the kitchen. Each evening before Violet May's bedtime they visited Grandma. Lamplight was perfect for making shadow figures. "You can make a rabbit like this. Put your wrists together . . . point these two fingers up like this to make the long ears . . . and these . . . like this to make the front legs." A rabbit appeared on the bedroom wall and wiggled its ears.[17]

Hello little rabbit, how do you do,
Hop away quickly so you won't become stew.

May was enchanted. Grandma said, "Now, say it with me. Hello little rabbit . . . ."

Then May wanted to make a rabbit too. Before long, two little rabbits were saying hello. Next night they added a goose. "Goosey, Goosey Gander. . ." The following night, a dog barked to scare away robbers. Then came a jester; they named him Hans Kuony. They had a marvelous time; but the days sped by. By the time the threshers were fed, Will's health appeared better. It was time for Edwy to take the family back to Brandon on a load of wheat.

I miss them terribly and it doesn't help to know that Mrs. Bellhouse is also moving away.[18] *She is the only other woman I have got to know in all these many years. It was a holiday for me, being with her and Emily at The Palace.*

Their harvest, after all the worry, was actually good. The root vegetables were abundant and they harvested the highest number of bushels ever.[19] The price being satisfactory, the family needn't go hungry, and Mr. Criddle extended his card playing binge to four days. He had just returned—Edwy was still unharnessing the horses—when Jim drove up with Minnie. "It's the twenty-third. We've come to celebrate two birthdays. I have the cakes. We'll have to leave right after."

Elise was thrilled; *it's been years since Minnie's come for my birthday.*[20]

---

17 Reprinted with permission from Algrove Publishing Limited. "The Classic Art of Hand Shadows" is available from Lee Valley Tools. www.leevalley.com

18 November 26, 1902. Bellhouse rented farm for five years to McLeods. ". . . glad to get rid of the Old Hag but sorry Miss Emily and the boys are going."

19 Oct 24, 1902. "Total 2300 (899 on I) of wheat and 242 of oats + oats unthreshed . . ."

20 Alice Nicol, born November 24. Elise Harrer, born November 24. Mr. Criddle claimed Elise's birthday to be November 25.

The visit was everything she might have hoped, unless Harry, and Isabel and her family could have joined the gathering. As they drove away, she heard Mr. Criddle say, "I like Mr. Brandon better than I did at first. He's a bit rough – but evidently very kind-hearted and straight. He seems to be jolly well off too."

Following the birthday celebration, Elise took a turn for the worse. Everything she ate disagreed with her. *They all say, 'Be good,' 'take care'. Percy is tired of patching me up.*[21] Alone and discouraged, Elise's thoughts turned to her loving mother. *Mama always wanted the best for me. When Percy and I were engaged, she said anxiously, "What would your papa say?" And every time Percy visited us she was on edge. "Do be careful with your Englishman. They have a reputation here. Don't let Percy have his way with you."*

But, I loved and trusted Percy.

I was packing to go with him to London when Mama asked me to sit down, "You and Wilhelm liked your Grossmutter and her stories. But she didn't tell you everything and I was wrong not to tell you sooner. You have a right to know why I worry." She took my hands, and looked at them between her worn ones. She hesitated, and then plunged in, "Just as you have, your Grossmutter let her lover have his way with her. It's right that you marry. Grossmutter did, but she found out soon enough that a lover's promises are easily forgotten. I'm telling you now, and pleading, please don't go!" Tears ran down her cheeks. "Catharina, that was your grandmother's name, loved your grandfather. Andreas was a talented musician had an education and a good position. They married. But, it was not long before she found out more about her husband. You remember her telling you about the cruel Württemburg soldiers.[22] *They came about the time your papa was born. Catharina had no food for her family. Her husband became bitter and cruel. Things got worse and worse. Grossmutter was hungry and frightened. When another baby, your mama's uncle Friedrich, was born she had very little milk. He cried and cried. . . . Her husband was furious. Catharina was afraid the wee boy was going to die. She was desperate! She knew Andreas loved the new baby. She thought, 'If I weren't here he would find a woman to nurse him. I cannot take my own life. Such a mortal sin would lead to terrible trouble, eternal trouble.' She made a desperate plan to get away.*[23] *It worked and baby Friedrich and your papa lived. Unfortunately, and to her everlasting grief, not her daughter. Never did she tell anyone how she fled to far away Hungary."*

---

21   November 29, 1902. "Dutchman not well again – She's forever ailing – first one thing – then another and takes no end of patching up."

22   *Geschichte der Stadt Radolfzell*, Gestaltet von Erich Holmann. *Württemburg* 1805-1810 Hegaus e. V. Hegau-Bibliothek Band 12, 1967.

23   Stadtarchiv, Radolfzell, Germany. Achim Fenner. "I looked in the church protocols and in Sept 20, 1808 p. 134 we have the following notation, Catharina left secretly in 1808 soon after Friedrich was born. . . ." Email, Oct. 14, 2004. Also Fenner's book on education, *Schule in Badischer Zeit, 1810-1918*.

My dear Mama, you pleaded with me. "My precious Elise, do not listen to sweet words . . . promises cost nothing. Are you sure you want to go . . . leave me, your brothers, your family. We love you so. . . . If you go, you will not be able to come back."

But Percy loved me, wanted me, and promised he would soon be a famous tenor. We would be married as soon as he got established. "Just give me time," he said. I cared for our babies; I thought he was keeping his promise. When his cousin Chaloner came home on leave from China,[24] he saw how Percy was living and stopped sending money. Henry's orders stopped, and Percy's business dried up. . . . Thank God for friends. With my sewing and the children at the point of striking out on their own, we were going to make it. And then Percy came with more promises! . . .

It's been difficult here: hunger, insults, degradation, lies, fevers, abscesses. . . . With God's help and my children, I am still here. Mama didn't understand Grossmutter leaving her little ones, but I know through my suffering to think better of her. . . . The right path is not always clear.

⊰⊱

Just before Christmas Edwy told his mother, "Emily's mother has invited us for Christmas. But I'm worried about you."

"They need your little ones to fill the empty places of their hearts. You must go, my son."

Early December 21 he and Emily came with their little ones to her room for goodbye hugs.

⊰⊱

Christmas day Elise was helped down the stairs to the table. During the meal she looked fondly at the 11 faces around the circle. *My how things have changed these 20 years! We've had good times and some not so good. They are dear to include me in the feast. . . . Isabel is cooking for the Knights. Minnie is with her Jim and his family. Edwy's gone to the Steers to make up for their two empty chairs. Where will Harry spend the day now the Dennys have left the farm? I thank you, dear God, for my Cecil. Yet I worry; how will it be for him when I, too, am missing?*

Before the year was out, Elise received another letter from Harry:

Dec 22nd, 1902

My dear Mama,

I am so sorry you have been unwell again. I am afraid you want me to see you again. I often think I am a good deal to blame for your bad health.

I hope you had a jolly Christmas though Edwy and Emily being away would not improve matters very much. I am sorry I have not been able to write more but I got hurt a little. I got your letter, the boys and Stuart. I have not heard from Mr. Tulk just lately. I expect he is very busy.

---

24 Alabaster, Adrian. *Quintet of Alabasters*. (Able Publishing, Knebworth, Herts. UK. 1999).

Some of these days you will have your old boy to see you. I daresay I have changed quite a bit but I am still able to join in any sport going on and to make more noise than ever. I only wish I could see you just for a little while just to make my Mama laugh a little.

Tell Bobo I am a worse tease than ever and that it is a good thing for her I am not there, she would have a roughish journey of it. . . .

I suppose the boys will be hard at hockey ere this reaches its resting place. I should like to assist them but that can't be yet.

Well Mama I must say goodbye now, be very good, love to all and a Happy New Year from your loving boy.

Harry.

P.S. Will you thank Norman for the nice little pictures and Will [Denny] wishes me to thank him for his card. He was simply delighted with it.

And, a newsy letter from Edwy.

Turtle River, Man. Dec 26. 1902

My dear Mother,

We arrived here safely Wednesday night at 7. All well and comfortable. When leaving Brandon the weather was mild but rather stormy with getting up wind. We got to Portage in a bad blizzard. Fortunately there was a bus right at the entrance to the car we got out of. The wind was very bad and it was rapidly getting cold. We got a very nice room at the best Hotel in Portage but some of the people had to change quarters during the night owing to snow blowing through windows, etc. etc. Jim Marshall (also coming up here) stayed in another Hotel and there all the people on the wind side had a high time of it. Marshall said there was snow a foot deep in his room, all over his bed as well and he couldn't keep warm.

We left Portage at 11.30 next morning, one hour and a half late. The train was stuck in a snow drift 400 yds from station. After we got started the train went first rate half the distance and gained time rapidly. Fifty miles from here we met a very heavy freight between two stations. The engine had gone bust, our engine was a light one and had a bad time clearing the track. However, it managed the job at last taking half of it to one Station and the other half of it to another ten miles farther on. We lost two hours so instead of getting to Makinak at 3.15, we arrived after five. The horses were there ready and waiting. We went to a hotel for a little while and got some milk and a good warm up for the youngsters before starting. The horses were in good shape and brought us here in an hour and ten minutes. There were lots of wraps so nobody got cold.

Yesterday was a nasty cold day. It was 35 below Thursday morning at daybreak and it certainly felt like it, the temperature has steadily gone up since (at 4 this afternoon 2 above zero) S.E. gale.

We had a pretty good time yesterday and lots to eat. We demolished a good sized pudding among other things, for dessert we had oranges, nuts, apples and candies. I don't know exactly when I shall get back, perhaps two weeks, but may be three. After spending so much time it seems foolish to race up here and back for nothing and I don't think it would make much difference to you at home, however I haven't settled it yet but will let you know next week.

Our love to everybody and a Happy New Year to all. I hope to find you a great deal stronger when I get back, so mind.

Your loving boy

Edwy

Elise settled back and closed her eyes. *What a comfort that boy is! Taking time for me in the midst of their festivities. . . . He wants me to be stronger when he gets back. . . . I would like to please him. . . .*

I am in God's hands.

The Palace. Emily with Rupert, Edwy and Thyra

Chapter Twenty-nine

Journey's End

Edwy wrote after Christmas, "We'll be in Brandon January 15. Will Cecil meet our train? If it's stormy we'll stay over. Mrs. Fleming would like to see the children."

Mr. Criddle reworked some of his musical arrangements for Mrs. Husband and made a copy to send to Germany. He told Elise, "I'm asking Elsa for a critique. Write a note to send along."

My niece plays Mendelssohn, Schubert, and Wagner. He's sending Adieu, Old Maid's Song, and Hush-a-bye Baby. Is he hinting she give up teaching and find a husband?

The day of the homecoming was clear and bright. When Edwy came up to the house to check on his mother, her face lit up. "You are all well? I feel better already."

"I'm glad we went. Thyra and Rupert had a high time of it with their aunts and uncles. We had that beastly storm going, but the weather was fine coming back. Our coach's window was clear so we could see the countryside. Sure has changed since we came in '82, ever so many big barns and new homes. Farmers have done well, given up their log houses."

"I'm finding ours more drafty this year. But, it's still here, in spite of all the many storms."

"I guess it will weather a few more. In case you're interested, I've totaled my miles for last year. I'll not ask you to guess—driving just over 3,100 miles, **and**, walking—almost 2000! Mr. Tulk rides his bike, but I expect he'll be impressed."[1]

They chatted for a few minutes about the children and then with a peck on his mother's cheek, he went back down to The Palace where Emily would have supper waiting.

During the latter part of February, Edwy didn't count any miles, either walking or driving. He was flat on his back. The first week was touch-and-go, and for several more weeks he seesawed between illness and health. Elise, in her little room at the top of the stairs, kept listening for his voice. When she heard Mr.

---

1 E. Vane distance records 1902. Driving, 3,154 miles; walking, 1,922 miles. The author saw Tulk's records also in Chertsey Archives, Surrey.

Köhler, Alma told her, "We're putting on the new dresses Cousin Louisa sent. It's to say thank you for all our nice things. Mama's picture is done already."

Alice Criddle.

Later that afternoon Forrest Cullen dropped by with his wife and little one. Elise recognized Jane's voice. *I'd like to see the baby!* [2] She dressed and was partway down the stairs when her slipper caught the edge of a step and down she bumped to land with a final thump on the floor. Stuart and Evelyn rushed to her aid and, without even a glimpse of the little one, they maneuvered her back up the stairs. Mr. Criddle followed them up,

Maida, Julia, Beatrice, Alma.

"Trying to kill yourself? You were told to wait for help! Don't try this dodge again! . . . You've not broken anything. I'll send something up for pain."[3]

Beatrice appeared with a cup and held it to her lips, "You're to drink all of this, Huckey." She helped Elise out of her clothes and, tucking in the blankets, said kindly, "Now, take care."

Alone with throbbing pain and the concoction's horrid taste, Elise chided herself. *I didn't make it. . . . I was stupid . . . . Dummkopf indeed![4] Oh! Oh, ohoooo... No broken bones . . . I feel like I'm on fire with pain. . . . Dear Papa, I remember you crying—"Joseph, Mary, Jesus." Over and over, "Joseph, Mary, Jesus help me." But I'm not a Catholic. . . . Gott im Himmel be merciful, help me. . . . Help me bear this pain. When Cecil comes in from the chores he'll sit awhile. . . .* Mercifully the medication took effect and she fell into a fitful sleep.

Down, she was falling, down, and down . . . into a flaming pit. Her heart throbbed, she gasped for a breath; the pain broke through to her that she was in her bed, alive. *I was dreaming! That painting of the last judgment. The screams of the dead as they fall into the flames; No, No! Gott im Himmel! Save me!. . . . I looked up and saw figures floating upward. Saw God's arms outstretched. . . . Reaching down for me . . . Oh dear God, I have tried. . . . I didn't know which way to turn . . . I've done*

2 February 24, 1903 visit. Jane Fortune married Forrest Cullen. She has many descendants.
3 February 24, 1903. "Dutchman been trying a new dodge of killing herself – and – nearly successful – is very feeble of late and the least thing seems to get her wrong."
4 Nitwit

wrong, but I can't go back. . . . I can only hold on to the promises of my baptism. . . . In all this pain can I remember? . . . Our catechism . . . baptism . . .⁵ She concentrated. When our hour shall come, grant us a blessed end . . . . take us from this vale of tears to himself into heaven. . . .

She was with her friends as they rhymed off the words in confirmation class. *Little we knew about this vale of tears and the blessed end. . .*

I'm not ready! Dear God, please give me a little longer. . . . More time with my grandchildren. . .

I can bear pain, but that horrid dream. . . . I have to get it out of my mind. . . . **Harre**, *meine Seele.⁶ . . . wait and trust . . . I am still a Harrer . . . one who waits. Help me, dear God, to stay true to my name . . .* **Harre**, *meine Seele . . .* **Harre**, *meine Seele.* Her lips moved, "Vater unser im Himmel, Hallowed be thy Name. Thy Kingdom come. Thy will be done on earth as it is in heaven. Give us this day our daily bread and forgive us our trespasses as we forgive them that trespass against us. And lead us not into temptation, but deliver us from evil."⁷ By habit she continued with her evening prayer: "Ich danke dir, himmlischer Vater,* **Harre**, *meine Seele. through Jesus Christ, Thy dear Son, that Thou hast graciously kept me this day, I pray keep me this night. For into Thy hands I commend myself, my body and soul. . . . Amen.*

And she slept.

With grippe in the household it was not surprising that Elise, already weakened, followed suit. For some days it seemed her survival was in doubt, but her will to live was strong. She told Cecil, "I'm waiting for you to finish your musical box . . . such lovely wood. How skillfully you cut the shells! How wonderfully you do the inlay."

By the time he finished she was a little stronger. "This is my best box ever. For you to send to your brother." ⁸/⁹

She took it in her boney hands, turned it from side to side admiring the maple inlay, the diamond border, and the patterned flowers. She opened the lid and listened to the music. . . . "Thank you, my son. Now, at last, I have something very special for my brother. Can you bring me my little desk? I'll add a note." She explained how Cecil made his 'river pearl'. He waited patiently until she folded her pages, placed them inside and closed the lid. Cecil packed it carefully, wrapped

---

5 Traditionally, all Lutherans memorized Luther's Small Catechism.
6 King James Bible. Psalm 27:14 "Wait on the Lord: be of good courage, and he shall strengthen thine heart. . ." *The Contemporary English Version* translates the verse, "Trust in the Lord! Be brave and strong and trust in the Lord."
7 The Lord's Prayer was part of the evening prayer ritual laid out by Martin Luther.
8 Cecil's letter to Harry, Feb. 12. '02. "I have made three other boxes this winter. One for Will and Dido, musical box for mama to send to Germany and one for Mr. C."
9 February 27, 1903. "Solomon has made a beautiful little box — really very handsome – over 200 bits of pearl mostly diamond and triangle shape inlaid! – took him many days to do."

and tied the package, and handing it back for her to address, he promised, "It will be on its way tomorrow."

Elise was feeling better by the time she received Friedrich's response.

Mannheim, March 1, 1903

Liebe Elise!

    Your dear letters of Dec. 10 and January 23 I have received.

    The little chest and ornaments have arrived and has given all of us great pleasure. The boy that made all this must be a regular artist for everything is made so exact and tastefully. We thank you and the boys.

    Also the music from Percy has arrived which I have forwarded to Elsa who thanks him for it. Since she is usually absent from here, (right now she again was away 6 weeks giving a course in cooking in Banschlott) she does not get to playing the piano very often. But she did attempt to play Percy's music and to study it, reading the written music is troublesome for her. To my understanding they are pretty melodies.

    We are all fairly well. I am passably well; the frequent cold winds after sunny spring days are not good for me and I have to protect myself as much as possible from them. I enclose a few postage stamps again with the hope that my letter finds all of you well.

    I remain with hearty greetings to all of you.

    Your loving brother,

    F. Harrer

***

As soon as Edwy recovered, he accepted a challenge from Stockton's hockey team. They were outsized, outplayed, and outscored. Cecil confessed to his mother, "It was our worst showing ever. We are not used to boards around the ice and the lights in our eyes. They're coming next week to play on the river. We sure hope to turn the tables."

From the opening face-off, Stockton used violent tactics. With 15 minutes to go Cecil's nose caught it with a stick. And then, barely back on his feet, a flying puck dropped him. After some frightening moments, he came around and Aweme won by a single point. Back home all bloodied and battered, Mr. Criddle checked him out. "Your eye is bloodshot, but I'm afraid of meddling. The doctors are either quacks or fools so I don't care to get their opinions." Edwy took Cecil's turn with his mother that evening. "Cecil helped us win. He's tired and gone to roost."[10]

Late in March, Grandma Elise was helped downstairs to attend a tea party in honour of Thyra's fourth birthday. The little girl was in her glory, the centre of attention. Rupert didn't care much for sitting on a chair waiting for his drop of

---

10 March 1, 1903 and March 8, 1903.

tea, but he enjoyed the cake. Elise couldn't help thinking: *this will be my last tea party.*

Edwy was laid up again on a stormy morning, so it was Cecil who went with Mr. Criddle when Mr. McLeod asked for help for his sick wife. In a matter of minutes, Mr. Criddle said, "Your wife is very ill. What with I don't know – possibly a very bad bilious attack – maybe typhoid fever coming on – or even diphtheria. I can't take responsibility. You have to get a doctor."[11]

"I can't leave her alone," McLeod said.

"Cecil can round up a neighbour to fetch Dr. Harman from Wawanesa."[12]

The neighbours told him, "It's foolhardy to start out in this weather. She'll have to wait."

Seeing the panic in the husband's face, Cecil said, "I'll go for you, Mr. McLeod, if I can take your team. I've never been past Treesbank, but I should be able to follow the tracks, even if they're drifted."

The relief on McLeod's face was all Cecil needed. Supplied with landmarks, the number of miles and turns, he started out. Striking off into the stormy whiteness, his largest worry was that Dr. Harman would also refuse to travel in the bad weather. Meanwhile, at home, Mr. Criddle peered out, "Damned infernal nuisance – comes of trying to help one's neighbors."

Cecil made it to Wawanesa and made his case to the doctor. Dr. Harman agreed to follow in his own rig and they eventually reached the patient. With his duty done, Cecil stabled the teams and walked home hoping for a word or two of praise. Instead, Mr. Criddle barked; "Where's the doctor? Didn't you ask him here for the night? I wanted to consult him about Mrs. Martin. Damn it! I shall have to chance catching him ere he departs in the morning."

His mother, unaware of Cecil's exploit had neither worried nor congratulated him.[13] Next evening, in his own unique style, Cecil unfolded his adventure at The Palace. Knowing a thing or two about navigating in bad weather, Edwy truly appreciated his little brother's achievement. "I'm proud of you. Congratulate yourself. You made it through a storm, on strange roads, and in the dark. I was over to the post office just before tea. McLeod said you saved his wife's life."

Elise was no better. In fact, everything she ate upset her and although sympathy might have softened her despair, she heard instead, "You shouldn't have eaten **that!**"

11 March 29, 1903.
12 Dr. C.M.Vanstone came to Wawanesa about 1895, joined by Dr. A.E.Harman until 1904. *Sipiweske*, p. 17.
13 March 30, 1903. "Dutchman is very feeble indeed – and I'm afraid she won't last much longer. Of late she has been making continued mistakes with her diet – No sooner is she got convalescent than some new complication occurs – in fact she has to be watched and treated like a child."

Cecil came in and sat on the edge of her bed, "I've a letter here from Harry. I'll read it."

Brownings Farm, Chigwell Row, Essex. April 11ᵗʰ, 1903

My dear Mamma,

> *I am so sorry to hear you have not been well again. I am afraid you have been naughty, it is a pity you can't be good while I am away.*

His mother broke in. "Falling down the stairs was naughty, I agree. But nothing seems to suit my stomach. I'm afraid I'll never enjoy another meal."

> *I am sorry Edwy has been bad too. There seems to be a lot of sickness since I have left.*
>
> *I am still with Will but there must be some change soon. I shall know more when Mr. Tulk gets back. Then I will let you know everything. I have one cow now and she is a beauty. I paid 24£ for her.*
>
> *Tell Cecil I played football on Good Friday. We won 3-0. I made 3 goals and practically a third from a pass to centre. I play again on Monday which I think will be about our last, I got three letters this morning from Cecil, Stuart, Edwy and Emily. I have not seen Olger for some time but I heard the other day she had been ill but was better again.*
>
> *I hope this will find you well, try and be good or I shall have to take the next ship.*
>
> *Good bye with love to all, your loving son, Harry*

"Did he say take the next ship?" Her heart skipped a beat before the irony sank in, "Harry's just talking." She held her tears until Cecil had gone. *I'll not see my Harry again.*

⤜⟡⤛

A spring cold had everyone coughing but with high winds and a shout of "Fire!" the boys had to go whether they were well or not.[14] It took all afternoon, but they returned victorious, only to discover Edwy's cow had not. They fanned out to search and when Stuart found her mired in the mud a mile north, he lit a smudge to signal the others. After much manoeuvering Fawn also made it home.

Elise heard snatches of their exploits and thought about the days when she had been on the front lines. *Fighting fires was not my favourite job . . . seems so long ago . . . .*

She was dozing when Cecil came with a letter. "You wanted news from your friend. Here it is. I'll read it."

"Please may it be good news."

---

14   April 16, 1903 "As there was a ¾ ESE gale – we soon had a dandy blaze and all hands were ordered out. . . .Stuart coughing continuously in a <u>hopeless sort of manner</u> – he's been doing it off and on for weeks and I'm getting anxious. That infernal hockey in cold weather is enough to play havoc with anyone's lungs . . . but of course it's of no use preaching against it."

Battersea S.W. April 28.1903

My dear Madame,

I was glad to hear from you, but sorry you are so sadly. I hope as the weather gets warm you will get better. I have been very ill. I did not think I should ever get well again. I am very weak and low and the weather has been so bad. I never remember such weather for the time of year. I have not heard from dear Harry for a long time. The Denny's were moving and as soon as things were settled he was going to let me know.

I have had a letter from Minnie. I am glad to hear she has had such a happy time and I pray all may go well with her. I wish I was near you all but I am afraid that will never be. I am glad dear Edwy and wife and family are all well. Give my love to Minnie and dear Cecil. Give my respects to Mr. Criddle. I am very pleased to hear that the family are so clever. It makes it nice for you to see pretty things.

. . . Things are very dull and quiet in London. There are so many out of work. The deaths are very sad. So many men are dieing [sic]and leaving wifes [sic] and children.

With love my dear Madam
I am your affectionate Friend,
E Foulger

"That's her letter, Mama. She doesn't sound like the jolly Olger I remember. It's been quite a day. I'm beat. I'll see you in the morning."

Thank goodness Minnie wrote her . . . poor dear . . . so little to cheer her. Harry must be busy.

Elise's condition improved with the warm, spring weather until another cold spell had her fighting again for her life—such a cough, not a moment's peace![15/16] *It's like whooping cough, only I'm the one that's coughing . . . disturbing others.* When a downpour found the old leak in her ceiling, she couldn't escape the drip, drip, drip. *That puddle has caused me plenty of grief . . . should run for a pot to put under it but I dare not get out of bed. . . . The dripping . . . the damp, the chill. . . .[17] If only I could get warm. And this awful cough.[18] Harre, meine Seele.*

❧━◦◦◦━❧

Elise unfolded her brother's letter hoping he would suggest something she might eat.

---

15 Apr. 28, 1903. "The Dutchman perhaps a little better – but she's terribly feeble and shrunken."

16 Catarrhus senilis. ". . . chronic bronchitis, occurring in persons advanced in life, and very apt to be converted into pneumonia, or to be greatly aggravated in degree during winter, or upon any accidental exposure. . . . An habitually congested state of that membrane, marked by some shortness of breath, and some expectoration (the process of coughing up and spitting out), and by the constant presence of some degree of crepitation (a dry, crackling sound) in the lower parts of the lungs. . . . they have pain in the lower breast or side, headache, heat and thirst: and at these periods the cough and expectoration are aggravated . . . ." Watson's *Practice of Physics.* p. 537.

17 May 17, 1903. "The house a trifle soppy in more than one place."

18 May 19, 1903. "Dutchman worse again – Caught cold the other day – has great difficulty in getting rid of mucus – and – this bad weather is much against her."

Mannheim 11 Mai 1903

Liebe Elise!

Today I received your letter from April 22 and I am very saddened that you are not well and that you have suffered much during the last weeks. I noticed it immediately on your letter that something was amiss, your handwriting showed me that you were weak. Let's hope to God that you will soon improve, something I heartily wish for you!

I too have digestive problems quite frequently and I have to be careful not to eat any food that is hard to digest. Namely at night I often suffer stomach cramps so that I cannot fall asleep for a long time. Anna also has not been well and she went to Heidelberg to Aunt Amalie to get some respite. One doesn't really know what is bothering her, often she is moody and quiet and loses weight. We thought it would be good for her to have a change of environment. She has been gone for 14 days now and probably returns by the weekend.

Elsa still has not received a job here nearby. The Secretary of the Women's Guild Karlsruhe has written to her that they have recommended her to Heilbronn, where in October they want to open a cooking school and she would take the leadership position. Hopefully this will materialize.

Dear Elise! You write that Percy wanted more critique from us on his music. As I wrote you, we like the music quite well but we aren't that knowledgeable, that we could critique it professionally. I refer to Richard Wagner, his operas were not appreciated when they were first performed and now he has so many fans. In Paris he was even "whistled out" and now they can't perform enough Wagner. That's how the taste changes or the understanding improves?

With this I send you a $1.00 dollar bill and some stamps. With the sincere wish that your health may improve I remain, with the heartiest greetings from all of us to you and Percy.

Your loving brother
Friedrich [19]

She refolded the letter, *Dear Friedrich; we must have the same trouble. Perhaps your dollar can get something for my cough.*

Mr. Criddle thought hydrochloric dil. would help but decided to consult Dr. Husband. He took his five boys to Treesbank to register for the forthcoming election—prohibition being the burning issue. Edwy drove Mr. Criddle to Wawanesa; Norman walked home; three stopped off at the river to fish. Elise's taste of fresh pickerel was better than medicine.[20]

Elise's cough almost disappeared by June. When Stuart was around he helped her down to the kitchen. On a few pleasant afternoons, she sat out in the warm sunshine. As the boys left for cricket one day, Edwy called from the wagon,

---

19   Friedrich died in 1911. Anna kept house for him and her sisters until her death in 1919. They taught in Mannheim. Elsa, into the thirties, and Julie, listed until 1941 as a high school teacher. Germany, as had England, lost so many young men in wars that tens of thousands of women were independent by necessity.
20   May 26, 1903. ". . . . Dr. Husband – discussion and wandering as usual – he'd nothing to advise re the Dutchman."

"Take care, Mama, we'll see you in the morning. Our punt will get us across to Sutcliffe's."

The punt . . . it set her thinking of Mr. Tulk and building the boat. *What year was that, I wonder?*

When Will brought his family out again, Isabel was surprised to find her mother sitting outdoors. Although pleased to see them, she soon asked, "Have you heard anything of Minnie?"

"No, not a word. You're anxious, but don't worry. She's busy; you'll hear from her one of these days."

Isabel wrote Harry and it wasn't long until their mother was reading his letter.

Brownings Farm, Chigwell Row June 5, 1903

My dear Mamma,

I am so glad to hear you feel so much better. You must be good and do just what you are told, so that you get quite strong.

I am having a bit of change here, I think, though I have not settled yet, so I can't say anything for sure. How is Mrs. Criddle? Is she quite well? I should very much like to just walk in to see how you all are.

I am thinking of buying up Wee Isle and getting a nice house for you to live in.

Be good and take care you get well.

With love from your boy, Harry

Elise smiled. *That boy! Things must be going well if he plans to buy an island, however small . . . and a house . . . . But he's just teasing. . . . A house of my own . . . what a fairy tale! But it's pleasant to think about.* She chuckled, *Harry and his wee island!*

❧⤜⟨◦⟩⤛

Mr. Criddle's mail did not leave him smiling: Mr. Tulk was going to India again. The list of projects awaiting the gentleman's board money had to be put on hold again.[21] Fortunately, Edwy won an $86 tender for more road work.

Cooler, wet weather brought on Elise's coughing.[22] In bed one lonely afternoon, she heard music. With every nerve strained, she listened—Beethoven's *Für Elise. I haven't heard my special piece since Percy played it on Mama's piano. Is he playing for me? . . . It doesn't sound like Percy. . . .* She was carried away to that long-ago time when she was in love with a young man who promised her the world. She remained under its spell after the sound died way. *I've never heard the little organ played like that! Who could it be?*

---

21   June 20, 1903 "I feel jolly vexed about the business as he gave me to understand some time since that he'd be here – and of course the change upsets a lot of my plans."
22   July 2, 1903. "Dutchman coughing a good deal these last 48 hours – a nasty irritating little helpless cough."

When Cecil came, she asked, "Do you know who was visiting this afternoon?"

"Came on foot, Mr. C called him Grainger, the music teacher from Wawanesa. He sure put him in a bad mood."[23]

"He played my favourite piece, and he played it beautifully. I wish you could have heard it." She started to hum the melody for him . . . but it set her coughing.

Mr. Criddle's bad mood carried over to his diary that night:

Mr. Grainger the music teacher of Wawanesa has honoured me by presenting me with a copy of one of his compositions – Dreadful stuff – How any man can have the conceit to publish when he hasn't the remotest knowledge of harmony, counterpoint or form is certainly amazing. This man too shows that he has no ability – no musical instinct – no power even to make a tune – so that no teaching could ever make anything out of him.

A bad storm that night might have frightened Elise, but, with the music still singing in her heart she felt calm. An extra strong gust of wind made the roof creak and glass splinter. . . . *Gracious, must be a window downstairs.* But her memories just kept blending with the thunder, the wind, and groaning walls until she drifted off to sleep. Downstairs Mr. Criddle busily wrote and rewrote his story, *The Actor's Daughter.* By 3:15 A.M. he had a finished copy, and since the wind had moderated somewhat, he turned in.

Elise improved enough to get up for a couple of hours in the afternoon to the window in boys' room to read her old letters, poetry, and church book. Some days, she was helped downstairs to sit by the fire, soak up its warmth, and wondered with the girls why Minnie hadn't written. The answer came at last; "I have a son, born June 26th. Everything is fine. Sorry it took so long to write. I hope you haven't been worrying."

That Minnie had such a positive aliby for neglecting her corresponence gave Grandmother Elise a new reason to hold on to life.

---

23 "Professor Albert Grainger returned to England in 1931. Came in 1885, worked as a farm hand. The family, home from church unexpectedly, caught him playing their piano. Totally amazed, they said, 'You'd better give up your job here and teach music.' He provided music education, piano and violin, from Dunrea to Brandon for 47 years. Organist, first at St. John's, Rounthwaite; after 1900, organist and choir director at St. Paul's in Wawanesa. Served faithfully and well seventeen Rectors, three Archbishops, and one Bishop before returning to England." *Sipiweske: One Hundred Years of Wawanesa and District.* pp. 94, 102, 194. He taught my mother, Ruth Clark.

Brownings Farm, July 22nd
1903

My Dear Mama,

I am glad to hear you are so much better and that everything looks bright. I believe you want me to look after you every now and then and make you laugh a bit.
It is raining just like old Sam Hill, so I don't know what to be at tomorrow. You see we have six men to find work for. Will leaves it to me to do.
Well I must finish this letter. I hope this finds you Jolly.
Love to all
From your affectionate boy,
Harry.

Minnie was more realistic about her mother's health and came as soon as she could. Elise's heart beat faster at the sound of her daughter's voice. *I'll see Minnie's baby . . . hold little Wesley in my arms.* Minnie came up the stairs, kissed her mother, and sat down beside her. "I'm sorry, Mama, I couldn't bring the baby, but I brought you some goodies to eat," and she opened her basket.

Elise grew weaker and more isolated. She learned only what the family thought suitable for an invalid. Sometimes she asked about a voice; "Was that Cullen's voice early this morning?"

"He brought the Charleson lad. He got kicked by a colt they bought from Dr. Vanstone.[24] Bronc-Buster Vanstone, Mr. C calls him. He might need surgery. Mr. C sent them to Brandon.[25] Don't worry, he'll be alright."

Another day Talbot came in all proud of himself. "I tried ploughing for a little while. It's boring spending all day sitting on the prairie watching cattle." But without him, 20 of Clay's cattle strayed and both Cecil and Talbot were on the hook to find them.

24　The doctor raised purebred draft horses. Pictures in Wawanesa Museum. It was Dr. Vanstone who helped my mother, 12-year-old Ruth Clark, with her first hive of bees in 1917.
25　July 20, 1903. "I don't want any surgical jobs – haven't the proper appliances."

But the surprise that capped everything was the arrival of Charles Alabaster, oldest son of Mr. Criddle's cousin, Henry Alabaster. He'd walked from Douglas with nothing but the scruffy clothes on his back. Furthermore, he settled in as if he were a member of the royal family, making himself at home in Mr. Criddle's chair, reading his books, and smoking his tobacco. The last straw was the discovery of an infestation of head lice.

What the devil Palacia could have been thinking of to let him come out - passes my comprehension entirely - had she sent him to the cape 'Twould have been a thousand times better.

Charlie's father had helped Mrs. Criddle and her son Percy in England, but Canada was the land of opportunity for those who worked. There was no patience for the pampered whippersnapper.[26] Elise was thankful to be upstairs, away from the brewing conflict. Cecil brought a candle and chair into his mother's room, "Let's write Harry. I'll bring your desk and prop you up."

Aweme Manitoba 6th of August (1903)

My Dear old boy!

I am trying to write so you can read it. I am still in bed, I just can get up for a couple of hours in the afternoon. How is it that you never mention Mr. Tulk? Have you given each other up? I should be very sorry if it was so. Your photograph in the hay I like very much, it is very clear. I suppose there is no more photographing for you now.

I heard through Emily that you saw Olger again, I have written yesterday to her. I suppose they have not told that Minnie has a son. She has been here to see me and bring a lot of delicacies. We have a cousin of P.C. here, a Mr. Alabaster, he wants to go and buy a farm. He is very weak and will never be able to work.

Now goodbye my dear boy, love from all.

I am your Affectionate Mama

Cecil also wrote. He had to tell Harry about their mother's health, but he wanted to do it gently. His words would flow in the same easy way he talked.

Aweme, Manitoba August 6th 1903

My dear Harry,

As I have a little time to spare I thought I would write you a few more lines.

We have been ploughing up on One for the past three weeks, that is Edwy and I. Norman is as usual ploughing with the oxen on Five. They have about finished the summer fallowing and we are now going to prepare for harvest. It all depends on the weather. The price of wheat

Cecil Vane

---

26 Aug. 5, 6, 1903. Charlie's father, Henry Alabaster, died in Siam. His mother Palacia, in England, with two other sons, hoped to find Charlie a home. Percy said, "I tried him at unloading a load of hay last night – not the remotest use – even Alma I believe would beat him. . . . does not improve on acquaintance - He's very weak – has no energy – is interested in nothing so far as I can make out bar feeding and is most distinctly lazy."

is good now, it's been 70 cents and likely to go up. Our oats are looking good in the swamp and the gardens are at about their best.

You will be glad to hear old boy that Mama is better, in fact she looks quite well but what hurts me Harry is that she cannot get up and stay up. She is only able to stay up for about two hours every day and then it is only to come in our room and sit and read. I should like to see her able to walk about a bit and go outside to get some fresh air.

Minnie and Jim were out here the other day but did not stay long and I was away ploughing so did not see them. Minnie says Mama looks much better than she expected to see her.

. . . This ought to reach you in time for your birthday. I wish you many happy returns of the day. I am a very poor hand at remembering birthdays, it's seldom that I remember even yours.

I must say goodbye now old boy hoping that you are quite happy and not working too hard. I remain yours,

Affectionately, Cecil

Elise saw little of her hardworking sons during harvest. Isabel managed to get out again and Harry wrote again.

Brownings Farm, Aug 29th, 1903

My dear Mama,

I am so pleased to hear you are better and have got a good appetite. You will soon get strong again, but you must take care of yourself. How is Mrs. Criddle and the Governor, are they well. I will write to the Governor next time. I am getting on alright and am respected by everyone about here. I had a bit of a row with an old farmer the other day. I told him just what I thought. I don't think he will bother me again. Crops are very bad here, spoilt by rain.

Mr. Tulk I don't think is going to India . . . Well, I must begin to close now and I hope this finds you well.

Love to you and everybody,

Your affectionate son,

Harry.

Bad weather wasn't confined to England. September's harvesting came to an abrupt halt with a nasty drizzle. Unable to be out harvesting, Stuart helped Elise down to the fire for an hour.[27] The rain turned to sleet and then to snow; the hope of having a good harvest had gone south once more. Elise shivered while her ceiling dripped.[28] In the fields stooks were sopping and the mown hay spoiled. Then came wind with heavy wet snow that broke branches and buried their vegetables. Harry's effort to be cheery did little to lighten the mood.

---

27 Sept. 3, 1903. "The Dutchman in kitchen sitting before the fire! Hasn't been downstairs for months!"

28 Sept. 7, 1903. "Puddles everywhere and roof dripping delightfully round stovepipes. Fancy nearly 1 ½ inch rain must be down!!"

Brownings Farm, Chigwell Row, Essex

My dear Mama,

 I am so pleased to hear you are better. I got a letter from Evelyn. I wish I had you over here so I could take care of you. There are all sorts of things I could get you. I am sorry to hear Mrs. Criddle has got the toothache. I think you want me over there to make you laugh a bit, you don't laugh enough. I have felt lonely of late as they Dennys have all gone away and the people are new. Having very wet weather the roads are flooded and plenty of cattle and horses have drowned.

 Well I must begin to close. You must take care of yourself and be good, and then you will get quite well, I should like to have a letter from you soon.

 Good Bye with love

 From your dear Harry

She sat quietly, thinking. *My dear Harry, writing won't bring you home, but you'll feel closer.*

Aweme Manitoba 16th Sept 03

My dear Harry!

 It is a chilly afternoon and I have to sit near the stove. They told you I am better. I am very thankful it was a great anxiety for everybody and lots of trouble, only thing is I can't walk by myself. I can manage to come in the kitchen now by being held up coming down, but difficult to haul me up. If Stuart is at home he carries me up. . . .

 I am glad you are all right in your place. I only wish you were near us. We had a horrible day last Saturday, great bit of wind and snow. The stacks are so wet they can't thresh them and I am afraid by the time they are dry it will rain again.

 They are all well and send their love to you. Now goodbye dear boy, writing a long letter is hard work for me.

 I am always your

 Affectionate

 Mama

Helped back to bed she thought. *They **tell me** I am well. But I know it's not so.*

Alone in her tiny room she had time to remember . . . *mama . . . papa, my brothers, grandparents—Schaaf . . . Haarbarth*[29] *. . . uncles . . . aunts . . . schoolmates.* Her mind flitted from scene to scene, and face to face, from laughter to tears. *So many memories. . . .*

Sounds from below called her back to her helpless body. *I have done my best. May God have mercy on me for what I have not done. . . . My tired old body can't go on. . . . I'll be free and through God's loving mercy . . . will see my little Mabel . . . and Wilhelm . . . Mama . . . Carl . . . Papa. It seems like yesterday we stood watching Papa's coffin being lowered into his grave. They told me, "Your papa was a fine man. You will meet him again someday."* In the wonderment of reunion she drifted into sleep.

❧ ❦ ❧

Elise heard her mother's voice, *"I had two fine sons. Then God answered my prayer for a daughter. I got you, my little Sabina Elise."* Mama loved to tell me about *my baptism, "a new little Protestant in Catholic Freiburg. We are a special family, because Papa is Catholic and I am Lutheran."* She dozed. *The Grand Duke had all his postal families move from town to town, helped understanding between peoples. We were always saying goodbye and finding new friends. It was sad to lose Papa, but we settled down in Heidelberg with Mama's family. No more moving . . .* She dozed. A door slammed, she roused. *Baptism, thinking of my baptism. How it happened that I was baptized Protestant in a Catholic town. Mama always said, "The Grand Duke knew I was coming." He found an old monastery in a valley. Had it taken down stone by stone and carted by wagon to Freiburg. They built a beautiful church, named it Ludwig Kirche after the Grand Duke. Mama liked to tell me, "Your baptism was a grand affair. Your papa in his official dress—dark uniform with gold braid, his hat and sword. He was as proud of his little girl as were your big brothers. Our Pharrer baptized you, Sabina Elise, after my Grossmutter."*

Ludwig Kirche, Staatsarchiv Frieburg

*I **was** Sabina Elise Harrer. . . . But my name is not known here. . . .*

She saw her father's gravestone: 'Carl Harrer, 1805-1849 Postmeister'. Fully conscious she asked herself. *How will they mark my grave? Not as my brother expects, Elise Criddle. If it has a name, it will be Vane. . . .* She wandered through tangled threads of thought. . . . *Vane, a good name and had it been mine, one to be proud of.*

---

29 Grandparents and family on her mother's side. Address books and Church Archives, Heidelberg, Germany.

Criddle was our name—the children pasted it on our trunks for the voyage. How they shrieked, "Our trunk. Someone's stolen our trunk!" But the trunk was there, only our name was stolen, replaced by a big black 'E. Vane', I shouldn't have been shocked. . . . I couldn't think. . . . Percy had our tickets. . . . The boys were to get land. . . . I tried to soothe them, told them Vane is a good name. . . . Reminded them of the stories Percy

Vane Tempest Stewart
Durham, England

told about Lord Harry Vane.[30] His was a grand house close to Buckingham Palace, an easy walk from Percy's boyhood home on Piccadilly.[31]

I didn't have an answer for my children because I never understood myself Percy's reasons for choosing 'Vane'. He often talked about his connection to the aristocratic family and how Lord Harry Vane helped his mother get recognition as an artist.[32] Sometimes he mentioned the Percys, another noble family from Northumberland. He liked to be called Percy Vane. When I registered our baby girls, he said, tell them the father's name is Percy Vane. . . . Did the connection between the Vane and Percy families have something to do with his mother naming him Percy? . . . Child of her old age? . . . Secrets are best left. I know all too well about women having to hide such things.

⤜◦⬥◦⤏

When I first arrived in England with my Percy he called me "my sweet Mabel," I liked it, until he took me to see a play. Percy loved the theatre . . . played a coachman once.[33] He cooed, "In the play 'Masques and Faces' you are going to meet Mabel."[34] He enjoyed every minute of the performance; I felt like I'd swallowed a stone.

---

30   Lord Harry Vane 1804-1891. Diplomat in Paris, Member of Parliament for Durham Southern until 1859. Resided within walking distance of the Piccadilly hat shop, where the Criddle family resided, and of Percy's mother's studio.

31   The Criddles had many addresses. Among them: 58 Piccadilly in '41 census, Percy born 1844 at 3 Upper Belgrave Place. [renamed Buckingham Palace Rd] On 1851 census lived over the straw hat shop at 115 Piccadilly with the employees. Harry B Criddle and Mary Ann Criddle, artist, are still listed separately in Post Office directory of 1855. She at her Sloan Street studio address. Percy's father died 1857 at 22 Notting Hill Terrace, Bayswater. Mrs. Criddle and Percy moved—1859 to Horton, Surrey, then 1860 to Addlestone, Surrey. Percy took music lessons in Heidelberg during winters, home for the summers from January of 1861 to spring of 1863 following his engagement to Elise. In 1868 he lived with Elise in Southwark until 1874. After his marriage he and Alice lived with his mother and they moved to the small cottage on J.A. Tulk's estate about 1878. Sources: letters, archives, census, and rate books and Percy Criddle's diary.

32   "The aristocratic surname 'Vane' survives in the surname, Vane-Tempest-Stewart. I would say that to the English, Criddle sounds working class and Vane aristocratic. One point worth bearing in mind is that 'Percy' as a Christian name came about because it was the surname of the Dukes of Northumberland. Could there be a connection? The Vanes came from the adjoining County and held much land in Northumberland too. What we need is some late 19th century 'gossipy' memoirs of high society in London!" Researcher Peter Towey, email, March 12, 2006.

33   London Times, 1873, lists Percy as the coachman in Sheridan's opera, *The Rivals.*

34   Charles Reade in collaboration with Tom Taylor, *Masks and Faces*: first produced in 1852.

She stiffened at the thought of that night. *Mr. Ernest Vane, a country squire, left his wife of six months to go up to London to settle an inheritance. That accomplished, he found his way to the theatre and fell head over heels for the talented and beautiful actress, Peg Woffington. Vane swore on his honour, he'd never loved before. Meanwhile, his lonely wife, Mabel, decided to go to him in London and found his residence filled with a crowd that included the actress. The people laughed at the lovers' dilemma. Mabel, diamond that she was, remained steadfast. "Even if it is true," she argued, "I will remain faithful . . . I'll always be the mistress of his household." In the end, on her knees, through tears, Mabel pleaded with the actress. "Have pity on me; give me back my husband's heart. You can enchant—can you not break your own spell?" Percy raved about the plot and clever lines. . . . He kissed me and said, "You are* **my** *Mabel." He was right. Percy counted on me. Mabel Vane would be a suitable name for my gravestone.*

But sweet Mabel didn't last. Percy started up in business close by and needed a respectable family. I became Mrs. Criddle, of St. George's Road . . . for eleven years we were Criddles, until . . . until that morning on the dock . . .

My poor head . . . can't think anymore. . . . My grave may not have a name at all. My children will know where I lie buried. . . . My precious ones. . . . What would I do without them?

She drifted into an uneasy sleep.

Half awake, Elise heard her pastor's voice, *"Commit these words to memory, someday you may need them . . . . 'Baptism works forgiveness of sins, and gives eternal salvation. . . . Christ says, he that believeth and is baptized shall be saved. . . .'"*

Minnie knows I'd like to have a minister to comfort my children. I've told them about the stained glass window . . . that Jesus goes before us into heaven. I trust it will be so. I can do no more. What I have done is done and what is not done is not done. May God have mercy on my soul.

By the end of October Elise became frailer, slept more, drank less, ate nothing, and sometimes mumbled in her own language, words no one understood. Isabel came with her husband and while he hunted, she sat with her mother. Clearly the end was near. When Will had to return to work, Mr. Criddle sent a letter for him to post in Brandon.

Aweme, Manitoba Oct 31, 1903

My dear Minnie,

I'm afraid your Mama can't last much longer. She was a bit better recently but has been going down steadily for some days past and the end may come at any time – in her sleep it is to be hoped. Dico was out on Tuesday with Will and went home yesterday. Your Mama took very little notice of her – in fact, barring a certain amount of grumbling now and again, she seems to take no interest in anything and just lies huddled up in bed as she won't (or can't) sit up at all now. Of course everything is being done that can be done, but she wastes away steadily – old age - and nothing can alter things.

. . . .

Mrs. Criddle wrote to you several weeks ago but has never got any answer. I hope you are all well your way – and – probably you'll be coming down here very soon – at least – we are expecting you. When you do come – perhaps I shall be able to discover what's wrong with the baby.
    Kind regards to Mr. Brandon.
    Yours affectionately,
    Percy Criddle

Next morning he wrote in his diary, "The poor Dutchman fast going down hill," and by four o'clock that afternoon added, "Doubt if the Dutchman will last 48 hours." She slept during the night; was still conscious in the morning. Minnie arrived at two that afternoon just in time to witness her mother's last few breaths.[35]

The household was quiet except for the sounds of sobbing from Elise's room where Cecil clung to his mother's body. Minnie tried to comfort him. After a time she said gently, "Go ask Beatrice for a basin of warm water. We need to wash Mama and do her hair. I'll look in her trunk for something nice to wear. She is so terribly thin, only a shadow of her old self. But we want her to look her best."

Minnie found her beautiful blue silk concert gown and the green dress her mother wore in steerage.[36] "These won't do," she told Cecil. "It's a wonder she kept them—such unhappy memories. I brought an extra dress, short for her, but we'll cover her feet with a blanket. Those old slippers aren't fit to be seen." And so they worked through their tears until they had her hair washed and put up in a tidy bun. Once dressed and with her poor knobby hands folded over her breast, she appeared to them to be sleeping. "That's all we can do." Minnie said, "You say Edwy is hauling grain? The boys will tell him. Come downstairs and we'll have a cup of tea with the girls. They're feeling it too. Emily and Edwy will be over."

Meanwhile Jim had been talking with Mr. Criddle.

"Minnie tells me you've been doctoring Martin's wife. Ask him to go to Brandon, tell Isabel about her mother, and fetch a casket. I've money for him. She wouldn't want anything fancy. If he goes first thing in the morning he'll be back by late afternoon. I understand you don't want her buried in the community

---

35 Nov. 1, 1903.
36 The dress survived in all probability due to the fact that Victorian servants wore black. At the time of writing in the care of the Burrough of the Gleann Museum, Glenboro, Manitoba.

cemetery. The soil here is very sandy . . . boys will need some lumber to keep the grave from falling in. Tell them where to dig."

Next morning Jim rose early and talked to Cecil, "When you're finished milking, harness my drivers. I'll take Mr. Criddle to Wawanesa. Minnie tells me she promised her mother to have a minister."

Mr. Criddle wasn't pleased, "Don't need an outsider – I planned to read the service."

"Don't worry," Jim responded, "I'll look after any expenses. Edwy tells me there's a young pastor in Wawanesa."

They found the Reverend at the parsonage. Jim introduced himself as a fellow Methodist and stated his mission. "My mother-in-law passed away yesterday afternoon. Mrs. Vane lived too far away to attend a church. She was a good woman, a believer—baptized as a Lutheran. My wife Minnie is the oldest of five. All of them hope you will give their mother a Christian burial."

The Reverend Mr. Cann expressed his sorrow at their loss. "You say she passed away yesterday? You'd like to have the funeral on the third day? I'll ask the class leader to take over for me here. I'll be pleased to help you out, Mr. Brandon."

Back at St. Albans the boys dug the grave; the girls arranged the sitting room; Will arrived with his family.

⁓⁓⁓

Word spread and by next morning rigs began to arrive. Women as a rule didn't attend funerals, but Mrs. Mair and Mrs. Sutcliffe both brought a basket of food. And Jane, long a friend of the Vane boys, came with her husband.[37]

When the Reverend Cann arrived, Jim was at hand and asked a neighbour to stable the horses. Shaking the pastor's hand, he said quietly, "The Vanes appreciate your coming. The Criddles though, are not church people. I suggest you temper your sermon, and don't issue any altar calls." He then pointed to the garden path and said, "The grave is down there, 150 yards."

Relieved of his top hat and coat, Reverend Cann began greeting each mourner with a handshake. "How do you do, Mr. Criddle . . . Mrs. Criddle . . . You're Mrs. Brandon. . . . I'm sorry for your loss." Minnie passed him to Isabel, "This is my sister, Mrs. Knight, her husband, Will, and daughter, May." He shook their hands. "I'm Edwy, her oldest son, and this is my wife, Emily, . . . our children and my brother, Cecil. Harry is over in England." He continued shaking hands right down to Alma and the neighbours.

With the formalities concluded, Reverend Cann said, "Before we open the casket for viewing, let us bow in prayer. 'Eternal God, before whose face the generations rise and pass away, we remember Elise Vane, most dear to us and now

37 Nov. 4, 1903.

among those who have trusted in Thee. And to Thy name, with the church on earth and the church in heaven, we ascribe all honour and glory, world without end. Amen.'"

Jim raised the lid of the coffin. Each of Elise's children kissed her a final goodbye. The younger Criddles bade farewell to their Mama Dutcheen; to others she was Huckey or Huddock; for neighbours, humble servant—Mrs. Vane. Meanwhile the Reverend filled out the church record with Mr. Criddle, and then donned his robes.[38] Jim gently closed the casket and took his seat beside Minnie. The pastor's voice broke the silence, "I am the Resurrection and the Life saith the Lord. He that believeth in me, though he were dead, yet shall he live; and whosoever liveth and believeth in me, shall never die.[39]

"Let us pray: 'Almighty and everlasting Father, with whom do live those who have loved and served thee: we thank thee for them. We thank thee that with faith and patience they have inherited thy promises and are now with thee in joy and peace. Grant that encouraged by their example we may be gathered into thy kingdom for ever: through the grace and mercy of Jesus Christ our Saviour. Amen.'"

His message began, "Every man born of women hath but a short time to live, his days are swifter than a weaver's shuttle. We all know this earthly house will be dissolved; the wise build their houses not made with hands, eternal in the Heavens." He elaborated on a mother's selfless labour on behalf of her family and concluded. "Mrs. Vane having reached her three score years, now reaps the fruit of her labour." He prayed for guidance and strength for all mourning her loss.

The Reverend motioned to the pallbearers. Stationing themselves on either side of the coffin, they lifted in unison and followed the pastor. Outdoors, he spoke from the head of the coffin, "I know that my redeemer liveth and that he shall stand at the latter day upon the earth, and though after my skin, worms destroy this body, yet in my flesh shall I see God. We brought nothing into this world, and it is certain we can carry nothing out. The Lord gave, and the Lord hath taken away; blessed be the name of the Lord." He turned and led the procession down from the house to the waiting grave.

The pallbearers lowered the coffin with ropes to its final resting place. Then, tall against the prairie sky, Reverend Cann spoke, "Man hath but a short time to live. He cometh up and is cut down as a flower; he fleeth as it were a shadow. Thou

38 Municipality of Oaklands. Elise Vane, Nov. 2, 1903. Place of Death: St Albans. Female, Age 62, Occupation: farmer. Religious Denomination: Lutheran. Where born: Germany. Certified cause of Death: Senile Decay. Duration of illness: Many months. Name and Residence of informant: Mr. Criddle, St Albans. Date of funeral service: November 4, 1903. Signature of Clergyman: W. F. Cann. United Church of Canada Archives, University of Winnipeg, Winnipeg, MB.
39 Service based on, The Order of the Burial of the Dead, *The Liturgy: or Formulary of Services* in use in the Methodist Church of Canada. Samuel Rose. Methodist Book-Room, 80 King Street East Toronto. 1875.

knowest, Lord, the secrets of our hearts; shut not thy merciful ears to our prayers and grant us divine comfort and strength."

He bent, picked up a handful of earth and while speaking let the sand fall slowly from his hand. "Forasmuch as it hath pleased Almighty God in his wise providence, to take out of the world the soul of the departed, we therefore commit her body to the ground; earth to earth, ashes to ashes, dust to dust." Then standing up he continued, "I heard a voice from Heaven saying, 'Behold, the dwelling of God is with all people. The voice of weeping shall no more be heard: and God shall wipe away all tears from their eye, and there shall be no more death, neither sorrow, nor crying, neither shall there be any more pain, for the former things are passed away.'"

Elise's children took the shovel in turn. Others followed until the earth formed a sandy brown mound. Emily reached into her coat above her bulging belly—great with child—and pulled out two stems of bright red geranium blossoms. She placed them into little Rupert's hands and Edwy helped the sturdy three-year-old lay them on his grandmother's grave.

The Reverend prayed, "O merciful God, the Father of our Lord Jesus Christ, who is the resurrection and the life; in whom whosoever believeth shall live, though he die, and whosoever liveth and believeth in him shall not die eternally."

Then raising his arms he blessed the little gathering of mourners. "The grace of our Lord Jesus Christ, and the love of God, and the fellowship of the Holy Ghost, be with us all evermore. Amen."

Elise's final wish had been fulfilled.

Back in the house, neighbours shared stories of Mrs. Vane's self-giving life. Cecil did his best to be sociable, but it wasn't long before he sought his mother's room, dropped to her bed and gave way to his grief.

That evening Edwy wrote at the bottom of the page recording the dates and miles travelled:

Nov. 4. Home. My dearly beloved Mother buried.

Picture of Elise's grave sent to Friedrich, 1905;

The Vanes Following Their Mother's Death

Percy Criddle, furious and frustrated by young Charlie Alabaster, beat him severely and threw him out. For Percy, no amount of money from the handicapped lad's mother in England was worth the aggravation. Emily and Edwy took Charlie in.

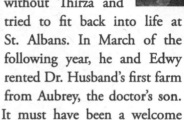

Back: Edwy, May, Harry
Front: Rupert, Cecil Ivan [John], Thyra, Emily

Harry returned from England in the spring of 1905 without Thirza and tried to fit back into life at St. Albans. In March of the following year, he and Edwy rented Dr. Husband's first farm from Aubrey, the doctor's son. It must have been a welcome change for Emily to have the large home for her children—Thyra, Rupert and John (Cecil Ivan), their lodger Charlie, and her sisters who came to stay from time to time. Edwy and Emily had two more daughters, Margaret [Madge] Elise, and Mona Iris, born after John's tragic death from meningitis at the age of eleven. Isabel and her daughter May also lived with Edwy and Emily after Will died of tuberculosis in 1907. May attended Millford School and then St. Mary's Academy in Brandon. Isabel went back to St. Albans to help Maida after her parents' death and Julia's marriage. In 1931, May married R. M. White and Isabel lived with them.

Alice, Mabel, Wesley, Bill Brandon

Minnie's children were Wesley, Percy, Mary [the latter two died in early childhood], Mabel, Alice, Gordon (Bill), and Helen. Unfortunately Jim Brandon, an automobile fan, was killed accidentally in 1915. The following year Minnie rented out the farm, sold other properties, and bought a two-story, very modern house in Kenton where she operated a boarding house and raised her family. Harry never married and died one month prior to his 102nd birthday.

Cecil suffered terribly from depression following his brothers' move. After

Harold, Lorna, Maurice with Cecil and Edie, 1924. Flora, a later arrival is inserted in the foreground.

years of invitations he finally broke away from the Criddle's for a weekend with Edwy and Emily. Edie, Emily's young sister, was visiting between secretarial positions in Indian Head and Winnipeg. Letters went back and forth until Cecil finally ventured to Winnipeg. With a great deal of encouragement from his brothers and Mr. Tulk, Cecil finally broke away in 1911 to marry Edie. They farmed the former Mair's place and had four children: Harold, Lorna, Maurice—tragically killed by a car as he crossed the road to get drinking water—and their youngest, Flora.

Mr. Tulk visited the Vanes regularly, staying in a little shanty John Harms built for him on the rented farm. When the Vanes bought McCauley's farm in 1917, they moved the little building. It became Charlie's until his death in 1945.

Edwy, Rupert, Thyra, and Harry Vane on the morning the brothers departed for England to visit Mr. Tulk in 1921.

Owning their own land, the Vane's built a new house called St. John's in 1919, and enjoyed several more visits from Mr. Tulk. He passed away in 1927.

Sifting out Elise's Story at St. Albans

Why is the knowing and telling of this story important?

My first goal is to free Great-Grandmother Elise from the mysterious 'mistress syndrome' that masks the depth of her sacrifice and her contribution to the children of both families.

I also hope to spare Elise's descendants from further embarrassment. Of the many examples, one involved a high school student, being refused a mark on her family research essay unless, and until, the word 'mistress' was used to describe her great-great-grandmother, Mrs. Vane. Another one was the embarrassing situation I experienced when attending a lecture celebrating the 85th anniversary of the Manitoba Naturalists Society. It was honouring one of the six little boys trying to keep warm in Elise's tent that first winter, an early naturalist, Norman Criddle. In introducing Norman's early life, the speaker began: "Percy Criddle arrived at Aweme with a wife, and his mistress, Mrs. Vane."

There was tittering in the audience; someone laughed outright. I felt humiliated as I had done on occasions in the past. The speaker went on with an excellent presentation of Norman's contributions to the Society. But I had learned too much about Elise's role at the homestead to be shamed into silence. In question time, I spoke up:

"Why in a speech to honour Norman Criddle, did you begin with the indiscretions of his father? I thought it offensive. I was hurt by the responding laughter. Surely Norman's contributions were sufficient to gain our respect. Do we, as an audience, need tantalizing tidbits to augment your tribute?"

With Elise's education and background in painting, she may very well have been Norman's mentor as he began drawing and painting the plants and flowers that led to his future success. All the Criddle descendants have impressed on me the following: "Make it very clear in your book, that Mrs. Vane was deeply appreciated and truly loved by all of us."

She was 'Huckey', sometimes 'Huddock', to the older children. In letters Mrs. Criddle also referred to her as 'Mama Dutcheen'. Mr. Criddle, from their arrival in Winnipeg until after her death, called her 'the Dutchman'. Elise lived out her Canadian life as the Criddle's servant, Mrs. Vane.

Other writers, from the national media to academics, have also seized upon the 'scandal' and ignored the woman herself. An article in the National Post,

Tuesday March 2, 2004, *How women won the West,* named Elise Vane as one of the few women to obtain a homestead in Western Canada, in spite of stringent conditions imposed by the Canadian Dominion Lands Act of 1872. History professor Ms. Carter wrote:

> Elisa [sic] Vane was a widow and the mistress of a married English wine merchant named Percy Criddle. Mr. Criddle had children with both his wife and Ms. Vane and when the Criddles emigrated to southern Manitoba, the Vanes followed suit. Ms. Vane established her homestead right next to the Criddle settlement.

Although Ms. Carter's subject was homesteading, she couldn't resist a little aside to quote another history professor. Kathryn McPherson suggested that the very proximity of the homesteads caused a problem later, "when a Criddle became enamoured with a Vane, the parents had to tell the young sweethearts they were in fact brother and sister." [1]

The account sounds plausible; nothing in the rules of homesteading need make it untrue. Yet, had she dug beneath the surface, she would have found it to be pure gossip.

What of those nearer in time and intimacy? Did the neighbours guess the children of the two families were half siblings? I asked this question to a woman whose grandfather had played hockey with the Criddle gang and enjoyed supper at St. Albans following the games. She was surprised by my question, "Oh no! Absolutely not! They were dressed so differently, treated so differently. We had no idea they were related."

Another descendant of early settlers in the Aweme district gave me a momentary glimpse of Elise's life when I asked, "Did your family ever talk about the Criddles? Any stories handed down?"

After a long pause, he answered, "Yes, they did. They talked about Mr. Criddle. How he was waited on hand and foot by his women."

"Oh?" I asked, "What women would they be?"

"His girlfriend and his wife," and then seeming a little unsure of himself added, "Well, his girlfriend."

Elise's everyday reality was indeed a life in the service of Percy Criddle, autocratic ruler of his little empire. Yet, she provided all the children, but especially her own, the moral leadership that served them well throughout their lives. I want the Vane descendants to celebrate their ancestry. The abuse of the past has to give up its power because healing begins when wounds are opened to the light.

—◦◦◦—

---

1 National Post, Tuesday, March 2, 2004 Page: A10 Section: News

Elise, the unknown woman in the Criddle home, was to be the focus of my book and I set out to find and sift out as many kernels of her life as possible. In addition to a few family stories, I studied materials from private family collections as well as archives and libraries in Germany, England and Canada.

- Correspondence to Elise from her brothers in Germany, plus their wills. [Primary sources]
- Elise's homestead applications and correspondence for NW 28.8.16. [Primary sources]
- Personal letters of Elise, her children, Percy and Alice Criddle, and Mr. Tulk. [Primary sources]
- Harry Vane's memoirs. [Primary source]
- Emily and Edwy's letters and his mileage records. [Primary sources]
- Mr. Criddle and Mr. Tulk's letters and diaries. [Primary sources]
- Norman Criddle's diary and writings. [Primary sources]
- Old family photographs. [Primary sources]
- Other original diaries of that period. [Primary sources]
- Manitoba community history books, especially those of Glenboro and Wawanesa.
- Alma Criddle's book, *Criddle-de-Diddle-Ensis*—Chapter 38: *Elise—Alias the Dutchman.*
- Newspaper articles, usually based on the above book.
- Linguistic Consultant Barbara Becker's analysis of letters: Elise, Mr. and Mrs. Criddle, and Mr. Tulk.

Through Elise's translated letters from her bothers, Karl and Friedrich, I found descendants of Elise's Uncle Friedrich. Dr. Hermann Harrer and his uncle, Hans Eugen Harrer, invited me to Germany and through them I reclaimed my lost heritage.

In England I mined every possible location for Percy Criddle's connections. I was seeking answers to my original questions: What was Percy's education? [2] Was his family aware of Elise and their children? Diligent research revealed primary sources contradicting much of the family lore, and paints a picture less flattering of Percy and more respectful of Elise.

Indoctrinated as I was from childhood that the Vanes and Criddles were friends; accepting Percy's genes as part of my genetic makeup has not come easily. Although he is my great-grandfather, I continue to refer to him as Mr. Criddle as my family always has.

---

2 Research on Percy's education was published in *The Alabaster Chronicle*, www.alabaster.org.uk

Preparatory Thoughts

Pictures of the Criddle family were taken in 1894 and '95 by neighbours.[3] English families often included in their pictures everyone connected to their household: butler, cook, coachman, gardener, governess and domestics. Group photography was a relatively new phenomenon and such family pictures were impressive. These pictures can mislead our generation into thinking the family was very large, unless we consider clues, like uniforms or clothing that differentiate the non-family members. After all, the family knew who was who and could never imagine that strangers more than 100 years later would be seeing their photographs.

This particular photograph was taken thirteen years after the family settled on the sandy soil of the homestead. Elise was fifty-five years old; Mr. Criddle spoke of her as 'an eyesore'. She appears reluctant to be in the photograph, almost hidden in her bonnet—a worn out old woman. Alma Criddle explained her appearance in her book, *Criddle-de-Diddle-Ensis*.

> Over the years, Elise's hair thinned and she lost the luxuriant braids that had formed a coronet around her head in youth. She grew careworn and aged, without that additional inherent factor which gave Alice [Mrs. Criddle] the aristocratic maturity which made her outstanding even with the advancing years.[4]

What caused Elise's rapid aging? Was it due to non-British lineage? For the answer I needed to know more about Elise's life on the homestead. At each institution where I enquired for Vane/Criddle information, I received the same response: "The best source is Alma Criddle's book, *Criddle-de-Diddle-Ensis*."

"I have both the book and her grandfather's diary." I explained, "I am searching for other primary documents."

Frustrated by my lack of success, I discussed one of the sources—Mr. Criddle's diary—with my philosopher son.

"Research historians," he cautioned, "understand that diaries are not considered accurate sources for factual data. A case for the Russian Revolution is not based on a soldier's diary; rather his account sheds light on one man's experience in that conflict." That seemed logical. He continued, "Only after evidence is firmly established from other reliable sources is a diary useful to shed light on individual experiences within the larger context. People write diaries to prove later they were right. Problematic in providing accurate information, a diary's real value lies mostly in revealing the character of its author."[5]

---

3 Taken by McVey in 1894. After Elise's severe illness, Köhler's the next year.
4 Criddle, Alma. p. 211
5 Veldhuis, Phillip A. BA (Hons.) M.A.

While considering this severe assessment, I opened the diaries I had kept as a young teacher. On somewhat yellowed pages, I read some daily accounts of that formative part of my life. Immediately, I realized my son was right; I had shown myself in a positive light, and because I had done the recording, I knew other happenings, more intimate in nature or not so flattering to my ego, were missing. Could Mr. Criddle have been guilty of a similar bias?

Many Victorian gentlemen kept diaries. As Mr. Criddle made plans to immigrate into the unsettled frontiers of Western Canada, he undoubtedly read accounts from earlier emigrants of life in the colonies. He intended to publish his own diary. Since the folks back home knew little of his circumstances, he had free range for story-telling. Who would blame him for tuning his diary for their enjoyment?

Following is an excerpt from his diary. Does it fit the mould of an event shaped to please the folks back home in England?

One Sunday morning before sunrise, I heard a violent ringing of our old dinner bell from the house – the preconcerted signal for anything wrong - and of course jumped up and went to our door. "Hullo – what's the matter?" shouted I – supposing the precious house must be on fire at least. Then I listened – and heard the Dutchman's voice from her half-opened door. "There's some great animal trying to break into the house from the back", she cried. "Is there?" said I – "All right, we'll soon see about that". And – out I presently ran in my nightshirt, minus even slippers, with my Rifle, over the preciously cold snow that lay on the ground – the back of the house being but 15 yards off, soon came under my eye & cautiously lifted Rifle – and – there sat our little friend the Woodpecker, clinging onto & hammering a log. Other "great animal" was there none – so I went back to bed in a hurry after reassuring the Dutchman – merely noting that Mr. W. was observing me with his head remarkably on one side as I hooked it round the corner – evidently wondering what the deuce I could be up to – at that unearthly hour. We didn't forget to roast the Dutchman most preciously for a day or so afterwards – but she didn't seem to mind it much. [January, 1883]

It's a good story; an example for my scrutiny.

The people and their location were factual; their circumstances were as follows. At the time of this event Mr. Criddle, his wife, and their youngest child resided in a small heated shanty. Elise and eight children (her own five and three Criddle boys) had lived in a tent from their arrival in August to December 17th, the date given for her move into the uncompleted log house.

It began with the violent ringing of 'our old dinner bell', which gave me conflicting feelings between the wild new land and a peaceful manor in England.

Had they brought this dinner bell from home I would have expected it to reappear later in the diary to warn of danger. I never found it.

'Mr. Woodpecker', we understand, had regularly awakened Mr. Criddle in his shanty. It must also have roused Elise since the tent was close by, and canvas, I have the misfortune to know, provides zero sound proofing, especially from a woodpecker. Furthermore, Elise spent most of her time outdoors, cooking, securing firewood, melting snow, and washing. Was she not therefore, equally acquainted with 'Mr. Woodpecker'? Elise and the children had just moved from four months in the tent to the security of four sturdy walls. Could a familiar sound be so frightening? Or was it another, larger animal, frightened away by the commotion before Mr. Criddle peered around the corner?

An English reader might imagine just such a barefoot romp in the early hours of a British winter. But according to Brandon newspaper reports around December 17, 1882, when Elise and the children reportedly moved from their tent, Manitobans were enduring severe 30 below temperatures; dangerously cold, even for a suitably dressed outdoorsman. We are given a fellow clad only in his nightshirt with 'slipperless feet'. The distance was not great, but at that temperature the frost can literally take your breath away, so consider the effect on other body parts, clad only in a thin nightshirt.

Further to 'friend woodpecker'; would it not, on that coldest hour of a bitterly cold morning be perched on a sheltered limb with feathers fully fluffed?

The British had fought the Dutch many times in their colonial conquests and because of that long standing hostility, the name 'Dutchman', was an insulting stereotype. The use of this common English slur made Elise appear a not-so-bright person and a suitable victim for a joke.

Finally, Mr. Criddle had not written in his diary from the day after their arrival until the end of January. Convalescing indoors in late January to early February, he filled in those first six months with an eye to publication.

From my analysis I concluded that just as I was the hero in my diary, he was the hero of his. Had his story appeared in print, it would have entertained his friends in England. But I wanted to write more than tall tales.

Maintaining his sense of identity was another factor in Mr. Criddle's recording of his story. In observing his immigrant companions, Robert Louis Stevenson described them as the 'broken men of England' seeking a new start.[6] They were escaping from the humiliations and constraints of the motherland.

---

6 Stevenson , Robert Louis, *The Amateur Emigrant:* "We were a company of the rejected; the drunken, the incompetent, the weak, the prodigal, all who had been unable to prevail against circumstances in the one land, were now fleeing pitifully to another; and though one or two might still succeed, all had already failed. We were a shipful of failures, the broken men of England." http://etext.library.adelaide.edu.au/s/stevenson/robert_louis/s848ae/. Viewed. October, 2008.

The future was all that mattered. Mr. Criddle was no exception. Although a failed London merchant, he planned to be a gentleman, a genteel land owner. Such a dream was impossible in England where birth determined a man's status. Sensing an opportunity for prestige, he cultivated the image and sought positions of importance, e.g. Justice of the Peace, Game Warden, and Aweme School chair and secretary of the board.

Others masqueraded: Grey Owl (Belaney) with his beavers and Frederick Philip Grove (Greve) with his writing. Both reveal "how much the public needs and enjoys its myths and how much it hates to be fooled." Once their deceptions were uncovered, harsh words like "charlatans, impostors and pathological liars"[7] were applied to both Belaney and Grove and for many years their real contributions were overlooked.

The Criddles brought their Britishness with them; attitudes and traditions embedded in the pages of Charles Dickens, and Thomas Hughes's *Tom Brown's School Days*. British males were referred to as Mr. Burnett; Canadians as Lonsbury, Mair Junior, Upper, and even Old Clark. Females were Miss Bellhouse, Miss Steer, or Mrs. Bruner. Friend and benefactor John Augustus Tulk was informally known as Tulk, or J A, but never John. He in turn spoke of Percy Criddle's wife, as Mrs. Criddle.

In addition to Mr. Criddle, two other family members wrote of life on the homestead. Elise Vane's second son, Harry, wrote a brief memoir and, although his mother is not named, she was among the 'rest of us'.

> 1882 Lonsbury, Pete Smith & Bruner built a shanty. Mr. & Mrs. Criddle and the young ones lived in that for the first winter. The rest of us lived in the big tent until Christmas.

Norman Criddle, writing in *The Canadian Field-Naturalist*, described his life after leaving England:

> My memory of the next few years is somewhat confused, the period was one of extreme depression, crops had been poor & prices low. Hunger generally accompanied us in our daily work.... substitute for bread learned to eat Cree Turnips[8] a root for which I retain a liking ... father tried to shoot a deer without success.[9]

There were many other sources. Members of the Manitoba Genealogical Society encouraged and guided me through their collection of books, maps

7 Abley, Mark, *Beyond Forget: Rediscovering the Prairies. (Douglas & McIntyre, Toronto) p.55*
8 *Psoralea esculenta*: Latin name for plant known as Indian Breadroot, once a prairie staple, with large edible underground tubers. The plant takes two to four years to develop from seed to tubers and has become rare due to lack of habitat.
9 The Canadian Field-Naturalist Vol. XLVII Ottawa Canada, Nov. 1933 No. 8. p 177. Manitoba Archives

and beyond. Names, addresses and occupations of all the neighbours are listed in Henderson's directories. The Archives of Manitoba holds fascinating pioneer records. Research days sped by so quickly I had to be reminded by a firm voice, "Closing time." Museums large and small, community history books, municipal offices, Universities of Brandon and Manitoba's archives, Church records, and both Brandon and Winnipeg public libraries have all added to my store of local information.

Books of the era were also enlightening. Nellie McLung's *Clearing in the West* described her family's arrival in 1879 and her early life on the Mooney homestead. Her first novel, *Sowing Seeds in Danny*, was based in her fictionalized Millford, only a few miles from the Criddles. Heroine Pearlie Watson and her poor Irish family shone light on class differences and society beyond the Criddles. Because the Mooneys were Canadian and Methodist, as were my mother's family, the Clarks, they were looked down upon by the Criddles. Life was not easy for any of the pioneers. Had the Criddles been open to the many experienced farmers in their midst, much of the hardship the Criddle family endured could have been avoided.

Recent books expose an unacknowledged history of our foremothers. One especially, *Walk toward the Gallows: the Tragedy of Hilda Blake, Hanged 1899*, provides an eye-opening glimpse of 'upper crust' life in Brandon in contrast to the conditions of poor domestics.[10] On a happier note, *Gully Farm*,[11] a biography of a young English girl who with her parents, emigrated to Canada as part of the Barr Settlement is a must read. Her account of pioneer life is guaranteed to inform and delight.

Most precious of all to inform my understanding of Elise's life within the Criddle household are the personal letters written by Elise's children to her, and to each other, and she to them.

―――❦―――

I had done five years of research and people were asking, "How is your book coming?"

"I'm working on it." I said. But, I was not making much progress.

My son said, "Better hurry Mother, if you don't get it done soon all the people wanting to read your story will be gone."

What was holding me back? The answer came on a very clear, forty-below day in January when my husband said, "I'll put away the lunch things; you go upstairs and start writing."

---

10   Kramer, Reinhold & Mitchell, Tom. *Walk Toward the Gallows: The Tragedy of Hilda Blake, Hanged 1899* (Oxford University Press, Canada. 2002)

11   Hiemstra, Mary, *Gully Farm*, (McClelland & Stewart Ltd. Toronto, 1955)

My little second floor office in our home has a window over my left shoulder. The bright blue sky echoed my husband, "Get going on that keyboard. No excuses, don't worry about the quality, just let the words flow."

I was doggedly typing when I became aware of a sound. Determined to let nothing interfere, I kept my fingers moving. . . . The sound got closer, footsteps . . . on the roof? I tried to keep my mind on the words I was typing. Crunch, crunch, the steps came closer. I tried to concentrate. But I couldn't ignore them—heavier and closer. My fingers stopped in midair. Someone was on our roof—the crunching directly above me. I glanced up at the window and saw pieces of snow falling, as if pushed over the edge of the roof. Startled, I stood up to look more closely. Craning my neck for the source, I saw a man's arm, clothed in a heavy coarse overcoat and big brown knitted mitt reach out from the roof's edge and swing down like the arm of a railway crossing.

He'll fall! He's crazy to be leaning over the edge like that! I raced downstairs calling, "Art, Art, someone's on the roof." My husband was reading, and reluctantly pulled his eyes away from the page. I tried to explain, but he wasn't impressed.

Convinced somebody was up there; I grabbed my parka and ran out the back door. The frigid air was dead-still. Nothing moved in the winter sunshine. There was no one on the roof. No indentations to show that the snow had been disturbed causing some to fall.

I was unnerved and shaken. It was too cold to walk off my upsetting experience outdoors, so I attacked the week's ironing. I've had some interesting dreams, but never while fully conscious. The arm swung down as if to block the way. That mitted hand was so real. Was it saying, "Stop! Do not proceed?" Was my subconscious trying to tell me something? Did I not want to write this story? After a night of brooding I told myself, "Yes, difficult as it is, I want to chronicle my great-grandmother's life."

Was someone sending me a message? I pondered. Who doesn't want this book written? It wasn't Great-Grandmother Elise; the hand was a man's. Was it Mr. Criddle? No, the coat and mitts were common. Besides, he wouldn't be on a roof. My father? I didn't think so. Was it his father, Edwy Vane?

Was I breaking my grandpa's promise? Elise's eldest son had, along with his brothers and sisters, promised never to tell the truth about their father. It had to be Edwy. Gathering courage, I decided to face my much loved grandfather.

"Grandpa," I said, "you promised to keep the secret. But, I did not. I'm going to write this book to the best of my ability, even if it kills me."

My Grandpa Vane did not come again. I was able to begin writing the story of the woman who served—with a gracious heart—everyone who came her way at St. Albans.

Harrer Decendant Chart

Matteus Harrer & Anna Maria Joller

They were married before the record book began in 1790
Stockach, Outer Austria.

Franz Joseph Harrer 1701 - 1795
Maria Eva Thumm 1719 - ?
Stockach, Outer Austria

Andreas Harrer 1764-1836
Maria Catharina Reuthemann 1780 - 1849
Radolfzell, Outer Austria/Baden

Carl Harrer 1805 - 1848	Friedrich Harrer 1808 - 1874
Susanna Haarbarth 1809 - 1885	Caroline Friederang 1821-1869
Radolfzell/Heidelberg, Baden	Radolfzell/Lörrach, Baden
Sabina Elise Harrer 1840 - 1903	Hermann Harrer 1840 - 1904
Percy Criddle 1844 - 1917	Charlotte Sattler 1858 - 1956
Heidelberg/London/Aweme, MB	Lörrach, Germany
Edwy Vane 1871 - 1955	Hermann Harrer 1878 - 1959
Emily Louise Steer 1871 - 1947	Elizabeth Vogelbach 1887 - 1975
Aweme/Treesbank, MB	Lörrach, Germany
Harry Rupert Vane 1900 - 1977	Herbert Harrer 1911 - 1995
Annie Lucinda Ruth Clark 1905 - 2010	Brigitte Reischach 1924 - ?
Treesbank/Stockton, MB	Lörrach, Germany
Oriole Amelia Vane	Hermann Harrer
Atze (Art) Veldhuis	Sabine Niederhofer
Stockton/Winnipeg, MB	Lörrach, Germany

Appendix 2

Europe 1870

Carl Harrer, Elise's father, was a Grand Duke of Baden Postmaster. All officials were regularly transferred, as the Grand Duke tried to bring harmony between the Catholic population of the south and the Protestants in northern Baden.

From 1690, the Harrers were an often mentioned family in Stockach—part of Outer Austria and later Baden. Elise's Grandfather Andreas moved to Radolfzell to teach in 1801. Born there, Carl began his postal career in Stockach, then transferred to Heidelberg, and later Mannheim. He married Susanna Haarbarth in Heidelberg, where Friedrich and Karl were born. Elise was born in Freiburg, then back to Heidelberg where Wilhelm was born. Postmaster Harrer died in Donaueschingen and Susanna returned to her family in Heidelberg where Elise spent her youth. Later Friedrich and Marie settled in Mannheim, Karl and Amalie in Karlsruhe.

Appendix 3

Community mid–1880s

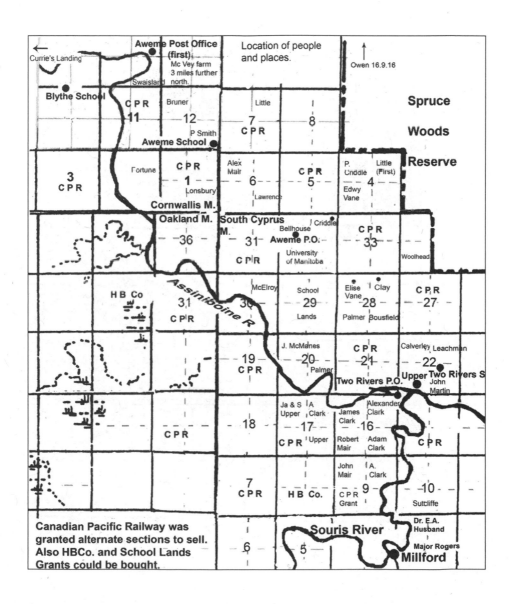

Location of people and places.

Currie's Landing

Aweme Post Office (first). Mc Vey farm 3 miles further north.

Owen 16.9.16

Swaisland

Blythe School

CPR **11** Bruner

12 P Smith

Aweme School

Little **7** CPR

8

Spruce

Woods

Reserve

3 CPR

Fortune

CPR **1** Lonsbury

Alex Mair **6** Lawrence

CPR **5**

P. Criddle

Edwy Vane

Little (First) **4**

Cornwallis M.

Oakland M. **36**

South Cyprus M. **31**

Bellhouse Aweme P.O.

J Criddle

University of Manitoba

CPR **33**

Woolhead

HB Co **31** CPR

Assiniboine R.

30

McElroy School **29** Lands

Elise Vane **28** Palmer Bousfield

Clay

CPR **27**

19 CPR

J. McManes **20** Palmer

CPR **21**

Two Rivers P.O.

Calverley Leachman **22**

Upper Two Rivers S John Martin

18 CPR

Ja & S Upper Clark **17** CPR Upper

James Clark **16** Robert Mair

A Clark

Alexander Clark

Adam Clark

CPR

7 CPR

HB Co.

John Mair CPR Grant **9**

A. Clark

10 Sutcliffe

Canadian Pacific Railway was granted alternate sections to sell. Also HBCo. and School Lands Grants could be bought.

6

Souris River

5

Dr. E.A. Husband

Major Rogers **Millford**

Community mid–1890s

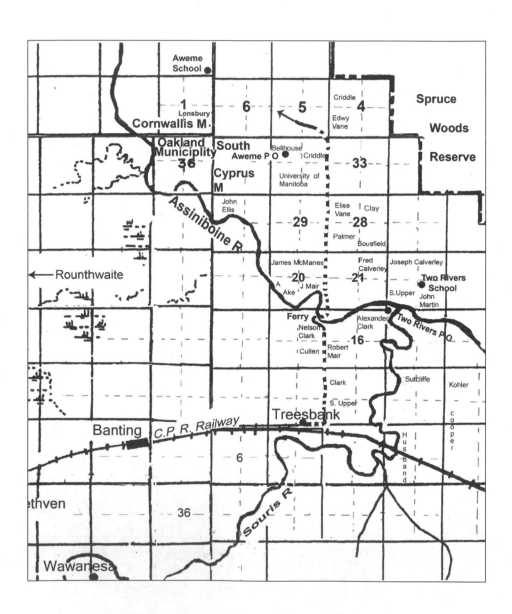

Elise Vane's First Homestead Application – July 26, 1889

Statement *Made and Sworn to by* _____ 159596

Elise Vane _____ *in support*

of his application for _4d_ *Patent for* _N.W._ *of*

Section _28_ *Thp.* _8_ *Rge.* _16 W of_ _1st_ *Meridian.*

Homestead _N.W._ _____ *Pre-emption* _____

1. What is your name in full, age and Post Office address? — *Elise Vane Age 47 Avenue. British*

2. Are you a British subject by birth or naturalization? If naturalized, when and where? — *British*

3. What is your trade, profession or calling? — *Farming*

4. When did you obtain entry for this homestead? — *3 May 86*

5. When did you build your house thereon? — *End of February 89.*

6. When did you perfect your entry to your homestead by taking up your own person possession of the land and beginning continuous residence thereon and cultivation thereof? — *3rd of May 86 residing on S.E. of S. 16 W.* *within 2 miles*

7. What portion of each year since that date have you resided thereon? State each month. — *from 3rd May 86 till 25th March 89 residing on S.E. ¼ S. 16 W. from 25th March 89 until 1st July 89 upon N.W.*

8. When absent from your homestead where have you resided, and what has been your occupation? — *Residing on S.E. 32 8. 16 W*

9. Of whom does your family consist; when did they first commence residence upon this homestead, and for what portion of each year since that date have they resided upon it? — *8 Children resided with me on the place within 2 miles.*

10. How much breaking have you done upon your homestead in each year since you obtained entry, and how many acres have you cultivated each year? — *86 broke 23a 87 " 15 Cropped 23a 88 " 20 " 38 89 " " " 35*

11. How many horned cattle, horses, sheep, and pigs have you had on your homestead each year since date of perfecting entry? Give number in each year. — *Team Oxen working the place*

12. What is the size of your house, and what is its present cash value? — *16 6in X 19 6in — 50.*

13. What extent of fencing have you made, and what is the present cash value thereof? — *None*

14. What other buildings have you erected? What other improvements have you made, and what is the cash value of the same? — *Granary. No value.*

15. Are there any indications of minerals or quarries on your homestead? If so, state nature of same, and whether it is more valuable for agricultural than any other purpose — *No. Land is fit for mix farming.*

16. Have you had any other homestead entry? If so, when and where, and what became of it? — *No.*

17. Have you assigned or transferred or agreed to assign or transfer your homestead or pre-emption right or any part thereof? If so, when and to whom. — *No.*

Form No. 132.

(Continued on next page)

487

Back of the Homestead application signed by applicant. The buildings and other improvements made to the quarter section were usually depicted.

15959

I, *Elise Vane* do solemnly swear that the answers to the foregoing questions are true and correct in every particular. That I claim a Patent for this Homestead under the provisions of *the Lands Act*

That I obtained an entry, and claim a Patent for the same for my own benefit, and not in the interest or for the benefit of any other person or persons whomsoever.

Sworn before me at *Brandon*

this ___ day of *July* 1889 .

having been read over and explained to the said applicant.

Elise Vane

_____
Local Agent of Dominion Lands for the District.

I recommend the foregoing application for Patent, believing that the homestead requirements of the "Dominion Lands Act" have, in this case, been complied with.

_____
Local Agent of Dominion Lands for *Souris* District.

Winnipeg, 188

Accepted as sufficient

_____
Commissioner.

Diagram showing the location of animal shelter and the house below. The road to Two Rivers passed over the land from the upper left to the lower right.

Elise Criddle's Registered Letter

Confirmation that the registered letter sent by notary Stricker to 'Elise Crittel' October 10, 1896 was received on November 8, 1896. Postmaster Bellhouse signed and stamped it the following April 17, 1897. Received in Germany long after the estate was settled, it was dated and filed with the documents.

State Archives Karlsruhe, Baden-Württemburg, Germany.
Reference B 270/IV Karlsruhe, Nr 28187

Percy Criddle's Will and Statement of Relationship, 1912

[handwritten manuscript reproduction of the will]

This is the last Will of me, Percy Criddle of Aweme Manitoba, Gentlemen. I direct that my remains be buried in the plainest and least expensive manner at the entrance [?] of my Estate. I bequeath to my daughter Beatrice Ellis one hundred dollars to Mabel Knight 100 dollars to Edwy Vane fifty dollars and to Harry Vane Cecil Vane and Minnie Brandon each twenty five dollars or the heirs of any of them free of legacy duty together with such souvenirs from my personal effects as may be deemed appropriate by my Executors herein after named. The remainder of my property whatsoever I give with power to act in all things connected therewith as they may determine in their discretion to my sons Norman and Evelyn in Trust for the use and benefit jointly of my Wife my four sons and such of my daughters as may continue to be unmarried during the lifetime of my said Wife so long as she is a Widow. At her death or remarriage I give the said Remainder of my property absolutely to such of my said sons and then unmarried daughters as survive at that time share and share alike Provided that any of my said daughters marrying previous to my said Wifes death or remarriage Then said daughter or daughters shall be given a marriage portion of five hundred dollars that is to say five hundred dollars to each of them that they may marry. Provided also that any of my said sons have died leaving issue previous to the death or remarrying of my said Wife then said issue if still living shall take the place of the parent And I hereby appoint my said sons Norman and Evelyn Executors hereof and constitute them together with my said Wife guardian of my daughter Alma now a minor until she attains the age of twenty one years-

Dated at Aweme Manitoba this fourteenth day of February in the year nineteen hundred and twelve--- Percy Criddle

Signed by the above named testators in the presence of [and] in presence at the same time, who in his presence in the presence of each other, and at his request, have hereunto—subscribed our names as witnesses.   John F Harms Laurence Mason.   Stamped Exhibit B, 20th day of May A.D. 1918

This is the will of Percy Criddle deceased referred to in affidavits made by us respectively in applying for probate.   Norman Criddle   Evelyn Criddle

Lawyer's Statement after Percy's death in 1918: Cecil is missing from the list.

Statement of Relationship

Canada :
Province of Manitoba

The Succession Duties Act

IN THE SURROGATE COURT OF *the Central* JUDICIAL DISTRICT.

In the matter of *the Estate of Percy Criddle deceased* deceased, late of the *municipality* of *South Cypress* in the *Province* — of *Manitoba*.

NAME	RELATIONSHIP	ADDRESS	PROPERTY	PASSING	VALUE
Beatrice Ellis	Daughter	Treesbank	Legacy		$100
Isobel Knight	his niece	"	Legacy		$100
Edwy Vane	his niece	"	Legacy		$50
Harry Vane	his niece	"	Legacy		$25
Minnie Brander	his niece	Kenton	Legacy		$25
Norman Criddle	Son	Treesbank			
Evelyn Criddle	Son	"			
Stuart Criddle	Son	"			$10,671.58
Maida Criddle	Daughter	"			
Julia Criddle	Daughter	"			
Talbot Criddle	Son	"			

This is the Statement of Relationship marked "B" referred to in the Affidavit of Value and Relationship of *Norman Criddle and Evelyn Criddle*

Sworn before me on the   *3d*   day of *June*   A.D. 1918

J H Donaldson

A Commissioner, etc., or Notary Public, etc.

491

Norman Criddle's Will and Statement of Relationship, 1926

(Second) I give devise and bequeath unto:— My sister Beatrice Ellis Two thousand ($2000) dollars; To my sister Julia Gowan Two thousand dollars ($2000) To my brother Talbot Criddle Two ($200) thousand dollars; To Mrs William Knigh one hundred dollars ($100). The rest of my property real or personal, to which I a in any way entitled, I leave absolutely to my Brothers and Sister Evelyn Criddle, Stuart Criddle and Maida Criddle or to such of them as survive me, share and share alike. And I reserve my life rent and full power to alter, innovate, or revoke these presents i whole or in part and I dispence with the delivery here of—

In witness Whereof I have subscribed the presents written by my self at Treesbank, Manitoba this twelfth day of November Nineteen–hundred–and–twenty-six –

Norman Criddle

At the time of writing his will in 1926 Norman's mind was still closed to the reality that the Vanes were his father's children and his half-brothers and sisters. Notice that he only includes one 'unrelated' Vane in his will. Isabel, Mrs. William Knight, lived and worked at St. Albans helping Maida serve him and his naturalist assistants.

Statement of Relationship

Canada
Province of Manitoba } Under "The Succession Duty Act"

In the Surrogate Court of CENTRAL Judicial District

In the Matter of NORMAN CRIDDLE
deceased, late of the Municipality of South Cypress
in the Province of Manitoba

NAME OF BENEFICIARY	RELATIONSHIP Trace to deceased, describing nephew or niece as son or daughter of brother or sister.	ADDRESS	Age last birthday of Life Tenant or Annuitant	Nature of Bequest or Property Passing	VALUE
Beatrice Ellis	Sister	Wawanesa, Manitoba		Legacy	$2000.00
Julia Gowan	Sister	Treesbank, Manitoba		Legacy	$2000.00
Talbot Criddle	Brother	Treesbank, Manitoba		Legacy	$2000.00
Mrs. Wm. Knight	Not related	Lethbridge, Alberta		Legacy	$ 100.00
Evelyn Criddle	Brother	Treesbank, Manitoba	}	Residuary Legatees	$7497.11
Stuart Criddle	Brother	Treesbank, Manitoba	}		$7497.11
Maida Criddle	Sister	Treesbank, Manitoba	}		$7497.11

Bibliography

Abbott, Elizabeth. *A History of Marriage*, Penguin Canada, Toronto, 2010.

Abley, Mark. *Beyond Forget: Rediscovering the Prairie*, Douglas & McIntyre, Vancouver, 1986.

Alabaster, Adrian. *A Quintet of Alabasters*, Able Publishing, Knebworth, Hertfordshire, 1999.

Austen, Jane. *Emma*. Ed. Stephen M. Parish, Norton, New York, 1972.

Boyd, Nancy. *Three Victorian Women Who Changed Their World*, Oxford University Press, New York/Oxford, 1982.

Brook-Shepherd, Gordon. *The Austrians: A Thousand-Year Odyssey*, Harper Collins, London, 1996.

Burns, Wayne. *Charles Reade: A Study in Victorian Authorship*, Bokman Associates, New York, 1961.

Cahill, Susan. *Wise Women*, W.W. Norton, New York, 1996.

Callow, Philip Louis. *A Life of Robert Louis Stevenson*, Ivan R. Dee, Chicago, 2001.

Carter, Sarah. *Capturing Women: The Manipulation of Cultural Imagery in Canada's Prairie West*, McGill-Queen's University Press, 1997.

Cather, Willa. *My Antonia*, Virago Press, London, 1918.

Catlow, Agnes and Maria E. *The Children's Garden and What They Made of It*, illustrations by Mrs. Harry [Maryann Alabaster] Criddle, Cassell, Petter & Galpin, London, 1865.

Cattermole, Wm. *Emigration: The Advantages of Emigration to Canada*, Simpkin and Marshall, London, 1831.

Cherry, Debora. *Painting Women: Victorian Women Artists*, Routledge, London and New York, 1993.

—*Beyond the Frame: Feminism and Visual Culture*, Britain 1850-1900, Routledge, London, 2000.

Cole, Robert. *Lives of Moral Leadership*, Random House, New York, 2000.

Conner, Ralph. *The Foreigner*, Westminster Press, Toronto, 1909.

Cornwallis Centennial Committee. *Municipal Memories: Municipality of Cornwallis*, 1884-1984.

Criddle, Alma. *Criddle-De-Diddle Ensis*, D.W. Friesen, Steinbach, Manitoba, 1973.

Douglas Historical Book Club. *Echoes of a Century: Douglas Centennial 1882-1892*, Friesen Printers, Altona, Manitoba.

Edward, Arnold. *A Summer on the Canadian Prairie*, London, 1910.

Fenner, Achim. *Schule in Badischer Zeit 1810-1918*, Primo-Verlag, Stockach, 1987.

Festschrift zur 700-Jahr-Feier der Stadt Stockach, *1283-1983*, n.p., n.d.

Fitzgibbon, Mary. *A Trip to Manitoba*, Rose-Belford, Toronto, 1880.

Gissing, George. *The Odd Woman*, ed. Arlene Young, Broadview Press, Peterborough, Ontario, 1998.

Glenboro and Area Historical Society. *Beneath the Long Grass*, Derksen Printers, Steinbach, Manitoba, 1979.

Götz, Franz, ed. *Geschichte der Stadt Radolfzell*, Stadt Radolfzell and Verein für Geschichte des Hegaus, Radolfzell, 1967.

Gowan, Frank, ed. *The Western Canada Photographers List*, 1860 to 1925, 1997.

Grove, Frederick Phillip. *Over Prairie Trails*, 1879-194, Macmillan Canada, Toronto, 1929.

Guillet, Edwin C. *The Great Migration: The Atlantic Crossing by Sailing Ship since 1770*, University of Toronto Press, Toronto, 1963.

Hall, Mrs. Cecil. *A Lady's Life on a Farm in Manitoba*, W.H. Allen, London, 1884.

Hammet, Michael. *Plays by Charles Reade*, Cambridge University Press, Cambridge, 1986.

Hancock, Carol. *No Small Legacy: Canada's Nellie McClung*. Woodlake Books, Winfield, 1986.

Hart, James D, ed. *From Scotland to Silverado: Robert Louis Stevenson*, Harvard University Press, Cambridge, Massachusetts, 1966.

Hawksley, Lucinda. *Katey: The Life and Loves of Dickens's Artist Daughter*, Doubleday, London, 2006.

Hiemstra, Mary Pinder. *Gully Farm*. McClelland & Stewart, Toronto, 1955.

Hughes, Thomas. *Tom Brown's School Days*, University Press, John Wilson & Son, Cambridge, 1890.

—*Tom Brown at Oxford*. Donohue, Denneberry, Chicago, n. d.

Kramer, Reinhold & Mitchell, Tom. *Walk Toward the Gallows: The Tragedy of Hilda Blake*, Oxford University Press, Don Mills, Ontario, 2002.

Lawrence, Margaret. *Dance on the Earth: A Memoir, McClelland & Stewart*, Toronto, 1989.

Macewan, Grant. *...and Mighty Women Too: Stories of Notable Canadian Women*, Western Producer, Saskatoon, Saskatchewan, 1975.

McClung, Nellie. *Clearing in the West: My Own Story*, Thomas Allen, Toronto, 1935.

—*Sowing Seeds in Danny,* Grosset & Dunlap, New York, 1908.

Millar, Nancy. *The Unmentionable History of the West*, Red Deer Press, Calgary, Alberta, 2006.

Pennefather, *John P. Thirteen Years on the Prairies: From Winnipeg to Cold Lake*, Kegan, Trench, Trubner, London. 1892.

Reade, Charles. *Peg Woffington*, T. Nelson & Sons, n.p., n.d.

Rose, Phyllis. *Parallel Lives: Five Victorian Marriages*, Alfred A. Knopf, New York, 1984.

Ross, Ellen. *Love and Toil: Motherhood in Outcast London*, 1870-1918, Oxford University Press, New York, 1993.

Schama, Simon. *The Fate of Empire*, 1776-2000, vol 3, A History of Britain, BBC, London, 2002.

Shepherd, George. *West of Yesterday*, McClelland & Stewart, Toronto, 1965.

Sidgwick, Mrs Alfred. *Home Life in Germany*, Macmillan, n.p., 1912.

Siggins, Maggie. *Revenge of the Land*, McClelland & Stewart, Toronto, 1991.

Smith, Elton. *Charles Reade*, Twayne Publishers, Boston, 1976.

Spence, Lewis. *Germany: Myth and Legends*, Bracken Books, London, 1985.

Stevenson, Robert Louis. *The Amateur Emigrant*, Harvard University Press, Cambridge, Massachusetts, 1966.

Stokes, Richard, ed. *The Book of Lieder, chosen, translated & introduced the original texts of over 1000 songs*, Faber & Faber, London, 2005.

Taylor, Tom. *Charles Reade Masks and Faces: Or before and behind the Curtain*, Oxford University Press, Oxford, 1854.

Töpfer, Rudolf. *Das Königlich Württembergische Postamt Balingen in der Zeit von 1806 bis 1918/20*, Südwestdeutsche Postgeschichtliche Blätter der Oberpostdirektion Freiburg, Freiburg, 1986.

Trollop, Anthony. *Barchester Towers*, J. M. Dent, London, 1968.

Tyman, John Langton. *By Section Township and Range*, Brandon University, Brandon, Manitoba, 1995.

Wagner, Hans. *Aus Stockachs Vergangenheit*, Herausgegeben Von Fur Geschichte Des Hegaus E. V. , Konstanz, 1981.

Watson, Thomas. *Lectures on the Principles and Practice of Physic.* Lea & Blanchard, Philadelphia, 1845.

Wawanesa & District History Book Committee. *Sipiweske: Light through the Trees*, 100 Years of Wawanesa and District, Friesen Printers, 1988.

Weise, Wolfgang. *Heidelberg Castle: A Guide to the Castle Enclosure*, Administration of State Palaces and Gardens, Baden-Württemberg, 2002.

Wells, Ronald A. *Letters from a Young Emigrant in Manitoba*, University of Manitoba Press, Winnipeg, 1981.

Wiebe, Rudy. *Of this earth: A Mennonite Boyhood in the Boreal Forest,* Vintage Canada, Toronto, 2007.

Yalom, Marilyn. *A History of the Wife*, Harper Collins, New York, 2001.

Zinsser, William. *Investigating the Truth: The Art and Craft of Memoir*, Houghton Miffin, Boston, 1998.

Wagon at the entrance to the Canadian Transportation Museum and Heritage Village, near Kingsville, Ontario. The author's Clark ancestors' original cabin is one of the homes in the heritage village.

Pictures without captions throughout the book: